LODGINGS

FOR LESS

NORTHEAST AND MIDWEST

N 15 3
SALE
$ 357 E A

PRENTICE HALL

Important

Budget lodgings are scarce, and even nonexistent in many major cities and resort areas. Consequently, these cities will have listings which are higher in their rates for two persons than noted on the cover of this Guide. Please refer to the State Information page for the areas that fall into these categories and their price ranges. All lodgings listed within each city are available for the given price or less and are considered to be a good value for their particular area.

Lodgings for Less selects a representative cross section of accommodations which gives the traveler a wide range of choice in both type and price. Space limitations necessitate the omission of many fine places; however, no adverse criticism is implied or should be inferred.

Published in 1989 by Prentice Hall Trade Division
A Division of Simon & Schuster, Inc.
Gulf + Western Building
One Gulf + Western Plaza
New York, NY 10023

ISBN 0-13-586926-9
ISSN 0899-9627

Manufactured in the United States of America
10 9 8 7 6 5 4 3 2 1

Contents

Introduction

States

Hotel/Motel Toll-Free "800" Numbers

This selected list is a handy guide for hotel/motel toll-free reservation numbers. You can save time and money by using them in the continental United States and Canada; Alaska and Hawaii are not included. Although these '800' numbers were in effect at press time, the *Mobil Travel Guide* cannot be responsible should any of them change. Many establishments do not have toll-free reservation numbers. Consult your local telephone directory for regional listings. The toll-free numbers designated 'TDD' are answered by a telecommunications service for the deaf. Don't forget to dial "1" before each number.

AMRES (American Reservation System)
800-241-3848

Best Western International, Inc.
800-528-1234 Cont'l USA and Canada
800-528-2222 TDD

Budgetel Inns
800-4-BUDGET Cont'l USA

Comfort Inns
800-228-5150 Cont'l USA

Courtyard by Marriott
800-321-2211 Cont'l USA

Davis Bros Motor Lodges
800-841-9480 Cont'l USA

Days Inn
800-325-2525 Cont'l USA

Dillon Inn
800-253-7503 Cont'l USA

Downtowner-Passport Motor Inns
800-238-6161 Cont'l USA exc TN
800-582-6173 TN

Drury Inns
800-325-8300 Cont'l USA

Econo Lodges of America
800-446-6900 Cont'l USA & Canada

Exel Inns of America
800-356-8013 Cont'l USA

Friendship Inns of America Int'l
800-453-4511 Cont'l USA

Hampton Inn
800-HAMPTON Cont'l USA

Holiday Inns, Inc.
800-HOLIDAY Cont'l USA & Canada
800-238-5544 TDD

Howard Johnson
800-654-2000 Cont'l USA & Canada
800-654-8442 TDD exc OK

Imperial Inns
800-368-4400 Cont'l USA exc VA
800-572-2200 VA

La Quinta Motor Inns, Inc.
800-531-5900 Cont'l USA

L-K Penny Motels, Inc.
800-848-5767 Cont'l USA exc OH
800-282-5711 OH

Master Hosts Inns
800-251-1962 Cont'l USA

Preferred Hotels
800-323-7500 Cont'l USA & Canada

Quality Inns
800-228-5151 Cont'l USA & Canada

Ramada Inns
800-2-RAMADA Cont'l USA
800-228-3232 TDD

Red Carpet/Scottish Inns
800-251-1962 Cont'l USA & Canada

Red Lion-Thunderbird
800-547-8010 Cont'l USA & Canada

Red Roof Inns
800-848-7878 Cont'l USA & Canada

Regal 8 Inn
800-851-8888 Cont'l USA

Rodeway Inns International
800-228-2000 Cont'l USA

Shilo Inns
800-222-2244

Sundowner/Best Value/Superior
800-322-8029

Super 8 Motels
800-843-1991 Cont'l USA & Canada

Susse Chalet Motor Lodges & Inns
800-258-1980 Cont'l USA exc NH
800-572-1880 NH

The Northwest Connection
800-648-6440 Cont'l USA

Travelodge International Inc./Viscount Hotels
800-255-3050 Cont'l USA & Canada

Treadway Inns Corp
800-752-3297 Cont'l USA

Vagabond Hotels Inc.
800-522-1555 Cont'l USA
800-468-2251 Canada

Introduction

Finding economical ways to travel is essential, and for years the *Mobil Travel Guide* has been a reliable resource to help direct travelers to lodgings and restaurants which suit their tastes and their budgets. Now *Lodgings for Less* makes choosing a reasonably priced accommodation even easier, while still insisting upon the high standards of maintenance and cleanliness for which *Mobil Travel Guide* is known.

Lodgings for Less includes establishments across the country that offer economical prices for two persons (double). There are three regional *Lodgings For Less Guides;* The Northeast And Midwest, The West, and The South. Features noted in the listings indicate the availability of senior citizen discounts, free lodging for children, recreational facilities on or nearby the premises, coin laundry, free coffee in rooms, picnic facilities, and the hours of restaurants on the premises or the availability of nearby dining. At the back of the book you will also find discount offerings for attractions and lodgings throughout the region.

Every establishment is inspected by experienced field representatives who submit detailed reports to the editorial offices. From these reports, the editors extract factual information for listings and ascertain that establishments to be recommended are clean, well-maintained, and well-managed.

During the inspection of establishments, field representatives identify fire protection equipment. The inspection does not extend to every room nor does it determine whether the equipment is working properly. The 🔲 symbol appearing at the end of a listing indicates the presence of smoke detectors and/or sprinkler systems. Travelers wishing to gain more information on fire protection systems at properties should contact the establishment directly to verify the installation and working conditions of their systems.

The rating for each establishment—motel, motor hotel, hotel, inn, resort, guest ranch—is measured against others of the same type. The criteria for rating accommodations are related to the number and quality of facilities, guest services, luxury of appointments and attitude and professionalism of staff and management. Because each type of establishment is viewed also in terms of its own style, unique characteristics and ambience, these additional qualities are also considered in determining a rating.

This introduction section explains the features of *Lodgings for Less* in more detail and provides useful travel advice.

How to Read the Listings

Each listing of a motel, motor hotel, hotel, inn, resort and guest ranch gives the quality rating, name, address, directions (when there is no street address), phone number (local and 800), room rates, seasons open (if not year-round), and number and type of rooms available. The listings also contain information on recreational and dining facilities on or adjacent to the establishment, credit cards, foreign languages spoken and Lodging Discount participation, noted with the 🅢 symbol.

You will find that many lodgings have received a check mark (✔) which appears before the quality rating. This denotes an unusually good value, relatively inexpensive. The criteria for this designation are found in the Good Value Check Rating section. Occasionally, an establishment may go out of business or change ownership just after our publication deadline. By calling ahead for reservations you can avoid the disappointment of discovering a closed or changed establishment. Space limitations necessitate the omission of many fine places; however, no adverse criticism is implied or should be inferred. There is no charge to an establishment for inclusion in *Lodgings for Less.*

Neither Prentice Hall nor Mobil Oil Corporation can be held responsible for changes in prices, name, management or deterioration in services—there is no contractual agreement between management and *Mobil Travel Guide* to guarantee prices or services.

Motels

Motels provide lodging facilities in low-rise structures that are easily accessible to parking areas. Lodges located in recreational areas also fall into our motel category.

Limited services are offered at these properties as the staff is frequently small. In higher-rated properties, however, services are more varied and the staff ratio per guest is higher.

Lobbies are functional, offering limited sitting areas. Shops and service businesses are not often found in motels. Some recreational facilities are offered, such as pools, which may be outdoor more often than indoor. In higher-rated properties, the recreational facilities will be more extensive.

Food services may be located adjacent to or opposite the establishment. The variety of restaurants within a motel or lodge varies with the level of luxury of the property.

Motor Hotels

Motor hotels range from low-rise structures to multi-storied buildings with varied facilities. The decision as to category is based upon its compatibility with the rating criteria.

Frequently offering dual room entry, motor hotels may provide lobbies with sitting areas, dining facilities, 24-hour front desk service and switchboard services. Often they will offer bellmen and valet services, room service and one or more pool areas. Because the following features and services apply to most establishments, they are not shown in the listing of motels and motor hotels:

- Year-round operation with a single rate schedule
- European plan (meals not included in room rate)
- Bathroom with tub and/or shower in each room
- Air-conditioned/heated, often with individual room control
- Cots
- Daily maid service
- Free parking
- Phones in rooms
- Elevators

The distinction between motor hotels and hotels in metropolitan areas is minor.

Hotels

To be categorized as a hotel, the establishment must have most of the following facilities and services: multiple floors, a restaurant and/or coffee shop, elevators, room service, bellhops, valet services, spacious lobby and some recreational facilities.

A hotel offers its guests a broad spectrum of lodging experiences. Because the following features and services apply to most establishments, they are not shown in the listing:

- Year-round operation with a single rate structure
- European plan (meals not included in room rate)
- Bathroom with tub and/or shower in each room
- Air-conditioned/heated, often with individual room control
- Daily maid service
- One-day laundry/cleaning service (check with desk clerk)
- Room service during hours restaurant is open
- Elevator
- Phones in rooms
- Bellhops
- Oversize beds available

Resorts

Resorts are establishments specializing in stays of one week or more. They usually offer American Plan and/or housekeeping facilities, with an emphasis on recreational facilities, often providing the services of a social director.

Food services are of primary importance at a resort. Guests must be able to obtain three meals a day on the premises or be provided with grocery stores to enable them to obtain food for meal preparation without leaving the premises.

When horseback riding is indicated, phone ahead to inquire about English saddle availability; Western style is assumed.

Inns

Frequently thought of as a small hotel, an inn is a place of homelike comfort and warm hospitality. It is often a structure of historic significance, located in an equally interesting environmental setting.

Meals are a special time at an inn and frequently tea will be served in the late afternoon. Rooms are usually individually decorated, featuring antiques or furnishings representative of the locale. Phones and bathrooms may not be available in every room.

Guest Ranches

Like resorts, guest ranches specialize in stays of a week or more. Guest ranches also offer meal plans and extensive outdoor activities such as horseback riding. Stables and trails exist on the ranch; daily, expert instruction is part of the program. Ranging from casual to rustic, many guest ranches are working ranches and guests are encouraged to participate in various aspects of ranch life. Eating is often family style and may also include cookouts as part of morning, midday or evening trail rides. Phone ahead to inquire about English saddle availability; Western style is assumed.

Cottage Colonies

Cottage colonies are housekeeping cottages and cabins that are usually found in recreational areas. When dining or recreational facilities are available on the premises, you will find it noted in the listing.

Prices

Because of inflation and changing wage and hour laws, costs and prices continue to rise. All prices quoted in *Lodgings For Less* are expected to be in effect at the time of publication and during the entire year; however, prices cannot be guaranteed.

Neither Prentice Hall nor Mobil Oil Corporation can be held responsible for changes in prices, name, management or deterioration in services. There is no contractual agreement between management and the *Mobil Travel Guide* to guarantee prices or services.

In some localities there may be short-term price variations because of special events or holidays. Whenever possible, these price changes are noted. Certain resorts have complicated rate structures that vary with the time of year—it's a good idea to contact the management to confirm specific rates. State and city sales taxes added to rooms and meals are not included in listed prices. Many places now add a special room tax; some establishments also charge a flat rate for telephone use in addition to the published room rates. Listings do not include either of these rates. Always secure a confirmation of rates prior to registration to avoid any misunderstanding.

Explaining the Ratings

The rating categories, ★ through ★★★, apply nationally. The principal areas of evaluation are quality of physical structure, furnishings, maintenance, housekeeping, overall service and food service. Climate, historic, cultural and artistic variations representative of regional differences are major factors in each rating. No rating is ever final, since each is subject to annual review; hence each establishment must continue to earn its rating and has a chance to improve it as well.

Every effort is made to assure that ratings are fair and accurate: the designated ratings are published to serve as an aid to travelers and should not be used for any other purpose.

A further rating designation exists and that is Unrated. When major changes have occurred during the one-year period prior to publication, there will be no star rating. These changes may be in management, ownership or general manager. If an establishment is undergoing major renovation/refurbishment or has been in operation less than one year, it will also appear unrated. The decision to list an establishment "unrated" is the responsibility of the Rating Committee.

Every establishment listed in *Lodgings for Less* is inspected by experienced field representatives who submit detailed reports to the editorial offices. From these reports, the editors extract factual information for listings and ascertain that establishments to be recommended are clean, well-maintained, well-managed and above average.

Ratings are based upon the inspection reports, written evaluation of staff members who stay and dine anonymously at establishments throughout the year, and an extensive review of guest comments received by the *Mobil Travel Guide* editorial offices.

The rating for each establishment—motel, motor hotel, hotel, inn, resort or guest ranch—is measured against others of the same type. The criteria for rating accommodations are related to the number and quality of facilities, guest services, luxury of appointments and attitude and professionalism of staff and management. Because each type of establishment is viewed also in terms of its own style, unique characteristics and ambience, these additional qualities are also considered in determining a rating.

Star Ratings

One-Star Rating: A 1-Star establishment should be clean, comfortable and well-maintained. It offers a minimum of service, probably having limited phone service, but frequently will have a small outdoor pool and restaurant serving breakfast adjacent to the establishment.

Two-Star Rating: A 2-Star establishment offers all of the qualities of a 1-star plus additional services such as 24-hour front desk facilities, indoor or outdoor pool, coffee shop on the premises and larger, more attractive rooms.

Three-Star Rating: A 3-Star establishment represents an excellent lodging accommodation. Very often beautifully appointed, the range of facilities is extensive, offering full service restaurants, wake-up services, suites and many other exceptional qualities to make a stay appealing and comfortable.

Good Value Check Rating

The check mark designation appearing in front of the star rating of a listing indicates "an unusually good value, relatively inexpensive." It will appear with the listing in the following manner:

✔ ★ Prentice Motor Inn

Lodging establishments rated with a good value check mark have been determined to be clean and well-maintained, offering some appointments such as room phones, free television, pools and breakfast on or adjacent to the premises, at economical prices.

Due to the fact that prevailing rates vary regionally, we are able to be more selective in our good value rated establishments in some areas than in others. However, you will find a wide range of these properties to visit in all locales.

Rate Information

Budget lodgings are scarce, and often nonexistent in many major cities and resort areas. Consequently, these cities will have listings which are higher in their rates for two persons than noted on the cover of this Guide. Please refer to the State Information page for the areas that fall into these categories and their price ranges. All lodgings listed within each city are available for the given price or less and are considered to be a good value for their particular area.

Lodgings for Less selects a representative cross section of accommodations which gives the traveler a wide range of choice in both type and price. Space limitations necessitate the omission of many fine places; however, no adverse criticism is implied or should be inferred.

Credit Cards

The major credit cards honored by each establishment are indicated by initials at the end of the listing. Many establishments do not honor any credit cards; some honor cards other than those listed. Please remember that Mobil Oil Corporation credit cards cannot be used for payment of meals and room charges. Be sure the credit cards you plan to use in your travels are current and will not expire before your trip is over. If you should lose one, report the loss immediately.

The following letters indicate credit cards that are accepted by the listed establishments:

A-American Express
C-Carte Blanche
D-Diners Club
DS-Discover
ER-enRoute
MC-MasterCard
V-Visa

Terms and Abbreviations

The following terms and abbreviations are used consistently throughout the listings. See "How to Read the Listings" on the inside front cover for an explanation of symbols used in the listings.
AP   Indicates American plan (lodging plus all meals)
Bar   Liquor, wine and beer are served at a bar or in a cocktail lounge usually with meals unless otherwise indicated (e.g., "wine, beer")

Cafe   Any type of restaurant or dining room except a cafeteria

Ck-in; ck-out   Check-in time; check-out time

Coin lndry   Self-service laundry

Continental bkfst   Usually coffee and a roll or doughnut

D   Followed by a price; indicates room rate for two persons in one room (one or two beds; charge may be higher if two double beds are offered)

Each addl   Extra charge for each additional person beyond the stated number of persons for a given price

Early   In referring to season openings or closings, approximately the first third of a month (May 1 to May 10); check with management for exact date

EP   Indicates European plan (lodging only)

Exc   Except

Exercise equipt   Two or more pieces of exercise equipment on the premises

Exercise rm   When an instructor is on the premises, this term is used to indicate both exercise equipment and room

Golf privileges   Privileges at a course within 10 miles

Hols   Holidays

In-rm movies   Videotaped movies available for use with video cassette player

Kit. or kits.   A kitchen or kitchenette with stove, sink, and refrigerator that is either part of the room or a separate room. If the kitchen is not fully equipped, the listing will indicate "no equipt" or "some equipt"

Late   In referring to season openings or closings, approximately the last third of a month (May 21 to May 31); check with management for exact date

MAP   Indicates Modified American Plan (lodging plus two meals)

Mid   In referring to season openings or closings, approximately the middle third of a month (May 11 to May 20); check with management for exact date

Min   "Minimum" is the smallest check per person in a restaurant; generally it may be made up of food and/or drinks

No elvtr   In a hotel with more than two stories, it is assumed there is an elevator, so it is not noted; only its absence is noted

No phones   Only the absence of phones is noted

Private club   A cocktail lounge or bar available to members and their guests (in Motels and Hotels where these clubs exist, registered guests can usually use the club as guests of the management; frequently the same is true of restaurants)

Res   Reservations required

S   Followed by a price; indicates room rate for one person

Serv bar   Where drinks are prepared for dining patrons only

Serv charge   Service charge is the amount added to restaurant check in lieu of tip

Serv plate   Charge for an extra plate when meal is shared

Snow skiing downhill/x-country   Downhill and/or cross-country skiing within 20 miles of property

Tennis privileges   Privileges at tennis courts within 5 miles

TV   Indicates color television; B/W indicates black-and-white television

Under 18 free   Children under a specific age not charged if staying in room with one or both parents

Handicapped Traveler Information

Lodgings For Less handicapped symbol noted in accommodations is intended to serve travelers with limited handicaps, temporary impairments or the semi-ambulatory.

When the handicapped symbol ♿ appears following a listing, the establishment is equipped with facilities to accommodate persons in wheelchairs, on crutches or the aged in need of easy access to doorways and restroom facilities. Severely handicapped persons, the hard of hearing and blind persons should not assume establishments bearing our symbol will offer facilities to meet their needs. We suggest these persons phone an establishment before their visit to ascertain if their particular needs will be met.

The following facilities must be available at all lodging properties bearing our handicapped symbol:

Public Areas

- Handicapped parking near access ramps
- Ramps at entryways to buildings
- Swinging entryway doors (32″ width)
- Restrooms on main level with room to operate a wheelchair; handrails at commode areas
- Elevators equipped with grab bars; lowered control buttons
- Restaurants on main level, easy-access doorways; restrooms with room to operate wheelchair; handrails at commode areas

Rooms

- 32″ width entryway to rooms
- Low-pile carpet
- Telephone at bedside
- Bed placed at wheelchair height
- 32″ width doorway to bathroom

- Bath, open sink—no cabinet; room to operate wheelchair
- Handrails at commode areas; tub handrails

Many useful hints may be picked up from several excellent books written specifically for the handicapped traveler. *Access to the World,* by Louise Weiss (Facts on File, 460 Park Avenue South, New York, NY 10016, 1983), at $16.95, is a good source of travel information for the disabled, including chapters on various modes of travel, destination sources, access guides and health care. Also available is the magazine entitled *Itinerary: The Magazine for Travelers with Disabilities,* published every month; a year's subscription is $9. For more information write to *Itinerary,* P.O. Box 1084, Bayonne, NJ 07002.

Other informative material on facilities for the handicapped may be obtained from local chapters of the Easter Seal Society for Crippled Children and Adults. To obtain information on programs and books, call Library of Congress, 800/424-8567.

Many national parks have facilities specially constructed for handi-capped people—ramps, wide doors, Braille trails, emergency equipment and other features.

Lodging Discounts

Lodgings For Less continues to offer travelers discounts of 10% off each night's stay during the calendar year of 1989. Participating establishments will appear with a 🛇 symbol at the end of their listing.

You will find many hotel and motel properties participating in this discount program. When placing advance reservations, identify yourself as a *Mobil Travel Guide Lodgings For Less* Discount user. You will be required to show your Identification Card <u>at the time of registration</u>. This card may be found near the back of this Guide.

This discount may not be used in combination with other discounts or promotions offered at participating establishments. Reservations made through travel agents are not eligible for this discount.

This discount offering is made possible through the generosity of the participating quality-rated establishments. The *Lodgings For Less Guide* and Prentice Hall may not be held responsible for the failure of any participating management to honor these discounts.

Travel Tips

Lodging

Many hotels in major metropolitan areas offer special weekend package plans. These plans offer considerable savings on rooms and often include breakfast, cocktails and some meal discounts as well. Information on specific pricing for these specials is not available because prices change frequently throughout the year. We suggest you phone to obtain current information prior to your trip.

Traveling with Pets

Before taking your pet on a trip, make several test drives. Don't forget to carry a certificate of good health and proof of a rabies shot. Always use a leash for your dog; keep your cat in a well-ventilated carrier. Bring plenty of food and water and plan to stop frequently for exercise. The establishments accepting pets show a pet symbol at the end of a listing. We recommend you phone ahead to verify this accessibility.

10 Tips for Worry-Free Travel

1. Be sure to notify local police and leave a phone number where you can be contacted in case of emergency.
2. Lock doors and windows, but leave shades up and lights on (or on an automatic timer).
3. Stop newspaper deliveries and discontinue garbage pickups.
4. Remove food and defrost refrigerator; store valuables in a safe place; disconnect electrical appliances; turn off gas jets, including hot water heater; turn off water faucets and drain pipes in severe weather.
5. Remember to pack personal medicines and duplicate prescriptions; spare eyeglasses or the prescription; sunglasses; suntan lotion; First Aid kit; insect spray; towels and tissues; writing materials.
6. Make sure that proof of car insurance is in your glove compartment; also take along your driver's license and those of other passengers (check expiration dates); car registration; copies of birth certificates (if driving outside U.S.); traveler's checks. Be sure you have a duplicate set of car keys.
7. Check to see that you have a jack, spare tire, repair kit, emergency tools, flashlights, tire chains, spare fan belt, windshield scraper, auto fuses, lug wrench and work gloves. A pre-trip tune-up won't hurt—and, of course, be sure to "fill up" before you start out.

8. Also check vehicle's battery, oil and air filters, cooling system, brakes and lights.
9. Remember "extras" like hunting/fishing licenses and equipment; camera and film; bathing suits, beach accessories, sports equipment; portable radio and/or TV; picnic accessories.
10. Buckle up your seat belt, and have a nice trip!

Interstate Highway System

State towns are listed alphabetically showing cities that are within 10 miles of indicated interstate highways.

Weather Information

Average temperatures are listed for the entire state. Averages are given for specific regions if significant differences exist.

Visitor Information

Immediately following each state heading you will find statistics on population, elevation, Capital, and many other interesting facts. A Visitor Information section, which gives the names of places to write to or call for further information on the state, is also provided.

Room Rate Information

Major cities and resort areas frequently have higher room rates for two (double) than indicated on the cover of this Guide. Towns falling into these categories are listed with their rates for two (double) in each State Introduction section.

Attraction Discount Coupons

The Attraction Discount Coupons at the back of this book offer considerable savings for the traveler with discounts in varying amounts. All coupons note the amount of savings a family may anticipate.

All of the special admission prices are made available by the participating attractions. The *Lodgings For Less Guide* does not reimburse the managements, nor do they pay to be included. The *Lodgings For Less Guide* is not responsible for any changes in terms, discounts or performances offered by the participants in the Discount Coupon program subsequent to publication of this book. The *Guide* is not responsible for the failure of any management to honor the coupons nor for any injury or loss sustained by anyone using these Discount Coupons. Remember, the coupons are not always accepted in conjunction with other discount coupons. Since some places are not open during the entire year and others honor coupons only during certain seasons, please read all information on the back of each coupon before presenting it.

The editors welcome comments from users of the Discount Coupon program as well as any other general reactions to *Lodgings For Less.* Please address letters to: *Mobil Travel Guide,* Prentice Hall, 108 Wilmot Road, Suite 450, Deerfield, IL 60015.

Savings for Seniors

Lodgings For Less notes senior citizen rates in lodgings. Always call ahead to confirm that the discount is being offered. Carry proof of age, such as a passport, birth certificate or driver's license. Medicare cards are often accepted as proof. Contact the following organizations for additional information:

1. American Association of Retired Persons (AARP), 1909 K Street NW, Washington, DC 20049
2. National Council of Senior Citizens, 925 15th Street NW, Washington, DC 20005

The mature traveler on a limited budget should look for the senior citizen discount symbol in lodging listings. Also, pay special attention to all listings in the Guide highlighted by a check mark (✔).

Car Care

Familiarize yourself with the owner's manual for your car. It provides valuable advice for service and maintenance. Get a lubrication and oil change, an inspection of tires, fan belts and cooling system, and a check of engine performance, lights and brakes. Any other regular services recommended by the car manufacturer should be performed as well.

Once your car is ready for the road, make certain your insurance is paid up—and don't forget your registration certificate, insurance information, driver's license and an extra set of keys.

Keep your seat belt and harness fastened. Watch your instrument panel closely—your panel gauges or indicators will alert you to potential problems. If a problem arises, get to a service station as soon as possible.

A world of convenience is yours with a Mobil credit card. Mobil's gasoline, oil and tires, as well as many other products and services may be charged at Mobil dealers in the U.S. as well as at certain other dealers throughout Canada.

Road Emergencies

The best insurance against an emergency is proper maintenance of your car. Despite care, however, the unexpected can happen. Here are a few tips for handling emergencies:

Accidents. If you should have an accident, observe the following:

- Do not leave accident scene
- Help the injured but don't move them unless necessary
- Call police—ask for medical help if needed
- Get names, addresses, license numbers and insurance company of persons involved
- Get names and addresses of at least two witnesses
- Get description and registration number of cars involved
- Report accident to your insurance company
- Diagram the accident showing cars involved

Breakdowns. If your car breaks down, get out of traffic as soon as possible, pulling off the road if you can. Turn on your emergency flashers and raise the hood. If you have no flashers, tie a white cloth to the roadside door handle or antenna. Stay near your car but off the road. Carry and use flares or reflectors to keep your car from being hit.

Blowout. Do not overreact if you have a tire blowout. Hold the wheel steady—do not jerk it. Gradually let up on the gas pedal, steer straight and coast to a stop. If you have to brake, do so very gently.

Collision. "If a collision is imminent, you will need to make these split-second decisions," advises the National Safety Council's Defensive Driving Course. "Drive right, away from the oncoming vehicle. Drive with control, don't skid off the road. If you are forced to drive off the road, look for something either soft, like bushes or small trees, or something fixed, like a break-away pole or a fence to break your impact. A fixed object has no momentum and the crash will be less intense than if you had hit the oncoming vehicle. If you are unable to ride off the road, try to collide with the oncoming vehicle at an angle. A glancing blow is less dangerous than hitting a vehicle head on."

Flat tire. Drive off the road, even if you risk ruining your tire. Set the parking brake firmly, but remember it may not hold if a rear wheel is off the ground. Put wooden blocks, bricks or stones tightly against the front and rear of the tire diagonally opposite the flat. After removing the hubcap, loosen each wheel nut about one-half turn. Position the jack exactly as the instructions indicate, then raise the car an inch or two to determine how the jack fits. (If it appears to be about to slip, stop and wait for help.)

Jack the car until the flat is about three inches off the ground, remove the wheel nuts and put them in the hubcap. Keep your body away from the car. Handle the tire from the sides; never put your hand above or underneath the tire.

Slide the spare tire into place, using the wrench as a lever. You may have to raise the jack a little farther. Screw the nuts on firmly and jack the car down, standing at the side, not in front of the car. Finally, fully tighten the wheel nuts and leave the hubcap off as a reminder to have the flat fixed.

Skids. When your car skids, let up on the gas gently, keeping some power going to the wheels. Steer into the direction of the skid and brake only after you have the car under complete control.

Stuck wheels. If you get stuck in the mud or snow, don't spin the wheels. Rock the car by gently accelerating ahead and back in rhythm with the car's natural tendency.

Equipment. The following checklist describes the necessary equipment to carry at all times:

- ☐ Spare tire; tool kit; first aid kit
- ☐ Road flares; flashlight
- ☐ Jumper cables; gloves
- ☐ Can of oil; a can opener
- ☐ Empty one-gallon container (Note: Check local laws governing type of container to use for gasoline.)
- ☐ Spare parts, fan belt and fuses (especially for foreign cars)
- ☐ In winter: chains, ice scraper, de-icer in spray can, shovel, "liquid chain" or a one-gallon milk carton filled with dry sand
- ☐ Mobil credit card and auto club identification

Connecticut

Population: 3,107,576

Land area: 4,872 sq mi (12,618 sq km)

Elevation: 0–2,380 ft (0–725 m)

Highest point: Mount Frissel (Litchfield Co)

Entered Union: Fifth of original 13 states (January 9, 1788)

Capital: Hartford

Motto: *Qui transtulit sustinet* (He who transplanted, still sustains)

Nickname: Constitution State

State flower: Mountain laurel

State bird: American robin

State tree: White oak

Time zone: Eastern

Interstate Highway System

The following alphabetical listing of Connecticut towns in *Mobil Travel Guide* shows that these cities are within 10 miles (16 kilometers) of the indicated Interstate highways. A highway map should be checked for the nearest exit.

INTERSTATE 84: Danbury, Farmington, Hartford, Manchester, Southbury, Stafford Springs, Vernon, Waterbury.

INTERSTATE 91: Enfield, Hartford, Meriden, Middletown, New Haven, Wallingford, Wethersfield, Windsor, Windsor Locks.

INTERSTATE 95: Branford, Bridgeport, Clinton, Darien, Fairfield, Greenwich, Groton, Guilford, Madison, Milford, Mystic, New Haven, New London, Norwalk, Old Saybrook, Stamford, Stonington, Stratford, Westport.

Weather Statistics*

	WINTER	SPRING	SUMMER	FALL
Statewide	28°F (-2°C)	46°F (8°C)	70°F (21°C)	52°F (11°C)
Hill Country	16°F (-9°C)	37°F (3°C)	60°F (15°C)	42°F (5°C)

*Average mean temperatures are listed for the entire state. Averages for specific regions are given if significant differences exist.

Visitor Information

State of Connecticut Department of Economic Development, 210 Washington St, Hartford 06106; toll-free 800/243-1685 (Maine through Virginia, except CT), 800/842-7492 (in CT), 203/566-3977 or -3385, distributes pamphlets on vacationing in Connecticut. Other pamphlets may be obtained at any Highway Tourist Information Center. *Connecticut*—a monthly magazine available at newsstands—gives a listing of activities around the state.

Room Rate Information

The following major cities have higher room rates for two (double) than indicated on the cover of this Guide. However, the lodgings listed in these cities offer a good value when compared to others of their type in the area.

Hartford	$70	New Haven	$80

Danbury

Settled: 1685 **Pop:** 60,470 **Elev:** 378 ft (115 m) **Area code:** 203 **Zip:** 06810

Motel

 ★SUPER 8. *3 Lake Ave Ext, I-84 Lake Ave exit. 203/743-0064.* 86 rms, 4 story. S $46.88–$51.88; D $46.88–$61.88; each addl $5; under 12 free. TV. Free coffee. Ck-out 11 am. Cr cds: A, C, D, DS, MC, V.

Darien

Pop: 18,892 **Elev:** 60 ft (18 m) **Area code:** 203 **Zip:** 06820

Motel

 ★★COMFORT INN. *50 Ledge Rd, I-95 exit 10. 203/655-8211.* 99 rms, 3 story. S, D $49.95–$91; each addl $5; suites $150–$180; under 12 free; wkend rates. Crib free. TV; cable. Pool. Cafe 7 am–2 pm, 5–10 pm. Rm serv. Bar 5:30 pm–midnight. Ck-out noon. Meeting rms. Bellhops. Cr cds: A, C, D, DS, MC, V. Ⓕ

Enfield

Settled: 1680 **Pop:** 42,695 **Elev:** 150 ft (46 m) **Area code:** 203 **Zip:** 06082

Motel

 ★RED ROOF INN. *5 Hazard Ave. 203/741-2571.* 109 rms, 2 story. S $33.95–$35.95; D $39.95–$41.95; under 18 free. Crib free. Cafe adj 6:30–12:30 am. Ck-out noon. X-country ski 1 mi. Cr cds: A, C, D, DS, MC, V.

Greenwich

Settled: 1640 **Pop:** 59,578 **Elev:** 71 ft (21 m) **Area code:** 203 **Zip:** 06830

Inn

 ★★STANTON HOUSE. *76 Maple Ave. 203/869-2110.* 30 rms, 20 baths, 3–4 story. No elvtr. Some rm phones. S $39–$85; D $49–$95; each addl $10. Children over 8 yrs only. TV avail. Complimentary continental bkfst. Ck-out 11 am, ck-in 3 pm. Some refrigerators. Picnic tables. Built late 1800s; antiques. Cr cds: A, MC, V. Ⓔ Ⓕ

Hartford

Settled: 1623 **Pop:** 136,392 **Elev:** 50 ft (15 m) **Area code:** 203

Hotel

★RAMADA INN-CAPITOL HILL. *440 Asylum St (06103), opp State Capitol Bldg. 203/246-6591.* 96 rms, 9 story. S $71–$81; D $67–$78; each addl $10. Crib free. TV. Cafe 6:30 am–11 pm. Bar 11 am–midnight. Ck-out noon. Meeting rms. Garage. Cr cds: A, C, D, DS, MC, V. Ⓔ Ⓕ

Lakeville

Settled: 1740 **Pop:** 1,200 (est) **Elev:** 764 ft (233 m) **Area code:** 203 **Zip:** 06039

Motels

✔ ★★**IRON MASTERS.** *Main St, on US 44, ½ mi E of CT 41. 203/435-9844.* 26 rms, 6 kits. Apr–Nov: S $42–$75; D $46–$75; each addl $6–$12; kit. units $6 addl; under 12 free; higher rates special events; lower rates rest of yr. Crib $6. TV; cable. Heated pool. Coffee in rms. Cafe 7 am–11 pm. Bar. Ck-out 11 am. Cr cds: A, D, MC, V. Ⓕ

★★**SHARON MOTOR LODGE.** *(CT 41, Sharon 06069) 7 mi S on CT 41. 203/364-0036.* 22 rms. May–Oct: D $52–$75; lower rates rest of yr. Crib free. TV; cable. Pool. Cafe opp 6:30 am–8 pm. Ck-out 11 am. Downhill/x-country ski 10 mi. Picnic tables. Ⓓ Ⓕ

Manchester

Settled: 1672 **Pop:** 49,761 **Elev:** 272 ft (83 m) **Area code:** 203 **Zip:** 06040

Motel

✔ ★**CONNECTICUT MOTOR LODGE.** *400 Tolland Tpke, at I-84 exit 63. 203/643-1555.* 31 rms. S $38.50; D $41.50; each addl $4; under 14 free. Crib free. TV. Cafe adj 7 am–11 pm; Sat to midnight. Ck-out 11 am. Cr cds: A, MC, V.

Meriden

Settled: 1661 **Pop:** 57,118 **Elev:** 144 ft (44 m) **Area code:** 203 **Zip:** 06450

Motel

✔ ★**SUSSE CHALET.** *(462 Queen St, Southington 06489) I-84 exit 32. 203/621-0181.* 116 rms, 2 story. S $33.70; D $37.70; each addl $4. Crib $2. TV; cable. Pool. Cafe adj 7 am–11 pm. Ck-out 11 am. Coin lndry. Cr cds: A, D, MC, V. Ⓔ Ⓕ

Milford

Settled: 1639 **Pop:** 50,898 **Elev:** 89 ft (27 m) **Area code:** 203 **Zip:** 06460

Motels

✔ ★★**HAMPTON INN.** *129 Plains Rd, I-95 exit 36. 203/874-4400.* 148 rms, 3 story. S $48–$60; D $54–$66; under 18 free. TV; cable, in-rm movies. Continental bkfst. Ck-out noon. Meeting rms. Valet serv. Some refrigerators. Cr cds: A, C, D, DS, MC, V. Ⓔ Ⓘ

★★★**HOWARD JOHNSON.** *1052 Boston Post Rd (US 1), at I-95 exit 39A. 203/878-4611.* 158 rms, 1–5 story. S, D $45–$85; each addl $8; suites $105–$130; under 18 free; higher rates special events. Crib free. TV. 2 pools, 1 indoor. Playground. Cafe open 24 hrs. Bar 11:30–1 am; Fri, Sat to 2 am. Ck-out noon. Meeting rms. Bellhops. Valet serv. Sundries. Miniature golf. Exercise equipt; weight machines, bicycles, whirlpool, sauna. Rec rm. Most refrigerators. Private patios, balconies. Picnic tables. Cr cds: A, C, D, DS, MC, V. Ⓕ

New Haven

Settled: 1638 **Pop:** 126,109 **Elev:** 25 ft (8 m) **Area code:** 203

Motor Hotels

★★**HOLIDAY INN-NEW HAVEN.** *30 Whalley Ave (06511), near Yale Univ.* *203/777-6221.* 160 units, 8 story. S $69–$82; D $77–$90; each addl $10; suites $95; under 18 free; higher rates Yale special events. Crib free. TV. Pool. Cafe 7 am–2 pm, 5–10 pm. Rm serv. Bar 11 am–midnight. Ck-out noon. Meeting rms. Bellhops. Valet serv. Covered parking. Cr cds: A, C, D, DS, MC, V.

★★**HOWARD JOHNSON.** *400 Sargent Dr (06511). 203/562-1111.* 153 rms, 8 story. Jan–May: S $66; D $72; each addl $8; under 18 free; higher rates Yale graduation; lower rates rest of yr. Crib free. TV. Pool. Cafe open 24 hrs. Bar 11–1 am. Ck-out noon. Meeting rms. Free area transportation. Cr cds: A, C, D, DS, MC, V.

✔★**SUPER 8.** *(7 Kimberly Ave, West Haven 06516) I-95 exit 44. 203/932-8338.* 82 rms, 2 story. S $46–$50; D $47.10–$55.30; suites $69–$87; under 12 free. Crib $3. TV; cable. Free continental bkfst. Ck-out 11 am. Meeting rms. Cr cds: A, C, D, DS, MC, V.

New London

Settled: 1646 **Pop:** 28,842 **Elev:** 33 ft (10 m) **Area code:** 203 **Zip:** 06320

Motel

✔★★**TRAVELODGE CONNECTICUT YANKEE.** *(Box 479, Niantic 06357) At jct I-95 exit 74 & CT 161. 203/739-5483.* 50 rms, 2 story. July–Labor Day: S $38–$83; D $42–$83; each addl $7; under 17 free; lower rates rest of yr. Crib free. TV; cable. Pool; sauna. Free bkfst. Rm serv. Bar. Ck-out 11 am. Meeting rms. Valet serv. Game rm. Beach privileges. Cr cds: A, C, D, DS, MC, V. Ⓓ Ⓘ

New Preston

Pop: 1,209 **Elev:** 700 ft (213 m) **Area code:** 203 **Zip:** 06777

Inn

✔★★**HOPKINS INN.** *Hopkins Rd, 2 mi N; ½ mi W of CT 45. 203/868-7295.* 10 units, 9 baths, 3 story. No A/C. No elvtr. No rm phones. Apr–Dec: S, D $45–$53; each addl $5; suite $62. Closed rest of yr. Cafe 8:30–9:30 am, noon–2 pm, 6–9 pm; Fri to 10 pm; Sat 5:30–10 pm; Sun 12:30–8:30 pm. No rm serv. Bar. Ck-out 11 am. Lake Waramaug opp. Established 1847. Ⓓ Ⓕ

Stamford

Settled: 1641 **Pop:** 102,453 **Elev:** 10 ft (3 m) **Area code:** 203

Motor Hotel

✔★**SUPER 8.** *32 Grenhart Rd (06902), I-95 exit 6. 203/324-8887.* 99 rms, 4 story. S $45.88; D $50.88; each addl $5; suite $45.88–$55.88; under 18 free. Crib free. TV; cable. Free coffee. Ck-out 11 am. Meeting rms. Cr cds: A, C, D, DS, MC, V. Ⓔ Ⓕ

Wethersfield

Settled: 1634 **Pop:** 23,013 **Elev:** 45 ft (14 m) **Area code:** 203 **Zip:** 06109

Motel

✔ ★ ★ **GREAT MEADOW INN.** *(1499 Silas Deane Hwy, Rocky Hill 06067) At I-91 exit 24. 203/529-7446.* 83 rms, 2 story. S, D $45–$75; each addl $6.50; studio rms $50–$65; kit. units $575–$750/month; under 18 free; higher rates special events. Crib free. TV; cable. Pool. Cafe 6–1 am. Ck-out 11 am. Coin lndry. Meeting rms. Valet serv. Sundries. Airport transportation. Cr cds: A, C, D, MC, V.

Woodbury

Pop: 6,942 **Elev:** 264 ft (80 m) **Area code:** 203 **Zip:** 06798

Inn

✔ ★ **CURTIS HOUSE.** *506 Main St S. 203/263-2101.* 18 rms, 12 with bath, 12 A/C, 3 story. S, D $26–$69; each addl $10. Many rms with B/W TV; cable. Cafe noon–2 pm, 5–9 pm; Sun noon–8 pm. Bar. Ck-out 11 am, ck-in 1 pm. Tennis, golf, racquetball, health club nearby. Downhill/x-country ski 5 mi. Oldest inn in state; since 1754. Cr cds: MC, V.

Delaware

Population: 594,317
Land area: 1,982 sq mi (5,133 sq km)
Elevation: 0–442 ft (0–135 m)
Highest point: Ebright Road (New Castle Co)
Entered Union: First state to ratify Constitution (December 7, 1787)
Capital: Dover
Motto: Liberty and Independence
Nicknames: First State, Small Wonder, Diamond State, Blue Hen State
State flower: Peach blossom
State bird: Blue hen chicken
State tree: American holly
State fair: Late July 1989, in Harrington
Time zone: Eastern

Interstate Highway System

The following alphabetical listing of Delaware towns in *Mobil Travel Guide* shows that these cities are within 10 miles (16 kilometers) of the indicated Interstate highway. A highway map should, however, be checked for the nearest exit.

INTERSTATE 95: Newark, New Castle, Wilmington.

Weather Statistics*

	WINTER	SPRING	SUMMER	FALL
Statewide	39°F (4°C)	64°F (18°C)	74°F (23°C)	57°F (14°C)

*Average mean temperatures are listed for the entire state. Averages for specific regions are given if significant differences exist.

Visitor Information

Delaware Tourism Office, 99 Kings Highway, Box 1401, Dover 19903, will provide business and tourist information. Phone 800/282-8667 in Delaware or 800/441-8846 if calling from outside the state.

An excellent reference for history and local color is *Delaware, A Guide to the First State* (Hastings House, New York, revised 1955), one of the American Guide Series.

Visitor centers provide information and brochures on points of interest in the state. Their locations are as follows: Delaware Memorial Bridge Plaza, jct I-295 and the bridge at New Castle (daily, 8 am–8 pm); I-95 Rest Area, Greater Wilmington Convention and Visitors Bureau, Wilmington (Mon–Fri, 9 am–5 pm), phone 302/737-4059; Margaret O'Neill Information Center, Court St, Dover (daily, 8 am–4:30 pm), phone 302/736-4266; Smyrna, 1 mi N on US 13 (daily, 8 am–8 pm); Southern Delaware Visitor and Convention Center, 204 NE Front St in Milford, phone 800/345-4444.

Bethany Beach

Founded: 1901 **Pop:** 330 **Elev:** 8 ft (2 m) **Area code:** 302 **Zip:** 19930

Motel

★**SEA CREST.** *(Box F) Garfield Pkwy at Atlantic Ave. 302/539-7621.* 14 rms, 2 story. Mid-June–early Sep: D $55–$65; each addl $7; lower rates mid-Apr–May, after Labor Day–mid-Nov. Closed rest of yr. Crib $7. TV; cable. Free continental bkfst. Cafe adj 8 am–9 pm. Ck-out 11 am. Bellhops. On oceanfront. Cr cds: DS, MC, V.

Lewes

Settled: 1631 **Pop:** 2,197 **Elev:** 10 ft (3 m) **Area code:** 302 **Zip:** 19958

Motel

★**ANGLER'S.** *(Box 511) Angler's Rd at Market St, ½ blk NE of Canal Bridge. 302/ 645-2831; res: 800/523-3312.* 25 rms, 1–2 story, 2 kits. Mid-May–mid-Sep (3-day min wkends, hols): S $50–$63; D $55–$69; each addl $5; kit. units $60–$69; lower rates rest of yr. Crib free. TV; cable. Cafe adj. Ck-out 11 am. Picnic tables, grills. Sun deck. Overlooks canal, marina opp. Boat docking, truck parking. Cr cds: A, D, MC, V.

Newark

Settled: 1685 **Pop:** 25,247 **Elev:** 124 ft (38 m) **Area code:** 302

Motels

✔ ★ ★**COMFORT INN.** *1120 S College Ave (DE 896) (19711), at I-95 exit 1 (N). 302/368-8715.* 102 rms, 2 story. S $42–$45; D $51–$53; each addl $4; under 6 free. Crib free. TV. Pool; lifeguard. Cafe adj 6:30–1 am. Ck-out noon. Meeting rm. Some refrigerators. Cr cds: A, C, D, DS, MC, V.

★ ★**HOLIDAY INN-WILMINGTON AREA.** *1203 Christiana Rd (19713). 302/737-2700.* 144 rms, 2 story. S $52–$58; D $55–$61; each addl $6; under 19 free. Crib free. TV. Pool; lifeguard. Cafe 6:30 am–10 pm. Rm serv. Bar 11–1 am. Ck-out noon. Meeting rms. Valet serv. Sundries. Cr cds: A, C, D, DS, MC, V. ⒹⒺ

✔ ★**McINTOSH INN.** *100 McIntosh Plaza (19713). 302/453-9100.* 108 rms. S $31.95; D $38.95; each addl $3; 3–4, $41.95–$44.95. Crib $3. TV. Cafe open 24 hrs. Ck-out 11 am. Cr cds: A, MC, V.

New Castle

Settled: 1651 **Pop:** 4,907 **Elev:** 19 ft (6 m) **Area code:** 302 **Zip:** 19720

Motel

✔ ★ ★**DUTCH VILLAGE.** *111 S du Pont Hwy (US 13, 40, 301), 3 mi S of DE Memorial Bridge. 302/328-6246.* 41 rms. May–Aug: S $41–$54; D $43–$61; each addl $5; under 16 free. Crib $5. TV. Pool; lifeguard. Cafe adj 7 am–10 pm. Ck-out noon. Meeting rms. Valet serv. Airport, bus depot transportation. Some refrigerators. Cr cds: A, C, D, DS, MC, V. Ⓔⓘ

Rehoboth Beach

Settled: 1872 **Pop:** 1,730 **Elev:** 16 ft (5 m) **Area code:** 302 **Zip:** 19971

Motels

✔ ★**ADAMS OCEAN FRONT.** *(4 Read Ave, Dewey Beach) 1 mi S on DE 1. 302/227-3030; res: 800/448-8080.* 23 rms, 3 story. No elvtr. July–Sep: S $30–$74; D $35–$101; each addl $5; lower rates mid-Mar–mid-June, Oct. Closed rest of yr. Crib $5. TV; cable. Free continental bkfst. Ck-out 11 am. Refrigerators $5. On beachfront. Cr cds: A, MC, V.

✔ ★**COMMODORE.** *154 Rehoboth Ave. 302/227-9446; res: 800/245-2112.* 97 units, 1–4 story, 10 kits. S $32–$99; D $35–$99; each addl $6; kits. $45–$145; under 12 free; higher rates wkends. Crib free. TV; cable. Pool. Free coffee. Cafe nearby. Ck-out 11 am. Meeting rms. Some refrigerators. Cr cds: A, D, DS, MC, V. Ⓓ

District of Columbia

Population: 638,432	
Land area: 63 sq mi (163 sq km)	
Elevation: 1–410 ft (0–125 m)	
Highest point: Tenleytown	
District flower: American Beauty rose	
District bird: Wood thrush	
Founded: 1790	
Time zone: Eastern	

Visitor Information

Washington DC Convention and Visitors Association, 1575 Eye St NW, Suite 250, Washington, DC 20005. For brochures and schedules of events phone 202/789-7000 (Mon–Fri, 9 am–5 pm) or 800/422-8644. For daily recorded calendar of events phone 202/737-8866. In town, the Washington Visitor Information Center, 1455 Pennsylvania Ave NW, provides literature, maps and touring information (daily exc Sun; closed major hols).

The National Park Service maintains information kiosks at seven key points in the city.

International Visitors Information Service, 733 15th St NW, 20005. Phone 783-6540.

The average mean temperatures for the District of Columbia are 56°F (13°C) in spring; 76°F (24°C) in summer; 59°F (15°C) in fall; and 37°F (3°C) in winter.

NOTE: By writing to your representative or senator ahead of time, you can get two special tour privileges. One is a ticket for a White House tour that differs from the normal tour; you don't have to wait in a long line and the tour group is smaller. These 30-minute tours start at 8:30 and 8:45 am (Tu–Sat); you'll be assigned a specific time. The other ticket entitles you to watch congressional sessions in progress from the Visitors' Galleries. (Without a ticket you can only view the area when congress is not in session).

Write your senator at the United States Senate, Washington, DC 20510. Address your representative at the United States House of Representatives, Washington, DC 20515. All tickets are free, but in peak season, which starts in spring, White House tickets may be limited. In your letter, include the date you'll be in Washington, first and second-choice dates for the tours and the number of people in your party. Also include your home phone number should your representative's or senator's aide need to contact you. You can also get tickets, if available, directly from the office of your senator or representative after you arrive in Washington.

Room Rate Information

The District of Columbia is considered a major city and has higher room rates for two (double) than indicated on the cover of this Guide. However, the lodgings in this city offer a good value when compared to others of their type in the area. The lodgings listed for the District of Columbia have double room rates of $80 or less.

Washington

Area code: 202

Motel

✔ ★**DAYS INN CONNECTICUT AVE.** *4400 Connecticut Ave (20008). 202/244-5600.* 155 rms, 6 story. S $64–$79; D $69–$84; each addl $6; suites $90; under 18 free; wkend, hol rates. TV; cable, in-rm movies. Free continental bkfst. Ck-out noon. Bellhops. Free parking, some covered. 2 blks from Metro. Cr cds: A, C, D, DS, MC, V. Ⓔ Ⓕ

Motor Hotels

✔★★DAYS INN-CAPITOL CENTRE. *(55 Hampton Park Blvd, Capitol Heights, MD 20743) 301/336-8900.* 191 rms, 6 story. Apr–Aug: S $53–$65; D $59–$74; each addl $6; under 12 free; lower rates rest of yr. Crib free. TV; cable, in-rm movies. Pool; lifeguard. Cafe 6 am–10 pm. Ck-out noon. Meeting rms. Valet serv. Daily tours. Cr cds: A, D, DS, MC, V. ⑤ Ⓔ Ⓕ

🛇 🐾 ➰ ⊘ Ⓢ Ⓢ ⓢⓒ Ⓢ

★★QUALITY INN DOWNTOWN. *1315 16th St NW (20036). 202/232-8000; res: 800/368-5689.* 135 kit. units, 10 story. S $72–$105; D $80–$118; each addl $10; under 16 free; wkend rates. Crib free. Garage $6. TV; cable, in-rm movies. Pool privileges. Cafe 7 am–10 pm. Rm serv 7 am–2 pm, 5–9:30 pm. Bar 11:30–1 am. Ck-out noon. Meeting rms. Bellhops. Health club privileges. Refrigerators. Cr cds: A, C, D, DS, ER, MC, V. Ⓔ Ⓕ

➰ ⊘ ⊘ ⓢⓒ Ⓢ

Hotels

✔★CARLYLE SUITES. *1731 New Hampshire Ave NW (20009). 202/234-3200.* 170 units, 8 story, 156 kits. S $59–$89; D $69–$99; each addl $10; suites, kit. units $125–$150; under 17 free; wkend rates. Crib $10. TV; in-rm movies. Cafe 7 am–midnight. No rm serv. Bar 11–2 am. Ck-out 1 pm. Meeting rms. No bellhops. Health club privileges. Many refrigerators. Cr cds: A, C, D, MC, V. ⑤ Ⓔ Ⓕ Ⓘ

🐾 ⊘ ⊘ ⓢⓒ

★★RAMADA INN CENTRAL. *1430 Rhode Island Ave NW (20005). 202/462-7777.* 186 kit. suites, 10 story. S $69–$99; D $79–$109; each addl $10; under 18 free; wkend rates. Crib free. Garage $5.60. TV; cable. Pool; lifeguard. Cafe 7–11 am, 11:30 am–2:30 pm, 5–10 pm. Bar 2:30 pm–midnight. Ck-out noon. Health club privileges. Many bathrm phones. Cr cds: A, C, D, DS, MC, V. ⑤ Ⓔ Ⓕ

➰ ⊘ ⊘ ⓢⓒ

Inns

★EMBASSY. *1627 16th St NW (20009). 202/234-7800.* 41 rms, 5 story. S $59–$79; D $69–$89; each addl $10; under 14 free. Crib free. TV. Free continental bkfst, sherry, tea. Ck-out noon, ck-in 1 pm. Historic bldg; antiques. Cr cds: A, C, D, MC, V. Ⓔ Ⓕ Ⓘ

⊘ ⓢⓒ

✔★KALORAMA. *1854 Mintwood Pl NW (20009), follow Connecticut Ave N of Dupont Circle, right on Columbia Rd. 202/667-6369.* 31 units, some shared baths, in 4 townhouses, 3 story. S $40–$75; D $45–$80; each addl $10; suites $70–$100; wkly rates. Free continental bkfst. Ck-out 11 am. Free lndry facilities. Limited parking avail. Victorian townhouses (1890s); rms individually decorated, antiques. Garden. Cr cds: A, D, MC, V.

⊘ ⓢⓒ

★WINDSOR. *1842 16th St NW (20009). 202/667-0300.* 48 units, 4 story, 9 suites. No elvtr. S $59–$79; D $69–$89; each addl $10; suites $105–$150; under 15 free. Crib free. TV. Free continental bkfst. Cafe nearby. Ck-out noon, ck-in 1 pm. Historic bldg (1900s). Cr cds: A, C, D, MC, V. Ⓔ Ⓕ Ⓘ

⊘ ⓢⓒ

Illinois

Population: 11,427,414	
Land area: 55,646 sq mi (144,123 sq km)	
Elevation: 279–1,235 ft (85–376 m)	
Highest point: Charles Mound, near Galena	
Entered Union: December 3, 1818 (21st state)	
Capital: Springfield	
Motto: State Sovereignty-National Union	
Nickname: Land of Lincoln	
State flower: Wood violet	
State bird: Cardinal	
State tree: White oak	
State fair: August 10–20, 1989 in Springfield	
Time zone: Central	

Interstate Highway System

The following alphabetical listing of Illinois towns in *Mobil Travel Guide* shows that these cities are within 10 miles (16 kilometers) of the indicated Interstate highways. A highway map should be checked, however, for the nearest exit.

INTERSTATE 55: Bloomington, Brookfield, Chicago, Cicero, Collinsville, Downers Grove, East St Louis, Edwardsville, Hinsdale, Joliet, La Grange, Lincoln, Naperville, Oak Lawn, Springfield.

INTERSTATE 57: Arcola, Benton, Cairo, Champaign/Urbana, Charleston, Chicago, Chicago Heights, Effingham, Homewood, Kankakee, Marion, Mattoon, Mt Vernon, Oak Lawn, Rantoul, Salem.

INTERSTATE 64: Belleville, Collinsville, East St Louis, Mt Vernon.

INTERSTATE 70: Altamont, Collinsville, East St Louis, Edwardsville, Effingham, Greenville, Marshall, Vandalia.

INTERSTATE 74: Bloomington, Champaign/Urbana, Danville, Galesburg, Moline, Peoria.

INTERSTATE 80: Chicago, Chicago Heights, Geneseo, Homewood, Joliet, Lockport, Moline, Morris, Ottawa, Peru, Princeton, Rock Island.

INTERSTATE 88: Aurora, Brookfield, Chicago, Chicago O'Hare Airport Area, Cicero, De Kalb, Dixon, Downers Grove, Elmhurst, Geneseo, Geneva, Glen Ellyn, Hillside, Hinsdale, Itasca, La Grange, Moline, Naperville, Oak Brook, Oak Park, St Charles, Sterling, Wheaton.

INTERSTATE 90: Algonquin, Arlington Heights, Chicago, Chicago O'Hare Airport Area, Cicero, Elgin, Elmhurst, Hillside, Itasca, Oak Park, Palatine, Rockford, Schaumburg, Union.

INTERSTATE 94: Calumet City, Chicago, Chicago Heights, Chicago O'Hare Airport Area, Evanston, Glenview, Grayslake, Gurnee, Highland Park, Highwood, Lake Forest, Libertyville, Northbrook, Skokie, Waukegan, Wheeling, Wilmette, Winnetka.

INTERSTATE 290: Arlington Heights, Chicago, Chicago O'Hare Airport Area, Cicero, Elmhurst, Glen Ellyn, Hillside, Itasca, Libertyville, Northbrook, Oak Brook, Oak Park, Palatine, Schaumburg.

INTERSTATE 294: Arlington Heights, Calumet City, Chicago, Chicago Heights, Chicago O'Hare Airport Area, Cicero, Elmhurst, Evanston, Glen Ellyn, Glenview, Highland Park, Highwood, Hillside, Itasca, Lake Forest, Libertyville, Northbrook, Oak Brook, Oak Park, Palatine, Skokie, Wheeling, Wilmette, Winnetka.

Weather Statistics*

	WINTER	SPRING	SUMMER	FALL
Northern	22°F (-6°C)	59°F (15°C)	74°F (23°C)	52°F (11°C)
Central	28°F (-2°C)	64°F (18°C)	78°F (26°C)	57°F (14°C)
Western	26°F (-3°C)	61°F (16°C)	76°F (24°C)	55°F (13°C)
Southern	37°F (3°C)	69°F (21°C)	81°F (27°C)	62°F (17°C)

*Average mean temperatures are usually listed for the entire state. Averages for specific regions are given if significant differences exist.

Visitor Information

For specific information about Illinois attractions and activities contact the Illinois Travel Information Center, 310 S Michigan Ave, Suite 108, Chicago 60604; 312/793-2094 or the Office of Tourism, State of Illinois Center, 100 W Randolph, Chicago 60601; 312/917-4732 (daily, 8:30 am–5 pm). For toll-free travel information in Illinois phone 800/223-0121; from Indiana, Iowa, Kentucky, Michigan, Minnesota, Missouri, Tennessee, or Wisconsin, 800/637-8560.

Periodicals that are helpful are *Illinois* (10 issues/yr), Box A, Benton 62812 and *See Illinois* (6 issues/yr), 601 S Future, Marion 62959.

Locations of Illinois visitor centers: May–Oct: off I-80 (eastbound) near Rapid City; off I-57 near Monee; May–Nov: off I-24 near Metropolis; off I-57 (northbound) near Anna; off I-70 (eastbound) near Highland; May–Dec: off I-90 (southbound) near Rockford; off I-70 (westbound) near Marshall; off I-57 (southbound) near Benton; off I-94 at the Lake Forest Oasis.

Room Rate Information

The following major city and suburbs have higher room rates for two (double) than indicated on the cover of this Guide. However, the lodgings listed in these cities offer a good value when compared to others of their type in the area.

Arlington Heights	$65	Itasca	$60
Chicago	85		

Altamont

Pop: 2,389 **Elev:** 619 ft (189 m) **Area code:** 618 **Zip:** 62411

Motels

★**ALOHA INN.** *(Rte 2) ¼ mi S on IL 128, 1 blk S of I-70 exit 82. 618/483-6300.* 25 rms, 2 story. S $22.95; D $28.95; each addl $3; under 12 free. Crib free. TV; cable. Playground. Cafe adj 6 am–9:30 pm. Ck-out 11 am. Coin lndry. Cr cds: A, C, D, MC, V.

✔ ★ ★**BEST WESTERN STUCKEY'S CARRIAGE INN.** *(Box 303) 1 mi S on IL 128, 1 blk N of I-70 Altamont exit. 618/483-6101.* 38 rms, 2 story. May–mid-Oct: S $25–$32; D $33–$39; each addl $3; under 12 free; lower rates rest of yr. Crib $2. TV; cable. Pool. Cafe 5:30 am–9:30 pm. Rm serv. Bar 4 pm–midnight. Ck-out noon. Meeting rms. Sundries. Cr cds: A, C, D, DS, MC, V.

Alton

Founded: 1817 **Pop:** 34,171 **Elev:** 500 ft (152 m) **Area code:** 618 **Zip:** 62002

Motel

★★**RAMADA INN.** *1900 Homer Adams Pkwy. 618/463-0800.* 128 rms, 2 story. S, D $48–$59; under 18 free; wkend rates. Crib free. TV; cable. Pool. Cafe 6 am–10 pm. Rm serv. Bar 11–1 am, Sat from noon, Sun 4–11 pm; entertainment, dancing Tu–Sat. Ck-out 2 pm. Meeting rms. Free local airport, RR station transportation. 9-hole golf adj, greens fee $3.75. Cr cds: A, C, D, DS, MC, V. Ⓔ

Arlington Heights

Settled: 1836 **Pop:** 66,116 **Elev:** 700 ft (213 m) **Area code:** 312

Motel

✔ ★**RED ROOF INN.** *22 W Algonquin Rd (60005). 312/228-6650.* 136 rms, 2 story. S $35.95–$38.95; D $37.95–$45.95; under 18 free. Crib free. TV; in-rm movies. Cafe opp open 24 hrs. Ck-out noon. Meeting rm. Sundries. Cr cds: A, C, D, DS, MC, V. Ⓔ

Motor Hotels

DILLON INN. (Too new to be rated) *2120 S Arlington Heights Rd. 312/593-9400.* 125 rms, 3 story. S, D $42; each addl $6; under 18 free. TV; in-rm movies. Cafe adj open 24 hrs. Ck-out noon. Meeting rms. Valet serv. Some refrigerators. Balconies. Cr cds: A, C, D, DS, MC, V. Ⓔ

★**HOLIDAY INN-MT PROSPECT.** *(200 E Rand Rd, Mount Prospect 60056) 5 mi SE on US 12. 312/255-8800.* 147 rms, 3 story. S $55–$67; D $62–$72; each addl $7; under 18 free; wkend packages. Crib free. TV; cable, in-rm movies. Pool. Cafe 6:30 am–10 pm. Rm serv. Bar 4:30 pm–midnight. Ck-out noon. Coin lndry. Meeting rms. Bellhops. Valet serv. Free airport transportation. Health club privileges. Cr cds: A, C, D, DS, MC, V. Ⓓ Ⓔ Ⓕ Ⓘ

Aurora

Settled: 1834 **Pop:** 81,293 **Elev:** 676 ft (206 m) **Area code:** 312

Motels

✔ ★ ★**BEST WESTERN FOX VALLEY INN.** *2450 N Farnsworth (60505). 312/851-2000.* 108 rms, 2 story. S $40; D $48; each addl $5; under 12 free. Crib $3. TV; in-rm movies. Pool. Cafe 6:30 am–2 pm, 5–10 pm; Sun to 2 pm. Bar noon–12:30 am, Fri, Sat to 1 am; entertainment, dancing exc Sun. Ck-out noon. Meeting rms. Sundries. Cr cds: A, D, DS, MC, V.

★**REGAL 8 INN.** *2380 N Farnsworth (60504). 312/851-3600.* 118 rms, 3 story. No elvtr. S $24.88; D $29.88. Crib free. TV. Indoor pool. Free coffee. Cafe adj 4 am–10 pm. Ck-out 1 pm. Cr cds: A, C, D, DS, MC, V.

Motor Hotels

★ ★**DAYS INN.** *(306 S Lincolnway, N Aurora 60542) 3 mi N on IL 31, at I-88 (E-W Tollway). 312/892-6481.* 118 rms, 2 story. S $44–$65; D $48–$72; each addl $6; suites $75–$140. Crib free. TV; cable. Pool. Cafe 6:30 am–2 pm, 5–10 pm; Sat, Sun from 7 am. Rm serv. Bar 4 pm–1 am; Fri, Sat to 2 am. Ck-out noon. Meeting rms. Valet serv. Cr cds: A, DS, MC, V.

✔ ★ ★**SARATOGA.** *(311 S Lincolnway, N Aurora 60542) 3 mi N on IL 31 at I-88 (E-W Tollway). 312/896-0801; res: 800/942-1042 (exc IL), 800/942-1032 (IL).* 240 rms, 4–5 story. S $40–$70; D $48–$70; each addl $6; under 18 free. Crib free. TV; in-rm movies. Indoor pool. Playground. Cafe 6 am–2 pm, 5–10 pm. Rm serv 7 am–9 pm. Bar 11–1 am; entertainment, dancing exc Sun. Ck-out noon. Meeting rms. Bellhops. Putting green. Game rm. Picnic area. Cr cds: A, C, D, DS, MC, V. Ⓔ

Belleville

Founded: 1814 **Pop:** 41,580 **Elev:** 529 ft (161 m) **Area code:** 618

Motor Hotels

✔ ★★**HYATT LODGE.** *2120 W Main St (62223). 618/234-9400.* 85 rms, 1–2 story. S $34–$42; D $44–$54; each addl $6; suites $39–$75; under 16 free. Crib free. TV; cable. Pool. Cafe 7 am–midnight. Bar 11:30–1 am; wkends to 2 am. Ck-out noon. Meeting rms. Valet serv. Cr cds: A, C, D, DS, MC, V.

★**TOWN HOUSE.** *400 S Illinois (62220). 618/233-7881.* 55 rms, 2 story. S $30.90; D $40.90; each addl $4; under 12 free. Crib $2. TV. Cafe 6 am–10 pm. Rm serv 8 am–9 pm. Bar 4 pm–2 am; entertainment some nights. Ck-out noon. Meeting rms. Picnic tables. Cr cds: A, C, D, DS, MC, V.

Bloomington

Founded: 1843 **Pop:** 44,189 **Elev:** 829 ft (253 m) **Area code:** 309 **Zip:** 61701

Motels

✔ ★ ★**HAMPTON INN.** *604½ I.A.A. Dr, I-55 to Veteran's Pkwy, S to IL 9, W to I.A.A. Dr. 309/662-2800; res: 800/426-7866.* 108 rms, 3 story. S $39–$43; D $41–$49; under 18 free; higher rates Corvette show. Crib free. TV; in-rm movies. Heated pool. Cafe adj open 24 hrs. Ck-out noon. Meeting rm. Valet serv. Sundries. Transportation. Cr cds: A, C, D, DS, MC, V.

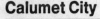

✔ ★**HOWARD JOHNSON.** *(Box 486) 2½ mi SW on Veterans Parkway, ¼ mi NW of I-74 exit 134B. 309/829-1211.* 111 rms, 2 story. S $29.95; D $34.95; each addl $5; higher rates special events. Crib free. TV; cable, in-rm movies. Heated pool. Cafe nearby. Ck-out noon. Sundries. Airport transportation. Cr cds: A, C, D, DS, ER, MC, V.

Calumet City

Pop: 39,697 **Elev:** 589 ft (180 m) **Area code:** 312 **Zip:** 60409

Motel

✔ ★**MOTEL 6.** *(17003 S Halsted, Harvey 60426) W on I-80/294, exit Halsted N. 312/596-7470.* 156 rms, 2 story. S $23.95; D $28.95; each addl $4; under 18 free. TV; cable. Cafe adj open 24 hrs. Ck-out noon. Coin lndry. Cr cds: D, DS, MC, V.

Carbondale

Founded: 1852 **Pop:** 26,414 **Elev:** 415 ft (126 m) **Area code:** 618 **Zip:** 62901

Motels

✔ ★**GIANT CITY LODGE & COTTAGES.** *(Rte 1, Makanda 62958) Exit I-57 at IL 13, W to Carbondale, then Giant City Rd (US 51) S 15 mi to Giant City State Park. 618/457-4921.* 34 cottages. Feb–mid-Dec: S, D $35–$70; each addl $5. Closed rest of yr. TV. Pool. Cafe 8 am–8:30 pm. Bar 8 am–10 pm. Ck-out noon. Game rm. Cr cds: MC, V.

★ ★★**HOLIDAY INN.** *(Box 2646) 800 E Main St. 618/529-1100.* 141 rms, 2 story. S $50.95–$56.95; D $54.95–$60.95; each addl $6; suites $115–$160; under 18 free; higher rates:

late Oct, DuQuoin State Fair, SIU special events. Crib free. TV; cable. Indoor pool; whirlpool. Cafe 6:30 am–2 pm, 5–10 pm; Fri, Sat to 11 pm. Rm serv. Bar 11–1:30 am; entertainment, dancing exc Sun. Ck-out noon. Meeting rms. Valet serv. Free airport transportation. Cr cds: A, C, D, DS, MC, V.

🛆 🐾 🏊 ⊘ 🐾 SC

✔ ★SUPER 8. *1180 E Main, 1½ mi E on IL 13. 618/457-8822.* 63 units, 3 story. No elvtr. S $27.88–$32.88; D $34.88–$42.88; suites $34.88–$38.88; under 12 free. Crib $1. TV; cable. Cafe adj 6 am–midnight. Ck-out 11 am. Cr cds: A, C, D, DS, MC, V.

🛆 🐾 ⊘ 🐾 SC

Champaign/Urbana

Settled: Urbana, 1822 **Pop:** Champaign, 58,133; Urbana, 35,978 **Elev:** Champaign, 742 ft (226 m); Urbana, 727 ft (222 m) **Area code:** 217 **Zip:** Urbana, 61801

Motels

(Rates may be higher for special university wkends)

✔ ★ ★BEST WESTERN LINCOLN LODGE. *(403 W University, Urbana) ½ mi W on US 45, 150 (IL 10), 1 mi S of I-74 Lincoln Ave exit. 217/367-1111.* 31 rms, 1–2 story. S $40; D $48; each addl $6; under 6 free. Crib free. TV; cable, in-rm movies. Pool. Cafe 6:30 am–9:30 pm; Sun 7 am–1:30 pm. Rm serv. Ck-out noon. Cr cds: A, C, D, MC, V. Ⓓ

🐾 ⊘

✔ ★ ★BEST WESTERN PARADISE INN. *(1001 N Dunlap, Savoy 61874) I-57 exit 229 E to US 45 N, 3½ mi S of Champaign/Urbana. 217/356-1824.* 62 rms, 1 kit, 1–2 story. S $32–$39; D $42–$49; each addl $4; under 12 free. Crib $3. TV; cable, in-rm movies. Heated pool; wading pool. Playground. Free coffee in rm. Free continental bkfst. Cafe adj 11 am–9 pm. Rm serv. Ck-out 11 am. Meeting rms. Free airport transportation. Game rm. Picnic tables. Cr cds: A, C, D, DS, MC, V.

🐾 🏊 🐾 SC

★DAYS INN. *(914 W Bloomington Rd, Champaign 61821) ½ mi E of I-74 Prospect Ave exit. 217/356-6000.* 107 rms, 2 story. S $30–$35; D $35–$40; each addl $5; under 18 free. Crib free. TV; satellite. Pool. Cafe adj 5 am–9:30 pm. Rm serv. Ck-out noon. Cr cds: A, C, D, DS, MC, V.

🐾 🏊 ⊘ 🐾 SC

✔ ★ ★HOWARD JOHNSON. *(222 N State St, Champaign 61820) 1 mi S of I-74 Neil St exit. 217/359-9180.* 113 rms, 5 story. S $34–$46; D $38–$58; each addl $8; under 18 free. Crib free. TV; satellite, in-rm movies. Pool. Cafe 6 am–9:30 pm. Bar 4–11 pm. Ck-out noon. Coin lndry. Meeting rms. Valet serv. Balconies. Park opp. Cr cds: A, C, D, DS, ER, MC, V.

🛆 🐾 🏊 🏃 ⊘ 🐾 SC

★ ★HOWARD JOHNSON. *(Box 605, Urbana) I-74 & US 45, 1¾ mi N on US 45; I-74 Cunningham exit 184A. 217/367-8331.* 105 rms, 2 story. S $45–$60; D $52–$75; each addl $6; suites $100; under 18 free; higher rates special events. Crib free. TV; satellite. Indoor/outdoor pool; sauna. Free coffee. Cafe 6 am–11 pm. Rm serv from 8 am. Bar 11 am–11 pm. Ck-out noon. Meeting rms. Bellhops. Valet serv. Private patios, balconies. Cr cds: A, C, D, DS, MC, V.

🐾 🏊 ⊘ SC 💲

✔ ★ ★LA QUINTA. *(1900 Center Dr, Champaign 61820) 1 blk N of I-74 Neil St exit. 217/356-4000.* 122 rms, 2 story. S $38–$41; D $43–$46; each addl $5; under 18 free. Crib avail. TV; satellite. Heated pool. Free coffee. Cafe adj open 24 hrs. Ck-out 1 pm. Meeting rms. Valet serv. Cr cds: A, C, D, DS, MC, V.

🛆 🐾 🏊 ⊘ 🐾 SC

★TRAVELODGE. *(409 W University Ave, Urbana) 6 blks W on US 45, 150 (IL 10), 1½ mi SE of I-74 Lincoln Ave exit. 217/328-3521.* 58 rms, 2 story. S $36–$49; D $40–$59; each addl $3; under 17 free. Crib free. TV; cable. Pool. Free coffee. Cafe nearby. Ck-out noon. Some balconies. Cr cds: A, C, D, DS, ER, MC, V.

🛆 🏊 ⊘ 🐾 SC 💲

Chicago

Settled: 1803 **Pop:** 3,005,072 **Elev:** 579–673 ft (176–205 m) **Area code:** 312

Motor Hotels

✔ ★COMFORT INN. *601 W Diversey Pkwy (60614). 312/348-2810.* 74 rms, 4 story. S $55–$75; D $60–$85; each addl $5; under 16 free. TV. Free continental bkfst. Ck-out noon. Health club privileges. Cr cds: A, C, D, DS, MC, V. Ⓔ

Ⓚ SC

★HOLIDAY INN-MIDWAY AIRPORT. *7353 S Cicero Ave (IL 50) (60629). 312/581-5300.* 161 rms, 5 story. S $60–$72; D $66–$74; each addl $7; under 18 free; wkend rates. Crib free. TV; cable. Cafe 6 am–10 pm. Rm serv from 7 am. Bar 11–2 am; entertainment, dancing Tu–Sat. Ck-out noon. Meeting rms. Bellhops. Sundries. Free Midway Airport transportation. Cr cds: A, C, D, DS, MC, V.

Ⓗ Ⓒ ⤳ Ⓢ Ⓚ SC Ⓢ

✔ ★MIDWAY AIRPORT INN. *5400 S Cicero Ave (60638), at edge of Midway Airport. 312/581-0500; res: 800/621-0127 (exc IL), 800/238-0638 (IL).* 200 rms, 2 story. S $50–$55; D $55–$60; each addl $5; suites $65; under 16 free; wkend rates. Crib $5. TV; in-rm movies. Heated pool; lifeguard. Cafe 7 am–11 pm. Rm serv. Bar to 4 am; dancing. Ck-out noon. Meeting rms. Bellhops. Valet serv. Sundries. Gift shop. Free transportation Midway Airport, McCormick Place. Refrigerator avail. Cr cds: A, C, D, MC, V.

Ⓗ Ⓒ ⤳ Ⓢ Ⓚ SC Ⓢ

Hotel

★ESSEX INN. *800 S Michigan Ave (60605). 312/939-2800; res: 800/621-6909.* 255 rms, 15 story. S $74–$98; D $84–$108; each addl $10; suites $150–$250; under 18 free; wkend packages. Crib free. TV; cable, in-rm movies. Heated pool; lifeguard, sauna. Cafe 7 am–midnight. Bar 11–4 am; pianist, band. Ck-out 1 pm. Valet parking. Airport transportation. Health club privileges. Game rm. Minibars; refrigerators in suites. Cr cds: A, C, D, DS, MC, V. Ⓔ

Ⓗ Ⓒ ⤳ Ⓚ SC Ⓢ

Collinsville

Pop: 19,613 **Elev:** 550 ft (168 m) **Area code:** 618 **Zip:** 62234

Motels

★BEST WESTERN BO-JON INN. *2 mi N on IL 159, 1 blk NE of I-55, I-70 exit 15 B. 618/345-5720.* 40 rms, 2 story. Apr–early Sep: S $29–$38; D $40–$49; each addl $5; lower rates rest of yr. TV. Pool. Ck-out 11 am. Picnic tables. Cr cds: A, C, D, DS, MC, V.

⤳ SC

✔ ★ ★DRURY INN. *602 N Bluff, just N of jct IL 157, I-55. 618/345-7700.* 123 rms, 4 story. S $38–$45; D $44–$53; each addl $5; under 18 free. Crib free. TV; satellite. Indoor pool. Free continental bkfst. Cafe adj open 24 hrs. Ck-out noon. Valet serv. Cr cds: A, C, D, MC, V.

Ⓗ Ⓒ ⤳ Ⓢ SC Ⓢ

✔ ★HOWARD JOHNSON. *301 N Bluff Rd. 618/345-1530.* 91 rms, 2 story. June–Aug: S $30–$40; D $35–$58; each addl $5; under 12 free; lower rates rest of yr. Crib $5. TV; cable. Pool; wading pool. Cafe 6 am–midnight; Sat to 1 am. Rm serv 9 am–11 pm. Bar noon–midnight; Fri, Sat to 3 am; dancing. Ck-out noon. Coin lndry. Valet serv. Private patios. Cr cds: A, C, D, DS, MC, V.

⤳ SC Ⓢ

Danville

Founded: 1827 **Pop:** 38,985 **Elev:** 597 ft (182 m) **Area code:** 217 **Zip:** 61832

Motel

✔ ★ ★**RAMADA INN.** *Lynch Rd, 1 blk N of I-74 exit 220. 217/446-2400.* 131 rms, 2 story. S $40–$56; D $46–$62; each addl $6; suites $86–$90; under 18 free. Crib free. TV; satellite. Heated pool. Free in-rm coffee. Cafe 6 am–10 pm. Rm serv. Bar 11–2 am, Sun 1 pm–midnight; entertainment, dancing Tu–Sat. Ck-out noon. Meeting rms. Bellhops. Sundries. Gift shop. Free airport transportation. Exercise equipt; weights, bicycles. Wet bar in suites. Cr cds: A, C, D, DS, MC, V.

Decatur

Founded: 1829 **Pop:** 94,081 **Elev:** 670 ft (204 m) **Area code:** 217

Motels

✔ ★ ★**BEST WESTERN SHELTON.** *450 E Pershing Rd (62526), at jct US 51, IL 47, 48, 121. 217/877-7255.* 150 rms, 2 story. S $39–$41; D $42–$46; each addl $3. TV; cable. Pool. Cafe 6:30 am–10 pm, Sun to 8 pm. Rm serv. Bar 11–1 am, Sun to 10 pm. Ck-out noon. Meeting rms. Bellhops. Free airport, RR station, bus depot transportation. Cr cds: A, C, D, DS, MC, V.

★**LAKEVIEW.** *16 S Country Club Rd (62521), US 36, IL 121. 217/428-4677.* 25 rms, 2 story. S $22.88; D $26.88–$31.88; up to 2 addl free. Crib free. TV; cable. Free coffee. Ck-out 11:30 am. Cr cds: A, D, MC, V. ⓓ

Hotel

✔ ★ ★**AMBASSADOR.** *(Box 883, 62523) 141 S Main. 217/428-8611; res: 800/624-6356 (exc IL), 800/851-2826 (IL).* 100 rms, 8 story. S $32.95–$39.95; D $39.95; each addl $5; suites $125; studio rms $37.95–$45.95; under 16 free; wkly rates. Crib free. TV. Free coffee. Heated pool; poolside serv. Cafe 6:30 am–9 pm; Fri, Sat to 10 pm; Sun 8 am–8 pm. Bar 11–1 am, Fri, Sat to 2 am; entertainment, dancing Tu–Sat. Ck-out noon. Meeting rms. Airport, bus depot transportation. Cr cds: A, MC, V.

De Kalb

Pop: 33,099 **Elev:** 880 ft (268 m) **Area code:** 815 **Zip:** 60115

Motels

★**GEORGETOWN MOTEL.** *1321 W Lincoln Hwy. 815/756-1451.* 60 rms, 2 story. S $26–$45; D $30–$49; under 15 free; wkly rates. Crib $3. TV; cable. Free coffee. Ck-out noon. Some balconies. Cr cds: A, C, D, MC, V.

✔ ★ ★**INN OF DE KALB.** *1212 W Lincoln Hwy, ¾ mi W on IL 38. 815/758-8661.* 114 rms, 2 story. S $32–$48; D $35–$54; each addl $6; under 18 free. Crib free. TV; satellite. Heated pool; poolside serv. Cafe 7 am–10 pm. Rm serv 7 am–2 pm, 5–9 pm. Bar 11–1 am. Ck-out noon. Coin lndry. Meeting rms. Valet serv. Near Northern Illinois Univ campus. Cr cds: A, C, D, DS, MC, V.

★**MOTEL 6.** *1116 W Lincoln Hwy. 815/756-3398.* 111 rms, 2 story. S $20.95; D $26.95; under 18 free. Crib free. TV; in-rm movies. Heated pool. Ck-out noon. Near Northern Illinois Univ campus. Cr cds: C, D, DS, MC, V.

East St Louis

Pop: 55,200 **Elev:** 410 ft (125 m) **Area code:** 618

Motel

★★**DRURY INN.** *(12 Ludwig Dr, Fairview Heights 62208) 618/398-8530.* 107 rms, 4 story. S $42–47; D $49–$57; each addl $6; under 18 free. Crib free. TV. Pool. Cafe 6 am–11 pm; Fri, Sat to midnight. Ck-out noon. Meeting rms. Valet serv. Cr cds: A, C, D, MC, V.

Motor Hotel

★★**RAMADA INN.** *(I-64 & IL 59, Fairview Heights 62208)* ½ blk N of jct IL 159, I-64. *618/632-4747.* 161 rms, 5 story. S $46–$52; D $52–$58; each addl $6; suite $85; under 18 free. TV. Pool. Cafe open 24 hrs. Rm serv. 2 bars 11–1 am; entertainment, dancing. Ck-out noon. Meeting rms. Bellhops. Valet serv. Cr cds: A, C, D, DS, MC, V.

Effingham

Settled: 1853 **Pop:** 11,270 **Elev:** 592 ft (180 m) **Area code:** 217 **Zip:** 62401

Motels

★**BUDGET HOST LINCOLN LODGE.** *(Box 634) 2 mi N on US 45, 1 blk N of I-57, I-70 exit 162. 217/342-4133.* 25 rms, 1–2 story. S $27.95; D $29.95–$34.95; each addl $3. Crib free. TV; in-rm movies. Pool. Cafe adj 6 am–9 pm. Ck-out 11 am. Cr cds: A, C, D, MC, V.

★**CARRIAGE HOUSE.** *W Fayette Ave, 1¼ mi W of US 40, 1 blk W of I-57, I-70 exit 159. 217/342-4121.* 65 rms, 2 story. May–mid-Sep: S $28.95–$33.95; D $32.95–$39.95; each addl $3; family rates; lower rates rest of yr. Crib $1. TV; cable. Pool. Cafe 6–11 am, 5–10 pm. 2 bars 5 pm–1 am; entertainment, dancing. Ck-out noon. Cr cds: A, C, D, DS, MC, V.

★★**DAYS INN.** *(Box 1168) W Fayette Rd, 1½ mi W on US 40, 2 blks E of I-57 & I-70, exit 159. 217/342-9271.* 122 rms, 2 story. Apr–mid-Sep: S $29.88–$32.88; D $30–$39; each addl $5; under 18, $1; lower rates rest of yr. Crib $1. TV; cable. Pool. Cafe open 24 hrs. Bar 11–1 am. Ck-out 11 am. Cr cds: A, D, DS, MC, V.

★★**HOLIDAY INN.** *(Box 187) W Fayette Rd, 1½ mi W of US 40, 1 blk E of I-57, I-70 exit 159. 217/342-4161.* 137 rms, 2 story. S $35–$43; D $40–$48; each addl $5; suites $61; under 17 free. Crib free. TV; cable. Pool. Cafe 6 am–10 pm. Rm serv. Bar noon–1 am; Sun to 10 pm. Ck-out noon. Meeting rms. Airport, RR station, bus depot transportation. Cr cds: A, C, D, DS, MC, V.

★★★**RAMADA KELLER.** *(Box 747) 1 mi NW on IL 32, 33, 1 blk N of I-57, I-70. 217/342-2131.* 169 rms, 2 story. S $40–$56; D $47–$63; suites $55–$85; each addl $7; under 18 free. Crib free. TV; cable. Indoor/outdoor pool. Playground. Cafe 6 am–10 pm. Rm serv. Bar 11 am–midnight; entertainment, dancing. Ck-out noon. Meeting rms. Sundries. Package store. Free airport, RR station, bus depot transportation. Miniature golf. Exercise equipt; weights, bicycles, whirlpool, steam rm, sauna. Bowling alley. Game rm. Some in-rm whirlpools. Balconies. Cr cds: A, C, D, DS, MC, V.

Freeport

Settled: 1838 **Pop:** 26,266 **Elev:** 780 ft (238 m) **Area code:** 815 **Zip:** 61032

Motel

★**TOWN HOUSE.** *1156 W Galena Ave. 815/232-2191.* 30 rms. S $27–$30; D $33–$36; each addl $3; under 12 free. Crib $2. TV; cable. Free coffee. Cr cds: A, D, DS, MC, V. Ⓓ

Hotel

✔ ★★**STEPHENSON.** *109 S Galena. 815/233-0300.* 75 rms, 8 story. S $45–$53; D $51–$63; each addl $6; suites $125–$150; under 18 free; wkend rates. Crib free. TV; cable. Cafe 6 am–10 pm. Bar 11–1 am; entertainment wkends. Ck-out noon. Meeting rms. Concierge. Airport, RR station, bus depot transportation. Balconies. Picnic tables, grills. Cr cds: A, C, D, DS, MC, V.

Galena

Founded: 1826 **Pop:** 3,876 **Elev:** 609 ft (186 m) **Area code:** 815 **Zip:** 61036

Motels

★**GRANT HILLS.** *(RR 2) 1 mi E on US 20, IL 84. 815/777-2116.* 35 rms, 1–2 story. S $25–$38; D $38–$47; family rates. Crib free. TV. Heated pool. Playground. Cafe nearby. Ck-out 11 am. Downhill ski 8 mi; x-country ski 6 mi. Picnic tables. High on hill; view of 3 states. Antique auto museum on premises.

✔ ★★**PALACE.** *(RFD 1) 2 mi W on US 20, IL 84. 815/777-2043.* 51 rms in motel, guest houses, main bldg, 1–2 story. S $24; D $38–$70; suites $91; rms in Civil War mansion $56–$71. Crib $3. TV. Pool; whirlpool. Free coffee in lobby. Cafe nearby. Ck-out 11 am. Downhill ski 9 mi; x-country ski 6 mi. Lawn games. Rec rm. Hayrides, outdoor movies avail adj campground. Picnic tables, grills.

Inns

✔ ★**COLONIAL GUEST HOUSE.** *1004 Park Ave. 815/777-0336.* 5 rms, some A/C, 3 story. No rm phones. S $40; D $45; each addl $5; suites $80. Crib free. TV; cable. Ck-out 11 am. Downhill/x-country ski 7 mi. Some refrigerators. Porches. Antiques.

★**VICTORIAN MANSION.** *301 S High St. 815/777-0675.* 9 rms, 3 story. D $45–$63. No children. Ck-out 11 am. Downhill ski 10 mi. Colonial woodwork, fireplaces; rooms furnished with antiques. Cr cds: DS, MC, V.

Galesburg

Settled: 1837 **Pop:** 35,305 **Elev:** 773 ft (236 m) **Area code:** 309 **Zip:** 61401

Motels

★**GALESBURG INN.** *565 W Main St. 309/343-3191.* 55 rms, 2 story. S $23; D $28–$37; each addl $4; under 17 free; wkend rates. Crib $2. TV; cable. Free coffee in lobby. Cafe adj 6 am–9 pm. Ck-out noon. Bellhops. Game rm. Sun deck. Balconies. Cr cds: A, C, D, DS, MC, V.

✔ ★★**REGAL 8 INN.** *1487 N Henderson St. 309/344-2401.* 80 rms, 2 story. S $24.88; D $29.88; 2–4, $34.88; suites $39.88. Crib free. TV; cable. Heated pool. Cafe adj 5:30 am–11 pm. Ck-out 1 pm. Bellhops. Refrigerator in suites. Cr cds: A, C, D, DS, MC, V.

★**STARLITE.** *1966 N Henderson St. 309/344-1515.* 23 rms. S $21; D $27; each addl $4; under 12 free. Crib $1.50. TV; free in-room movies. Free coffee in lobby. Cafe nearby. Ck-out noon. Cr cds: A, DS, MC, V.

Motor Hotel

✔ ★★★**JUMER'S CONTINENTAL INN.** *E Main St, at I-74. 309/343-7151; res: 800/645-8637 (exc IL), 800/635-8637 (IL).* 148 rms, 2 story. S $38–$60; D $47–$69; each addl $6; studio rms, kit. units, suites $90; under 18 free; wkend rates. Crib free. TV; cable. Indoor pool; whirlpool, sauna. Cafe 6:30 am–10 pm; Fri to 10:30 pm; Sat to 11 pm; Sun from 7 am. Rm serv. Bar 11–1 am, Sun from noon. Ck-out 1 pm. Meeting rms. Bellhops. Valet serv. Sundries. Gift shop. Airport, RR station transportation. Putting green. Many private patios. Cr cds: A, D, MC, V.
Ⓓ Ⓔ

Geneva

Settled: 1833 **Pop:** 9,881 **Elev:** 720 ft (219 m) **Area code:** 312 **Zip:** 60134

Motel

★**GENEVA.** *(Box 183) 1½ mi E on IL 38. 312/232-7121.* 26 rms, 1–2 story, some kits. S $30–$34; D $35–$37; each addl $4. Crib $3. TV. Free morning coffee. Ck-out 11 am. Cr cds: A, C, D, MC, V.

Harrisburg

Pop: 10,410 **Elev:** 403 ft (123 m) **Area code:** 618 **Zip:** 62946

Motels

✔ ★★**GATEWAY INN.** *(Box 27, Muddy 62965) 2 mi NE on US 45. 618/252-6354.* 81 rms, 2 story. S $33; D $40; each addl $3; suite $50; under 19 free. Crib free. TV; cable. Pool. Cafe 6:30 am–2 pm, 5–10 pm; Sat, Sun from 7 am. Rm serv. Bar 11–2:30 am; entertainment, dancing Wed, Fri, Sat. Ck-out noon. Meeting rms. Package store. Cr cds: A, C, D, DS, MC, V.

★**GRAY PLAZA.** *411 E Poplar St. 618/253-7651.* 46 rms, 2 story. S $25; D $31; each addl $4; under 12 free. Crib free. TV; cable. Cafe nearby. Ck-out noon. Exercise equipt; weights, bicycles, whirlpool. Cr cds: A, C, D, MC, V.

Hinsdale

Pop: 16,726 **Elev:** 725 ft (221 m) **Area code:** 312 **Zip:** 60521

Motor Hotel

✔ ★★**DAYS INN.** *(300 S Frontage Rd, Burr Ridge 60521) Off I-55 County Line Rd S exit. 312/325-2900.* 120 rms, 3 story. S $39–$49; D $53–$58; each addl $5; suites $80–$100; under 18 free; wkend rates. Crib free. TV. Pool. Cafe 6:30 am–2 pm, 4–10 pm; Sat, Sun 7 am–10 pm. Rm serv. Bar 11–1 am; Sat 11–2 am. Ck-out noon. Coin lndry. Valet serv. Golf. Racquetball. Cr cds: A, C, D, MC, V. Ⓔ

Homewood

Pop: 19,724 **Elev:** 650 ft (198 m) **Area code:** 312 **Zip:** 60430

Motels

★**BUDGETEL INN.** *(17225 Halsted St, South Holland 60473) Just N of jct I-80, I-294, on IL 1.* 312/596-8700. 102 rms, 2 story. S $32.95; D $38.95; each addl $5; under 19 free. Crib free. TV. Free coffee. Cafe adj open 24 hrs. Ck-out noon. Valet serv. Cr cds: A, C, D, DS, MC, V.

✔ ★**DAYS INN.** *(17220 S Halsted St, East Hazelcrest 60429) S of jct I-80, I-294, exit IL 11.* 312/957-5900. 145 rms, 5 story. S $28; D $36; each addl $4; under 18, $1; under 2 free. TV; satellite. Pool. Playground. Cafe adj open 24 hrs. Ck-out noon. Cr cds: A, MC, V.

Itasca

Pop: 7,129 **Elev:** 686 ft (209 m) **Area code:** 312 **Zip:** 60143

Motels

✔ ★**HAMPTON INN.** *(100 Busse Rd, Elk Grove Village 60007) 6 mi NE via IL 83, at jct IL 83 & IL 72.* 312/593-8600. 125 rms, 4 story. S $49–$59; D $53–$62; under 18 free; wkend packages. Crib free. TV; satellite. Free continental bkfst. Cafe adj 6 am–10 pm. Ck-out noon. Meeting rm. Valet serv. Sundries. Free airport transportation. Cr cds: A, C, D, DS, MC, V. Ⓔ

✔ ★**LA QUINTA.** *(1900 Oakton St, Elk Grove Village 60007)* 312/439-6767. 142 rms, 4 story. S $53–$55; D $58–$60; each addl $5; under 18 free; wkend rates. Crib free. TV; cable. Heated pool. Cafe opp 6 am–10 pm; Fri, Sat open 24 hrs. Ck-out 1 pm. Meeting rms. Valet serv. Health club privileges. Cr cds: A, C, D, DS, MC, V. Ⓔ

Joliet

Settled: 1831 **Pop:** 77,956 **Elev:** 564 ft (172 m) **Area code:** 815

Motels

✔ ★**MANOR.** *(RFD 3, 60436) Jct IL 6 & I-55 exit 248.* 815/467-5385. 77 rms, 1–2 story. S $27.36–$31.80; D $36.04; each addl $5.30; under 12 free; long-term rates. Crib $5.50. TV. Pool. Cafe opp 6 am–9 pm. Ck-out 11 am. Meeting rms. Cr cds: A, C, D, MC, V.

★**MOTEL 6.** *1850 McDonough St (60436).* 815/729-2800. 132 rms, 2 story. S $22.95; D $27.95; each addl $4; under 19 free. TV; in-rm movies. Cafe adj 6 am–2 pm, 5–10 pm. Ck-out noon. Coin lndry. Cr cds: C, D, DS, MC, V. Ⓔ

Kankakee

Founded: 1855 **Pop:** 30,141 **Elev:** 663 ft (202 m) **Area code:** 815 **Zip:** 60901

Motel

✔ ★**REGAL 8 INN.** *(IL 50 & Armour Rd, Bourbonnais 60914) ½ mi S of I-57 exit IL 50.* 815/933-2300. 98 rms, 3 story. No elvtr. S $25.88–$30.88; D $30.88–$35.88. Crib free. TV; cable.

Heated pool. Free coffee. Cafe adj open 24 hrs. Ck-out 1 pm. Meeting rms. Cr cds: A, C, D, DS, MC, V.

[icons]

Motor Hotels

✓ ★★**DAYS INN.** *1975 E Court, jct IL 17, I-57. 815/939-7171.* 98 rms, 4 story. S $36; D $42; each addl $6; under 16 free. Crib free. TV; cable. Pool. Cafe 5:30 am–11:30 pm. Rm serv. Bar 2 pm–midnight. Ck-out noon. Meeting rms. Cr cds: A, D, DS, MC, V.

[icons]

★★★**HOLIDAY INN.** *(800 N Kinzie Ave, Bradley 60915)* ½ mi S of I-57 exit 315. 815/ 939-3501. 160 rms, 2–5 story. S $45–$63; D $48–$69; each addl $5; suites $95; under 18 free. Crib free. TV; cable. Heated pool; wading pool, poolside serv. Cafe 6 am–2 pm, 5–10 pm. Bar 11:30–2 am. Ck-out noon. Meeting rms. Bellhops. Putting green. Game rm. Holidome. Balconies. Cr cds: A, C, D, DS, MC, V.

[icons]

Lincoln

Founded: 1853 **Pop:** 16,327 **Elev:** 591 ft (180 m) **Area code:** 217 **Zip:** 62656

Motels

✓ ★★**CROSSROADS.** *1305 W Woodlawn Rd. 217/735-5571.* 30 rms, 1–2 story. S $27–$33; D $33–$39; each addl $4; suites $46–$59. Crib free. TV; cable, some in-rm movies. Pool. Cafe 6:30 am–11 pm. Ck-out 11 am. Sundries. Refrigerators. Balconies. Picnic tables, grills. Cr cds: A, D, DS, MC, V.

[icons]

✓ ★★**HOLIDAY INN.** *2011 N Kickapoo St. 217/735-1202.* 61 rms. S $34–$40; D $38–$42; each addl $7; under 19 free; higher rates special events. Crib free. TV; cable. Indoor pool. Cafe 6:30 am–2 pm, 5–10 pm. Rm serv. Bar 4 pm–1 am; entertainment. Ck-out noon. Meeting rms. Bellhops. Sundries. Free airport transportation. Cr cds: A, C, D, DS, MC, V.

[icons]

★**LINCOLN COUNTRY INN.** *1750 5th St. 217/732-9641.* 62 rms, 2 story. S $26.95–$34.95; D $34.95–$40.95; each addl $2. Crib free. TV; cable. Pool. Cafe nearby. Ck-out noon. Picnic table. Cr cds: A, C, D, MC, V.

[icons]

Macomb

Founded: 1830 **Pop:** 19,863 **Elev:** 700 ft (213 m) **Area code:** 309 **Zip:** 61455

Motels

✓ ★★**HOLIDAY INN.** *1400 N Lafayette. 309/833-5511.* 150 rms, 2 story. S $45–$49; D $51–$55; each addl $5. Crib free. TV; cable. Pool; wading pool, poolside serv. Playground. Cafe 6 am–2 pm, 5–10 pm. Bar 4 pm–1 am; entertainment, dancing Fri, Sat. Ck-out noon. Coin lndry. Meeting rms. Valet serv. Cr cds: A, D, DS, MC, V.

[icons]

★**TIME OUT MOTOR LODGE.** *311 University Dr at US 67. 309/837-4838.* 32 rms, 2 story. S $26; D $25–$32; each addl $3; under 10 free. Crib $4. TV; cable, in-rm movies. Cafe adj 6 am–10:30 pm. Ck-out 11 am. Cr cds: A, DS, MC, V.

[icons]

Marion

Founded: 1839 **Pop:** 14,031 **Elev:** 448 ft (137 m) **Area code:** 618 **Zip:** 62959

Motels

★**GRAY PLAZA.** *On IL 13, ½ mi E of I-57 exit 54A. 618/993-2174.* 30 rms, 2 story. S $20.75; D $28.95. Crib free. TV; cable. Cafe nearby. Ck-out 11:30 am. Cr cds: A, MC, V.

▣ ▣ ▣

✔**REGAL 8 INN.** *I-57 & Route 13, exit 54B. 618/993-2631.* 80 rms, 2 story. S $24.88–$29.88; D $29.88–$34.88; suites $39.88. Crib free. TV; free in-rm movies. Pool. Cafe adj open 24 hrs. Ck-out 1 pm. Playground. Cr cds: A, D, DS, MC, V.

▣ ▣ ▣ ▣ ▣ ▣ ▣

Mattoon

Founded: 1854 **Pop:** 19,055 **Elev:** 726 ft (221 m) **Area code:** 217 **Zip:** 61938

Motel

★ ★**HOLIDAY INN.** *1½ mi E, just off IL 16 on access rd, 1 mi E of US 45, 1 mi W of I-57 exit IL 16 (W). 217/235-0313.* 124 rms, 2 story. S $45–$67; D $50–$69; each addl $5; suites $79–$95; under 20 free. Crib free. TV; cable. 2 pools, 1 indoor. Cafe 6 am–10 pm. Bar 11:30–1 am; dancing Mon–Sat. Ck-out 11 am. Coin lndry. Meeting rms. Free airport, RR station, bus depot transportation. Exercise equipt; weights, bicycles, whirlpool, steam rm. Holidome. Putting green. Rec rm, game rm. Cr cds: A, C, D, DS, MC, V.

▣ ▣ ▣ ▣ ▣ ▣ ▣

Moline

Founded: 1848 **Pop:** 46,278 **Elev:** 580 ft (177 m) **Area code:** 309 **Zip:** 61265

Motels

★**EXEL INN.** *2501 52d Ave. 309/797-5580.* 104 rms, 2 story. S $26.95; D $31.95–$36.95; each addl $2–$4; under 18 free. Crib free. TV; satellite. Cafe adj open 24 hrs. Ck-out noon. Downhill ski 15 mi. Cr cds: A, C, D, DS, MC, V.

▣ ▣ ▣ ▣ ▣

✔ ★ ★**HAMPTON INN.** *6920 27th St, near jct I-74 & I-280; adj to airport. 309/762-1711.* 140 rms, 2 story. S, D $32–$43; under 18 free. TV; satellite. Heated pool. Continental bkfst. Cafe adj 7 am–10:30 pm. Ck-out noon. Meeting rms. Valet serv. Free airport transportation. Cr cds: A, C, D, DS, MC, V.

▣ ▣ ▣ ▣ ▣ ▣

★ ★**HOWARD JOHNSON.** *Quad City Airport, Airport Rd at jct US 150, I-74, I-280. 309/797-1211.* 96 rms, 2 story. S $41–$55; D $46–$60; each addl $5; under 18 free. Crib free. TV; satellite. Heated pool. Free coffee. Cafe 6 am–11 pm. Ck-out noon. Meeting rm. Private patios, balconies. Cr cds: A, C, D, DS, MC, V.

▣ ▣ ▣

✔ ★ ★**LA QUINTA MOTOR INN.** *Airport Rd & US 150. 309/762-9008.* 130 rms, 2 story. S $34–$39; D $34–$44; suites $49; under 18 free. Crib free. TV; satellite. Pool. Free continental bkfst. Cafe nearby. Ck-out 1 pm. Free airport transportation. Some in-rm steam baths. Cr cds: A, C, D, DS, MC, V.

▣ ▣ ▣ ▣ ▣

✔ ★**REGAL 8 INN.** *Airport Rd, 1 blk W of US 150. 309/764-8711.* 144 rms, 2 story. S $25.88–$30.88; D $35.88; suites $45.88; under 18 free. Crib free. TV; cable. Pool. Free coffee in lobby. Cafe adj. Ck-out 1 pm. Cr cds: A, C, D, DS, MC, V.

▣ ▣

★ ★**STARDUST.** *19th St at 12th Ave, ½ mi N on US 150, IL 92. 309/764-9644; res: 800/221-2291 (exc IL), 800/322-7388 (IL).* 96 rms, 1–3 story. S $47–$62; D $54–$67; each addl $4; suites $85; studio rms $50; under 12 free; wkend rates. Crib $2. TV; satellite. Heated pool.

Cafe 6:30 am–2 pm, 5–10 pm. Rm serv to 9 pm. Bar 4 pm–midnight. Ck-out 1 pm. Meeting rms. Valet serv. Free airport transportation. Sun deck. Cr cds: A, C, D, DS, MC, V.

 SC S

Mt Vernon

Pop: 17,193 **Elev:** 500 ft (152 m) **Area code:** 618 **Zip:** 62864

Motels

✔ ★ ★**DRURY INN.** *(Box 805) 2 mi W just off IL 15, ½ blk E of jct I-57, I-64. 618/244-4550.* 82 units, 3 story. No elvtr. S $35–$38; D $42–$49; each addl $4; under 18 free. Crib free. TV; cable. Pool. Free coffee. Cafe adj open 24 hrs. Ck-out noon. Meeting rm. Game rm. Cr cds: A, C, D, MC, V.

★ ★**HOLIDAY INN.** *(Box 1328) I-57 & IL 15. 618/244-3670.* 188 rms, 4 story. S $45–$51; D $51–$57; each addl $6; under 18 free; wkend rates. Crib free. TV; in-rm movies. Indoor pool; whirlpool, sauna, poolside serv. Cafe 6 am–10 pm. Rm serv from 7 am. Bar; entertainment, dancing exc Sun. Ck-out noon. Meeting rms. Bellhops. Valet serv. Free airport, bus depot transportation. Game rm. Rec rm. Cr cds: A, C, D, DS, MC, V.

★**REGAL 8 INN.** *333 S 44th St. 618/244-2383.* 80 rms, 2 story. S $24.88–$29.88; D $34.88. Crib free. TV; satellite, in-rm movies. Pool. Free coffee. Cafe nearby. Ck-out 1 pm. Cr cds: A, C, D, DS, MC, V.

Naperville

Settled: 1831 **Pop:** 42,601 **Elev:** 700 ft (213 m) **Area code:** 312

Motels

★**EXEL INN.** *1585 N Naperville/Wheaton Rd (60540). 312/357-0022.* 124 rms, 3 story. S $36.95–$38.95; D $41.95–$43.95; each addl $4; under 18 free. Crib free. TV. Free coffee. Cafe nearby. Ck-out noon. Airport transportation. Racquetball privileges. Cr cds: A, C, D, DS, MC, V. E

★ ★**HAMPTON INN.** *1087 Diehl (60566). 312/505-1400.* 127 rms, 4 story. S $48; D $53; under 18 free. Crib free. TV; cable. Pool; poolside serv. Continental bkfst. Rm serv 5 am–11 pm. Serv bar. Ck-out noon. Meeting rms. Valet serv. Airport transportation. Exercise equipt; weight machine, bicycles. Game rm. Cr cds: A, C, D, DS, MC, V.

✔ ★**TRAVELODGE.** *1617 N Naperville/Wheaton Rd (60540), I-88 exit Naperville/ Wheaton Rd. 312/355-9500.* 106 rms, 3 story. S $48; D $54; each addl $4; under 18 free; wkend rates. Crib free. TV; satellite. Free continental bkfst. Ck-out noon. Meeting rms. Valet serv. Airport transportation. Cr cds: A, C, D, DS, ER, MC, V.

Nauvoo

Settled: 1839 **Pop:** 1,133 **Elev:** 659 ft (201 m) **Area code:** 217 **Zip:** 62354

Motels

★**NAUVOO.** *(Box 272) 150 N Warsaw St. 217/453-6527.* 32 units, 12 kit. units. May–Oct: S $25.20–$28.35; D $31.50–$37.80; each addl $3; kit. units $29.20–$57.25; under 12 free; lower rates rest of yr. Crib $2. TV. Ck-out 11 am. Coin Indry. Free airport, RR station, bus depot transportation. Some refrigerators. Cr cds: A, MC, V.

★**VILLAGE INN.** *(Box 191) 1350 Parley St. 217/453-6634.* 14 rms, 2 story, 3 kits. (no equipt). S $19; D $24.50–$32.50; each addl $2; family rates. Crib free. TV; cable. Playground. Ck-out 11 am. On hill at edge of state park.

Inn

✔★★**HOTEL NAUVOO.** *(Box 398) 1290 Mulholland, center of town on IL 96.* 217/453-2211. 8 rms. No rm phones. S, D $40–$50; each addl $5; suites $50–$80. Closed mid-Nov–mid-Mar. TV. Cafe 5–9 pm; Sun 11 am–3 pm. Bar. Ck-out 11 am. Bellhops. Restored historic inn (1840), originally a private residence; early Mormon architecture.

Northbrook

Pop: 30,778 **Elev:** 650 ft (198 m) **Area code:** 312 **Zip:** 60062

Motels

✔★**ECONO LODGE.** *(1246 S River Rd, Prospect Heights 60070) Jct of Milwukee Ave & River Rd.* 312/537-2000. 75 units, 2 story, 25 kits. Apr–Sep: S $41.95–$44.95; D $48.95–$53.95; each addl $5; kits. $41.95–$53.95; under 18 free; wkly rates; lower rates rest of yr. Crib free. TV; cable, in-rm movies. Playground. Free continental bkfst. Cafe adj 6 am–10 pm. Bar noon–10 pm. Ck-out 11 am. Free airport transportation. Some in-rm whirlpools. Picnic tables. Cr cds: A, C, D, DS, MC, V.

★**EXEL INN.** *(540 Milwaukee Ave, Prospect Heights 60070) Jct River Rd.* 312/459-0545. 124 rms, 3 story. S $36.96; D $41.95–$45.95; each addl $5; under 18 free. Crib free. TV; cable, in-rm movies. Ck-out noon. Cr cds: A, C, D, DS, MC, V.

Oak Brook

Pop: 6,641 **Elev:** 660 ft (201 m) **Area code:** 312 **Zip:** 60521

Motel

✔★★★**COURTYARD BY MARRIOTT.** *(6 Trans Am Plaza Dr, Oak Brook Terrace 60181)* 312/691-1500. 148 rms, 3 story. S, D $48–$70; suites $68–82; under 18 free; wkend rates. TV; cable. Indoor pool. Cafe 6 am–2 pm, 5–10 pm. Bar noon–2 pm, 4–11 pm. Ck-out 1 pm. Coin Indry. Meeting rms. Valet serv. Exercise equipt; weights, bicycles, whirlpool. Refrigerators in suites. Cr cds: A, C, D, DS, MC, V. Ⓔ Ⓕ

Oregon

Settled: 1833 **Pop:** 3,559 **Elev:** 702 ft (214 m) **Area code:** 815 **Zip:** 61061

Motels

★**VIP MOTEL.** *1326 IL 2 N.* 815/732-6195. 12 rms, 1 story. Apr–Oct: S $26.50; D $31.80; each addl $5.30; under 12 free; wkly rates; lower rates rest of yr. Crib free. TV; cable. Playground. Free coffee. Ck-out 11 am. Coin Indry. Cr cds: MC, V.

✔★**WHITE PINES LODGE.** *(6712 Pine Rd, Mt Morris 61054) 7½ mi W on Pines Rd in White Pines Forest State Park.* 815/946-3817. 25 rms in 1–4 rm log cabin units. Apr–Oct, Nov wkends: S $28; D $37; cabins for 4–8, $63–$135; cabins for 8–12, $60–$144. Closed Dec–Mar. Crib free. TV. Cafe 8 am–7:30 pm. Ck-out noon. Sundries. Picnic tables. Rustic. State-owned.

Ottawa

Founded: 1830 **Pop:** 18,166 **Elev:** 480 ft (146 m) **Area code:** 815 **Zip:** 61350

Motels

★**SANDS.** *1215 N La Salle St. 815/434-6440.* 46 rms, 2 story. S $22–$29; D $28–$32; each addl $3. Crib free. TV; cable, in-rm movies. Cafe nearby. Ck-out 11 am. Cr cds: A, C, D, DS, MC, V.

★**SURREY.** *IL 23 & I-80, ¼ mi S of I-80 on IL 23. 815/433-1263.* 22 rms. S $22–$29; D $28–$32; each addl $3; wkly rates off season. Crib free. TV; cable. Free coffee in rm. Ck-out 11 am. Cr cds: A, C, D, DS, MC, V.

Motor Hotel

✔ ★★**OTTAWA INN-STARVED ROCK.** *3000 Columbus St, at jct IL 23, I-80. 815/434-3400.* 135 rms, 2 story. S $39–$46; D $39–$48; each addl $6; suites $75; under 18 free; wkend rates. Crib free. TV; cable, in-rm movies. Heated pool. Cafe 6 am–2 pm, 5–10 pm. Rm serv 7 am–9 pm. Bar 11 am–midnight; Fri, Sat to 1 am. Ck-out noon. Meeting rms. Bellhops. Airport transportation. Cr cds: A, MC, V. ①

Peoria

Settled: 1691 **Pop:** 124,160 **Elev:** 510 ft (155 m) **Area code:** 309

Motels

✔ ★**DAYS INN.** *2726 W Lake Ave, exit 89 (61615). 309/688-7000.* 120 rms, 2 story. S $34; D $39; each addl $5; under 18, $1. Crib free. TV; cable. Pool. Free bkfst. Cafe nearby. Ck-out noon. Cr cds: A, D, DS, MC, V.

✔ ★**DAYS INN EAST.** *(300 N Main St, East Peoria 61611) 2 mi SE on US 150, IL 116. 309/694-4261.* 150 rms, 2 story. Apr–Sep: S $33–$37; D $39–$46; each addl $5; under 18, $1; lower rates rest of yr. Crib free. TV; satellite. Pool. Cafe 6 am–10 pm. Bar 3 pm–1 am exc Sun; entertainment, dancing. Sundries. Ck-out noon. Cr cds: A, C, D, MC, V.

★**RED ROOF INN.** *4031 N War Memorial Dr (61614). 309/685-3911.* 109 rms, 2 story. S $27.95–$32.95; D $29.95; 3–4, $36.95; under 18 free. Crib free. TV; in-rm movies. Free coffee. Ck-out noon. Cr cds: A, C, D, DS, MC, V.

✔ ★**TOWNE HOUSE.** *1519 N Knoxville Ave (61603). 309/688-8646.* 42 rms, 2 story. S $23–$26; D $27–$33.25; each addl $3–$4; kit. units $120–$169/wk. Crib $3. TV; cable. Free coffee; continental bkfst Mon–Fri. Cafe nearby. Ck-out 11 am. Refrigerators. Cr cds: A, D, DS, MC, V.

Motor Hotel

★★★**HOLIDAY INN BRANDYWINE.** *4400 N Brandywine Dr (61614). 309/686-8000.* 197 rms, 3–4 story. S $50–$70; D $54–$74; each addl $6; suite $100; studio rms $52–$61; under 12 free. Crib free. TV; in-rm movies. Indoor pool; whirlpool, sauna. Cafe 6 am–2 pm, 5–10 pm.

Rm serv. Bar 5 pm–1 am; entertainment, dancing. Ck-out noon. Coin lndry. Meeting rms. Bellhops. Free airport transportation. Holidome. Cr cds: A, D, DS, MC, V.

Peru

Settled: 1830 **Pop:** 10,886 **Elev:** 500 ft (152 m) **Area code:** 815 **Zip:** 61354

Motels

✔ ★ ★HOLIDAY INN. *(Box 626) 4 mi N on US 51, at I-80. 815/224-1060.* 168 rms, 2 story. S $40–$55; D $46–$61; each addl $6; under 18 free. Crib free. TV; in-rm movies. Pool; poolside serv. Cafe 6:30 am–2 pm, 5–10 pm. Rm serv. Bar 11–1 am; entertainment, dancing Mon–Sat. Ck-out 11 am. Meeting rms. Bellhops. Valet serv. Game rm. Cr cds: A, C, D, DS, MC, V. Ⓔ

✔ ★ ★HOWARD JOHNSON. *(I-80 & US 51, LaSalle 61301) 4 mi N on US 51 at I-80 exit 75. 815/224-2500.* 104 rms, 2 story. S $39–$53; D $45–$61; each addl $7; under 18 free; higher rates May–Sep. Crib free. TV; cable. Pool. Free continental bkfst. Cafe 6 am–midnight. Bar 11–1 am. Ck-out noon. Coin lndry. Meeting rms. Valet serv. Sundries. Cr cds: A, C, D, DS, MC, V.

Quincy

Settled: 1822 **Pop:** 42,554 **Elev:** 601 ft (183 m) **Area code:** 217 **Zip:** 62301

Motels

★ ★ ★HOLIDAY INN. *201 S Third St. 217/222-2666.* 156 rms, 4 story. S $48–$55; D $55–$64; each addl $7; suites $99; studio rms $30; under 18 free. Crib free. TV; satellite. Indoor pool; poolside serv. Rm serv. Bar 11–1 am; entertainment, dancing. Ck-out noon. Coin lndry. Meeting rms. Bellhops. Valet serv. Free airport, RR station, marina transportation. Game rm. Rec rm. Cr cds: A, C, D, DS, MC, V.

✔ ★QUINCY MOTOR INN. *200 Maine St, at E end of Quincy Memorial Bridge. 217/223-6610; res: 800/637-9183 (exc IL), 800/252-8436 (IL).* 154 rms, 3–4 story. S $34–$41; D $43; each addl $5; under 12 free. Crib $5. TV; cable. Pool. Cafe 6 am–11 pm. Rm serv to 9 pm. Bars 5 pm–11 pm; Sat 7 pm–1 am. Ck-out 1 pm. Coin lndry. Meeting rms. Barber. Free airport, RR station transportation. View of Mississippi River. Cr cds: A, D, MC, V.

Rantoul

Pop: 20,161 **Elev:** 748 ft (228 m) **Area code:** 217 **Zip:** 61866

Motels

★ ★BEST WESTERN HERITAGE INN. *420 S Murray Rd. 217/892-9292.* 50 rms, 2 story. S $32–$52; D $37–$57; each addl $5; under 15 free. Crib free. TV; cable. Heated pool; whirlpool, sauna, hot tub. Playground. Free coffee. Cafe opp 6 am–midnight. Ck-out noon. Meeting rms. Valet serv. Cr cds: A, C, D, DS, MC, V.

✔ ★ ★HOLIDAY INN I-57. *On US 136 at I-57. 217/893-0700.* 82 rms, 2 story. S $33–$36; D $36–$42; each addl $6; under 18 free; higher rates Univ of Illinois events. Crib free. TV; cable. Heated pool. Cafe 6:30 am–2 pm, 5:30–10 pm; Sun from 7 am. Rm serv. Bar 4 pm–midnight; entertainment Wed–Sat. Ck-out noon. Meeting rms. Bellhops. Sundries. Holidome. Cr cds: A, C, D, DS, MC, V.

Rockford

Founded: 1834 **Pop:** 139,712 **Elev:** 721 ft (220 m) **Area code:** 815

Motels

★★**BEST WESTERN COLONIAL INN.** *4850 E State St (61108).* 815/398-5050. 97 rms, 2–3 story. S $41–$56; D $50.75–$61; studio rms $70–$77; under 12 free. Crib $3. TV. Cafe adj 6 am–11:30 pm. Bar noon–2 am. Ck-out noon. Meeting rms. Beauty shop. Whirlpool. Rockford College adj. Cr cds: A, C, D, DS, MC, V.

 ⊘ SC

✓★★**CHESTNUT INN.** *4419 S 11th St (61109), at Samuelson Rd.* 815/397-4000. 112 rms, 1–2 story. S $24.95; D $29.95; each addl $5; under 16 free. Crib free. TV; in-rm movies. Heated pool; poolside serv. Cafe 5:30 am–11 pm. Rm serv. Bar 10–2 am. Ck-out noon. Coin lndry. Meeting rms. Bellhops. Valet serv. Airport, bus depot transportation. Putting green. Lawn games. Cr cds: A, C, D, DS, ER, MC, V.

⛐ ⚫ ⊘ SC

★★★**COURTYARD BY MARRIOTT.** *US 20 (61108), I-90 exit US 20 Business.* 815/397-6222. 148 units, 2–3 story. S $48–$59; D $48–$67; each addl $8; suites $64–$82; under 12 free; wkend rates. Crib free. TV; cable. Indoor pool; whirlpool. Free coffee in rms. Cafe 6 am–11 pm. Bar 4–11 pm. Ck-out 1 pm. Coin lndry. Meeting rms. Valet serv. Exercise equipt; weights, bicycles. Balconies. Cr cds: A, C, D, MC, V. Ⓔ

⚫ 🏃

★**EXEL INN.** *220 S Lyford Rd (61108), at I-90.* 815/332-4915. 102 rms, 2 story. S $26.95; D $33.95; each addl $4; under 18 free. Crib free. TV; satellite. Free coffee. Cafe opp open 24 hours. Ck-out noon. Meeting rms. Valet serv. Cr cds: A, MC, V.

 ⊘ SC

✓★★**HOWARD JOHNSON.** *3909 S 11th St (61109), at IL 251 Bypass 20.* 815/397-9000. 146 rms, 2 story. S $42–$62; D $46–$63; each addl $5; studio rms $53–$60; kit. apts $600/month; under 18 free; wkend rates. Crib free. TV; satellite. Indoor pool. Playground. Cafe. Bar 4 pm–1 am; Sun to 11 pm. Ck-out noon. Coin lndry. Meeting rms. Valet serv. Sundries. Free airport transportation. Rec rm. Tennis. Sun deck. Private patios, balconies. Cr cds: A, C, D, DS, MC, V.

⛐ 🔍 ⚫ SC

✓★★**SWEDEN HOUSE LODGE.** *4605 E State St (61108).* 815/398-4130. 107 rms, 2–3 story. S $31.75–$37.75; D $33.75–$45.75; suites $45.75–$55.75; each addl $2–3; under 18 free. Crib free. TV; cable, in-rm movies. Indoor pool; whirlpool. Free continental bkfst. Ck-out noon. Meeting rms. Valet serv. Sundries. Airport transportation. Game rm. Cr cds: A, C, D, DS, MC, V. Ⓔ

⚫

St Charles

Settled: 1838 **Pop:** 17,492 **Elev:** 697 ft (212 m) **Area code:** 312 **Zip:** 60174

Motels

✓★**BEST WESTERN INN OF ST CHARLES.** *1635 E Main St.* 312/584-4550. 54 rms, 2 story. S $37–$47; D $44–$54; each addl $5; under 18 free. Crib free. TV. Heated pool; whirlpool. Cafe adj 6 am–11 pm. Ck-out noon. Sundries. Cr cds: A, C, D, DS, MC, V.

⚫ ⊘ SC

✓★**DU WAYNE.** *(27 W 641 North Ave, W Chicago 60185) 2 mi E of IL 59.* 312/231-1040. 33 rms, 1–2 story. S $31–$36; D $36–$50; each addl $3; kit. units $3 addl. Crib free. TV. Heated pool. Playground. Cafe adj 6:30 am–8 pm. Ck-out 11 am. Coin lndry. Sundries. Cr cds: A, C, D, MC, V.

Salem

Pop: 7,813 **Elev:** 544 ft (166 m) **Area code:** 618 **Zip:** 62881

Motels

✔ ★ ★**DAYS INN.** *1812 W Main St, 2 mi W of I-57 exit 113.* 618/548-4212. 100 rms, 2 story. S $29.95–$32.95; D $34.95–$37.95; each addl $5; under 18 free; wkly rates. Crib free. TV; cable. Pool; wading pool, poolside serv. Cafe 6 am–9 pm. Rm serv. Bar 11 am–midnight; Sat, Sun from 4 pm. Ck-out 1 pm. Coin lndry. Meeting rms. Valet serv. Some refrigerators. Cr cds: A, C, D, DS, MC, V.

★**LAKEWOOD.** *1500 E Main, 2½ mi E of I-57, E on US 50.* 618/548-2785. 19 rms, 1–2 story. S $19; D $20–$23; each addl $2. Crib $2. TV; cable. Playground. Free coffee. Cafe nearby. Ck-out 11 am. Picnic tables. Grills. Cr cds: A, C, D, DS, MC, V.

Springfield

Settled: 1819 **Pop:** 100,054 **Elev:** 600 ft (183 m) **Area code:** 217

Motels

(Rates are generally higher during state fair)

✔ ★**DAYS INN.** *3000 Stevenson Dr (62703).* 217/529-0171. 210 rms, 2 story. S $32–$36; D $37–$41; each addl $5–$10; under 18 free; higher rates special events. Crib free. TV; cable. Pool. Cafe 6 am–10 pm. Ck-out noon. Meeting rms. Picnic tables. Cr cds: A, C, D, DS, MC, V.

✔ ★ ★**HOLIDAY INN-SOUTH.** *625 E St Joseph St (62703).* 217/529-7131. 121 rms, 2 story. S $47.75–$52.75; D $49.75–$54.75; each addl $7; suites $90–$110; under 18 free. Crib free. TV; cable. Pool. Playground. Free coffee. Cafe 6 am–10 pm. Rm serv from 7 am. Bar 11–1 am; Sun 1–10 pm. Ck-out noon. Coin lndry. Meeting rms. Bellhops. Valet serv. Cr cds: A, C, D, DS, MC, V.

★**RED ROOF INN.** *3200 Singer Ave (62703), off I-55S exit 96B.* 217/753-4302. 109 rms, 2 story. S $26–$29; D $32–$34; under 18 free. Crib free. TV. Free coffee. Cafe nearby. Ck-out noon. Cr cds: A, C, D, DS, MC, V.

✔ ★**REGAL 8 INN.** *Toronto Rd (62703), 7 mi S, 1 blk E of I-55 Toronto Rd exit 90S.* 217/529-1633. 100 rms, 2 story. S $22.88–$29.88; D $29.88–$32.88; suites $42.88. Crib free. TV; cable, in-rm movies. Indoor pool. Cafe 6 am–10 pm. Ck-out 1 pm. Meeting rms. Cr cds: A, C, D, DS, MC, V.

★ ★ ★**SHERATON MOTOR INN.** *3090 Adlai Stevenson Dr (62703).* 217/529-6611. 124 rms, 2 story. S $50–$60; D $50–$62; each addl $6; under 19 free. Crib free. TV; cable, in-rm movies. Indoor pool; whirlpool, sauna. Cafe 6 am–10 pm. Rm serv. Bar 11–1 am, Sun from 4 pm; entertainment, dancing exc Sun. Ck-out 1 pm. Meeting rms. Valet serv. Free airport, RR station transportation. Picnic tables. Cr cds: A, C, D, MC, V.

Motor Hotel

✔ ★**MANSION VIEW LODGE.** *529 S 4th St (62701), at Edwards St, opp Governor's Mansion.* 217/544-7411; res: 800/252-1083 (IL). 108 rms, 2–4 story. S $32–$42; D $40–$50;

each addl $2; under 16 free. Crib $1. TV; cable. Pool; wading pool. Free continental bkfst. Rm serv. Bar 2–11 pm. Ck-out noon. Cr cds: A, C, D, MC, V.

Starved Rock State Park

(2 mi S of La Salle on IL 351, then 4 mi E on IL 71) **Area code:** 815

Resort

✔ ★ ★STARVED ROCK LODGE. *(Box 471, Utica 61373) In state park, NW entrance on IL 178, 3 mi S of I-80 Utica exit. 815/667-4211.* 45 lodge rms, 23 units in log cabins, 5 with connecting baths, 5 rms in Tepee House. S $25–$30; D $35–$50; each addl $9. Crib free. TV in lobby. Playground. Dining rm 8–10 am, noon–2 pm, 6–8 pm. Box lunches. Snack bar. Bar. Ck-out noon, ck-in 3 pm. Meeting rms. Bellhops. Tennis. Golf privileges. Canoeing. X-country ski on site. Sleighing. Tobogganing. Large lobby, stone fireplace, Indian mementos. Rolling, wooded country.

Sterling

Founded: 1839 **Pop:** 16,281 **Elev:** 645 ft (197 m) **Area code:** 815 **Zip:** 61081

Motels

★INN OF STERLING. *2610 E Lincolnway. 815/625-9010.* 106 rms, 2 story. S $26.95–$38; D $35–$46; each addl $4–$12; under 16 free; wkly rates. Crib $4. TV; cable. Pool. Free coffee. Cafe 11:30 am–2 pm, 5–9 pm; Fri–Sat 5–10 pm. Closed Sun. Ck-out noon. Meeting rms. Cr cds: A, C, D, MC, V.

✔ ★ ★RAMADA INN. *(2105 S 1st Ave, Rock Falls 61071) 1 blk S of jct US 30 and I-88. 815/626-5500.* 118 rms, 2 story. S $38–$50; D $43–$55; each addl $6; under 18 free. Crib free. TV. Indoor pool; whirlpool. Cafe 6:30 am–10 pm; Sun to 9 pm. Rm serv 8:30 am–9:30 pm. Bar 11–1 am; entertainment, dancing Mon–Sat. Ck-out noon. Meeting rms. Sundries. Cr cds: A, C, D, DS, MC, V.

Indiana

Population: 5,490,260

Land area: 35,936 sq mi (93,074 sq km)

Elevation: 320–1,257 ft (98–383 m)

Highest point: Near Bethel (Wayne Co)

Entered Union: December 11, 1816 (19th state)

Capital: Indianapolis

Motto: The Crossroads of America

Nickname: The Hoosier State

State flower: Peony

State bird: Cardinal

State tree: Tulip tree

State fair: August 16–27, 1989 in Indianapolis

Time zone: Eastern and Central

Interstate Highway System

The following alphabetical listing of Indiana towns in *Mobil Travel Guide* shows that these cities are within 10 miles (16 kilometers) of the indicated Interstate highways. A highway map should, however, be checked for the nearest exit.

INTERSTATE 64: Corydon, Jeffersonville, New Albany, Wyandotte.

INTERSTATE 65: Columbus, Gary, Indianapolis, Jeffersonville, Lafayette, Lebanon, New Albany, Remington, Scottsburg, Seymour.

INTERSTATE 69: Anderson, Angola, Fort Wayne, Huntington, Indianapolis, Marion, Muncie, Noblesville.

INTERSTATE 70: Brazil, Greencastle, Greenfield, Indianapolis, New Castle, Richmond, Terre Haute.

INTERSTATE 74: Batesville, Crawfordsville, Indianapolis.

INTERSTATE 94: Gary, Hammond, Michigan City, Portage.

Weather Statistics*

	WINTER	SPRING	SUMMER	FALL
Statewide	28°F (-2°C)	63°F (17°C)	75°F (24°C)	55°F (13°C)
Northern region	25°F (-4°C)	58°F (14°C)	73°F (23°C)	53°F (11°C)
Southern region	33°F (.6°C)	65°F (18°C)	78°F (25°C)	58°F (14°C)

*Average mean temperatures are listed for the entire state. Averages for specific regions are given if significant differences exist.

Visitor Information

Ten-issue subscriptions to *Outdoor Indiana* may be obtained by writing Dept of Natural Resources, Information & Education Div, 612 State Office Bldg, Indianapolis 46204. This official publication of the Dept of Natural Resources is $7.50 for 1 year or $13.50 for 2 years.

Brochures on camping and other activities, calendar of events, information about historic sites and other subjects are available from the Indiana Dept of Commerce, Tourism Development Div, One N Capitol St, Suite 700, Indianapolis 46204; 317/232-8860 or 800/2-WANDER.

There are travel information centers located at highway rest areas throughout Indiana. Those who stop by will find information and brochures most helpful in planning stops at points of interest. All are open daily, 24 hours.

Angola

Pop: 5,486 **Elev:** 1,055 ft (322 m) **Area code:** 219 **Zip:** 46703

Motels

✔ ★**COUNTRY MEADOWS RESORT.** *(Box 215, Fremont 46737) N on I-69, Pokagon State Park exit; IN 120 at I-69. 219/495-4525.* 13 rms, 3 family units. S $34; D $45; each addl $5; family units $75; under 12 free; golf plans. Closed Nov–Mar. Crib $5. TV. Pool; whirlpool. Playground. Cafe 6 am–10 pm. Bar from 10 am. Ck-out 11 am. Tennis. 18-hole golf, putting green, pro. Picnic tables. On 40 acres. Cr cds: MC, V.

★**RED CARPET INN.** *(Box 392, Rte 7) I-69 at US 20. 219/665-9561.* 96 rms, 2 story. S $33–$35; D $39–$41; each addl $5; under 12 free. Crib $5. TV; cable, in-rm movies. Pool. Cafe adj 6 am–10 pm. Rm serv. Meeting rms. Bar 4 pm–midnight exc Sun. Ck-out noon. X-country ski 1 mi. Picnic tables. Cr cds: A, MC, V.

Resort

✔ ★ ★ ★**POTAWATOMI INN.** *(Box 180, Rte 2) 6 mi N on IN 127, ½ mi W of I-69 in Pokagon State Park (entrance fee, Apr–Oct; wkends Nov–Mar). 219/833-1077.* 54 rms in 2-story hotel, annex; 16 cabin rms, 10 motel rms. S $31; D $36. Crib $3. TV. Indoor pool; whirlpool, sauna. Cafe 7 am–8 pm. Box lunches. Ck-out noon, ck-in 4 pm. Meeting rms. Gift shop. Grocery in summer. Tennis. X-country ski on site. Hayrides. Private beach; lifeguard in summer. Dock, boats. Tobogganing. Lawn games. Fireplace. Rms vary. Facilities of Pokagon State Park. On Lake James. Cr cds: A, MC, V.

Aurora

Founded: 1819 **Pop:** 3,816 **Elev:** 501 ft (153 m) **Area code:** 812 **Zip:** 47001

Motel

★**HILLCREST.** *(Box 318, Rte 3) 3 mi W on US 50. 812/926-1991.* 25 rms. S $25–$30; D $29–$35; each addl $5; under 6 free. Crib $4. TV; cable. Free coffee. Cafe nearby. Ck-out 11 am. Sundries. Cr cds: A, C, D, MC, V.

Bloomington

Settled: 1818 **Pop:** 52,044 **Elev:** 745 ft (227 m) **Area code:** 812 **Zip:** 47401

Motels

(Rates may be higher during special college wkends)

✔ ★ ★**BEST WESTERN FIRESIDE INN.** *4501 E 3d St. 812/332-2141.* 96 rms, 2 story. S $34–$38; D $41–$45; each addl $4; under 17 free. Crib free. TV; cable, in-rm movies. Pool. Free coffee in rm. Cafe 7 am–10 pm; Fri, Sat to 11 pm; Sun 8 am–9 pm. Bar 11 am–midnight. Ck-out noon. Meeting rms. Sundries. Downhill ski 9 mi; x-country ski 12 mi. Health club privileges. Picnic tables. Cr cds: A, C, D, DS, MC, V.

✔ ★ ★**HAMPTON INN.** *2100 N Walnut, IN 37 exit College to Walnut. 812/334-2100.* 123 rms, 4 story. S $37; D $41–$49; under 18 free. Crib free. TV; cable. Pool. Continental bkfst. Cafe adj open 24 hrs. Ck-out noon. Meeting rms. Valet serv. Airport transportation. Health club privileges. Cr cds: A, C, D, DS, MC, V.

⬡ ⬡ ⬡ ⬡ ⬡

★★HOLIDAY INN. *2601 N Walnut (IN 37). 812/332-9453.* 140 rms, 2 story. Late Mar–mid-Sep: S $41–$51; D $44–$53; each addl $6; under 19 free; lower rates rest of yr. Crib free. TV; cable, in-rm movies. Heated pool. Cafe 6:30 am–2 pm, 5–10 pm; Sun 7 am–2 pm. Rm serv. Bar 4 pm–1 am. Ck-out noon. Meeting rms. Valet serv. Sundries. Downhill/x-country ski 20 mi. Cr cds: A, C, D, MC, V.

⬡ ⬡ ⬡ ⬡ ⬡ ⬡ ⬡

Motor Hotel

✔ ★★HOWARD JOHNSON. *1722 N Walnut St (IN 37). 812/332-7241.* 95 rms, 4 story. S $38–$50; D $44–$54; each addl $5; studio rms $44–$54; under 18 free; higher rates bike race. Crib free. TV; in-rm movies. Pool. Ck-out noon. Meeting rms. Valet serv. Sundries. Tennis. Downhill ski 12 mi; x-country ski 15 mi. Cr cds: A, C, D, MC, V.

⬡ ⬡ ⬡ ⬡ ⬡ ⬡ ⬡

Columbus

Settled: 1820 **Pop:** 30,614 **Elev:** 656 ft (200 m) **Area code:** 812

Motels

(Rates may be higher during Indianapolis "500," Kentucky Derby)

✔ ★★DAYS INN. *3445 Jonathan Moore Pike (47201), IN 46 W. 812/376-9951.* 120 rms, 2 story. S $38.95; D $42.95; each addl $6; under 16 free; Indianapolis "500" (2-day min). Crib free. TV; cable. Heated pool. Free continental bkfst. Cafe nearby. Bar 4 pm–2 am; DJ Mon–Thurs, entertainment Fri & Sat, dancing. Ck-out noon. Meeting rms. Downhill ski 16 mi. Cr cds: A, C, D, MC, V.

⬡ ⬡ ⬡ ⬡ ⬡ ⬡

★★KNIGHTS INN. *101 Carrie Ln (47201), jct I-65, IN 46, exit 68. 812/378-3100.* 100 units, 11 kits. S $30.50; D $36; each addl $3; kit. units $34.50; studio rms $32.50; under 18 free. Crib $5. TV; cable, in-rm movies. Pool. Cafe opp 6 am–10 pm. Ck-out noon. Meeting rm. Cr cds: A, C, D, ER, MC, V.

⬡ ⬡ ⬡ ⬡ ⬡

✔ ★★LEES INNS. *(2180 E King, Franklin 46131) 18 mi N on I-65, exit Franklin 90. 812/736-8000.* 100 rms, 2 story. S $37; D $42; each addl $5; "500" (3-night min). TV. Pool; poolside serv. Cafe 6 am–10 pm; Sun to 8 pm. Rm serv. Bar 4 pm–1:30 am; entertainment, dancing Tu–Sat. Ck-out noon. Meeting rm. Cr cds: A, C, D, MC, V.

⬡ ⬡

Motor Hotel

★★RAMADA INN. *2485 Jonathan Moore Pike (IN 46) (47201), just E of jct I-65. 812/376-3051.* 119 rms, 2 story. S $44–$48; D $50–$58; each addl $6; suites $65–$101; under 18 free; 2-day min Indianapolis "500;" ski, golf, wkend packages. Crib free. TV; cable. Pool. Free continental bkfst. Cafe 6 am–10 pm; Fri, Sat to 11 pm; Sun 5:30–8 pm. Rm serv. Bar 11–2 am, Sun 2–8 pm; entertainment, dancing exc Sun. Ck-out noon. Meeting rms. Bellhops. Valet serv. Sundries. Free airport transportation. Lighted tennis. Boating; 16-acre lake. Private patios, balconies. Cr cds: A, C, D, DS, MC, V.

⬡ ⬡ ⬡ ⬡ ⬡

Connersville

Founded: 1813 **Pop:** 17,023 **Elev:** 835 ft (255 m) **Area code:** 317 **Zip:** 47331

Motels

(Rates may be higher during the Indianapolis "500")

★HEIM. *N on IN 1. 317/825-5118.* 20 rms. S $25; D $30; suites $32–$50. TV; cable, in-rm movies. Cafe adj 6 am–6 pm. Ck-out 11 am. Free airport transportation. Some refrigerators. Cr cds: MC, V.

✔★★INN OF CONNERSVILLE. *IN 1 at 37th St. 317/825-7531.* 95 rms, 2 story. S $31–$42; D $35–$46; each addl $4; under 12 free. Crib free. TV; cable. Heated pool; poolside serv. Cafe 6 am–1:30 pm, 5–9:30 pm. Rm serv. Bar 11 am–midnight, Thurs, Fri to 2 am, Sat 6 pm–2 am, Sun 6 pm–midnight; dancing exc Sun. Ck-out noon. Meeting rms. Valet serv. Free airport transportation. Cr cds: A, D, DS, MC, V.

[icons]

Crawfordsville

Settled: 1822 **Pop:** 13,325 **Elev:** 769 ft (234 m) **Area code:** 317 **Zip:** 47933

Motels

★GENERAL LEW WALLACE. *309 W Pike St, 3 blks SW of town center. 317/362-8400.* 36 rms, 2 story. S $30.50; D $36.50; each addl $7.50; kit. cottages $450/month; under 12 free; higher rates Indianapolis "500" (2-day min). Crib $7.50. TV; cable. Cafe 5:30 am–10 pm. Bar. Ck-out noon. Sundries. Cr cds: A, C, D, MC, V.

[icons]

✔★★HOLIDAY INN. *2500 N Lafayette Rd, jct US 231, I-74. 317/362-8700.* 150 rms, 2 story. S $45–$51; D $51–$57; each addl $4; under 20 free; higher rates Indianapolis "500" (2-day min). Crib free. TV; cable, in-rm movies. Heated pool. Cafe 6 am–10 pm. Rm serv. Bar 11–1 am, Fri, Sat to 2 am, Sun 4–10 pm; entertainment, dancing. Ck-out noon. Coin Indry. Meeting rms. Valet serv. Sundries. Game rm. Cr cds: A, C, D, DS, MC, V. ①

[icons]

Elkhart

Founded: 1832 **Pop:** 41,305 **Elev:** 748 ft (228 m) **Area code:** 219

Motels

(Rates higher during Mobile Home Show, football wkends)

★★HOLIDAY INN. *2725 Cassopolis St (IN 19) (46514). 219/264-7502.* 201 rms, 2 story. Mid-July–Nov: S $49–$58; D $53–$62; suites $91–$114; studio rms $49–$58; under 12 free; lower rates rest of yr. Crib free. TV; cable, in-rm movies. Indoor pool; whirlpool, sauna, poolside serv. Cafe 6 am–2 pm, 5–10 pm; Sat, Sun from 7 am. Rm serv. Bar 5 pm–1 am exc Sun; Fri, Sat to 2 am; dancing. Ck-out noon. Coin Indry. Meeting rms. Valet serv. Sundries. Putting green. Downhill/x-country ski 10 mi. Rec rm. Game rm. Cr cds: A, C, D, DS, MC, V.

[icons]

★★★RAMADA INN. *3011 Belvedere Rd (46514). 219/262-1581.* 145 rms, 2 story, 3 kits. S $45–$54; D $50–$59; each addl $6; suites, kit. units $78; studio rm $47–$52; under 18 free; ski packages. Crib free. TV; cable. 2 pools, 1 indoor; whirlpool, sauna, poolside serv. Playground. Cafe 6:30 am–10 pm; Sat from 7 am; Sun, hols 7 am–8:30 pm. Rm serv 7 am–9 pm. Bar 11–1 am, Fri, Sat to 2 am, Sun 12:30–8:30 pm; entertainment, dancing Tu-Sat. Ck-out noon. Meeting rms. Valet serv. Sundries. Game rm. Putting green. Downhill ski 8 mi. Health club privileges. Cr cds: A, C, D, DS, MC, V.

[icons]

✔★RED ROOF INN. *2902 Cassopolis St (IN 19) (46514). 219/262-3691.* 81 rms, 2 story. S $28.95–$39; D $34.95–$44; under 19 free; 2-night min football wkends. Crib free. TV; in-rm movies. Cafe adj open 24 hrs. Ck-out noon. Downhill ski 10 mi. Cr cds: A, C, D, DS, MC, V.

[icons]

★**TURNPIKE.** *52042 IN 19N (46514). 219/264-1108.* 18 rms, 2 kits. S $24–$38; D $28–$36; each addl $3; kit. units $38; higher rates special events, football wkends (2-day min, full deposit); Crib $3. TV; cable. Cafe nearby. Ck-out 11 am. Downhill ski 20 mi. Picnic table. Cr cds: A, DS, MC, V.

Evansville

Founded: 1819 **Pop:** 130,496 **Elev:** 394 ft (120 m) **Area code:** 812

Motels

✔ ★★**BEST WESTERN WILLIAMSBURG INN.** *100 S Green River Rd (47715). 812/473-0171.* 109 rms, 2 story. S $41–$51; D $47–$59; each addl $6; suites $50–$84; under 18 free; monthly rates. Crib free. TV; cable, in-rm movies. Indoor pool; poolside serv. Cafe 6 am–10 pm. Rm serv. Bar 3 pm–2 am, Sun to midnight; entertainment, dancing Wed–Sun. Ck-out noon. Meeting rms. Sundries. Package store. Indoor tennis, racquetball privileges. Exercise equipt; weights, bicycles, whirlpool, steam rm, sauna. Picnic table. Cr cds: A, C, D, DS, ER, MC, V.

✔ ★★**DRURY INN.** *3901 US 41 (47711). 812/423-5818.* 154 rms, 4 story. S $38–$43; D $42–$47; each addl $4; under 18 free. Crib free. TV; cable, in-rm movies. Pool. Free bkfst. Cafe adj open 24 hrs. Ck-out noon. Meeting rms. Free airport transportation. Cr cds: A, C, D, MC, V.

★**ESQUIRE.** *1817 US 41N Business (47711). 812/422-6000.* 67 rms. S $25–$27.50; D $28.50–$31; each addl $3; under 18 free. Crib $3. TV; cable. Free continental bkfst in lobby. Cafe nearby. Ck-out noon. Sundries. Some refrigerators, in-rm steam baths. Covered picnic tables. Cr cds: A, C, D, MC, V.

✔ ★**REGAL 8 INN.** *4201 US 41N (47711). 812/424-6431.* 103 rms, 2 story. S $25.88–$30.88; D $30.88–$35.88; 3–4, $34.88. Crib free. TV; cable. Indoor pool. Playground. Free coffee. Cafe adj open 24 hrs. Ck-out 1 pm. Picnic table. Cr cds: A, C, D, DS, MC, V.

★**TRAVELODGE.** *701 1st Ave (47710). 812/424-3886.* 59 rms, 2 story. S $35–$37; D $40–$45; each addl $4; under 17 free. Crib free. TV; cable. Pool. Free continental bkfst. Cafe nearby. Ck-out noon. Meeting rm. Sundries. Some balconies. Cr cds: A, C, D, DS, ER, MC, V.

Motor Hotel

✔ ★★**SHERATON INN.** *5701 US 41N (47711), near airport. 812/464-1010.* 120 rms, 3 story. S $42–$47; D $44–$53; each addl $5; kit. suites $85–$95; studio rms $26–$45; under 18 free. Crib free. TV; cable. Indoor pool; whirlpool, sauna. Cafe 6 am–2 pm, 5–10 pm. Bar 2 pm–2 am; entertainment, dancing Wed–Sun. Ck-out noon. Meeting rms. Sundries. Free airport transportation. Cr cds: A, C, D, DS, MC, V.

Fort Wayne

Settled: ca 1690 **Pop:** 172,028 **Elev:** 767 ft (234 m) **Area code:** 219

Motels

★★**CARLTON LODGE.** *1619 W Washington Center Rd (46818), I-69 exit 111B. 219/489-1500.* 142 units, 2 story, 5 kits. S $47–$56; D $52–$61; each addl $8; suites $56–$150; kit. units $75; under 18 free; wkend rates. Crib free. TV; cable, in-rm movies. Heated indoor/outdoor pool; whirlpool. Free coffee, bkfst buffet. Ck-out noon. Meeting rms. Valet serv. Sundries. Game rm. Refrigerator in some suites. Cr cds: A, C, D, MC, V.

✔ ★ ★ ★**DON HALL'S GUESTHOUSE.** *1313 W Washington Center Rd (46825), I-69 exit 111B. 219/489-2524; res: 800/348-1999.* 130 rms, 2 story. S $42–$50; D $48–$50; suites $70; wkend rates. Crib free. TV; cable. 2 pools, 1 indoor; whirlpool, sauna. Free coffee in rms, free continental bkfst. Cafe 6 am–midnight; Sun to 11 pm. Rm serv. Bar 11–1 am, Sun noon–11 pm; entertainment exc Mon. Ck-out 2 pm. Meeting rms. Sundries. Cr cds: A, C, D, DS, MC, V. Ⓓ Ⓔ Ⓕ

🏊 🚭 SC

★**KNIGHTS INN.** *2901 Goshen Rd (46808), jct US 33, 30 and I-69. 219/484-2669.* 100 units, 10 kits. S $28.50–$30.50; D $34–$36; each addl $3; kit. units $38.50–$44; under 18 free. Crib $3. TV; cable, in-rm movies. Pool. Free coffee in lobby. Cafe adj open 24 hrs. Ck-out noon. Meeting rm. Some refrigerators. Cr cds: A, C, D, MC, V.

♿ 🏊 🚭 🐾 SC

★ ★**RAMADA.** *1212 Magnavox Way (IN 14) (46804). 219/432-0511.* 150 rms, 2 story. S $49–$59; D $54–$59; each addl $5; suites $59–$64; under 18 free; wkend rates. Crib free. TV; cable. Heated pool. Playground. Cafe 6 am–2 pm, 5–9 pm. Rm serv. Bar 4–11 pm, closed Sun; entertainment Tu–Sat. Ck-out noon. Meeting rm. Bellhops. Valet serv. Cr cds: A, D, MC, V.

♿ 🏊 🚭 🐾 SC

✔ ★**RED ROOF INN.** *2920 Goshen Rd (US 33, 30) (46808). 219/484-8641.* 79 rms, 2 story. S $28.95–$30.95; D $34.95–$36.95; under 18 free. Crib free. TV; cable, in-room movies. Free coffee in lobby. Cafe opp open 24 hrs. Ck-out noon. Cr cds: A, C, D, DS, MC, V.

🐾 🚭 🐾 SC

✔ ★ ★**SIGNATURE INN.** *1734 W Washington Center Rd (46818). 219/489-5554.* 100 rms, 2 story. S $41; D $47; each addl $6; under 19 free; some wkend rates. Crib free. TV; cable. Pool. Free continental bkfst. Ck-out noon. Meeting rms. Valet serv. Sundries. X-country ski 10 mi. Game rm. Cr cds: A, C, D, DS, MC, V.

♿ 🐾 🏊 🚭 🐾 SC

French Lick

Founded: 1811 **Pop:** 2,265 **Elev:** 511 ft (156 m) **Area code:** 812 **Zip:** 47432

Motel

★**LANE MOTEL.** *(Box 224) ½ mi N on IN 56, 1½ mi S of US 150. 812/936-9919.* 39 rms. S $28–$30; D $35; each addl $4. Crib $2. TV; cable. Pool. Playground. Cafe nearby. Ck-out 11 am. Picnic table. Cr cds: MC, V.

♿ 🐾 🏊 🐾

Hammond

Pop: 93,714 **Elev:** 591 ft (180 m) **Area code:** 219

Motor Hotels

✔ ★ ★**DAYS INN.** *4000 Calumet Ave (46327). 219/931-0900.* 160 rms, 4 story. S $29.95–$33; D $34.95–$41.95; each addl $4; under 12 free. Crib free. TV; cable. Heated pool. Playground. Cafe 6 am–10 pm. Rm serv 7 am–9 pm. Bar 4 pm–midnight. Ck-out noon. Coin lndry. Meeting rms. Bellhops. Valet serv. Cr cds: A, C, D, DS, MC, V.

🏊 🚭 🐾 SC

★ ★**QUALITY INN.** *3830 179th St (46323). 219/844-2140.* 149 rms, 4 story. S $35–$45; D $39–$51; each addl $6; under 16 free. Crib free. TV; in-rm movies. Pool; wading pool, poolside serv. Playground. Cafe 6 am–2 pm, 5:30–10 pm. Rm serv. Bar 11–1 am; Fri, Sat to 3 am; Sun 1–10 pm. Ck-out noon. Coin lndry. Meeting rms. Bellhops. Valet serv. Sundries. O'Hare Airport transportation. Racquetball privileges. Balconies. Cr cds: A, C, D, DS, MC, V.

♿ 🐾 🏊 🚭 🐾 SC

Indianapolis

Founded: 1820 **Pop:** 774,800 **Elev:** 717 ft (219 m) **Area code:** 317

Motels

(Rates are usually higher during Indianapolis "500" and state fair; may be 3-day min.)

✔ ★ ★**CHEZ JEAN RESTAURANT FRANCAIS & INN.** *(9027 S IN 67, Camby 46113) SW on Kentucky Ave (IN 67).* 317/831-0870. 14 units. S $27.30–$31.50; D $31.50–$36.75; suites $64.05–$74.50; wkly rates. TV. Free coffee & tea; free continental bkfst in suites. Cafe 6–10 pm exc Sun. Bar. Ck-out 11 am–2 pm. Some refrigerators. Antiques in suites. Picnic tables. Cr cds: A, C, D, MC, V. ⒺⒻ

🅿🚫

★**DAYS INN-SOUTH.** *450 E Bixler Rd (46227).* 317/788-0811. 104 rms, 2 story. S $25–$30; D $30–$35; each addl $5; under 12 free. Crib free. TV; in-rm movies. Pool; wading pool. Playground. Free continental bkfst in lobby. Cafe nearby. Coin lndry. Meeting rm. Cr cds: A, C, D, DS, MC, V.

🅿🔜🚫sc Ⓢ

★ ★**DILLON INN.** *9090 Wesleyan Rd (46268).* 317/875-7676. 116 units, 3 story. S $39; D $45; each addl $6; suites $55; under 18 free; some wkend rates. Crib free. TV; cable, in-rm movies. Pool. Free coffee, continental bkfst. Cafe nearby. Ck-out noon. Meeting rms. Balconies. Cr cds: A, C, D, DS, MC, V.

🅿🔜🚫🚫sc

✔ ★ ★**DRURY INN.** *9320 N Michigan Rd (46268).* 317/876-9777. 110 rms, 4 story. S $40–$45; D $49–$54; each addl $6; under 18 free; some wkend rates. Crib free. TV; cable, in-rm movies. Pool. Free bkfst. Cafe opp. Rm serv 6 am–11 pm. Ck-out noon. Meeting rms. Sundries. Cr cds: A, C, D, MC, V.

🅿🔜🚫🚫sc Ⓢ

★**EXECUTIVE INN.** *3740 N High School Rd (46224).* 317/293-6550. 158 rms, 2 story. S $32–$34; D $35–$39; each addl $5–$8; suites $55; under 18 free. Crib free. TV. Pool; wading pool. Cafe 7–1 am; Fri, Sat to 3 am; Sun to midnight. Ck-out noon. Meeting rms. Sundries. Cr cds: A, C, D, DS, MC, V.

🅿🔜🔜🚫🚫sc

✔ ★ ★**HAMPTON INN-NORTHEAST.** *6817 E 82d St (46250).* 317/576-0220. 129 units, 4 story. S $42–$50; D $46–$56; suites $60–$76; under 18 free; monthly rates. Crib free. TV; cable. Indoor pool. Continental bkfst. Cafe opp 11 am–9 pm. Ck-out noon. Meeting rm. Valet serv. Refrigerator in suites. Cr cds: A, C, D, DS, MC, V. Ⓔ

🅿🔜🚫🚫

✔ ★ ★**HOWARD JOHNSON-SPEEDWAY.** *2602 N High School Rd (46224).* 317/291-8800. 125 rms, 2 story. S $29–$40; D $35–$50; each addl $5; under 18 free; higher rates special events. Crib free. TV; cable, in-rm movies. Pool. Playground. Cafe 6 am–10 pm. Ck-out noon. Meeting rms. Valet serv. Sundries. Free airport transportation. Private patios, balconies. Cr cds: A, C, D, ER, MC, V.

🔜🚫sc

★**INNTOWNER.** *401 E Washington St (46204).* 317/637-6464. 100 units, 2 story. S $36; D $45; each addl $5; under 12 free; wkly rates; some lower rates winter. TV; cable, in-rm movies. Cafe 5–10 am, 5–10 pm. Rm serv. Bar 11 am–11 pm. Ck-out 11 am. Coin lndry. Meeting rms. Cr cds: A, C, D, MC, V.

🅿🚫sc

★**KNIGHTS INN.** *7101 E 21st St (46219).* 317/353-8484. 99 units, 11 kits. S $27.50–$39.50; D $33.50–$45.50; each addl $3.30; kit. units $46.50; under 18 free; wkly rates (for kit. units). Crib $3. TV; cable, in-rm movies. Pool. Cafe adj 6 am–10 pm. Ck-out noon. Meeting rm. Some refrigerators. Cr cds: A, C, D, MC, V.

🅿🔜🔜🚫🚫sc

★**LA QUINTA-EAST.** *7304 E 21st St (46219). 317/359-1021.* 122 rms, 2 story. S, D $40–$45; each addl $5–$10; under 18 free. Crib free. TV; cable, in-rm movies. Heated pool. Free coffee in lobby. Cafe adj open 24 hrs. Ck-out 1 pm. Valet serv. Cr cds: A, C, D, DS, MC, V.

★**RED ROOF INN-NORTH.** *9520 Valparaiso Ct (46268). 317/872-3030.* 109 rms, 2 story. S $28.95–$30.95; D $34.95–$36.95; each addl $2; under 18 free. Crib free. TV; cable. Free coffee. Cafe nearby. Cr cds: A, C, D, DS, MC, V.

★**REGAL 8 INN-AIRPORT.** *5421 W Bradbury Ave (46241). 317/248-1231.* 134 rms, 3 story. S $25.88; D $30.88–$35.88; suites $45.88. TV; cable. Pool. Cafe adj open 24 hrs. Ck-out 1 pm. Cr cds: A, C, D, DS, MC, V.

✔ ★ ★ ★**SHERATON NORTHEAST.** *7701 E 42d St (46226). 317/897-4000.* 192 rms, 2 story. S $46–$65; D $50–$72; each addl $5–$10; suites $85–$125; studio rms $54–$72; under 18 free. Crib free. TV; cable. Heated pool. Free bkfst. Cafe 6:30 am–10 pm; Sat, Sun from 7:30 am. Rm serv. Bars 11–2 am, Fri, Sat to 3 am, Sun noon–midnight; entertainment, dancing. Ck-out 11 am. Meeting rms. Bellhops. Valet serv. Sundries. Cr cds: A, C, D, DS, ER, MC, V.

✔ ★ ★**SIGNATURE INN-NORTH.** *3910 Payne Branch Rd (46268). 317/875-5656; res: 800/822-5252.* 145 rms, 2 story. May–Oct: S $45; D $51; each addl $6; under 18 free; wkend rates (winter); lower rates rest of yr. Crib free. TV; cable. Pool. Free continental bkfst. Cafe nearby. Ck-out noon. Meeting rms. Valet serv. Sundries. Game rm. Cr cds: A, D, MC, V.

Jasper

Pop: 9,097 **Elev:** 472 ft (144 m) **Area code:** 812 **Zip:** 47546

Motels

✔ ★ ★**BEST WESTERN DUTCHMAN INN.** *(US 231 N & 22d St, Huntingburg 47542) Approx 6 mi S on US 231. 812/683-2334.* 94 rms, 2 story. S $38–$42; D $48–$53; each addl $4; under 18 free. Crib free. TV; cable. Pool. Cafe 6 am–10 pm; Sun to 9 pm. Bar 3 pm–2 am, Sun to midnight; entertainment, dancing Fri, Sat. Ck-out noon. Meeting rms. Valet serv. Some in-rm steam baths ($2). Cr cds: A, C, D, DS, MC, V.

✔ ★ ★**DAYS INN.** *(Box 762) Jct IN 162, IN 164. 812/482-6000.* 84 units, 2 story. S $28–$36.50; D $33–$45; each addl $5; under 18 free. Crib free. TV; cable. Pool. Cafes 6 am–10 pm. Rm serv. Bar to 1 am; Sun to 10 pm. Ck-out noon. Meeting rms. Valet serv. Sundries. Downhill ski 20 mi. Health club, racquetball privileges. Some refrigerators. Cr cds: A, C, D, DS, MC, V.

Jeffersonville

Founded: 1802 **Pop:** 21,220 **Elev:** 448 ft (137 m) **Area code:** 812 **Zip:** 47130

Motels

(Rates are generally much higher during Kentucky Derby)

✔ ★ ★**BEST WESTERN GREENTREE INN.** *(1425 Broadway St, Clarksville 47130) N of Louisville on I-65 at IN 131 exit. 812/288-9281.* 108 rms. S $35–$38; D $38–$44; each addl $3. Crib free. TV; cable. Heated pool. Cafe adj open 24 hrs. Ck-out noon. Bathrm phones. Cr cds: A, C, D, DS, ER, MC, V.

★**COLONIAL INN.** *(Box 2009, Clarksville 47130) On I-65, ½ blk W of IN 131 exit. 812/283-7921.* 104 rms, 2 story. S $22; D $28; each addl $4; under 12 free. TV; cable, in-rm movies. Cafe open 24 hrs. Rm serv. Bar 2 pm–3 am; entertainment, dancing exc Sun. Ck-out noon. Meeting rms. Sundries. Cr cds: A, C, D, MC, V.

🐕

✔ ★DAYS INN. *350 Eastern Blvd, ½ blk E of I-65 exit. 812/288-9331.* 172 rms, 3 story. S $27; D $34; each addl $4. Crib free. TV; cable, in-rm movies. Pool. Playground. Cafe 6 am–10 pm. Ck-out 11 am. Sundries. Cr cds: A, D, MC, V.

🛏️ 🐕 ➡️ 🚫 sc

Kokomo

Founded: 1842 **Pop:** 47,808 **Elev:** 810 ft (247 m) **Area code:** 317

Motels

✔ ★ ★HOWARD JOHNSON. *2808 S Reed Rd (46902). 317/457-8211.* 93 rms, 2 story. S $36–$46; D $45–$55; each addl $6; studio rms $42–$59; under 18 free; higher rates Indianapolis "500" wknd (2-day min). Crib free. TV; cable, in-rm movies. Pool; lifeguard. Cafe adj 5:30 am–midnight. Bar 11–1 am; Sun to 11:30 pm. Ck-out noon. Meeting rms. Valet serv. Balconies. Cr cds: A, C, D, MC, V.

➡️ 🚫 🎿 sc

★ ★RAMADA INN. *1709 E Lincoln Rd (46902). 317/459-8001.* 132 rms, 3 story. Service elvtr. S $45–$60; D $51–$66; each addl $6; under 18 free; wkend rates; higher rates Indianapolis "500" wknd (2-day min). Crib free. TV; cable, in-rm movies. Indoor pool; sauna. Cafe 6 am–2 pm, 5–10 pm; Sat, Sun from 7 am. Rm serv 7 am–10 pm; Sat, Sun from 8 am. Bar 11–2 am, Thurs–Sat to 3 am, Sun noon–midnight; entertainment, dancing. Ck-out 1 pm. Meeting rms. Valet serv. Free airport transportation. Picnic tables. Cr cds: A, C, D, DS, ER, MC, V.

🛏️ ➡️ 🚫 🎿 sc

★WORLD INN. *268 US 31S (46902), 3 mi SE. 317/453-7100.* 119 rms, 2 story. S $25.95; D $30.95; each addl $4; under 18, $1; higher rates Indianapolis "500." Crib $1. TV. Pool adj. Cafe 5:30 am–9 pm. Ck-out noon. Cr cds: A, C, D, MC, V.

🐕 ➡️ 🚫 🎿 sc

Lafayette

Founded: 1825 **Pop:** 43,011 **Elev:** 560 ft (171 m) **Area code:** 317

Motels

✔ ★ ★DAYS INN OF LAFAYETTE. *400 Sagamore Pkwy S (47905). 317/447-4131.* 180 rms, 2 story. S $31–$53; D, suites $36–$58; each addl $4; studio rms $40–$45; under 16 free; higher rates Indianapolis "500," football & special event wkends. Crib free. TV; cable. Heated pool. Cafe 6:30 am–2 pm, 5–10 pm; Sun 7 am–2 pm. Rm serv. Bar 3 pm–2 am; Sun 8 pm–midnight. Ck-out noon. Meeting rms. Valet serv. Free airport transportation 6 am–4 pm. Cr cds: A, C, D, DS, MC, V. D E

♿ 🐕 ➡️ 🚫 🎿 sc S

✔ ★PRESTIGE INN. *1217 Sagamore Pkwy W (47906). 317/463-1531.* 48 rms. S $21.88; D $26.88–$31.88; each addl $5; under 12 free; wkly, monthly rates. Crib free. TV; cable, in-rm movies. Pool. Cafe adj 6 am–10 pm. Rm serv. Ck-out noon. Lndry. X-country ski 2 mi. Health club privileges. Game rm. Some refrigerators. Cr cds: A, C, D, DS, MC, V. E

🐕 ➡️ 🚫 🎿 sc

Motor Hotel

★ ★HOLIDAY INN-NORTH. *5601 IN 43 (47906). 317/567-2131.* 150 rms, 4 story. S $50; D $52; each addl $6; under 18 free; higher rates football games, Indianapolis "500." Crib free. TV; in-rm movies. Indoor pool; sauna. Cafe 6 am–10 pm. Rm serv. Bar 11–1 am, Sun 12:30

pm–midnight; dancing. Ck-out noon. Free lndry. Meeting rms. Valet serv. Tennis. Golf privileges. Game rm. Lawn games. Cr cds: A, C, D, DS, ER, MC, V. Ⓔ

Lincoln Boyhood National Memorial & Lincoln State Park

(4 mi W of Santa Claus on IN 162)

Motel

★**STONE'S.** *(RR 1, Dale 47523) On IN 231, 1½ mi S of I-64 exit 57. 812/937-4448.* 23 motel rms, 10 lodge rms, 1–2 story. S $27; D $34; each addl $2. Crib $2. TV. Cafe 6 am–11 pm. Bar 3 pm–midnight; Sat, Sun from noon. Ck-out 11 am. Sundries. Picnic tables, grills. Near Lincoln State Park & Holiday World. Cr cds: A, C, D, DS, MC, V.

Marion

Settled: 1826 **Pop:** 35,874 **Elev:** 815 ft (248 m) **Area code:** 317

Motel

✔ ★**BROADMOOR.** *1323 N Baldwin Ave (46952). 317/664-0501.* 61 rms. S $27.95; D $30.50; each addl $3.50; suites $45.50; under 10 free; higher rates Indianapolis "500" wkend. Crib $3. TV; cable, in-rm movies. Heated pool; whirlpool. Cafe adj 5 am–11 pm; wkends to 11:30 pm. Ck-out 11 am. Refrigerators. Cr cds: A, C, D, MC, V.

Motor Hotel

✔ ★ ★**SHERATON.** *501 E 4th St (46952). 317/668-8801.* 122 rms, 5 story. S $43–$51; D $48–$53; each addl $5; under 18 free. Crib free. TV; cable. Heated pool. Cafe 6 am–3 pm, 5–10 pm; Sat from 7 am; Sun 7 am–3 pm, 5–9 pm. Rm serv 7 am–9 pm. Bar 11–3 am, Sun 4 pm–midnight; entertainment, dancing exc Sun. Ck-out noon. Meeting rms. Valet serv Mon–Fri. Racquetball privileges. Cr cds: A, C, D, DS, ER, MC, V.

Merrillville

Pop: 27,677 **Elev:** 661 ft (201 m) **Area code:** 219 **Zip:** 46410

Motels

✔ ★**KNIGHTS INN.** *8250 Louisiana St, 1 blk SE of jct I-65, US 30. 219/736-5100.* 130 units, 14 kits. S $29.50–$30.50; D $30.50–$36.50; each addl $3; studio rms $31.50–$43.50; kit. units $39.50–$51.50; under 18 free. Crib $3. TV; cable. Pool. Cafe nearby. Ck-out noon. Meeting rm. Some refrigerators. Cr cds: A, C, D, MC, V.

✔ ★**LA QUINTA.** *8210 Louisiana St, 1 blk SE of jct I-65, US 30. 219/738-2870.* 122 rms, 2 story. S $43–$48; D $48–$53; each addl $5; under 19 free. Crib free. TV; cable. Heated pool. Free coffee in lobby, continental bkfst. Cafe nearby. Ck-out 1 pm. Meeting rms. Valet serv. Sundries. Cr cds: A, C, D, DS, MC, V.

★**RED ROOF INN.** *8290 Georgia St, ½ mi SW of jct I-65, US 30. 219/738-2430.* 109 rms, 2 story. S $27.95–$29.95; D $33.95–$35.95; each addl $2; under 18 free. Crib free. TV;

cable. Free coffee 6–10 am. Cafe opp open 24 hrs. Ck-out noon. Balconies. Cr cds: A, C, D, DS, MC, V.

🉐 🚫 🐾 SC

Michigan City

Founded: 1833 **Pop:** 36,850 **Elev:** 600 ft (183 m) **Area code:** 219 **Zip:** 46360

Motels

★**AL & SALLY'S.** *3221 W Dunes Hwy. 219/872-9131.* 16 rms. May–early Sep: S $30–$32; D $35–$40; each addl $5; higher rates Memorial, Labor Day wkends; lower rates rest of yr. Crib $2. TV. Heated pool. Playground. Free coffee in rms. Cafe nearby. Ck-out 11 am. Lighted tennis. Downhill ski 15 mi; x-country ski 3 mi. Lawn games. Some refrigerators. Picnic tables. Located in Indiana Dunes National Lakeshore. Cr cds: A, MC, V.

🉐 🐾 🚫 SC

★**KNIGHTS INN.** *201 W Kieffer Rd, near jct I-94, US 421. 219/874-9500.* 103 units, 12 kits. S $27.50–$29.50; D $33–$35; studio rms $29.50–$35; kit. units $37.50–$43; under 18 free. Crib $5. TV; in-rm movies. Pool. Free coffee. Cafe adj 6 am–10 pm. Ck-out noon. Meeting rm. Sundries. Cr cds: A, C, D, MC, V.

🉐 🚫 🐾 SC

★**RED ROOF INN.** *110 W Kieffer Rd. 219/874-5251.* 79 rms, 2 story. S $25.95–$30.95; D $31.95–$36.95; under 18 free. Crib free. TV; cable. Free morning coffee. Cafe opp 6 am–10 pm. Ck-out noon. Sundries. Balconies. Cr cds: A, C, D, DS, MC, V.

🉐 🚫 🐾 SC

Muncie

Founded: 1818 **Pop:** 77,216 **Elev:** 950 ft (290 m) **Area code:** 317

Motels

★**HOLIDAY INN.** *3400 S Madison St (47302). 317/288-1911.* 150 rms, 2 story. S $42–$48; D $44–$59; each addl $5; suites $85; under 18 free; higher rates Memorial Day wkend. Closed Dec 25. Crib free. TV; cable, free in-rm movies. Pool. Cafe 6:30 am–2 pm, 5–10 pm; Sun 7 am–10 pm. Rm serv. Bar 11–2 am; entertainment exc Sun, dancing. Ck-out noon. Meeting rms. Bellhops. Cr cds: A, C, D, DS, MC, V.

🉐 🉐 🐾 SC

✔ ★**QUALITY INN.** *2000 N Broadway (47303). 317/288-9953.* 120 units, 2 story. S $32–$35; D $40–$50; each addl $5; suites $45–$65; under 16 free; higher rates Indianapolis "500," Memorial Day. Crib free. TV; cable. Pool. Free continental bkfst. Cafe 6:30 am–2 pm, 5–9 pm; Sat from 7 am; Sun 7–11 am. Rm serv. Bar 11–1 am; Sun to midnight. Ck-out noon. Meeting rms. Cr cds: A, C, D, DS, MC, V.

🉐 🐾 🚫 SC

★★**SIGNATURE INN.** *3400 N Chadam Ln (47302), near jct McGalliard Rd & Bethel Pike. 317/284-4200.* 102 rms, 2 story. S $41; D $47; each addl $6; studio rms $41–$45; under 17 free; wkend rates. Crib free. TV; cable. Pool. Free continental bkfst. Cafe nearby. Ck-out noon. Valet serv. Meeting rms. Cr cds: A, C, D, MC, V.

🉐 🐾 🚫

New Albany

Founded: 1813 **Pop:** 43,880 **Elev:** 450 ft (137 m) **Area code:** 812 **Zip:** 47150

Motel

.(Rates are generally higher for the Kentucky Derby events. Reservations necessary)

✔ ★★DAYS INN. (7618 IN 60 W, Sellersburg 47172) 7 mi N at jct IN 60, I-65 Hamburg exit 7. 812/246-4451. 115 rms, 2 story. S $31; D $39; each addl $5; under 16 free. Crib free. TV; cable. Pool. Playground. Free continental bkfst. Cafe 6–11 am. Ck-out noon. Sundries. Cr cds: A, MC, V.

🏊 🔁 ⊘ SC $

Motor Hotel

★★★HOLIDAY INN. 411 W Spring St. 812/945-2771. 134 rms, 5 story. S $47–$52; D $52–$55; each addl $6; studio rms $53–$58; suites $98–$120; under 18 free; wkend rates. Crib free. TV; cable. Indoor pool; poolside serv. Cafe 6:30 am–2 pm, 5–10 pm; Fri, Sat from 7 am. Rm serv. Bar 11–2 am, Sun 12:30 pm–12:30 am; entertainment, dancing. Ck-out noon. Coin lndry. Meeting rms. Bellhops. Valet serv. Sundries. Balconies. Cr cds: A, C, D, DS, MC, V.

♿ 🏊 🔁 🚶 ⊘ SC

New Castle

Founded: 1819 **Pop:** 20,056 **Elev:** 1,055 ft (322 m) **Area code:** 317 **Zip:** 47362

Motels

✔ ★★BEST WESTERN RAINTREE INN. 4400 S Memorial Dr. 317/521-0100. 72 rms, 2 story. S $33–$38; D $38–$44; each addl $5; studio rms $33–$44; under 16 free; higher rates "500." Crib free. TV; cable. Pool. Cafe 6:30 am–2 pm, 5–9 pm. Rm serv. Bar noon–midnight. Ck-out noon. Coin lndry. Meeting rms. Valet serv. Sundries. Cr cds: A, C, D, DS, MC, V.

♿ 🔁 ⊘ SC

✔ ★★L-K. (RR 2) 7 mi SW on IN 3 at I-70 New Castle exit. 317/987-8205. 85 rms, 1–2 story. S $31–$38; D $39–$49; each addl $6; under 18 free; higher rates "500." Crib free. TV; in-rm movies. Pool. Cafe 6 am–10 pm; Fri, Sat to midnight. Ck-out noon. Meeting rm. Cr cds: A, C, D, DS, MC, V.

🏊 🔁 ⊘ SC

★NEW CASTLE INN. 2005 S Memorial Dr 317/529-1670. 53 rms. S $19.95–$30; D $24.95–$35; each addl $5; kit. unit $26–$32; under 12 free; wkly rates; higher rates Indianapolis "500" (2-day min). Crib $5. TV; cable, in-rm movies. Pool; whirlpool. Cafe nearby. Ck-out noon. Meeting rm. Game rm. Cr cds: A, C, D, DS, MC, V.

🔁 ⊘ SC

Peru

Founded: 1826 **Pop:** 13,764 **Elev:** 656 ft (200 m) **Area code:** 317 **Zip:** 46970

Motel

✔ ★L-K. 675 US 31 S, S of US 24. 317/472-3971. 31 rms, 1–2 story. S $36–$40; D $39–$46; each addl $6; under 18 free. Crib free. TV; cable, in-rm movies. Free coffee, rolls. Cafe opp 6 am–10 pm. Ck-out noon. Meeting rm. Cr cds: A, C, D, DS, MC, V.

🏊 ⊘ 🐾 SC

Portage

Pop: 27,409 **Elev:** 643 ft (196 m) **Area code:** 219 **Zip:** 46368

Motel

✔ ★★HOWARD JOHNSON. 6161 Melton Rd. 219/762-2136. 118 rms, 2 story. S $45–$51; D $45–$57; each addl $6; under 18 free. Crib free. TV; in-rm movies. Indoor pool;

whirlpool, sauna. Cafe 6 am–11 pm. Bar 11:30 am–midnight. Ck-out noon. Valet serv. Sundries. O'Hare Airport transportation. Downhill ski 10 mi. Some refrigerators. Private patios, balconies. Cr cds: A, C, D, DS, ER, MC, V.

Motor Hotel

★ ★ HOLIDAY INN. *6200 Melton Rd. 219/762-5546.* 160 rms, 2–4 story. S, D $47–$58; each addl $6; suites $60–$75; studio rms $47–$60; under 18 free. Crib free. TV; in-rm movies. 2 pools, 1 indoor; whirlpool, sauna, poolside serv. Cafe 5:30 am–10 pm; Sat, Sun from 6 am. Rm serv 7 am–10 pm. Bar 4 pm–3 am, Sun 12:30 pm–midnight; entertainment, dancing. Ck-out noon. Meeting rms. Bellhops. Valet serv. Sundries. O'Hare Airport transportation. Tennis, golf, racquetball privileges. Downhill ski 10 mi. Game rm. Rec rm. Some patios. Cr cds: A, C, D, DS, MC, V.

Princeton

Pop: 8,976 **Elev:** 500 ft (152 m) **Area code:** 812 **Zip:** 47670

Motor Hotel

✔ ★ ★ PRINCETON INN. *(Box 33) Jct US 41, IN 64. 812/386-1200.* 94 rms, 4 story. S $40–$44; D $40–$46; each addl $5; suites $95; under 18 free. Crib free. TV; cable. Indoor pool; whirlpool. Cafe 6 am–2 pm, 5–10 pm; Sat, Sun 7 am–2 pm. Rm serv. Bar 4 pm–midnight, Fri, Sat to 2:30 am; entertainment, dancing Fri, Sat. Ck-out noon. Coin lndry. Meeting rms. Valet serv. Sundries. Game rm. Cr cds: A, C, D, DS, MC, V.

Richmond

Settled: 1806 **Pop:** 41,349 **Elev:** 980 ft (299 m) **Area code:** 317 **Zip:** 47374

Motels

(Rates may be higher during the Indianapolis "500")

✔ ★ BEST WESTERN IMPERIAL. *3020 E Main St. 317/966-1505.* 44 rms, 2 story, 3 kits. S $24–$29; D, suites $30–$38; each addl $3–$4; kit. units $5 addl; under 12 free. Crib $2. TV; cable. Heated pool. Free continental bkfst. Cafe nearby. Ck-out noon. Cr cds: A, C, D, DS, MC, V.

★ GOLDEN INN. *(7701 National Rd E, New Paris OH 45347) 1 mi E of I-70 on US 40, exit 156 B. 513/437-0722.* 16 rms. S $23–$28; D $27–$32; each addl $2. TV; cable, in-rm movies. Cafe nearby. Ck-out 11 am. Cr cds: DS, MC, V.

★ ★ ★ HOLIDAY INN. *4700 National Rd E. 317/962-5551.* 160 rms, 2 story. S $46–$59; D $52–$66; each addl $4; under 18 free. Crib free. TV; cable, in-rm movies. Heated pool. Cafe 6 am–10 pm; Sat, Sun 7 am–9 pm. Rm serv. Bar 11–1 am; entertainment exc Sun. Ck-out noon. Coin lndry. Meeting rms. Bellhops. Valet serv. Sundries. Golf nearby. Cr cds: A, C, D, DS, MC, V.

✔ ★ KNIGHTS INN. *419 Commerce Dr. 317/966-6682.* 104 units, 10 kits. S $28.50; D $34; each addl $3; kit. units $37; under 18 free. Crib $3. TV; cable. Pool. Free coffee in lobby. Cafe opp 6 am–10 pm; Fri, Sat open 24 hrs. Ck-out noon. Meeting rm. Some refrigerators. Cr cds: A, C, D, MC, V.

★ SPIRIT OF '76. *540 W Eaton Pike. 317/966-7591.* 95 rms, 1–2 story. Mar–Oct: S $25.80; D $31.80–$33.80; each addl $4; wkly, family rates; lower rates rest of yr. Crib $3. TV;

cable. Pool. Cafe nearby. Ck-out 11 am. Coin lndry. Sundries. Miniature golf privileges. Picnic table. Cr cds: A, D, DS, MC, V.

★**VILLA.** *533 W Eaton Pike (US 40). 317/962-5202.* 26 rms. S $20.50; D $21.50. Crib $2.50. TV. Playground. Cafe opp 6 am–11 pm. Ck-out 11 am. Cr cds: MC, V.

Scottsburg

Pop: 5,068 **Elev:** 570 ft (174 m) **Area code:** 812 **Zip:** 47170

Motels

✔ ★ ★ ★**BEST WESTERN SCOTTSBURG INN.** *¼ mi W on IN 56 at I-65. 812/752-2212.* 95 rms, 2 story. S $37–$45; D $42–$50; each addl $6; under 12 free; higher rates Kentucky Derby wkend (2-day min). Crib $2. TV; cable. Pool. Playground. Cafe 6 am–10 pm. Rm serv. Bar 3 pm–1:30 am, Sun to 11 pm; entertainment, dancing exc Sun, Mon. Ck-out noon. Meeting rms. Bellhops. Valet serv. Cr cds: A, C, D, DS, ER, MC, V.

★ ★**MARIANN TRAVEL INN.** *6 blks W on IN 56 at I-65. 812/752-3396.* 98 rms, 2 story. S $27–$29; D $34–$36; each addl $2.50; under 11 free; wknd rates (winter); higher rates Kentucky Derby. Crib free. TV; cable, in-rm movies. Heated pool; wading pool. Playground. Cafe 6 am–9:30 pm. Ck-out 11 am. Sundries. Lawn games. Cr cds: A, C, D, DS, MC, V.

Seymour

Pop: 15,050 **Elev:** 605 ft (184 m) **Area code:** 812 **Zip:** 47274

Motels

(Rates may be higher during Kentucky Derby, Indianapolis "500")

★**ALLSTATE.** *2 mi E on US 50 at I-65. 812/522-2666.* 50 rms, 2 story. S $20.94; D $26; each addl $4; family rates; some wkend rates; higher rates special events. TV; cable. Cafe adj open 24 hrs. Ck-out 11 am. Cr cds: A, D, DS, MC, V.

✔ ★ ★**BEST WESTERN.** *220 E Frontage Rd, at I-65. 812/522-8000.* 63 rms, 2 story. S $25–$30; D $32–$40; each addl $4; under 12 free. TV; cable, in-rm movies. Pool. Cafe 11 am–10 pm. Ck-out 11 am. 18-hole golf privileges. Cr cds: A, C, D, DS, MC, V.

✔ ★ ★**DAYS INN.** *302 E Frontage Rd, at I-65. 812/522-3678.* 120 rms, 2 story. S $28–$32; D $32–$37; each addl $5; children $1; golf plan; some wkend rates. Crib free. TV; cable. Pool. Playground. Cafe 6 am–9 pm. Ck-out noon. Sundries. 18-hole golf privileges. Cr cds: A, D, MC, V.

★ ★**HOLIDAY INN.** *2025 Tipton St. 812/522-6767.* 100 rms, 2 story. S $45; D $50; each addl $5; under 18 free. Crib free. TV; cable. Pool. Cafe 6 am–2 pm, 5–9:30 pm. Rm serv. Bar 4 pm–midnight exc Sun. Ck-out noon. Meeting rms. Bellhops. Valet serv. Golf privileges. Cr cds: A, C, D, DS, MC, V.

South Bend

Founded: 1823 **Pop:** 109,727 **Elev:** 710 ft (224 m) **Area code:** 219

64 Indiana

Motels

(Rates may be higher football wkends)

★**BUDGETEER MOTOR INN.** *52825 US 33 N (46637). 219/272-9000.* 111 rms, 2 story. June–Sep: S $25.95–$29.95; D $32.95–$36.95; each addl $4; under 16 free; wkly, monthly rates; lower rates rest of yr. TV; in-rm movies. Ck-out noon. Meeting rms. X-country ski 10 mi. Cr cds: A, C, D, DS, MC, V.

✔ ★**DAYS INN.** *52757 US 31N (46637). 219/277-0510.* 180 rms, 3 story. S $32–$37; D $35–$45; each addl $5; under 18, $1. Crib free. TV; cable, in-rm movies. Pool. Playground. Cafe 6 am–10:30 am, 5–9 pm. Ck-out noon. Meeting rm. Downhill/x-country ski 20 mi. Some in-rm steam baths. Cr cds: A, C, D, DS, MC, V.

★**HICKORY INN.** *50520 US 31 N (46637). 219/272-7555.* 23 rms, 6 kits. S $18.85; D $22.95; each addl $3.20; kit. units $21.85–$23.95; under 18 free; wkly rates Sep–Apr. Crib $2.50. TV; cable. Coffee in rm. Cafe opp 5 am–3 pm. Ck-out 11 am. Downhill ski 9 mi; x-country ski 4 mi. Some in-rm whirlpools. Cr cds: MC, V.

✔ ★ ★**HOWARD JOHNSON.** *52939 US 31N (46637). 219/272-1500.* 108 rms, 2 story. May–Oct: S $29–$75; D $32–$85; each addl $8; under 18 free; higher rates special events; lower rates rest of yr. Crib free. TV; cable, in-rm movies. Heated pool. Cafe 6 am–9 pm. Bar 4–11 pm. Ck-out noon. Meeting rms. Valet serv. Downhill ski 15 mi; x-country ski 10 mi. Garden. Cr cds: A, C, D, DS, ER, MC, V.

✔ ★ ★**KNIGHTS INN.** *236 Dixie Way N (46637). 219/277-2960.* 108 rms, 9 kits. S $31.50–$43; D $32.50–$44; each addl $3; studio rms $33.50–$45; kit. units $35.50–$47; under 18 free. Crib $5. TV; cable, in-rm movies. Pool. Cafe adj 6 am–9 pm. Ck-out noon. Meeting rm. X-country ski 15 mi. Cr cds: A, C, D, MC, V.

Terre Haute

Founded: 1816 **Pop:** 61,125 **Elev:** 507 ft (155 m) **Area code:** 812

Motels

★**REGAL 8 INN.** *I-70 & US 41 (47802). 812/238-1586.* 120 rms, 2 story. S $23.88–$25.88; D $33.88–$35.88; suite $40.88–$45.88; family rates. Crib free. TV; cable, in-rm movies. Indoor pool. Playground. Free coffee. Ck-out 1 pm. Cr cds: A, C, D, DS, MC, V.

✔ ★ ★**SIGNATURE INN.** *3033 Dixie Bee Rd (47802), I-70 & US 41. 812/238-1461; res: 800/822-5252.* 155 rms, 3 story. S $41–$53; D $47–$59; each addl $7; under 18 free; some wkend rates; higher rates special events. Crib free. TV; cable. Pool; whirlpool. Ck-out noon. Meeting rms. Valet serv. Sundries. Game rm. Cr cds: A, C, D, DS, MC, V.

★**SUPER 8.** *3089 S 1st St (47802). 812/232-4890.* 118 units, 3 story. S $25.88–$29.88; D $29.88–$38.88; each addl $2; suites $29.88–$42.88. Crib $3. TV; cable. Continental bkfst in lobby. Ck-out 11 am. Sundries. X-country ski 4 mi. Cr cds: A, C, D, DS, MC, V.

Motor Hotels

✔ ★ ★**BEST WESTERN OF TERRE HAUTE.** *3325 Dixie Bee Rd (47802). 812/234-7781.* 96 rms, 7 story. May–Oct: S $42–$44; D $46–$48; each addl $5; suites $99–$150; under 12 free; higher rates Memorial Day wkend; lower rates rest of yr. Crib free. TV, cable. Pool; whirlpool, sauna. Cafe 6:30 am–1 pm, 5–9 pm; Sun to 1 pm. Rm serv. Bar 5 pm–11 pm. Ck-out noon.

Meeting rms. Valet serv. Sundries. Racquetball nearby. Some bathrm phones. Some balconies. Cr cds: A, C, D, DS, MC, V.

⚓ 🚫 SC

✔ ★ ★PARK INN INTERNATIONAL. *2800 S Dixie Bee Rd (47802)*. *812/238-2424*. 125 rms, 4 story. S $34.95–$41; D $34.95–$37; each addl $6; suites $58; under 18 free. Crib free. TV; cable, in-rm movies. Indoor pool; whirlpool, sauna. Cafe 6 am–10 pm. Rm serv 7 am–9 pm. Bar 11–1 am; entertainment Tu–Sat. Ck-out 1 pm. Meeting rms. Bellhops. Valet serv. Sundries. Golf, racquetball privileges. X-country ski 1 mi. Game rm. Cr cds: A, C, D, DS, MC, V.

🏊 ⚓ 🏋 🏌 🏃 🚫 🐾 SC

Turkey Run State Park

(2 mi N of Marshall on IN 47) **Area code:** 317

Motel

✔ ★ ★TURKEY RUN INN. *(RR 1, Box 444, Marshall 47859)* In Turkey Run State Park. *317/597-2211*. 72 rms, 2 story. S, D $34–$36. TV. Pool; lifeguard. Playground. Cafe 7 am–8 pm. Ck-out 11 am. Meeting rms. Gift shop. Lighted tennis. X-country ski on site. Game rm. Picnic tables, grills in park. 18- and 9-hole golf courses nearby, pro. 2 lakes & Sugar Creek nearby. Hiking trails; nature center. Cr cds: A, MC, V.

🏊 🚴 🏋 🔍 🏃 🚶 🐾 🚫

Valparaiso

Founded: 1865 **Pop:** 22,247 **Elev:** 738 ft (225 m) **Area code:** 219 **Zip:** 46383

Motel

★ ★CARLTON LODGE. *2301 E US 30*. *219/465-1700; res: 800/445-6343*. 111 units, 2 story. S $48–$55; D $53–$60; each addl $5; suites $61–$150. Crib free. TV; cable, in-rm movies. Heated indoor/outdoor pool; whirlpool. Free coffee, continental bkfst. Cafe nearby. Ck-out noon. Meeting rms. Valet serv. Sundries. Picnic tables, grills. Cr cds: A, C, D, MC, V.

♿ ⚓ 🏃 🚫 🐾 SC

Motor Hotel

✔ ★DAYS INN. *559 West St*. *219/464-8555*. 115 rms, 2–4 story. S $39–$45; D $44–$49; each addl $5; under 18 free. Crib free. TV; cable. Heated pool. Cafe 6 am–10 pm; Sun from 7 am. Rm serv 7:30 am–9:30 pm. Bar 11–1:30 am, Sun 4 pm–midnight. Ck-out noon. Coin lndry. Meeting rm. Balconies. Cr cds: A, C, D, DS, MC, V.

♿ ⚓ 🏋 🏃 🚫 🐾 SC

Vincennes

Founded: 1732 **Pop:** 20,857 **Elev:** 429 ft (130 m) **Area code:** 812 **Zip:** 47591

Motels

✔ ★ ★HOLIDAY INN. *600 Wheatland Rd, at US 41, 50 Cloverleaf*. *812/886-9900*. 132 rms, 2 story. S $32–$46; D $32–$52; each addl $6; under 20 free. Crib free. TV; cable. 2 pools, 1 indoor; whirlpool, poolside serv. Playground. Cafes 6 am–10 pm. Rm serv. Bar 11–2 am; Sun noon–midnight. Ck-out noon. Coin lndry. Meeting rms. Sundries. Free local airport transportation. Putting green. Holidome. Cr cds: A, C, D, DS, ER, MC, V.

♿ ⚓ 🏃 🐾 SC

★TRAVELODGE. *1411 Willow St*. *812/882-1282*. 39 rms, 2 story. S $23–$29; D $28–$40; each addl $3; under 16 free. Crib free. TV; cable. Pool. Free coffee. Cafe nearby. Ck-out noon. Balconies. Cr cds: A, C, D, DS, ER, MC, V.

♿ 🏃 🚫 🐾 SC 💲

Iowa

Population: 2,913,808

Land area: 55,965 sq mi (144,949 sq km)

Elevation: 480–1,670 ft (146–509 m)

Highest point: Near Ocheyedan (Osceola Co)

Entered Union: Dec 28, 1846 (29th state)

Capital: Des Moines

Motto: Our liberties we prize and our rights we will maintain

Nickname: The Hawkeye State

State flower: Wild rose

State bird: Eastern goldfinch

State tree: Oak

State fair: Aug 17–27, 1989 in Des Moines

Time zone: Central

Interstate Highway System

The following alphabetical listing of Iowa towns in *Mobil Travel Guide* shows that these cities are within 10 miles (16 kilometers) of the indicated Interstate highways. A highway map, however, should be checked for the nearest exit.

INTERSTATE 29: Council Bluffs, Missouri Valley, Onawa, Sioux City.

INTERSTATE 35: Ames, Clear Lake, Des Moines, Mason City, Osceola.

INTERSTATE 80: Atlantic, Avoca, Council Bluffs, Davenport, Des Moines, Grinnell, Iowa City, Newton, Walnut, Williamsburg.

Weather Statistics*

	WINTER	SPRING	SUMMER	FALL
Statewide	21°F (-6°C)	48°F (9°C)	73°F (23°C)	52°F (11°C)

*Average mean temperatures are listed for the entire state. Averages for specific regions are given if significant differences exist.

Visitor Information

The Tourism Bureau of the Department of Economic Development, 200 East Grand Ave, Des Moines 50309; 515/281-3100 or 800/345-IOWA has further information including pamphlets and an Iowa Calendar of Events. Margaret L. Posten's *This is the Place: Iowa* (Iowa State University Press, Iowa City, 1971) describes present-day Iowa; and *Portrait of Iowa*, by John M. Zienlinski et al (Adams Press, Minneapolis, 1974), depicts Iowa through photographs.

Two periodicals worth looking at are: *Annals of Iowa*, quarterly, Iowa State Historical Dept, Des Moines 50319; and *The Iowan*, quarterly, Mid-America Publishing Corp, Box 130, Shenandoah 51601.

There are eight interstate welcome centers in Iowa; visitors who stop by will find information and brochures most helpful in planning stops at points of interest. They are located near the following cities: Clear Lake, Davenport, Davis City, Des Moines, Sergeant Bluff, Underwood, Victor and Wilton. (Mid-May–mid-Oct, daily) For Iowa road condition information phone 515/288-1047 (mid-Oct–Apr).

Algona

Settled: 1854 **Pop:** 6,289 **Elev:** 1,200 ft (366 m) **Area code:** 515 **Zip:** 50511

Motels

✔ ★**BURR OAK.** *(Box 738) 3 mi SE on US 169. 515/295-7213.* 42 rms. S $27; D $29–$36. Crib $4. TV; cable. Free continental bkfst. Cafe adj 5–11 pm. Ck-out 10 am. Valet serv. Cr cds: A, C, D, DS, MC, V.

★**CANDLELITE.** *US 169S. 515/295-2441.* 19 rms, 1–2 story. S $20; D $24; each addl $5. Crib $1.50. TV; cable. Free coffee. Cafe nearby. Ck-out 10:30 am. Cr cds: MC, V.

★**SUPER 8.** *210 E Norwood Dr. 515/295-7225.* 30 rms, 2 story. S $24.88; D $27.88–$28.88; each addl $3. Crib $2. TV; satellite. Free coffee in lobby. Cafe adj open 24 hrs. Ck-out 11 am. Cr cds: A, D, DS, MC, V.

Amana Colonies

Settled: 1855 **Pop:** (7 colonies) 1,650 (est) **Elev:** 715 ft (218 m) **Area code:** 319 **Zip:** 52203

Motels

✔ ★★**BEST WESTERN COLONY HAUS MOTOR INN.** *(RR 2, Williamsburg 52361) Just off I-80 exit 225. 319/668-2097.* 120 rms, 1–3 story. No elvtr. S $30; D $45; each addl $4; under 16 free. Crib free. TV. Indoor pool; whirlpool, sauna. Playground. Cafe adj 6 am–10 pm; from 7 am in winter. Bar adj 11 am–10:30 pm. Ck-out 11 am. Coin lndry. Meeting rm. Sundries. Gift shop. Putting green. Lawn games. Cr cds: A, C, D, DS, MC, V.

★**GUEST HOUSE MOTOR INN.** *Main St, on IA 220. 319/622-3599.* 38 rms, 2 story. Apr–Dec: S $30.90–$42.90; D $37.90–$46.90; each addl $2; under 10 free; lower rates rest of yr. Crib free. TV; cable. Cafe nearby. Ck-out 11 am. Cr cds: A, MC, V. ⓓ

Inn

✔ ★★**DIE HEIMAT COUNTRY INN.** *(Homestead 52236) At jct US 6, 151. 319/622-3937.* 19 rms, 2 story. Mar–Nov: S $28–$35; D $35–$55; each addl $4; under 6, $1; some lower & wkend rates rest of yr. Crib $2. TV, some B/W; cable. Free bkfst. Ck-out 11 am. Some refrigerators. Restored 1858 inn; antiques. Cr cds: MC, V.

Ames

Settled: 1864 **Pop:** 45,775 **Elev:** 921 ft (281 m) **Area code:** 515 **Zip:** 50010

Motels

✔ ★★★**BEST WESTERN STARLITE VILLAGE.** *I-35 & 13th St. 515/232-9260.* 131 rms, 3 story. S $34–$38; D $44–$50; each addl $5; higher rates special events. Crib $5. TV; cable. Indoor pool; whirlpool, sauna. Cafe 6 am–11 pm. Rm serv to 10 pm. Bar noon–2 am. Ck-out noon. Meeting rms. Valet serv. Sundries. Airport transportation. Game rm. Cr cds: A, C, D, DS, MC, V.

★**HEARTLAND INN.** *I-35 & US 30. 515/233-6060; res: 800/334-3277.* 91 rms, 2 story. S $29–$35; D $35–$43.50; each addl $6; under 17 free. Crib free. TV; cable. Whirlpool, sauna. Free coffee. Cafe nearby. Ck-out noon. Airport transportation. Cr cds: A, C, D, DS, MC, V.

✔ ★ ★PARK INN INTERNATIONAL. *1206 S Duff. 515/232-3410.* 103 rms, 2 story. S $41; D $49; each addl $6; suites $107; studio rms $39–$49; under 19 free. Crib free. TV; cable. Pool. Cafe 6 am–2 pm, 5–10 pm; Sun 7 am–2 pm. Rm serv. Bar 11–2 am; entertainment, dancing Tu-Sat. Ck-out noon. Meeting rms. Sundries. Cr cds: A, C, D, MC, V.

🏊 sc

✔ ★TRAVELODGE. *229 S Duff Ave. 515/233-1714.* 48 rms, 2 story. S $30–$34; D $32–$36; each addl $2; under 18 free; wkday rates. Crib free. TV. Pool. Cafe adj. Ck-out noon. Valet serv. Balconies. Cr cds: A, C, D, MC, V.

🏊 🚭 sc 🅢

★ ★UNIVERSITY INN. *316 S Duff, I-35 S Ames exit. 515/232-0280; res: 800/422-5250.* 120 rms, 2 story. S $26–$50; D $32–$60; each addl $4; under 12 free. Crib free. TV; cable. Pool. Cafe nearby. Bar 4 pm–2 am; entertainment. Ck-out noon. Valet serv. Meeting rms. Cr cds: A, D, DS, MC, V.

🐾 🏊 🚭 sc

Atlantic

Pop: 7,789 **Elev:** 1,215 ft (370 m) **Area code:** 712 **Zip:** 50022

Motels

✔ ★ ★BEST WESTERN COUNTRY SQUIRE. *(Box 70) 8 blks E on US 6, 7 mi S of I-80. 712/243-4723.* 44 rms. S $30–$35; D $39–$47; each addl $4. Crib $2. TV; cable. Cafe open 24 hrs. Bar 11–1 am. Ck-out 11 am. Meeting rm. Sundries. Free airport transportation. Cr cds: A, C, D, DS, MC, V.

🚭 sc

★ECONO LODGE. *7 mi N on US 71, ½ mi S of I-80 exit 60. 712/243-4067.* 51 rms, 1–2 story. S $25–$31; D $36–$45; each addl $4. Crib $2. TV; cable. Cafe opp 6 am–10:30 pm. Ck-out 11 am. Meeting rm. Sundries. Cr cds: A, C, D, DS, MC, V.

🚭 sc

★HAWKEYE. *E 7th St, 1 mi E on US 6, 1 mi W of US 71. 712/243-1603.* 18 rms. S $23; D $30; each addl $3; suites $38; under 5 free. TV; cable. Ck-out 11 am. Sundries. Picnic tables. Cr cds: A, C, D, DS, MC, V.

🐾

Burlington

Settled: 1832 **Pop:** 29,529 **Elev:** 540 ft (165 m) **Area code:** 319 **Zip:** 52601

Motel

★VOYAGER INN. *1601 N Roosevelt Ave, at jct US 34, 61. 319/754-4681.* 44 rms. S $26–$29; D $28–$31; each addl $5; studio rms $30; under 10 free. Crib free. TV; cable. Pool. Cafe nearby. Ck-out 11 am. Meeting rm. Cr cds: A, D, DS, MC, V.

🐾 🏊 sc

Motor Hotels

★ ★ ★BEST WESTERN PZAZZ! MOTOR INN. *3001 Winegard Dr, just N of jct US 34, 61. 319/753-2223.* 111 rms, 3 story. S $45.75–$49.75; D $52.75–$56.75; each addl $4; suites $74–$111; studio rms $48–$58; under 12 free. Crib free. TV; cable. Indoor pool; whirlpool, sauna. Cafe 6:30 am–10 pm. Rm serv 7 am–2 pm, 5–9 pm. Bar 11:30–2 am; entertainment, dancing exc Sun. Ck-out noon. Balconies. Coin lndry. Meeting rms. Airport transportation. Gift shop. Barber, beauty shop. Game rm. Cr cds: A, C, D, DS, MC, V.

🛏 🐾 🏊 sc

✔ ★ ★ ★HOLIDAY. *(Box 639) 2759 Mt Pleasant St, at jct US 34, 61. 319/754-5781; res: 800/553-2379 (exc IA), 800/582-2382 (IA).* 200 rms, 2 story. S $38.50–$55.50; D $47.50–$55.50; each addl $6; under 17 free. Crib free. TV; cable. Indoor pool; whirlpool, sauna. Free full bkfst.

Cafes 6 am–10 pm. Rm serv. Bar 3:30 pm–1 am. Ck-out noon. Coin lndry. Meeting rms. Bellhops. Valet serv. Sundries. X-country ski 2 mi. Rec rm. Cr cds: A, C, D, DS, MC, V.

🏃 🛁 ⛷ 🏊 sc $

Cedar Rapids

Settled: 1838 **Pop:** 110,243 **Elev:** 730 ft (223 m) **Area code:** 319

Motels

★EXEL INN. *616 33d Ave SW (52404). 319/366-2475.* 104 rms, 2 story. S $23.95; D $28.95–$30.95; each addl $4; under 18 free. Crib free. TV; in-rm movies. Cafe nearby. Ck-out noon. Cr cds: A, C, D, DS, MC, V.

🏃 🛁 ⊘ sc

★RED ROOF INN. *3325 Southgate Court (52404), off 33d Ave exit I-380. 319/366-7523.* 109 rms, 2 story. S $23.95–$27.95; D $28.95–$30.95; each addl $2; under 18 free. Crib free. TV; in-rm movies. Free coffee. Cafe opp open 24 hrs. Ck-out noon. Cr cds: A, C, D, DS, MC, V.

🏃 🛁 ⊘

Motor Hotels

✔ ★★BEST WESTERN LONGBRANCH. *90 Twixtown Rd NE (52402), just off jct IA 150, US 151. 319/377-6386.* 103 rms, 4 story. S $33–$50; D $36–$56; each addl $4; suites $63–$118; under 12 free; wkend package plans. Crib $4. TV; cable. Heated pool. Cafe 6 am–10 pm; Sat 6:30–11 am, 5–11 pm; Sun 6:30 am–9 pm. Rm serv. Bars 11–2 am; entertainment, dancing Fri, Sat. Ck-out 1 pm. Meeting rms. Bellhops. Valet serv. Free airport transportation. Health club privileges. Cr cds: A, C, D, DS, MC, V. Ⓔ

🏊 sc $

✔ ★★★DAYS INN OF CEDAR RAPIDS. *4747 1st Ave SE (52402). 319/393-8800.* 161 rms, 1–3 story, 10 kits. S $43–$54; D $48–$59; each addl $5; under 18 free. Crib free. TV; satellite. 2 pools, 1 indoor; wading pool, whirlpool. Free coffee. Cafe 6 am–10 pm; Sat 7 am–11:30 pm; Sun 7 am–10 pm. Bar noon–midnight. Ck-out 1 pm. Coin lndry. Meeting rms. Bellhops. Valet serv. Rec rm. Cr cds: A, C, D, DS, MC, V.

🏊 ⊘ sc $

★★★HOLIDAY INN. *2501 Williams Blvd SW (52404), at IA 151, 16th Ave. 319/365-9441.* 189 rms, 2 story. S $46–$65; D $51–$72; each addl $4; under 19 free. Crib free. TV; cable. Indoor pool; whirlpool, sauna. Cafe 6 am–10 pm. Rm serv. Bar 11–2 am; Sun noon–10 pm. Ck-out noon. Coin lndry. Meeting rms. Free airport transportation. Holidome. Cr cds: A, C, D, DS, MC, V.

🏃 🛁 🏊 ⊘ sc

★★★SHERATON INN. *525 33d Ave SW (52404). 319/366-8671.* 157 rms, 6 story. S $44.50–$57.50; D $51.50–$65.50; each addl $7; suite $125–$155; under 18 free; wkend rates. Crib free. TV; satellite. Indoor pool; whirlpool, sauna, poolside serv. Cafe 6:30 am–10 pm; Sat 7 am–11 pm. Rm serv. Bar 11–2 am; Sun noon–10 pm; entertainment, dancing. Ck-out 1 pm. Meeting rms. Bellhops. Valet serv. Sundries. Gift shop. Free airport transportation. Rec rm. Game rm. Cr cds: A, C, D, DS, MC, V. Ⓔⓘ

🏃 🛁 🏊 ⊘ sc $

★★VILLAGE INN. *100 F Ave NW (52405). 319/366-5323.* 86 rms, 4 story. S $31.95–$37.95; D $40–$48; each addl $4; under 12 free. Crib $4. TV. Cafe 6–3 am; Sun to midnight. Rm serv. Bar 11–2 am exc Sun. Ck-out noon. Meeting rms. Valet serv. Cr cds: A, C, D, MC, V.

Charles City

Settled: 1852 **Pop:** 8,778 **Elev:** 1,000 ft (305 m) **Area code:** 515 **Zip:** 50616

Motels

✔ ★★**LAMPLIGHTER.** *1416 Gilbert St. 515/228-6711; res: 800/341-8000.* 47 rms, 2 story. S $25–$30; D $28–$35; each addl $2–$3; family rates. Crib free. TV; satellite. Indoor pool. Cafe nearby. Ck-out noon. Valet serv. Hot tub. Rec rm. Cr cds: A, D, DS, MC, V.

★**PARKVIEW.** *On US 218, ½ mi S of jct US 18. 515/228-5163.* 23 rms. S $17–$22; D $27–$38; each addl $5; under 18 free. Crib free. TV; cable. Cafe nearby. Ck-out 11 am. Park opp. Cr cds: ER, MC, V.

Cherokee

Pop: 7,004 **Elev:** 1,200 ft (366 m) **Area code:** 712 **Zip:** 51012

Motels

✔ ★★**BEST WESTERN LA GRANDE HACIENDA.** *1401 N 2d St. 712/225-5701.* 56 rms, 2 story. S $30–$40; D $40–$55; each addl $8; suites $40–$60; under 12 free. Crib $2. TV; cable. Heated pool; whirlpool. Cafe 4–11 pm. Rm serv. Ck-out 11 am. Meeting rm. Sundries. Free airport transportation. Downhill ski 3 mi. Cr cds: A, D, DS, ER, MC, V.

★**LAMPLIGHTER.** *425 E Main St. 712/225-2577.* 30 rms, 2 story. S $27.50; D $37; each addl $4. Crib free. TV; cable. Free coffee. Cafe adj 5:30 am–10 pm. Ck-out 11 am. Downhill ski ½ mi. Cr cds: A, C, D, DS, ER, MC, V.

Council Bluffs

Settled: 1824 **Pop:** 56,449 **Elev:** 986 ft (301 m) **Area code:** 712 **Zip:** 51501

Motels

✔ ★★**BEST WESTERN FRONTIER MOTOR LODGE.** *2216 27th Ave, at jct I-29, I-80 exit S 24th St. 712/322-3150.* 108 rms, 2 story. S $42; D $44–$50; each addl $5; under 12 free. Crib free. Indoor pool; whirlpool, sauna. Playground. Cafe 6:30 am–10 pm. Rm serv. Bar 4 pm–2 am; entertainment, dancing Wed–Sat. Ck-out noon. Meeting rms. Rec rm. Putting green. Cr cds: A, C, D, DS, MC, V.

★**CHALET MOTOR LODGE.** *1530 Ave G. 712/328-3041.* 100 rms, 2 story. S $27–$38; D, studio rms $33–$45; each addl $3; suites, kit. units $39–$45; under 12 free. Crib free. TV; satellite. Cafe open 24 hrs. Bar 11–2 am. Ck-out 11 am. Sundries. Cr cds: A, C, D, DS, MC, V.

✔ ★★**HEARTLAND INN.** *1000 Woodbury Ave. 712/322-8400; res: 800/334-3277.* 91 rms, 2 story. S $31.50; D $37.50; each addl $6; suites $37.50–$43.50; under 16 free. Crib free. TV; cable. Free coffee in lobby. Cafe adj 6–1 am. Ck-out noon. Meeting rms. Valet serv. Downhill ski 7 mi. Whirlpool, sauna. Cr cds: A, D, DS, MC, V.

★**TIME OUT.** *(RR 1, Pacific Junction 51561) 16 mi S on I-29 exit 35. 712/622-8191.* 29 rms. S $26–$34; D $30–$39; each addl $5; under 12 free. Crib free. TV. Cafe 7 am–9 pm. Ck-out noon. Cr cds: ER, MC, V.

Davenport

Founded: 1808 **Pop:** 103,264 **Elev:** 589 ft (180 m) **Area code:** 319

Motels

★★★**BEST WESTERN STEEPLEGATE INN.** *100 W 76th St (52806). 319/386-6900.* 121 rms, 2 story. S $47–$58; D $54–$65; each addl $7; under 12 free; wkend rates. Crib $4. TV; cable. Indoor pool; whirlpool. Cafe 6 am–10 pm. Rm serv. Bar 11–2 am; entertainment, dancing. Ck-out noon. Meeting rms. Valet serv. Free airport, bus depot transportation. Game rm. Rec rm. Some refrigerators. Cr cds: A, C, D, DS, MC, V.

★**COMFORT INN.** *7222 Northwest Blvd (52806), just S of I-80 at exit 292. 319/391-8222.* 89 rms, 2 story. S, D $27.95; each addl $4. TV; satellite. Cafe adj 6 am–10 pm. Ck-out 11 am. Exercise equipt; weight machines, bicycle. Cr cds: A, C, D, DS, ER, MC, V.

✔★★**EL RANCHO.** *(2205 Kimberly Rd, Bettendorf 52722) 2½ mi S of I-80 off I-74 Middle Rd exit. 319/355-6471.* 67 rms, 1–2 story. S $25.95–$28.95; D $29.95–$32.95; each addl $4; under 18 free. Crib free. TV. Pool. Playground. Free continental bkfst. Cafe 10 am–11 pm exc Sun. Bar 11–1 am exc Sun. Ck-out noon. Meeting rm. Cr cds: A, C, D, DS, MC, V.

★**EXEL INN.** *6310 Brady St N (52806). 319/386-6350.* 104 rms, 2 story. S $25.95; D $27.95–$36.95; each addl $2; under 18 free. Crib free. TV; satellite. Free coffee. Cafe opp open 24 hrs. Ck-out noon. Cr cds: A, C, D, DS, MC, V.

✔★★**HAMPTON INN.** *3330 E Kimberly Rd (52807). 319/359-3921.* 138 rms, 2 story. S $33–$38; D $37–$43; under 18 free. Crib free. TV; satellite. Heated pool. Free continental bkfst. Ck-out noon. Bellhops. Free airport transportation. Cr cds: A, C, D, DS, MC, V.

✔★★★**RAMADA INN.** *6263 N Brady St (52806). 319/386-1940.* 179 rms, 2 story. S $42–$60; D $45–$60; each addl $6; under 18 free. Crib free. TV; cable. Indoor pool. Complimentary coffee. Cafe 6 am–2 pm, 5–10 pm. Rm serv. Bar 4 pm–1 am; Sun noon–10 pm; entertainment, dancing. Ck-out noon. Coin lndry. Meeting rms. Bellhops. Valet serv. Free airport, RR station, bus depot transportation. Exercise equipt; weights, bicycles, whirlpool, sauna. Game rm. Rec rm. Some refrigerators. Cr cds: A, C, D, DS, MC, V.

★**TWIN BRIDGES MOTOR INN.** *(221 15th St, Bettendorf 52722) Jct US 6, 67, I-74. 319/355-6451.* 69 rms, 2 story. S $25.95–$30.95; D $31.95–$36.95; each addl $3; under 13 free. Crib free. TV; satellite. Pool; whirlpool. Cafe 6–11 am, 4:30–9:30 pm; Sun 7–11 am. Rm serv. Bar 4 pm–midnight exc Sun ; Sat to 1 am. Ck-out noon. Valet serv. Cr cds: A, D, DS, MC, V.

✔★★**VOYAGER INN.** *4002 Brady St (52806), at jct US 6, 61. 319/391-5610.* 63 rms, 2 story. S $26–$29.95; D, studio rms $30–$33.95; each addl $4; suites $38–$42; under 13 free. Crib $2. TV; cable. Pool. Free coffee in rms. Cafe adj 6–2 am. Ck-out noon. Meeting rm. Sundries. Cr cds: A, C, D, MC, V.

Motor Hotel

✔★★**BEST WESTERN RIVERVIEW INN.** *227 Le Claire St (52801). 319/324-1921.* 150 rms, 6 story. S $40–$45; D $44–$50; each addl $4; studio rms $36–$43. Crib free. TV; satellite. 2 pools, 1 indoor; sauna, hot tub. Free coffee in rms. Cafe 6:30 am–2 pm, 5–10 pm. Rm serv. Bar 11–1 am; Sun to midnight. Ck-out noon. Coin lndry. Meeting rms. Bellhops. Valet serv. Sundries. Free airport transportation. Game rm. Rec rm. Refrigerators. Some rms with river view. Cr cds: A, C, D, DS, MC, V.

Des Moines

Founded: 1843 **Pop:** 191,003 **Elev:** 803 ft (245 m) **Area code:** 515

Motels

(Rates may be higher during state fair)

★ARCHER. *4965 NE Hubbell Ave (50317), at jct US 6, 65. 515/265-0368.* 29 rms. June–Aug: S $26.50–$35; D $29.50–$45; each addl $4–$5; family rates; lower rates rest of yr. Crib $3. TV; cable. Pool. Playground. Ck-out 11 am. Sundries. Picnic tables, grill. Amusement park adj. Cr cds: A, DS, MC, V.

🏊 ⊟ ⊛ SC

✔ ★ ★BEST WESTERN BAVARIAN INN. *5220 NE 14th St (50313), just N of jct I-35, I-80 exit 136. 515/265-5611.* 104 rms, 2 story. S $39–$45; D $45–$55; suites $69–$89; under 12 free; higher rates special events. Crib $2. TV; cable. Indoor pool; whirlpool. Playground. Cafe 6 am–2 pm, 5–10 pm; Sun to 9 pm. Rm serv. Bar 11 am–midnight. Ck-out noon. Meeting rms. Sundries. Cr cds: A, C, D, DS, MC, V.

⊟ ⊛ ⊛ SC $

✔ ★ ★BEST WESTERN WALNUT CREEK INN. *(1258 8th St, West Des Moines 50265) Just S of I-235 exit 3. 515/223-1212.* 68 rms, 2 story. S $48–$52; D $52–$57; each addl $5; suites $65–$75; under 12 free. Crib free. TV; cable. Heated pool. Free continental bkfst. Cafe adj open 24 hrs. Bar 4 pm–1:30 am exc Sun. Ck-out 1 pm. Meeting rm. Cr cds: A, C, D, DS, MC, V.

🏊 ⊟ ⊟ ⊛ SC

✔ ★ ★COMFORT INN. *(5908 Sutton Pl, Urbandale 50322) On Merle Hay Rd, just S of I-35/80 exit 131. 515/270-1037.* 63 rms, 2 story. S $30–$36; D $38–$43; under 17 free. Crib free. TV; cable. Indoor pool; whirlpool. Free continental bkfst. Cafe opp noon–midnight. Ck-out 11 am. Meeting rm. Game rm. Cr cds: A, D, DS, ER, MC, V. ⓓ

🖼 🏊 ⊟ ⊛ ⊛ SC

✔ ★ ★DAYS INN CAPITOL CITY. *3501 E 14th St (50316), at jct US 6, 65, 69. 515/265-2541.* 146 rms, 2 story. S $39–$51; D $44–$57; each addl $5; family rates. Crib free. TV; cable. Heated pool. Cafe 6 am–2 pm, 5–10 pm. Rm serv. Bar 4 pm–2 am. Ck-out noon. Coin lndry. Meeting rms. Cr cds: A, C, D, DS, MC, V.

🏊 ⊟ ⊛ ⊛ SC $

★ ★DRAKE INN. *1140 24th St (50311). 515/255-4000.* 52 rms, 2 story. S $45–$60; D $50–$60; under 18 free. Crib free. TV. Free coffee. Cafe adj 6 am–2 pm; Sun to 10 pm. Ck-out noon. Meeting rms. Valet serv. Sundries. Cr cds: A, C, D, MC, V.

🏊 ⊛ SC

★ECONO LODGE. *(I-35 & 1st St, Ankeny 50021) 6 mi N of I-80 at I-35 exit 92. 515/965-1995.* 54 rms, 2 story. S $26.75–$29.75; D $33.75–$36.75; each addl $5; under 18 free. Crib free. TV; satellite. Cafe 6 am–9 pm. Ck-out noon. Meeting rm. Cr cds: A, DS, MC, V.

♿ ⊟ ⊛ ⊛ SC

✔ ★ ★EXECUTIVE INN. *(3530 Westown Pkwy, West Des Moines 50265) 7 mi W on I-35, exit 35th St. 515/225-1144; res: 800/228-9669.* 100 rms, 2 story. S $39; D $47–$57; each addl $6; suites $55–$85; under 12 free. Crib $6. TV; satellite, in-rm movies. Pool. Free continental bkfst. Cafe 6 am–2 pm, 5–10 pm exc Sun. Rm serv. Bar 4 pm–2 am. Ck-out 11 am. Meeting rms. Sundries. Exercise equipt; weights, bicycles, whirlpool, sauna. Game rm. Refrigerators. Balconies. Cr cds: A, C, D, MC, V.

⊟ 🎿 ⊛ ⊛ SC

★ ★HAMPTON INN. *5001 Fleur Dr (50321). 515/287-7300.* 122 rms, 4 story. S $38–$43; D $44–$49; under 19 free; special package plans. Crib free. TV; cable. Pool. Free continental bkfst. Cafe nearby. Ck-out 11 am. Meeting rms. Bellhops. Valet serv. Airport, bus depot transportation. Cr cds: A, C, D, DS, MC, V.

♿ ⊟ ⊛ ⊛ SC

✔ ★ ★ ★RAMADA INN. *4685 NE 14th St (50313). 515/265-5671.* 141 rms, 2 story. S $32–$35; D $35–$40; each addl $6; under 18 free. Crib free. TV; cable. Heated pool. Playground.

Cafe 6 am–10 pm. Rm serv. Bar 4 pm–midnight. Ck-out noon. Meeting rms. Rec rm. Cr cds: A, C, D, DS, MC, V.

♿🕷➔🚫Ⓢ SC

★**RED CARPET INN.** *4845 Merle Hay Rd (50323), just off I-35, I-80 exit 131.* *515/ 278-5511.* 80 rms, 2 story, 14 kits. S $27.95; D $33.95; each addl $5; under 12 free. Crib free. TV; cable. Free coffee. Cafe adj open 24 hrs. Ck-out noon. Cr cds: A, C, D, DS, MC, V.

🕷🚫Ⓢ SC

✔★★**RODEWAY INN.** *4995 Merle Hay Rd (50322), just off I-35, I-80 exit 131.* *515/278-2381.* 122 rms, 2 story. S $40–$45; D $40–$50; each addl $5; suites $55–$75; under 17 free. Crib free. TV; cable. Indoor/outdoor pool; whirlpool, sauna. Cafe open 24 hrs. Bar 11–2 am. Ck-out noon. Coin lndry. Meeting rms. Some in-rm steam baths. Cr cds: A, C, D, DS, MC, V.

➔🚫Ⓢ$

Motor Hotels

✔★★**BEST WESTERN STARLITE VILLAGE.** *929 3d St (50309), at jct I-235.* *515/282-5251.* 165 rms, 7 story. S $44; D $50; each addl $6; suites $90–$125; under 12 free; hospital package plans. Crib free. TV; cable. Indoor pool. Cafe 6 am–10 pm; Sun 7 am–5 pm. Rm serv from 7 am. Bar 11–2 am. Ck-out noon. Meeting rms. Valet serv. Free airport, hospital transportation. Rec rm. Sun deck. Opp Veteran's Auditorium. Cr cds: A, C, D, DS, MC, V.

♿🕷➔🚫Ⓢ SC $

★**RAMADA HOTEL.** *6215 Fleur Dr (50321), opp airport.* *515/285-1234.* 194 rms, 1–3 story. S $44–$62; D $48–$66; each addl $6; studio rms $27; under 18 free. Crib free. TV; cable. Heated pool. Cafe 6 am–11 pm. Rm serv. Bar 11–2 am; entertainment Thurs-Sat. Ck-out noon. Meeting rms. Bellhops. Valet serv. Free airport transportation. Exercise equipt; weights, bicycles, sauna. Picnic tables, grill. Cr cds: A, C, D, DS, MC, V. D

➔🏃🚫Ⓢ SC

✔★★**SUPER 8 LODGE WESTMARK.** *(West Des Moines, 50265) At jct I-80, Ashworth Rd.* *515/223-6500.* 157 rms, 9 story. S $34.88; D $38.88; each addl $3. Crib free. TV; cable. Indoor pool. Cafe 6:30 am–2 pm, 5:30–10 pm. Rm serv. Bar; dancing. Ck-out 1 pm. Meeting rms. Valet serv. Airport, RR station, bus depot transportation. Lighted tennis. Exercise equipt; weights, treadmill, whirlpool, sauna. Some refrigerators. Cr cds: A, C, D, DS, MC, V.

♿🕷➔🏃🚫Ⓢ SC

Dubuque

Settled: 1833 **Pop:** 62,321 **Elev:** 650 ft (198 m) **Area code:** 319 **Zip:** 52001

Motels

★★**DODGE HOUSE.** *701 Dodge St, just W of jct US 52, 61, 151.* *319/556-2231; res: 800/553-0006 (exc IA), 800/942-0009 (IA).* 85 rms, 2 story. S $25; D $36; each addl $5; under 12 free. Crib $4. TV; cable. Cafe 6 am–9 pm. Bar 3 pm–1 am. Ck-out 11 am. Meeting rms. Sundries. Downhill ski 6 mi; x-country ski 8 mi. Cr cds: A, C, D, DS, MC, V.

🕷🎿

✔★★**HEARTLAND INN.** *4025 Dodge St (US 20).* *319/582-3752; res: 800/334-3277.* 91 rms, 2 story. S $31.50–$37.50; D $37.50–$43.50; each addl $6; under 17 free; ski, golf plans. Crib free. TV; cable. Free coffee. Cafe opp 7 am–10 pm. Ck-out noon. Meeting rm. Downhill/x-country ski 8 mi. Whirlpool, sauna. Some refrigerators. Cr cds: A, C, D, DS, MC, V.

♿🎿🚫 SC $

★★**HOLIDAY INN.** *1111 Dodge St.* *319/556-3340.* 198 rms, 2 story. S $46–$51; D $53–$58; under 18 free; family rates. Crib free. TV; cable. Pool. Cafe 6 am–10 pm. Rm serv. Bar 3:30 pm–midnight; Sun 3–10 pm. Ck-out noon. Meeting rms. Bellhops. Valet serv. Sundries. Free airport transportation. Cr cds: A, C, D, DS, MC, V.

♿🕷➔🚫 SC

✔★★**TIMMERMAN'S LODGE.** *(US 20, East Dubuque, IL 61025) 1 mi E on US 20.* *815/ 747-3181.* 74 rms, 3 story. S $32–$60; D $49–$74; each addl $5; suites $74; under 18 free. Crib free. TV; cable. Indoor pool; whirlpool, sauna, poolside serv. Cafe 5–10 pm; Fri, Sat to 11 pm. Rm serv. Bar 11–1 am; entertainment, dancing Fri–Sun. Ck-out noon. Coin lndry. Meeting rms. Sundries. Airport, bus depot transportation. Downhill ski 10 mi; x-country ski ¼ mi. Game rm. Rec rm. Private patios, balconies. Golf adj, greens fee $7.50. Cr cds: DS, MC, V.

Motor Hotel

✔ ★★JULIEN INN. *200 Main St. 319/556-4200.* 145 rms, 8 story. Apr–Oct: S $19.50–$43; D $34–$53; each addl $5; suites $60; under 14 free; lower rates rest of yr. Crib free. TV; cable. Cafe 6:30 am–10 pm. Rm serv. Bar 11:30–2 am. Ck-out noon. Meeting rms. Bellhops. Gift shop. Cr cds: A, C, D, MC, V.

Fort Dodge

Founded: 1853 **Pop:** 29,423 **Elev:** 1,030 ft (314 m) **Area code:** 515 **Zip:** 50501

Motels

✔ ★★★BEST WESTERN STARLITE VILLAGE. *(Box 1297) 2 mi NW at jct US 169, IA 7. 515/573-7177.* 120 rms, 1–2 story. S $33–$38; D $42–$48; each addl $5; studio rms $48. TV; cable. Indoor pool; whirlpool, sauna, poolside serv. Cafe 6 am–11 pm; Sun 7 am–9 pm. Rm serv 6 am–9 pm. Bar noon–2 am; dancing exc Sun. Ck-out noon. Meeting rms. Bellhops. Valet serv. Game rm. Cr cds: A, C, D, DS, MC, V.

★BUDGET TRAVELERS INN. *300 1st Ave S, just N off IA 7. 515/576-2191.* 59 rms, 3 story. S $22.36; D $30; each addl $5; under 12 free. TV; cable. Heated pool. Cafe nearby. Ck-out noon. Sundries. Some balconies. Cr cds: A, D, MC, V.

✔ ★★★HOLIDAY INN. *2001 US 169 S, at jct US 20. 515/955-3621.* 102 rms, 2 story. S $41–$43; D $51–$53; each addl $5; suites $51–$54; under 18 free. Crib free. TV; cable. Heated pool; wading pool. Playground. Cafe 6 am–10 pm. Rm serv. Bar 11–2 am; Sun 3–8 pm. Ck-out 1 pm. Coin lndry. Meeting rms. Cr cds: A, C, D, DS, MC, V.

Fort Madison

Settled: 1808 **Pop:** 13,520 **Elev:** 536 ft (163 m) **Area code:** 319 **Zip:** 52627

Motels

✔ ★★IOWAN MOTOR LODGE. *3 mi W on US 61, IA 2. 319/372-7510.* 150 rms, 2 story. S, D $34–$42; each addl $4; under 12 free; wkend rates. Crib free. TV; cable. Indoor pool; sauna. Cafe 6:30 am–10 pm; Sat from 7 am; Sun 7 am–8 pm. Bar. Ck-out 11 am. Meeting rms. Miniature golf. Rec rm. Balconies. Cr cds: A, C, D, DS, MC, V.

★MADISON INN. *3440 Ave L. 319/372-7740.* 20 rms. S $23–$25; D $26–$30; each addl $5. TV; cable. Cafe adj 6 pm–midnight. Ck-out 11 am. Cr cds: A, MC, V.

Iowa City

Founded: 1839 **Pop:** 50,508 **Elev:** 698 ft (213 m) **Area code:** 319 **Zip:** 52240

Motels

(Rates may be higher football wkends)

★**ABBEY RETREAT.** *(Coralville 52241) Approx 2 mi S of I-80 exit 242.* 319/351-6324. 18 units, 1–2 story. D $52–$62; suites $106–$127; under 12 free. Crib free. TV; satellite. Cafe adj 11:30 am–10 pm. Ck-out noon. Sundries. Free airport, bus depot transportation. Bathrm phones. Cr cds: A, C, D, DS, MC, V.

✔★★★**BEST WESTERN CANTEBURY INN.** *(704 1st Ave, Coralville 52241) 1 blk S of I-80 exit 242.* 319/351-0400. 129 rms, 2 story. S $41–$52; D $52–$62; each addl $5; bilevel suites $79–$127; wkend rates. Crib free. TV. Heated pool. Free continental bkfst. Cafe adj open 24 hrs. Bar 4 pm–2 am. Ck-out noon. Coin lndry. Valet serv. Barber, beauty shop. Exercise rm; instructor, weight machines, bicycles, whirlpool, sauna. Some refrigerators. Cr cds: A, C, D, DS, MC, V.

★**CAPRI LODGE.** *(705 2d St, Coralville 52241) 3 mi W on US 6, 1 mi S of I-80 exit 242.* 319/354-5100. 18 rms. S $21.50–$27; D $25.50–$30.50; each addl $2. Crib $2. TV; cable. Cafe nearby. Ck-out 11 am.

✔★★★**HIGHLANDER INN.** *(RR 2) Just N of I-80 exit 246.* 319/354-2000. 96 rms, 2 story. S $37.75–$47.75; D $46.75–$56.75; each addl $5; studio rms $55–$60; under 15 free. Crib free. TV; cable, in-rm movies. Indoor pool; whirlpool, sauna, poolside serv. Cafes 6:30 am–10 pm. Rm serv to 10 pm. Bar 11:30–1 am; Sun 4:30–9:30 pm; entertainment, dancing Tu–Sat. Ck-out noon. Meeting rms. Valet serv. Sundries. Some refrigerators. Cr cds: A, C, D, DS, MC, V. ⓓ Ⓔ

★★★**HOWARD JOHNSON.** *N Dodge St, 1 blk S of I-80 exit 246.* 319/351-1010. 82 rms, 2 story. S $41–$46; D $45–$51; each addl $5; under 18 free. Crib free. TV; cable. Indoor pool; whirlpool, sauna. Cafe open 24 hrs. Bar 2 pm–1 am. Ck-out noon. Meeting rms. Bellhops. Valet serv. Private patios, balconies. Cr cds: A, C, D, DS, MC, V.

✔★★★**RODEWAY INN.** *(I-80 & IA 965 exit 240, Coralville 52241)* 319/354-7770. 163 rms, 2 story. S $32–$44; D $40–$64.50; each addl $4; suites $50–$60; studio rm $32–$42; under 17 free; wkly rates. TV; cable. Indoor pool; whirlpool, sauna. Free coffee. Cafe 6:30 am–2 pm, 5–10 pm. Rm serv. Bar 4:30 pm–1:30 am. Ck-out noon. Meeting rms. Bellhops. Putting green. Hot tub. Game rm. Rec rm. Lawn games. Balconies. Cr cds: A, C, D, DS, MC, V. Ⓔ ⓘ

Keokuk

Settled: 1820 **Pop:** 13,536 **Elev:** 550 ft (168 m) **Area code:** 319 **Zip:** 52632

Motels

★★**KEOKUK MOTOR LODGE.** *(RFD 2) 2½ mi N on US 218, City 61.* 319/524-3252; res: 800/341-8000. 60 rms. S $28; D $33–$36; each addl $3. Crib $2. TV; cable, in-rm movies. Pool. Free coffee. Cafe opp 6 am–10 pm. Ck-out noon. Cr cds: A, C, D, DS, MC, V.

✔★★★**KEOKUK REGENCY.** *4th & Main Sts, on US 136.* 319/524-8000. 84 rms, 5 story. S $38–$44; D $39–$56; each addl $7; family rates. Crib free. TV; cable. Heated pool. Cafe 6:30 am–10 pm. Rm serv. Bar 11–2 am; entertainment. Ck-out noon. Meeting rms. Bellhops. Cr cds: A, C, D, DS, MC, V.

★**SUPER 8.** *3511 Main St.* 319/524-3888. 39 rms, 2 story. S $28.88–$33.88; D $35.88–$41.88; each addl $3; suites $38.88. Crib $2. TV; cable. Free continental bkfst. Cafe adj 11 am–10 pm. Ck-out 11 am. Cr cds: A, C, D, DS, MC, V.

Marquette

Settled: 1779 **Pop:** 528 **Elev:** 627 ft (191 m) **Area code:** 319 **Zip:** 52158

Motels

✔ ★**HOLIDAY SHORES.** *(Box 297, McGregor 52157) On US 18. 319/873-3449.* 33 rms, 2–3 story. No elvtr. S $28; D $28–$60. Crib $2. TV; cable. Indoor pool; whirlpool. Cafe nearby. Ck-out 10:30 am. Meeting rms. Balconies. Overlooks Mississippi River. Cr cds: MC, V.

★**NEW FRONTIER.** *(Box 295) At jct US 18, IA 76. 319/873-3497.* 20 rms, 2 story. May–Oct: S $25–$45; D $30–$50; each addl $5; lower rates rest of yr. Crib $4. TV; cable. Heated pool. Free coffee in rms. Cafe nearby. Sundries. Gift shop. X-country ski 4 mi. Overlooks Mississippi River. Cr cds: DS, MC, V.

★**PINK ELEPHANT.** *(Box 58) US 18 at Prairie du Chien Bridge. 319/873-3477.* 18 rms, 3 story. No elvtr. S $26; D $40–$45; suites $65; under 6 free. TV; cable. Free continental bkfst. Ck-out 10 am. Balconies. On bluff overlooking Mississippi River. Cr cds: MC, V.

Marshalltown

Founded: 1853 **Pop:** 26,938 **Elev:** 938 ft (286 m) **Area code:** 515 **Zip:** 50158

Motels

★**AMERICINN.** *403 E Church St. 515/753-7777.* 29 units, 2 story. S $26.90–$29.90; D $28.90–$32.90; each addl $4; suites $35.90–$39.90; under 12 free; wkly rates. Crib free. TV; cable. Free continental bkfst. Ck-out noon. Local airport, bus depot transportation. Picnic tables. Cr cds: A, C, D, DS, MC, V.

✔ ★ ★**BEST WESTERN REGENCY INN.** *3303 S Center, at jct US 30, IA 14. 515/752-6321.* 161 rms, 2 story. S $39; D $48; each addl $7; under 12 free. Crib free. TV; cable. Indoor pool; sauna. Cafe 6 am–9 pm. Rm serv. Bar 4 pm–2 am. Ck-out noon. Meeting rms. Bellhops. Valet serv. Free local airport transportation. Sundries. Gift shop. Game rm. Cr cds: A, C, D, DS, MC, V.

✔ ★ ★**BEST WESTERN THUNDERBIRD.** *2009 S Center St. 515/752-3631.* 30 rms. S $29–$35; D $33–$42; each addl $3; family rates. Crib $3. TV; cable. Heated pool. Free coffee. Cafe adj 11 am–2 pm, 5–10 pm; Sat from 5 pm; Sun to 2 pm. Rm serv. Ck-out 11 am. Meeting rm. Cr cds: A, C, D, DS, MC, V. Ⓓ

★**TRAVEL INN.** *3d Ave at Main, on IA 14. 515/753-6681.* 35 rms, 2 story. S $18–$20; D $27–$30; each addl $5; under 12 free. Crib $5. TV. Ck-out noon. Meeting rm. Cr cds: A, D, DS, MC, V.

Mason City

Settled: 1853 **Pop:** 30,144 **Elev:** 1,138 ft (347 m) **Area code:** 515 **Zip:** 50401

Motels

★**DAYS INN.** *2301 4th St SW. 515/424-0210.* 59 rms, 2 story. S, D $31; each addl $5; under 18 free. Crib free. TV; cable. Free continental bkfst. Cafe nearby. Ck-out noon. Cr cds: A, C, D, MC, V.

✔★★**SHERATON INN.** *(Box 1069) 2½ mi W on US 18. 515/424-1480.* 71 rms, 1–2 story. S $41–$47; D $49–$51; each addl $3; studio rms $36.50–$42.50; suites $80.50–$93.50; under 18 free. Crib free. TV; cable. Indoor pool; poolside serv. Cafe 7 am–10 pm; Sun 8 am–2 pm. Rm serv. Bar 4:30 pm–1 am exc Sun. Ck-out noon. Meeting rms. Valet serv. Sundries. Free airport transportation. Exercise equipt; bicycles, treadmill, whirlpool, sauna. Cr cds: A, C, D, DS, MC, V.

★**TRAVELODGE.** *24 5th St SW, at jct US 18W, 65. 515/424-2910.* 48 rms, 2 story. S $28–$30; D $33–$35; each addl $4; under 17 free. Crib free. TV; cable. Heated pool. Cafe nearby. Ck-out noon. Some balconies. Cr cds: A, C, D, DS, MC, V.

Muscatine

Founded: 1836 **Pop:** 23,467 **Elev:** 550 ft (168 m) **Area code:** 319 **Zip:** 52761

Motels

✔★★★**BEST WESTERN CANTEBURY INN.** *2402 Park Ave. 319/264-3337.* 100 rms, 2 story. S $38.85–$41.85; D $49.85–$58.85; each addl $5–$7; bi-level suites $60.85–$105.85; kit. units $58.85–$85.85; under 12 free, wkend rates. Crib free. TV. Indoor pool. Free bkfst. Cafe 5–9:30 pm. Bar 4 pm–midnight exc Sun. Ck-out noon. Coin lndry. Meeting rm. Exercise rm; instructor, weight machines, bicycles, whirlpool, sauna. Some refrigerators. Cr cds: A, C, D, DS, ER, MC, V.

★★★**HOLIDAY INN.** *(Box 56) 2½ mi N at jct US 61, IA 38. 319/264-5550.* 107 rms, 3 story. S $44–$49; D $44–$55; each addl $5; studio rms $48–$75; family rates; wkend rates. Crib free. TV: cable. Indoor pool; wading pool, whirlpool, sauna. Cafe 6 am–2 pm, 5–10 pm. Rm serv. Bar 4:30 pm–2 am. Coin lndry. Ck-out noon. Meeting rms. Bellhops. Rec rm. Some refrigerators. Cr cds: A, C, D, DS, MC, V.

Newton

Pop: 15,292 **Elev:** 950 ft (290 m) **Area code:** 515 **Zip:** 50208

Motels

✔★★**BEST WESTERN NEWTON INN.** *IA 14 at I-80 exit 164. 515/792-4200.* 118 rms, 2 story. S $35–$43; D $43–$56; each addl $6; under 12 free. Crib free. TV; cable. Indoor pool; whirlpool, sauna. Free full bkfst. Cafe 6 am–10 pm. Bar 4 pm–1 am. Ck-out noon. Meeting rms. Putting green. Rec rm. Cr cds: A, C, D, DS, MC, V.

★★**DAYS INN.** *(Box 1031) 2 mi S on IA 14 at I-80. 515/792-2330.* 58 rms, 2 story. S $32–$35; D $35–$48; each addl $3. Crib $2. TV; cable. Free continental bkfst 6:30–9:30 am. Cafe adj open 24 hrs. Ck-out 11 am. Cr cds: A, C, D, DS, MC, V.

★★**OAK TREE INN.** *(Box 277) On IA 14 at jct I-80. 515/792-8100.* 80 rms, 2 story. S $26.95; D $30.95–$34.95; each addl $4; under 5 free. Crib free. TV. Pool. Bar 5 pm–midnight. Ck-out noon. Meeting rms. Sundries. Free airport transportation. Cr cds: A, C, D, MC, V.

✔★★**TERRACE LODGE.** *(Box 577) 2 mi S on IA 14 at jct I-80. 515/792-7722.* 60 rms, 2 story. S $27.50–$29.50; D $35.50–$41.50; each addl $4; under 14 free. Crib $6. TV. Pool; whirlpool, sauna. Cafe 6 am–10 pm. Bar 4 pm–2 am exc Sun. Ck-out 11 am. Meeting rms. Cr cds: A, MC, V.

Okoboji

Founded: 1855 **Pop:** 559 **Elev:** 1,450 ft (442 m) **Area code:** 712 **Zip:** 51355

Motels

★**COUNTRY CLUB.** *(Box 287) 1 blk W on US 71. 712/332-5617; res: 800/831-5615 (exc IA), 800/262-4715 (IA).* 53 rms. Memorial Day–late Sep: S $25–$44; D $45–$56; lower rates rest of yr. Crib free. TV; satellite. Heated pool. Cafe nearby. Ck-out 11 am. Cr cds: A, DS, MC, V.

🏊 sc

✔ ★**CRESCENT BEACH RESORT.** *(Milford 51351) 3 mi NW of Milford on IA 86. 712/337-3351.* 115 units in lodges, cottages, 1–2 story, 70 kits. Some A/C, phones. Mid-June–late Aug: S, D $20–$40; suites $450–$1,025/wk; kit. units $59–$108; kit. cottages $108–$171; lower rates early June, late Aug–mid-Oct. Closed rest of yr. Crib $3. TV. Playground. Cafe 8 am–2 pm, 5:30–11 pm. Bar 5:30 pm–1 am; Sat to 2 am; entertainment, dancing exc Sun. Ck-out 11 am. Coin lndry. Meeting rms. Tennis. Rec dir (summer). Rec rm. Picnic tables, grills. Docks; paddleboats, boats, motor rentals. On West Okoboji Lake. Cr cds: A, MC, V.

🏖 🔍 🏊

✔ ★**FOUR SEASONS RESORT.** *(Box 87, Arnolds Park 51331) ½ mi S on US 71. 712/332-2103.* 31 units, 1–2 story, 14 kits. S $30–$80; D $34–$85; suites $60–$150; kit. units $30–$65. Crib $4. TV; cable. Cafe nearby. Bar 11–2 am. Ck-out 11 am. Free airport transportation. Whirlpool, sauna. Picnic tables, grills. Sand beach. Canoes, boat rentals. Many private patios, balconies. On lake. Cr cds: A, DS, MC, V.

🏖 🏊 🏊 sc

Ottumwa

Settled: 1843 **Pop:** 27,381 **Elev:** 650 ft (198 m) **Area code:** 515 **Zip:** 52501

Motels

✔ ★ ★**DAYS INN.** *206 Church St, at US 34, Business exit. 515/682-8131.* 135 rms, 1–2 story. S $36–$45; D $41–$50; each addl $5; under 18 free; wkend rates. Crib free. TV; cable. Pool; whirlpool. Cafe 6 am–10 pm. Rm serv to 9 pm. Bar 4 pm–2 am; dancing exc Sun. Ck-out noon. Meeting rms. Bellhops. Sundries. City park opp. Cr cds: A, C, D, DS, MC, V.

🏖 🏊 🚫 sc

★**INN TOWNER.** *111 N Court St. 515/682-8075.* 20 rms, 2 story. S $22; D $22–$28; each addl $3; under 12 free. Crib free. TV; cable. Coffee in rms. Cafe nearby. Rm serv. Ck-out noon. Opp park. Cr cds: A, D, DS, MC, V.

🏖

Sioux City

Settled: 1854 **Pop:** 82,003 **Elev:** 1,117 ft (340 m) **Area code:** 712

Motels

★**IMPERIAL.** *110 S Nebraska St (51101). 712/277-3151.* 68 rms, 2 story, 3 kits. S $28.75; D $28.75–$37.75; each addl $2; suites $40–$100; kit. units $5 addl; under 12 free. Crib $2. TV; cable. Pool. Free coffee. Cafe nearby. Bar 11–2 am. Ck-out noon. Coin lndry. Meeting rms. Some refrigerators. Cr cds: A, C, D, MC, V.

🏊 sc

★**PALMER HOUSE.** *3440 E Gordon Dr (51106). 712/276-4221.* 64 rms, 1–2 story. S $30; D $35–$38; each addl $2. Crib $3. TV; cable. Heated pool. Free coffee. Cafe adj open 24 hrs. Ck-out 11 am. Meeting rm. Sundries. Cr cds: A, DS, MC, V.

🏖 🏊 sc

★**SUPER 8.** *4307 Stone Ave (51106). 712/274-1520.* 60 rms, 2 story. Mid-May–mid-Oct: S $32.88; D $35.88–$41.88; each addl $3; lower rates rest of yr. Crib $2. TV; cable. Cafe open 24 hrs. Ck-out 11 am. Cr cds: A, C, D, DS, MC, V.

Motor Hotels

✔ ★ ★**BEST WESTERN REGENCY EXECUTIVE.** *2d & Nebraska Sts (51101), business exit 147B. 712/277-1550.* 115 rms, 2 story. S $42–$47; D $47–$53; each addl $6; suites $89–$97; under 12 free. Crib free. TV; cable. Heated pool. Cafe 6 am–11 pm; Sun to 10 pm. Rm serv 7 am–9 pm. Bar 4 pm–2 am. Ck-out noon. Coin lndry. Meeting rms. Free airport transportation. Cr cds: A, C, D, DS, MC, V.

★ ★**HOLIDAY INN.** *1401 Zenith Dr (51103), at I-29 Hamilton Blvd exit. 712/277-3211.* 156 rms, 2 story. S $47–$53; D $53–$59; each addl $6; under 18 free. Crib free. TV; cable. Heated pool. Cafe 6 am–10 pm. Rm serv. Bar 4 pm–2 am; entertainment, dancing exc Sun. Ck-out noon. Coin lndry. Meeting rms. Bellhops. Sundries. Free airport transportation. Cr cds: A, C, D, DS, MC, V.

★ ★**HOWARD JOHNSON.** *701 E Gordon Dr (51101). 712/277-9400.* 120 rms, 6 story. S $40–$46; D $49–$55; each addl $6; studio rms $43; under 18 free. Crib free. TV; cable. Indoor pool; whirlpool, sauna. Cafe open 24 hrs. Rm serv 7 am–10 pm. Bar 5 pm–2 am; dancing. Ck-out noon. Coin lndry. Meeting rms. Free airport transportation. Rec rm. Cr cds: A, C, D, DS, MC, V.

Hotel

✔ ★ ★ ★**HILTON INN.** *707 4th St (51101). 712/277-4101.* 190 units, 11 story. S $42–$66; D $50–$74; each addl $10; suites $125–$275; studio rms $56–$60; family rates; wknd rates. Crib $10. TV; cable. Indoor pool; sauna. Cafe 6 am–10 pm; dining rm 11 am–2 pm, 6–10 pm; Sun, Mon 11 am–2 pm. Bars 11–1 am. Ck-out noon. Meeting rms. Barber. Valet parking. Free airport transportation. Cr cds: A, C, D, DS, MC, V.

Spencer

Founded: 1859 **Pop:** 11,726 **Elev:** 1,321 ft (403 m) **Area code:** 712 **Zip:** 51301

Motels

★ ★**LAMPLIGHTER.** *1 mi S at jct US 18, 71. 712/262-3720; res: 800/242-5115.* 69 rms, 2 story. S $29; D $35–$45; under 12 free. Crib $5. TV; cable. Pool. Free coffee. Cafe nearby. Ck-out 11 am. Valet serv. Cr cds: A, C, D, DS, MC, V.

✔ ★ ★**PLAZA 1.** *1 mi S at jct US 18, 71. 712/262-6100; res: 800/255-2255, ext 1729.* 59 rms, 2 story. S $28–$37; D $34–$42; each addl $4–$5; suites $33–$48; under 12 free. Crib free. TV; cable. Pool. Cafe adj open 24 hrs. Ck-out 11 am. Valet serv. Some refrigerators. Cr cds: A, C, D, DS, MC, V.

★**SUPER 8.** *209 11th St SW, at jct US 18, 71. 712/262-8500.* 31 rms, 2 story. S $22.88; D $30.88–$34.88; each addl $4; higher rates county fair. Crib $2. TV; cable. Free coffee in lobby. Cafe nearby. Ck-out 11 am. Cr cds: A, D, DS, MC, V.

Storm Lake

Pop: 8,814 **Elev:** 1,435 ft (437 m) **Area code:** 712 **Zip:** 50588

Motels

✔ ★**LAMPLIGHTER.** *1504 N Lake Ave.* 712/732-2505; res: 800/383-7666. 50 rms, 2 story. S $28; D $35.50; each addl $3. TV; cable. Heated pool. Free coffee in lobby. Cafe adj. Ck-out 11 am. Meeting rm. Cr cds: A, D, DS, MC, V.

🏊 Ⓢ sc

★**PALACE.** *E Lake Shore Dr, 1½ mi SE on US 71, IA 7.* 712/732-5753. 27 rms. S $25; D $32.50; each addl $5. Crib $5. TV; cable. Free coffee in lobby. Ck-out 11 am. Lake opp. Cr cds: A, C, D, MC, V.

🐾

★**SAIL-INN.** *1015 E Lakeshore Dr.* 712/732-1160. 44 rms, 2 story. S $27; D $32–$35; each addl $4; family rates. Crib $2. TV; cable. Free coffee in lobby. Cafe nearby. Ck-out 11 am. Meeting rms. Free airport transportation. Some refrigerators. Cr cds: A, D, MC, V.

♿

★ ★**VISTA.** *1316 N Lake Ave.* 712/732-2342. 37 rms, 2 story. S $24–$31; D $32–$37; each addl $4. Crib $4. TV; cable. Free coffee in rms. Cafe adj open 24 hrs. Ck-out 11 am. Meeting rms. Cr cds: A, C, D, DS, MC, V.

♿ 💲

Waterloo

Settled: 1848 **Pop:** 75,985 **Elev:** 867 ft (264 m) **Area code:** 319

Motels

★**EXEL INN.** *3350 University Ave (50701).* 319/235-2165. 105 rms, 2 story. S $26.95–$31.95; D $32.95–$37.95; each addl $2; under 12 free. TV; satellite. Free coffee in lobby. Cafe nearby open 24 hrs. Ck-out noon. Cr cds: A, C, D, DS, MC, V.

♿ 🐾 Ⓢ sc

✔ ★ ★**HEARTLAND INN.** *1809 LaPorte Rd (50702).* 319/235-4461; res: 800/334-3277. 91 rms, 2 story. S $31.50–$37.50; D $37.50–$43.50; each addl $6; under 17 free. Crib free. TV; cable. Free coffee in lobby. Cafe nearby. Ck-out noon. Meeting rms. Sundries. Whirlpool, sauna. Picnic tables. Cr cds: A, C, D, DS, ER, MC, V.

♿ 🐾 Ⓢ sc 💲

Motor Hotel

★**CONWAY INNE.** *W 5th & Jefferson St (50701).* 319/235-0301. 97 rms, 5 story. S $23.95; D $31.50; each addl $5.50; under 12 free. Crib free. TV; satellite. Cafe 6 am–9 pm; Sun 7 am–2 pm. Rm serv. Bar 11–2 am exc Sun. Ck-out noon. Meeting rms. Cr cds: A, C, D, DS, ER, MC, V.

🐾 sc

Hotel

✔ ★ ★ ★**RAMADA.** *214 Washington St (50701).* 319/235-0321. 227 rms, 11 story. Jan–May, Sep–Aug: S $40–$44; D $40–$46; each addl $7; suites $75–$135; under 18 free; wkly rates; lower rates rest of yr. Crib free. TV; satellite. Indoor pool. Cafe 6 am–10 pm. Bar 10–2 am; entertainment, dancing exc Sun. Ck-out noon. Convention facilities. Airport, RR station, bus depot transportation. Cr cds: A, C, D, DS, MC, V.

♿ 🏊 Ⓢ sc

Waverly

Pop: 8,444 **Elev:** 919 ft (280 m) **Area code:** 319 **Zip:** 50677

Motel

★**STAR.** *2 mi E on IA 3. 319/352-4434.* 33 rms, 1–2 story. S $19.95–$26; D $25–$32; each addl $2. Crib $3. TV. Free coffee in rms. Cafe adj, summer 6:30 am–8 pm; winter from 7 am; Sun 8 am–2 pm. Ck-out 10 am. Meeting rm. Some fireplaces. Cr cds: A, MC, V.

Motor Hotel

✔ ★ ★ ★**BEST WESTERN RED FOX INN.** *½ mi W on IA 3. 319/352-5330.* 130 rms, 2–3 story. S $42–$48; D $52–$58; each addl $4; under 12 free. Crib $2. TV; cable. Indoor pool. Cafes 6:30 am–10 pm. Rm serv. Bar 11–2 am; entertainment, dancing Fri–Sat exc hols. Ck-out 1 pm. Meeting rms. Valet serv. Sundries. Some in-rm steam baths. Cr cds: A, C, D, DS, ER, MC, V. Ⓓ

Webster City

Settled: 1850 **Pop:** 8,572 **Elev:** 1,050 ft (320 m) **Area code:** 515 **Zip:** 50595

Motels

★ ★**BEST WESTERN NORSEMAN INN.** *(I-35 exit 144 & US 20, Williams 50271) 515/854-2281.* 33 rms. S $33; D $39–$44; each addl $4. Crib $2. TV; cable. Free continental bkfst. Cafe nearby. Bar. Ck-out noon. Cr cds: A, C, D, DS, MC, V.

✔ ★ ★**NEW CASTLE INN.** *1700 Superior St. 515/832-3631.* 40 rms, 2 story. S $28; D $31.95–$40.95. Crib free. TV; cable. Heated pool; sauna. Free continental bkfst in lobby. Cafe nearby. Ck-out 11 am. Cr cds: A, C, D, DS, MC, V.

Maine

Population: 1,125,030	
Land area: 30,995 sq mi (80,277 sq km)	
Elevation: 0–5,268 ft (0–1,606 m)	
Highest point: Mt Katahdin (Piscataquis Co)	
Entered Union: March 15, 1820 (23d state)	
Capital: Augusta	
Motto: *Dirigo* (I direct)	
Nickname: Pine Tree State	
State flower: Pine cone and tassel	
State bird: Chickadee	
State tree: Eastern white pine	
State fair: Mid-August, 1989 in Skowhegan	
Time zone: Eastern	

Interstate Highway System

The following alphabetical listing of Maine towns in *Mobil Travel Guide* shows that these cities are within 10 miles (16 kilometers) of the indicated Interstate highway. A highway map should, however, be checked for the nearest exit.

> **INTERSTATE 95:** Augusta, Bangor, Bath, Biddeford, Brunswick, Freeport, Houlton, Kennebunk, Kittery, Lincoln, Millinocket, Newport, Ogunquit, Orono, Portland, Saco, Scarborough, Waterville, Yarmouth, York.

Weather Statistics*

	WINTER	SPRING	SUMMER	FALL
Northern	11°F (-10°C)	49°F (9°C)	65°F (18°C)	44°F (7°C)
Southern	21°F (-6°C)	53°F (12°C)	68°F (20°C)	49°F (9°C)

*Average mean temperatures are usually listed for the entire state. Averages for specific regions are given if significant differences exist.

Visitor Information

Maine: A Guide to the Vacation State (Houghton Mifflin, Boston, rev 1969) and *Maine: A Guide "Downeast"* (Courier-Gazette, Inc, Rockland, rev 1970), two of the American Guide Series. *Maine: An Explorer's Guide* by Christina Tree (The Countryman Press, Woodstock, VT, rev 1987) is also an excellent source of information.

The Maine Publicity Bureau (97 Winthrop St, Hallowell 04347; 207/289-2423) publishes many pamphlets for distribution.

The Pequot Press (Old Chester Rd, Chester, CT, 06412) has several interesting publications on New England.

The pulp and paper industry mills throughout Maine offer tours of their woodlands and manufacturing facilities at various times of the year. For further information contact the Paper Industry Information Office, 133 State St, Augusta 04330; 207/622-3166.

There are 9 official information service centers in Maine; visitors who stop by will find information and brochures most helpful in planning stops to points of interest. Their locations are as follows: at Kittery, between I-95 and US 1; in Fryeburg (summer only), on US 302; in Bangor, at Bass Park, 519 Main St; in Calais, on Union St, off US 1; in Houlton, at jct of US 1 (exit 62), I-95; in

Orono (summer only), on Stillwater Ave (exit 51), I-95; in Bethel (summer only), on US 2; in Machias (summer only), on US 1; in Yarmouth, between I-95 (exit 17), & US 1. Allied offices are also located at more than 40 strategic points throughout Maine.

Room Rate Information

The following resort areas have higher room rates for two (double) than indicated on the cover of this Guide. However, the lodgings listed in these cities offer a good value when compared to others of their type in the area.

Bar Harbor	$65	Boothbay Harbor	$65

Augusta

Settled: 1628 **Pop:** 21,819 **Elev:** 153 ft (47 m) **Area code:** 207 **Zip:** 04330

Motels

★★**HOLIDAY INN.** *(Box 347) Western Ave & I-95. 207/622-6371.* 128 rms, 2 story. S $48–$63; D $50–$65; each addl $6; under 19 free. Crib free. TV; cable. Pool; wading pool. Cafe 7 am–10 pm. Rm serv. Bar 11–1 am; Sun noon–10 pm; entertainment, dancing exc Sun. Ck-out noon. Coin lndry. Bellhops. Valet serv. Sundries. Racquetball, health club privileges. Picnic table. Cr cds: A, C, D, DS, MC, V. ⓕ

★★**HOWARD JOHNSON.** *110 Community Dr, at jct ME 27, I-95 Augusta-Belgrade exit. 207/622-4751.* 103 rms, 2 story. S $42–$53; D $53–$63; each addl $8; under 18 free; higher rates: camp wkend, special events. Crib free. TV; cable. Pool. Cafe 6 am–10 pm. Rm serv. Bar noon–1 am. Ck-out noon. Sundries. Meeting rms. Adj to Augusta Civic Center. Cr cds: A, C, D, DS, MC, V. ⓕ

✔★★**SUSSE CHALET MOTOR LODGE.** *On Whitten Rd, just off ME Tpke, Augusta-Winthrop exit. 207/622-3776; res: 800/258-1980.* 58 rms, 2 story. S $31.70; D $35.70; each addl $3. Crib $3. TV; cable. Pool. Cafe nearby. Ck-out 11 am. Coin lndry. Cr cds: A, C, D, MC, V.

★**VALUE INN.** *18 Edison Dr. 207/622-0000.* 71 rms, 2 story. S $33; D $39; each addl $6; under 18 free. Crib free. TV; cable. Cafe adj 6:30 am–10 pm. Ck-out noon. Cr cds: A, MC, V. ⓕ

Bangor

Settled: 1769 **Pop:** 31,643 **Elev:** 61 ft (19 m) **Area code:** 207 **Zip:** 04401

Motels

✔★**BREWER MOTOR INN.** *(359 Wilson St, Brewer 04412) 2 mi E on US 1A. 207/989-4476.* 30 units, 3 story. No elvtr. July–Oct: S, D $40–$44; each addl $6; under 18 free; some wkend, wkly rates; lower rates rest of yr. Crib free. TV; cable. Cafes 6:30–11 am. Bar 4–11 pm. Ck-out 11 am. Balconies. Sun deck. Cr cds: A, C, D, DS, MC, V.

✔★**SUSSE CHALET MOTOR LODGE.** *1100 Hammond St. 207/947-6921.* 60 rms, 2 story. S $33.70; D $37.70; each addl $3. Crib $2. TV; satellite. Pool. Cafe nearby. Ck-out 11 am. Coin lndry. Cr cds: A, D, MC, V.

Bar Harbor

Pop: 4,124 **Elev:** 20 ft (6 m) **Area code:** 207 **Zip:** 04609

Motels

★**ANCHORAGE.** *51 Mt Desert St.* 207/288-3959. 48 rms, 2 story. July–Labor Day: S, D $32–$66; each addl $5–$6; kit. cottages $68; varied lower rates late May–June, after Labor Day–Oct. Closed rest of yr. Crib $5. TV; cable. Cafe nearby. Ck-out noon. Cr cds: A, C, D, MC, V.

✔ ★ ★**CROMWELL HARBOR.** *359 Main St, ½ mi S on ME 3.* 207/288-3201. 18 rms. No A/C. July–Labor Day: S, D $55–$68; each addl $5; 1 family unit $90; lower rates late May–June, after Labor Day–mid-Oct. Closed rest of yr. TV; cable. Cafe nearby. Ck-out 11 am. Cr cds: MC, V.
🚫

✔ ★ ★**EDENBROOK.** *(Rte 3) 96 Eden St, 1 mi N on ME 3.* 207/288-4975. 45 rms. No A/C. July–Aug: S, D $50–$75; each addl $6; varied lower rates late May–June, after Labor Day–late Oct. Closed rest of yr. Crib $4. TV; cable. Free coffee in rm. Cafe adj mid-June–Labor Day 7 am–10 pm. Ck-out 11 am. Some balconies. Cr cds: A, MC, V.
♿ 🚫

✔ ★**EMERY'S COTTAGES ON THE SHORE.** *(Box 172) Sand Point Rd, 6 mi NE of ME 3.* 207/288-3432. 21 cottages, 13 kits. (oven in 6), 1 kit. apt. No A/C. July–Labor Day: D $48; kit. units $54–$72; kit. apts $365–$495/wk; wkly rates; lower rates early May–June, Labor Day–Oct. Closed rest of yr. Crib free. TV; satellite. Free coffee. Ck-out 10 am. Coin lndry. Grocery 1 mi. Refrigerator in cottages without kit. Picnic tables, grills. Cr cds: A, MC, V.
🏊 🚫

★**FRENCHMAN'S BAY.** *Eden St.* 207/288-3321. 66 rms, 7 A/C, 2 story. July–Labor Day: D $64–$78; each addl $5; lower rates mid-Apr–June, after Labor Day–mid-Oct. Closed rest of yr. Crib free. TV; cable. Cafe 6–9:30 am. Ck-out 11 am. Ferry terminal opp; overlooks bay. Cr cds: A, MC, V.
🐟

✔ ★**HIGGINS HOLIDAY.** *43 Holland Ave.* 207/288-3829 res: 800/345-0305. 22 units, 1–2 story. No A/C. July–Labor Day: S $58–$62; D $62–$65; each addl $8–$10; kit units $90–$100; lower rates mid-May–June, Labor Day–Oct. Closed rest of yr. Crib $6. TV; cable. Free coffee in rm. Cafe nearby. Ck-out 11 am. Lawn games. Cr cds: MC, V.

★**HIGHBROOK.** *Eden St, 1 mi N on ME 3.* 207/288-3591; res: 800/338-9688. 26 rms. No A/C. July–Aug: S, D $55–$75; each addl $6; lower rates May–June, Sep–late Oct. Closed rest of yr. Crib free. TV; cable. Free coffee in rm. Cafe nearby. Ck-out 11 am. Cr cds: A, DS, MC, V.

★**SEA BREEZE.** *(RFD 1, Box 1080) 4 mi N on ME 3.* 207/288-3565. 31 rms. No A/C. July–Labor Day: S $54–$62; D $59–$75; each addl $10; lower rates mid-May–June, after Labor Day–mid-Oct. Closed rest of yr. Crib avail. TV; cable. Free in-rm coffee. Cafe adj. Ck-out 11 am. Refrigerators avail. Sun decks. View of Frenchman Bay; back from hwy. Cr cds: MC, V.

✔ ★ ★**TESTA'S HOTEL.** *53 Main St.* 207/288-3327. 16 rms, 3 story. Mid-July–mid-Sep: S, D $50–$52; each addl $8; lower rates late June–mid-July, mid-Sep–mid-Oct. Closed rest of yr. Crib $8. TV; cable. Cafe 7 am–midnight. Bar. Ck-out 11 am. Bellhops. Opp beach. Cr cds: A, C, D, MC, V.
🍴

✔ ★ ★**WONDER VIEW.** *(Box 25) Eden St, ½ mi NE on ME 3.* 207/288-3358; res: 800/341-1553 (exc ME). 82 rms, 1–2 story. No A/C. July–mid-Sep: S, D $51–$95; each addl $10; lower rates mid-May–June, mid-Sep–mid-Oct. Closed rest of yr. Crib $10. TV. Heated pool. Cafe 7–10:30 am, 5:30–9:30 pm. Bar. Ck-out 11 am. 18-hole golf privileges. Many balconies; most rms overlook bay. Cr cds: A, ER, MC, V.
⛳ 🏊

Inns

★ ★**BLACK FRIAR.** *10 Summer St, 5 blks from Main St & off Cottage St.* 207/288-5091. 6 rms, 3 story. No rm phones. May–Oct: S, D $60–$85. Closed rest of yr. Children over 12 yrs only. Free full bkfst, afternoon tea. Ck-out 11 am. Victorian decor; antiques. Totally non-smoking. Cr cds: A, MC, V.
🚫 🚫

★★**GREYCOTE.** *40 Holland Ave. 207/288-3044.* 12 units, 4 with bath, 3 story, 2 kits. No A/C. No elvtr. No rm phones. May–mid-Nov: S, D $55–$90; each addl $10; kits. $500/wk; wkly rates. Closed rest of yr. Children over 8 yrs only. Free full bkfst, tea, sherry. Ck-out 11 am, ck-in 2 pm. Free airport, ferry terminal transportation. Lawn games. Some balconies. Picnic tables, grills. Near ocean. Restored 19th century home; antiques, library. Cr cds: MC, V.

⊘ 🐾

★★**RIDGEWAY MANOR.** *11 High St. 207/288-9682.* 6 rms, 3 baths, 3 story. No A/C. Mid-June–mid-Oct: D $55–$95; each addl $10; lower rates rest of yr. Children over 12 yrs only. Free continental bkfst, evening tea. Wine. Ck-out 11 am, ck-in 3 pm. Former house of J.P. Morgan, built 1890. Free airport transportation; Nova Scotia ferry nearby. Balconies. Antique furnishings, quilts, pictures, Oriental rugs. Beach 2 blks. Totally nonsmoking. Cr cds: MC, V.

⊘ 🐾 SC

★★**STRATFORD HOUSE.** *45 Mount Desert St. 207/288-5189.* 10 rms, 8 with bath, 3 story. May–Oct: S, D $60–$125; each addl $15; under 5 free. Closed rest of year. Free continental bkfst 8–10 am. Ck-out 11 am. Music rm. English Tudor design, fireplaces, original Jacobean furniture. Cr cds: A, MC, V.

🐾

Bath

Pop: 10,246 **Elev:** 13 ft (4 m) **Area code:** 207 **Zip:** 04530

Motels

★★★**HOLIDAY INN.** *139 Western Ave, ¾ mi S on US 1. 207/443-9741.* 141 rms, 3 story. D $49–$109; each addl $6; under 19 free. Crib free. TV; satellite (fee). Pool. Cafe 6 am–2 pm, 5–9 pm; wkends 7–11:30 am, 5–9 pm. Bar 11–1 am; Sun from noon; entertainment Thurs-Sat. Ck-out noon. Meeting rm. Valet serv. Sundries. X-country ski 4 mi. Exercise equipt; weight machines, bicycles, whirlpool, sauna. Cr cds: A, C, D, DS, MC, V.

🏊 💆 🐾 🏌 ⊘ 🐾

✔★**NEW MEADOWS INN.** *(W Bath) 2 mi W on Bath Rd, ½ mi E of US 1 New Meadows Rd exit. 207/443-3921.* 10 rms in 2-story lodge, 12 units in 10 cottages. No A/C. S $30; D $36; cottage units for 2–4, $38–$53. Cottages closed mid-Oct–late May. Crib $5. B/W TV. Cafe 11:30 am–2 pm, 5–8:30 pm; Fri to 9 pm; Sat to 9:30 pm; Sun noon–8 pm. Bar 11:30 am–11 pm. Ck-out noon. Meeting rms. Porches on cottages. On river; dockage. Cr cds: A, C, D, MC, V.

🛏 🐾

Belfast

Settled: 1770 **Pop:** 6,243 **Elev:** 103 ft (31 m) **Area code:** 207 **Zip:** 04915

Motel

✔★★**COLONIAL GABLES.** *Searsport Ave, 3 mi NE on US 1, ME 3. 207/338-4000.* 13 motel rms, 45 cottages, 42 kits. No A/C. July–Labor Day: D $52–$54; each addl $4; cottages for 2–8, $50–$86; wkly rates; lower rates May–June, after Labor Day–Oct. Closed rest of yr. Crib free. TV; cable. Playground. Free coffee in motel rms. Cafe nearby. Ck-out 11 am. Sundries. Free airport transportation. Rec rm. Lawn games. Picnic tables, grills. Private sand beach on Penobscot Bay; beach fire 7–10 pm. Cottages with porches. Accommodations vary. Cr cds: MC, V.

Belgrade

Settled: 1774 **Pop:** 2,043 **Elev:** 268 ft (82 m) **Area code:** 207 **Zip:** 04917

Motel

✔ ★**VILLAGE INN.** *(Box 282, ME 27, Belgrade Lakes 04918) 14 mi N of I-95.* 207/495-3553. 12 rms, 8 baths, 2 story. No A/C. May–Nov: S, D $35–$65; each addl $10; suites $70. Closed rest of yr. Crib $6. Cafe 5–9 pm; Sun 11:30 am–2 pm, 5–9 pm. Bar. Ck-out 11 am. Gift shop. On lake. Cr cds: A, DS, MC, V.

Bethel

Settled: 1774 **Pop:** 2,340 **Elev:** 700 ft (213 m) **Area code:** 207 **Zip:** 04217

Motel

✔ ★ ★**RIVER VIEW.** *2 mi NE on US 2, ME 5, 26.* 207/824-2808. 32 kit. units, 2-bedrm. S, D $50; each addl $5. Crib $5. TV; cable. Ck-out 10:30 am. Tennis. Downhill ski 4 mi; x-country ski 3 mi. Game rm. Cr cds: A, MC, V.

Inn

★**NORSEMAN.** *Rumford Rd, 1 mi N on ME 2, 5, 26.* 207/824-2002. 10 rms, 3 shared baths, 2 story. No A/C. No rm phones. Dec–Mar: D $27–$30/person; lower rates rest of yr. Ck-out 11 am. Downhill ski 5 mi; x-country ski 4 mi. Cr cds: A, MC, V.

Biddeford

Settled: 1630 **Pop:** 19,683 **Elev:** 75 ft (22 m) **Area code:** 207 **Zip:** 04005

Motel

✔ ★**BIDDEFORD.** *560 Elm St.* 207/284-8924. 15 rms, 2 cottages. July–Labor Day: D $47–$54; each addl $3–$4; lower rates rest of yr. Crib free. TV; cable. Free coffee in rms. Cafe nearby. Ck-out 11 am. Free bus depot transportation. Cr cds: A, D, MC, V. ⓕ

Bingham

Settled: 1785 **Pop:** 1,074 **Elev:** 371 ft (113 m) **Area code:** 207 **Zip:** 04920

Motel

✔ ★ ★**BINGHAM MOTOR INN.** *(Box 683) 1 mi S on US 201.* 207/672-4135. 20 units, 4 kits. July–Labor Day: S $34–$40; D $40–$47; each addl $4; kit units $5 addl; wkly rates; lower rates rest of yr (exc hunting season). Crib $2. TV; cable. Pool. Playground. Cafe nearby. Ck-out 10 am. Free airport transportation. Downhill ski 3 mi. Lawn games. Some refrigerators. Picnic tables. Cr cds: A, MC, V.

Blue Hill

Settled: 1722 **Pop:** 1,644 **Elev:** 40 ft (12 m) **Area code:** 207 **Zip:** 04614

Motel

✔ ★ ★**HERITAGE MOTOR INN.** *Ellsworth Rd, ½ mi E on ME 172.* 207/374-5646. 23 rms, 2 story. No A/C. July–mid-Oct: D $50; each addl $8; lower rates May–June. Closed rest of yr. Crib $5. TV. Free coffee in rms. Cafe nearby. Ck-out 11 am. On hillside. View of bay. Cr cds: MC, V.

Inn

✔ ★★**BREEZEMERE FARM.** *(Rte 176, South Brooksville 04617) 207/326-8628.* 7 rms in inn (4½ bathrms), 9 cottages, 1–3 story. Early July–mid-Oct, MAP: S $60–$95; D $50–$63/person; family, wkly rates; lower rates Memorial Day–early July. Closed rest of yr. Cafe 8–9:30 am; 1 sitting 7 pm. Setups. Airport, bus depot transportation. Rowboats, sailboats, bicycles. Game rm. Rec rm. Lawn games. Sat night clambake. Blueberry picking. On ocean. Farm animals. Cr cds: MC, V.

Boothbay Harbor

Pop: 2,207 **Elev:** 16 ft (5 m) **Area code:** 207 **Zip:** 04538

Motels

★★**CAP'N FISH'S.** *65 Atlantic Ave. 207/633-6605.* 53 units, 2 story, 3 kits. Mid-June–Sep: D $60–$90; each addl $5; kit. units $100; lower rates rest of yr. Crib free. TV; cable. Cafe 7–10 am. Ck-out 11 am. Dockage. On harbor. Cr cds: A, MC, V.

✔ ★★**FLAGSHIP MOTOR INN.** *Townsend Ave (ME 27). 207/633-5094.* 85 rms, 2 story. Mid-May–mid-Oct: S, D $60–$70; each addl $5; lower rates rest of yr. Crib free. TV; cable. Pool; poolside serv. Cafe adj 7 am–10 pm. Bar 3–11 pm. Ck-out 11 am. Trolley service to town. Lawn games. Balconies. Picnic tables. Near ocean. Gardens. Cr cds: A, MC, V.

✔ ★★★**OCEAN GATE MOTOR INN.** *(Rte 27, Southport 04576)* 2½ mi E on ME 27. *207/633-3321; res: 800/221-5924 (exc ME).* 55 rms, 1–2 story, 3 kits., 2 kit. cottages. No A/C. July–Aug: S, D $45–$95; each addl $6; kit. units $50–$95; kit. cottages for 2–6, $159; wkly rates off season; lower rates May–June, Labor-Day–Nov. Closed rest of yr. Crib $5. TV. Pool. Playground. Free coffee in rms. Cafe 7 am–10 pm (May–Oct only). Bar from noon. Ck-out 11 am. Coin lndry. Meeting rm. Sundries. Gift shop. Tennis. Dock; boats. Private porch on some rms. Picnic tables. View of harbor. On 85 acres. On ocean. Cr cds: A, C, D, MC, V.

✔ ★★**THE PINES.** *(Box 693) Sunset Rd, 1¼ mi SE, off Atlantic Ave. 207/633-4555.* 29 rms. No A/C. July–Labor Day: D $63; each addl $5; lower rates May–late June, after Labor Day–late Oct. Closed rest of yr. Crib free. TV; cable. Heated pool. Playground. Bkfst avail. Ck-out 11 am. Tennis. Horseshoes. Refrigerators. Balconies, decks. In wooded area; view of harbor. Quiet, secluded. Cr cds: MC, V.

★★**ROCKTIDE INN.** *45 Atlantic Ave, ½ mi SE of ME 27. 207/633-4455; res: 800/762-8433.* 98 rms, 2 story. Mid-June–mid-Oct: D $65–$117; each addl $10; lower rates last 2 wks June. Closed rest of yr. TV; cable. Indoor pool. Full bkfst. Cafe 7:30–9:30 am, 5:30–9 pm. Bar 4–11 pm. Ck-out 11 am. Valet serv. Some balconies. On pier overlooking harbor; own dock. Trolley car transportation to business district. Cr cds: MC, V.

✔ ★**SEAGATE.** *124 Townsend Ave. 207/633-3900.* 25 rms. No A/C. Mid-June–mid-Sep: S, D $45–$70; each addl $5; 3 kit. units; lower rates rest of yr. Crib $5. TV; cable. Free coffee. Cafe nearby 7 am–8 pm. Ck-out 11 am. Sundries. Tennis, golf nearby. Picnic tables, grills. Cr cds: A, MC, V.

Inn

✔ ★★**OCEAN POINT.** *(East Boothbay 04544)* 6½ mi SE on ME 96 at Ocean Point. *207/633-4200.* 61 units, 1–2 story. No A/C. Late June–early Sep: S, D $55–$91; each addl $6; under 12, $3; lower rates late May–late June, after Labor Day–mid-Oct. Closed rest of yr. Crib $4. TV.

88 Maine

Pool. Cafe (in season) 7:30–10 am, 5:30–9 pm. Bar 5–10 pm. Ck-out 11 am, ck-in 2 pm. Shuffleboard. On peninsula at entrance to Linekin Bay. Units vary. Cr cds: A, DS, MC, V.

Bucksport

Settled: 1762 **Pop:** 2,853 **Elev:** 43 ft (13 m) **Area code:** 207 **Zip:** 04416

Motels

★**ELMAC.** *(Drawer BB) Main St, US 1, ½ mi NE on US 1, ME 3. 15. 15. 207/469-3111.* 23 rms. No A/C. D $35–$40; each addl $4. TV; cable. Free coffee in rms. Cafe nearby. Ck-out 11 am. Cr cds: A, MC, V.

✔ ★ ★**SPRING FOUNTAIN.** *(RFD 2, Box 710) 1 mi NE on US 1, ME 3. 207/469-3139.* 40 rms, 1–2 story, 15 kits. July–Labor Day: D $48–$58; each addl $5; kit. units $5 addl; family rates; wkly rates, lower rates rest of yr. Crib $5. TV. Pool. Playground. Cafe nearby. Ck-out 11 am. Coin lndry. Some patios, balconies. Rock garden. Penobscot River view. Cr cds: A, MC, V.

Camden

Pop: 3,743 **Elev:** 33 ft (10 m) **Area code:** 207 **Zip:** 04843

Motels

✔ ★ ★**MT BATTIE.** *(Box 570, Lincolnville 04849) 4 mi N on US 1. 207/236-3870.* 21 rms. July–Labor Day: S $32–$42; D $40–$46; each addl $7; suites $42–$55; under 3 $2; lower rates mid-Apr–June, Labor Day–Oct. Closed rest of yr. Crib $4. TV; cable. Free continental bkfst. Cafe nearby. Ck-out 11 am. Gift shop. Some rms view ocean. Cr cds: A, MC, V.

✔ ★ ★**SMARTS'.** *4 mi N on US 1. 207/236-3466.* 6 motel rms, 5 cottages, 4 kits. (3 without oven). No A/C. July–Labor Day: D $50–$55; each addl $5; kit. units $7 addl; kit. cottage for 2–3 (late June–Labor Day) $300/wk; lower rates mid-May–June, after Labor Day–mid-Oct. Closed rest of yr. Crib free. TV. Bkfst avail. Ck-out 11 am. Downhill/x-country ski 6 mi. Sun deck. View of ocean. Cr cds: A, MC, V.

✔ ★**SNOW HILL LODGE.** *(Star Rte, Box 550, Lincolnville 04849) 4½ mi N on US 1. 207/236-3452.* 30 rms, 1–2 story. No A/C. Mid-June–mid-Sep: D $42–$55; each addl $6; lower rates mid-Feb–mid-June, mid-Sep–Nov. Crib $6. TV; satellite. Free continental bkfst (early May–late Oct) 7:15–9:30 am. Cafe nearby. Ck-out 10 am. Downhill/x-country ski 4 mi. Lawn games. Picnic tables, grills. Tree-shaded grounds. View of bay. Cr cds: MC, V.

Caribou

Pop: 9,916 **Elev:** 442 ft (135 m) **Area code:** 207 **Zip:** 04736

Motel

✔ ★**KING HENRY'S MOTOR INN.** *(PO Box 57) Access Hwy. 207/493-3311.* 63 units, 2 story. June–Oct: S $34–$36; D $40–$46; each addl $7; under 12 free; monthly rates; lower rates rest of yr. Crib $7. TV; cable. Cafe 6 am–9 pm. Rm serv. Bar 3–11 pm; dancing. Ck-out 11 am. Meeting rms. Sundries. Refrigerators avail. Cr cds: A, C, D, MC, V. Ⓔ Ⓕ

Ellsworth

Settled: 1763 **Pop:** 5,179 **Elev:** 100 ft (30 m) **Area code:** 207 **Zip:** 04605

Motels

✔ ★**ELLSWORTH.** *24 High St. 207/667-4424.* 16 rms, 1–2 story. No A/C. July–Labor Day: S $35–$38; D $38–$50; each addl $5; varied lower rates rest of yr. Crib $4. TV; cable. Pool. Cafe nearby. Ck-out 10 am. Cr cds: A, MC, V.

★**HOMESTEAD MOTEL & COTTAGES.** *1 mi W on US 1, ME 3. 207/667-8193.* 14 rms in motel, cottages. No A/C. July–Aug: S $44–$48; D $46–$55; each addl $5; under 6 free; lower rates mid-May–June, after Labor Day–mid-Oct. Closed rest of yr. TV. Free coffee in lobby. Ck-out 11 am. Cr cds: A, MC, V.

✔ ★**TWILITE.** *1 mi W on US 1, ME 3. 207/667-8165.* 23 rms. July–Labor Day: S $36–$44; D $44–$58; each addl $5; lower rates May–June, after Labor Day–late Oct. Closed rest of yr. TV; some B/W. Continental bkfst. Ck-out 10 am. Picnic tables. Cr cds: A, C, D, MC, V.

Farmington

Pop: 3,583 **Elev:** 425 ft (130 m) **Area code:** 207 **Zip:** 04938

Motel

★**MT BLUE.** *(Box 5060) US 2. 207/778-6004.* 18 rms. S $30–$34; D $36–$42; each addl $4. Crib $2. TV; satellite. Cafe nearby. Ck-out 10 am. Sundries. Downhill/x-country ski 2 mi. Picnic tables. Cr cds: A, D, DS, MC, V.

Grand Lake Stream

Pop: 198 **Elev:** 300 ft (91 m) **Area code:** 207 **Zip:** 04637

Cottage Colony

★ ★**WEATHERBY'S.** *2 mi N of Princeton on US 1, then 11 mi W. 207/796-5558.* 16 units in 15 cottages. No A/C. MAP, May–Sep: S $70; D $52–$104/person; under 12, $32. Closed rest of yr. Crib avail. TV in rec rm. Cafe (public by res) 7–8 am, 6:30–7:30 pm. Box lunches. Rm serv. Ck-out 10 am. Cookout lunches with guides. Grocery 100 yds. Princeton airport bus, plane from Bangor Intl Airport. Tennis, basketball adj. Rec rm. Beach. Boats, motors; rowboats, canoes. Dockage. Fishing, guides; fish clean/store area. Lawn games. Fireplaces or Franklin stoves. Screened porches. Cabin boys bring ice, wood. Well-maintained rustic cottages. On spacious attractive grounds.

Greenville

Pop: 1,640 **Elev:** 1,038 ft (347 m) **Area code:** 207 **Zip:** 04441

Motels

✔ ★**CHALET MOOSEHEAD.** *(Box 327, Greenville Junction 04442) 1 mi W, just off ME 6, 15. 207/695-2950.* 8 kit. units, 2 rms, (no ovens); 1–2 story motel unit, 1 kit. cottage. No A/C. June–Dec: S, D $32–$39; each addl $7; cottage $39–$40; under 5 free; lower rates rest of yr.

Crib free. TV; cable. Cafe nearby. Ck-out 11 am. Private beach. Canoes. Seaplane rides. Lawn games. Picnic tables, grills. On Moosehead Lake. Cr cds: MC, V.

🅢 🅢 sc

✔ ★**GREENWOOD.** *(Greenville Junction 04442) 3 mi NW on ME 6, 15. 207/695-3321; res: 800/FOUR-FUN.* 14 rms, 2 story. No A/C. July–Sep, ski season: D $36; each addl $4; some lower rates rest of yr. Crib free. TV; in-rm movies. Pool. Free continental bkfst. Rm serv. Ck-out 10:30 am. 9-hole golf privileges opp. Lawn games. Picnic tables, grills. Guide serv. Downhill/x-country ski 3 mi. Cr cds: A, D, DS, MC, V.

🅢 🅢 🅢 🅢 sc

★**INDIAN HILL.** *(Box 367) ½ mi S on ME 15. 207/695-2623.* 15 rms. No A/C. S $36–$40; D $38–$44; each addl $5; also 3 kit. cottages, 2-bedrm $40–$45 mid-May–Sep only. TV. Morning coffee. Cafe nearby. Ck-out 10:30 am. X-country ski 6 mi. Trailer hookups. View of Moosehead Lake, mountains. Cr cds: MC, V.

🅢

Inn

✔ ★ ★ ★**GREENVILLE.** *(Box 1194) Norris St. 207/695-2206.* 15 units, 3 story. No rm phones. S $28–$60; D $34–$65; each addl $7; suites $64; kits. $55. Crib free. Cafe 7:30–9:30 am, 6–9 pm. Rm serv. Bar 5–11 pm; entertainment, dancing wkends. Ck-out 11 am, ck-in 2 pm. Airport transportation. Downhill/x-country ski 8 mi. Sauna. Game rm. Rec rm. Lawn games. Some refrigerators. Balconies. Complimentary sherry, tea. Former lumber baron home; built 1895. Cherrywood, mahogany antiques. Porches with view of mountains, lake; flower gardens. Cr cds: MC, V. Ⓓ Ⓕ

🅢 🅢 🅢

Houlton

Settled: 1805 **Pop:** 5,730 **Elev:** 366 ft (112 m) **Area code:** 207 **Zip:** 04730

Motels

✔ ★ ★**IVEY'S.** *Bangor Rd, 2 mi S on US 2A. 207/532-2236.* 45 rms, 1–2 story. S $30–$47; D $36–$48; each addl $4. Crib $4. TV; cable, in-rm movies. Heated pool. Cafe 4–10 pm exc Sun. Rm serv. Bar 4 pm–1 am. Ck-out 11 am. Meeting rms. Many refrigerators. Cr cds: A, C, D, ER, MC, V.

🅢

✔ ★ ★**SHIRETOWN.** *(RFD 3) North Rd 1 mi N on US 1, just N of I-95. 207/532-9421.* 52 rms. S $38–$51; D $42–$53; each addl $6; suites $50–$60. Crib $5. TV; cable, in-rm movies. Indoor pool. Free coffee in rms. Cafe 5:30–10 pm. Cafe opp open 24 hrs. Bar 2 pm–midnight. Ck-out 11 am. Coin lndry. Meeting rms. Tennis courts, 2 lighted. Exercise equipt; weights, bicycles, whirlpool, sauna. Refrigerators. Atrium supper club. Cr cds: A, C, D, MC, V. Ⓕ

🅢 🅢 🅢 🅢

★**STARDUST.** *(RR 3, Box 670) North Rd, 3 mi N on US 1, 2 mi N of I-95. 207/532-6538.* 12 rms. June–Nov: S $25–$32; D $32–$36; each addl $4; lower rates rest of yr. TV; satellite. Ck-out 11 am. Cr cds: MC, V. Ⓕ

🅢

Kennebunk

Settled: 1650 **Pop:** 6,488 **Elev:** 50 ft (15 m) **Area code:** 207 **Zip:** 04043

Motels

✔ ★ ★**FRIENDSHIP INN.** *(Box 575, West Kennebunk 04094) Alewive Rd, 2 mi N on ME 35 at ME Tpke exit 3S. 207/985-3541; 985-6525.* 40 rms. June–Oct: S $48–$65; D $48–$70; each addl $5; suites $10 addl; 1 unit, 2-rms, for 4–6 avail; under 16 free; lower rates rest of yr. Crib $4.

TV; cable. Heated pool. Playground. Ck-out 11 am. Rec rm. Lawn games. Some refrigerators. Cr cds: A, D, DS, MC, V. Ⓕ

★**TURNPIKE.** *Just off ME 35 at ME Tpke exit 3N. 207/985-4404.* 20 rms. Late June–Labor Day: S, D $55; each addl $3; lower rates Apr–late June, after Labor Day–early Dec. Closed rest of yr. Crib $3. TV: cable. Coffee in rms. Cafe nearby. Ck-out 11 am. Refrigerators. Wood-paneled rms. Cr cds: MC, V. Ⓕ

Kittery

Settled: 1623 **Pop:** 5,465 **Elev:** 22 ft (6 m) **Area code:** 207 **Zip:** 03904

Motels

✔ ★★**DAYS INN KITTERY/PORTSMOUTH.** *(Box 126) US 1 Bypass S. 207/439-5555.* 72 rms, 1–3 story. S $35–$75; D $41–$85; each addl $6; under 18 free; suites $65–$95. Crib free. TV; cable. Indoor pool; sauna. Cafe 7 am–9 pm. Bar from 11 am. Ck-out 11 am. Meeting rms. Valet serv. Sundries. Cr cds: A, D, DS, MC, V. Ⓕ

★**REX.** *½ mi N of bridge on US 1 Bypass; I-95 Dennett Rd-ME 103N, Berwick-Kittery S exits. 207/439-9002.* 13 rms. June–early Sep: S $28–$47; D $33–$60; each addl $3–$5; under 4 free; lower rates rest of yr. Crib $3. TV; cable. Pool. Free coffee in rms. Cafe opp 7 am–11 pm; Fri, Sat to midnight. Ck-out 11 am. Picnic tables. Cr cds: A, DS, MC, V. Ⓕ

Lubec

Pop: 2,045 **Elev:** 20 ft (6 m) **Area code:** 207 **Zip:** 04652

Motel

★**EASTLAND.** *(Box 200) 2½ mi W on ME 189. 207/733-5501.* 20 rms. No A/C. S $32–$37; D $42–$47; each addl $4; under 18, $2. Crib free. TV. Ck-out 10 am. Airport for small planes adj. Cr cds: D, MC, V.

Inns

✔ ★★**HOME PORT.** *45 Main St. 207/733-2077.* 6 rms, 5 baths, 2 story. No rm phones. May–Oct: S $50–$66; D $50–$65; each addl $10. Children over 7 yrs only. Closed rest of yr. TV in lobby. Free continental bkfst. Cafe 7:30–9 am. Ck-out 10 am, ck-in 2 pm. Picnic tables. Built 1880; antiques. Totally nonsmoking. Cr cds: MC, V.

✔ ★★**OWEN HOUSE.** *(Campobello, New Brunswick, CAN EOG 3HO) 2 mi from International Bridge. 506/752-2977.* 9 rms, 5 with bath, 4 share bath, 3 story. No rm phones. Memorial Day–mid-Oct: S $48; D $53–$63; each addl $15; suite $63–$74; group rates. Closed rest of yr. TV in lobby. Free full bkfst. Cafe nearby. Ck-out 11 am, ck-in noon. On ocean.

Machias

Settled: 1763 **Pop:** 1,277 **Elev:** 70 ft (21 m) **Area code:** 207 **Zip:** 04654

Motels

★**BLUEBIRD.** *(Box 45, US 1) 1 mi W on US 1. 207/255-3332.* 40 rms. No A/C. July–Labor Day: S $32–$36; D $40–$44; each addl $4; some lower rates rest of yr. Crib free. TV; cable. Ck-out 11 am. Valet serv. Cr cds: MC, V.

✔ ★MAINELAND. *(Rte 1, East Machias, 04630) 207/255-3334.* 30 rms. July–mid-Sep: S $30–$36; D $34–$45; each addl $4; lower rates mid-Sep–late Oct, May–June. Closed rest of yr. TV; cable. Free coffee. Cafe adj 7 am–9:30 pm. Ck-out 11 am. Picnic tables. Cr cds: MC, V.

Newport

Pop: 1,748 **Elev:** 202 ft (61 m) **Area code:** 207 **Zip:** 04953

Motel

✔ ★★LOVLEY'S. *(RFD 1)* ½ mi W at jct US 2, ME 11, 100, just N of I-95 Newport-Detroit exit 39. 207/368-4311. 53 rms, 3 kits. (no ovens, equipt). Phone jacks in some rms. S $24.90–$39.90; D $24.90–$59.90; each addl $3–$5; kit. units $5 addl. Crib $8. TV; satellite. Heated pool; whirlpool. Cafe nearby. Ck-out 11 am. 9-hole golf privileges, driving range. Lawn games, gliders. Picnic tables. Cr cds: A, DS, MC, V.

Northeast Harbor

Pop: 600 **Elev:** 80 ft (24 m) **Area code:** 207 **Zip:** 04662

Motel

★★KIMBALL TERRACE INN. *(Box 1030) Huntington Rd, 2 blks SE of ME 3. 207/276-3383.* 70 rms, 2–3 story. No A/C. May–Oct: S, D $55–$85; each addl $5; under 5 free; lower rates rest of yr. Crib free. TV. Pool; poolside serv in season. Cafe 7 am–9:30 pm. Rm serv 7:30 am–9:30 pm. Ck-out 11 am. Meeting rms. Tennis adj. Golf privileges. Overlooks harbor. Cr cds: A, MC, V.

Norway

Pop: 2,653 **Elev:** 383 ft (116 m) **Area code:** 207 **Zip:** 04268

Motels

★★GOODWIN'S. *(South Paris 04281)* ½ mi N on ME 26. 207/743-5121. 25 rms. S $27–$37; D $30–$45; suites $39–$51; under 12 free; higher rates special events. TV; cable. Cafe 6 am–midnight. Bar adj. Ck-out 11 am. X-country ski 6 mi. 2 family units. Cr cds: A, D, MC, V.

✔ ★★LEDGEWOOD. *1 mi S on ME 26. 207/743-6347.* 17 rms. Mid-May–mid-Oct: S $32–$40; D $38–$60; each addl $6–$12; higher rates: Oxford 250, campers wkends; lower rates rest of yr. Crib $4. TV; cable. Pool. Cafe 7–10 am. Ck-out 11 am. Cr cds: A, DS, MC, V.

✔ ★★MOLLYOCKET. *(Box 248, West Paris 04289)* 8½ mi N on ME 26. 207/674-2345. 18 rms, 1–2 story, 3 kits. (no oven). S $45–$50; D $50–$65; each addl $10; kit. units $60–$65. Crib $5. TV. Indoor pool; whirlpool, sauna. Playground. Free continental bkfst; coffee in rms. Ck-out 11 am. Meeting rm. Sunning rm. Cr cds: A, MC, V.

Inn

★★★WATERFORD. *(PO Box 49, Chadbourne Rd, East Waterford 04233)* 8 mi W via ME 118. 207/583-4037. 9 rms, 6 baths, 2 story. No rm phones. May–Feb: S, D $50–$75; each addl $15. Closed rest of yr. Cafe 8–9:30 am, 5–9 pm. Ck-out 11 am, ck-in 2 pm. Tennis, 9-hole golf privileges. Lawn games. Private patios, balconies. Built 1825; antiques. Parlor, library. Extensive grounds; flower gardens. Ⓕ

Ogunquit

Pop: 1,492 **Elev:** 40 ft (12 m) **Area code:** 207 **Zip:** 03907

Motels

 ★ ★ ★ANCHORAGE MOTOR INN. *(Box 2406) 55 Shore Rd, on Marginal Way. 207/646-9384.* 212 rms, 2–3 story, 2 kit. units. No elvtr. July–Aug: S, D $40–$130; each addl $6–$15; suites, kit. units $85–$140; lower rates rest of yr. TV; cable. 2 pools, 1 indoor; whirlpool, sauna. Cafe 7 am–7 pm. Bar (in season). Ck-out 11 am. Tennis. Refrigerators. Balconies. Overlooking ocean. Cr cds: D, DS, MC, V. ⓕ

✔ ★MARGINAL WAY HOUSE. *(Box 697) Wharf Ln, 1 blk E off Shore Rd. 207/646-8801.* 29 rms, 1–4 story, 1 cottage. No rm phones. Late June–Aug: S $53–$64; D $53–$89; each addl $3–$5; suites $701–$820/wk; cottage $750/wk; under 6 free; lower rates late Apr–late June, Sep–late Oct. Closed rest of yr. Crib free. TV; cable. Ck-out 11 am. Refrigerators. Private patios, balconies. Picnic tables, grills. On beach. ⓕ

Orono

Settled: 1774 **Pop:** 9,981 **Elev:** 80 ft (24 m) **Area code:** 207 **Zip:** 04473

Motel

✔ ★ ★UNIVERSITY MOTOR INN. *5 College Ave. 207/866-4921.* 49 rms, 2 story. Apr–Nov: S $40–$54; D $51–$76; each addl $4–$6; under 12 free; lower rates rest of yr. Crib $4–$6. TV; cable. Pool. Cafe. Bar. Ck-out noon. Sundries. Private patios, balconies. Cr cds: A, C, D, MC, V.

Portland

Settled: ca 1631 **Pop:** 61,572 **Elev:** 50 ft (21 m) **Area code:** 207

Motel

✔ ★SUSSE CHALET. *1200 Brighton Ave (04102). 207/774-6101.* 132 rms, 2 story. S $33.70; D $37.70; each addl $3. Crib $2. TV; satellite. Pool. Resfreshments in lobby. Cafe adj open 24 hrs. Ck-out 11 am. Coin lndry. Cr cds: A, C, D, MC, V.

Presque Isle

Settled: 1820 **Pop:** 11,172 **Elev:** 446 ft (136 m) **Area code:** 207 **Zip:** 04769

Motels

✔ ★ ★KEDDY'S MOTOR INN. *(Box 270) 1 mi S on US 1. 207/764-3321.* 151 rms, 127 A/C, 2 story. No elvtr. S $38–$46; D $42–$50; each addl $5; under 12 free; wkend rates. Crib free. TV; cable. Indoor pool; sauna. Cafe 6:30 am–2 pm, 5–10 pm; Sat, Sun 7 am–9 pm. Rm serv. Bar 11–1 am; entertainment, dancing Wed–Sat. Ck-out noon. Meeting rms. Sundries. On hill; scenic view. Cr cds: A, D, MC, V. ⓕ

★NORTHERN LIGHTS. *692 N Main St, 2 mi S on US 1. 207/764-4441.* 14 rms. S $24.95; D $35; each addl $5; under 10 free. Crib $4. TV; cable. Ck-out 11 am. Sundries. Picnic tables. Cr cds: A, MC, V.

SC

Rangeley

Settled: 1825 **Pop:** 1,023 **Elev:** 1,545 ft (471 m) **Area code:** 207 **Zip:** 04970

Motels

✔ ★**RANGELEY MANOR.** *Manor Rd, 1 mi W just off ME 4, 16.* 207/864-3340. 8 rms, 21 kit. cottages. No A/C. July–Labor Day, hol wkends: S, D $42–$47; each addl $4–$6; cottages for 2–4 (1-wk min July–Aug) $55–$70; lower rates mid-Apr–mid-June, after Labor Day–mid-Dec; wkly rates mid-Nov–mid-May. Crib free. B/W TV; color in lobby; avail in cottages. Playground. Ck-out 10 am. Free local airport transportation. Rec rm. Tennis. Private beach. Boats. Lawn games. Cottages with screened porch; some fireplaces. On Rangeley Lake. Cr cds: MC, V.

✔ ★**TOWN & LAKE.** *(Box 47) Main St, ¼ mi W on ME 4, 16.* 207/864-3755. 16 motel rms, 5 kits. (no ovens), 9 kit. cottages, 2-bedrm. No A/C. Late June–Labor Day, hol, ski wks: S $30; D $40–$48; each addl $5; kit. units $10 addl; cottages for 6–8 (1-wk min July–Aug) $400–$450/wk. Crib free. TV. Playground. Cafe nearby. Ck-out 11 am. Free local airport transportation. Boats. Launching ramp; dockage. Lawn games. Picnic tables, grills. On Rangeley Lake. Cr cds: A, MC, V.

Rockland

Settled: 1770 **Pop:** 7,919 **Elev:** 35 ft (10 m) **Area code:** 207 **Zip:** 04841

Motels

(Rates may be higher during Seafood Festivals)

★**GLEN COVE.** *(Box 35, Glen Cove 04846) 3 mi N on US 1.* 207/594-4062. 17 rms, 3 cottages. May–mid-Oct: S $28–$38; D $36–$46; each addl $4; lower rates Apr, mid-Oct–Dec. Closed rest of yr. Crib free. TV. Playground. Morning coffee. Cafe nearby. Ck-out 11 am. Cr cds: MC, V.

✔ ★**STRAWBERRY HILL MOTOR COURT.** *(RFD 1) 3 mi N on US 1.* 207/594-5462. 12 cottage units. No A/C. July–Labor Day: S $32–$47; D $40–$51; each addl $4; lower rates May–June, after Labor Day–Oct. Closed rest of yr. TV. Bkfst 7–10 am. Cafe nearby. Ck-out 10 am. Picnic tables. View of bay, islands. Cr cds: A, MC, V.

✔ ★**WHITE GATES.** *(RFD 1, Box 1442) 4 mi N on US 1.* 207/594-4625. 15 rms. June–Oct: S $40; D $44–$54; each addl $4; under 6 free; lower rates May. Closed rest of yr. Crib $4. TV. Cafe nearby. Ck-out 11 am. Some refrigerators. Cr cds: A, MC, V.

Searsport

Settled: 1770 **Pop:** 1,348 **Elev:** 60 ft (18 m) **Area code:** 207 **Zip:** 04974

Motels

✔ ★**LIGHT'S.** *1¼ mi NE on US 1, ME 3.* 207/548-2405. 14 rms. No A/C. July–Labor Day: S $27–$34; D $32–$46; each addl $3; family rates; lower rates mid-Apr–June, after Labor Day–mid-Nov. Closed rest of yr. Crib free. TV; cable. Cafe 7 am–9 pm. Bar. Ck-out 11 am. Cr cds: MC, V.

✔ ★**YARDARM.** *(Box 603) E Main St, ¾ mi NE on US 1, ME 3.* 207/548-2404. 18 rms. No A/C. July–Aug: S $28–$40; D $38–$51; each addl $5–$6; under 16 free; lower rates mid-May–June, Sep–mid-Oct. Closed rest of yr. Crib free. TV; some B/W; cable. Cafe. Bar. Ck-out 11 am. Game rm. Cr cds: A, C, D, MC, V.

Sebago Lake

Area code: 207 Zip: 04075

Motel

✔ ★**SUBURBAN PINES.** *(RFD 2, S Windham 04082) On US 302, 10 mi N of Portland, 1 mi S of jct US 202. 207/892-4834.* 9 rms. No A/C. July–Oct: S, D $42–$60; each addl $5; lower rates rest of yr. TV; cable. Ck-out 11 am. Maine State picnic area opp. Cr cds: A, ER, MC, V.

Sebasco Estates

Pop: 300 Elev: 10 ft (3 m) Area code: 207 Zip: 04565

Resort

★ ★**ROCK GARDENS INN.** *(Box 178) On ME 217, 12 mi S of Bath via ME 209, 217. 207/389-1339.* 4 rms in 2-story inn, 10 cottages, 2–4 bedrm. No A/C. AP, Mid-June–late Sep (1-wk min): S $63–$77; D $55–$66/person; family rates; some lower rates first 2 wks June, after Labor Day–late Sep. Closed rest of yr. Crib avail. Pool; lifeguard. Cafe (not open to public). Special diets. Box lunches; wkly lobster, New England cookout in season. Setups. Ck-out 10:30 am. Grocery 2 mi. Airport, bus depot transportation. Golf. Tennis. Rec bldg. Boat rentals; daily cruises. Lawn games. Library. Art workshops (June). TV. Enclosed sun porches. Fireplaces. Shares recreational facilities of Sebasco Lodge. Family resort on Casco Bay. Ⓕ

Skowhegan

Settled: 1771 Pop: 6,517 Elev: 175 ft (53 m) Area code: 207 Zip: 04976

Motels

✔ ★★**BELMONT.** *(PO Box 160) 425 Madison Ave. 207/474-8315; res: 800/235-6669 (exc ME), 800/445-8315 (ME).* 40 rms. July–Oct: S $35–$45; D $45–$55; each addl $5; suites $80–$95; higher rates: Skowhegan Fair, special events; lower rates rest of yr. TV; cable, in-rm movies. Pool. Cafe nearby. Ck-out 11 am. Meeting rm. Sundries. Downhill ski 5 mi; x-country ski 1 mi. Shuffleboard. Picnic tables. Cr cds: A, D, DS, ER, MC, V.

✔ ★**BREEZY ACRES.** *(RFD 3) Waterville Rd, 1½ mi S on US 201. 207/474-2703.* 14 rms, 4 A/C. Apr–Nov: S $30–$32; D $34–$38; each addl $3; higher rates: fair, racing, special events. Closed rest of yr. Crib free. TV. Pool. Playground. Free continental bkfst. Cafe nearby. Ck-out 11 am. Gift shop. Picnic tables, grill. View of mountains. Cr cds: A, MC, V.

✔ ★★**SOMERSET MOTOR LODGE.** *422 Madison Ave. 207/474-2227.* 31 cottages. No A/C. Mid-May–mid-Oct: S $34; D $34–$45; each addl $6; suites $55; higher rates: hols, fair, racing. Closed rest of yr. Crib $5. TV; cable. Pool. Free morning coffee in season. Cafe nearby. Ck-out 11 am. Lighted tennis. Driving range. Pond; boats. Rec rm. Lawn games. Barbecues in July–Aug. Picnic tables, grill. Some cottages with screened porches. Spacious grounds. Cr cds: MC, V.

★★**TOWNE.** *248 Madison Ave. 207/474-5151.* 31 motel rms, 6 kits. (no equipt). July–mid-Oct: S, D $47–$51; each addl $6; suites $54; kit. units (1-wk min) $58; higher rates: state fair, racing; lower rates rest of yr. Crib $1. TV; cable. Pool. Free continental bkfst. Cafe nearby. Ck-out 11 am. Coin lndry. Downhill/x-country ski 6 mi. Cr cds: A, DS, MC, V. Ⓕ

Southwest Harbor

Pop: 1,052 **Elev:** 50 ft (15 m) **Area code:** 207 **Zip:** 04679

Inn

✔ ★ ★**MOORINGS MOTOR SAIL INN.** *Shore Rd, 2 mi E, 1 mi E of ME 102A. 207/244-5523.* 9 rms in inn, 5 motel rms, 6 kits., 3 kit. cottages, 2-bedrm. No A/C. July: S $30–$37; D $40–$60; each addl $10; suites $45–$58; kit. cottage for 2 (1-wk min) $50–$69; lower rates May–June, Aug–Oct. Closed rest of yr. Crib free. TV in lounge. Free continental bkfst. Cafe 11 am–11 pm. Ck-out 11 am. Meeting rm. Bicycles. Private beach. Launching ramp; rowboats, canoes; motors, sailboats, instruction avail. Fireplace in cottages, lounge. Balconies, private screened decks. Picnic tables, grills. Oldest house in town, built 1784. On waterfront. Nautical motif. ⑤

Waterville

Settled: 1754 **Pop:** 17,779 **Elev:** 113 ft (34 m) **Area code:** 207 **Zip:** 04901

Motel

(Rates may be higher last two wkends in July, also special college wkends)

✔ ★ ★**AMERICAN MOTOR INN.** *Kennedy Memorial Dr at I-95 exit 33, Oakland, Waterville. 207/872-5577; res: 800/633-2200 (exc ME).* 49 rms, 2 story. May–early Nov: D $36–$56; each addl $4; higher rates summer camp wkends; lower rates rest of yr. Crib $6. TV; cable. Pool. Cafe open 24 hrs. Ck-out 11 am. Colby College ¼ mi. Cr cds: A, D, MC, V.

Wiscasset

Settled: 1653 **Pop:** 2,832 **Elev:** 50 ft (15 m) **Area code:** 207 **Zip:** 04578

Motel

✔ ★**WHITFIELD.** *3 mi S on US 1. 207/882-7137.* 13 rms, 2 story, 16 cabins, some heated. No A/C. May–mid-Oct: S, D $27–$45; each addl $4. Closed rest of yr. Crib $3. TV, B/W in cabins; cable. Pool. Full bkfst July–Labor Day 7:30–10 am. Ck-out 11 am. Cr cds: A, MC, V.

Yarmouth

Settled: 1636 **Pop:** 2,981 **Elev:** 100 ft (30 m) **Area code:** 207 **Zip:** 04096

Inn

✔ ★ ★ ★**HOMEWOOD.** *(Box 196) Drinkwater Point, on Casco Bay, 2 mi S off ME 88. 207/846-3351.* 14 motel rms, 6 kits., 13 rms in 2 guest houses, 11 cottages, 9 with kit. Some A/C. July–Labor Day (motel 2-day min, 3-day min wkends): D $53–$93; each addl $10; suites, cottages for 2 to 6 (5 day min) $125–$235; lower rates rest of yr. Crib free. TV; cable. Heated pool. Cafe 7:30–9:30 am, 6–9 pm; Mon to 9:30 am; Sat, Sun 7:30–10 am, 6–9 pm. Mon clambake by res only. Ck-out noon, ck-in 3 pm. Coin lndry. Rec rm. Tennis. Bicycles. Near sand beach. Free mooring, dockage. Most rms furnished with antiques; some with screened porch, fireplace. A resort-type inn. Cr cds: A, MC, V.

Maryland

Population: 4,216,941

Land area: 9,838 sq mi (25,480 sq km)

Elevation: 0–3,360 ft (0–1,024 m)

Highest point: Backbone Mountain (Garrett Co)

Entered Union: Seventh of original 13 states (April 28, 1788)

Capital: Annapolis

Motto: *Fatti maschi, parole femine* (Manly deeds, womanly words)

Nickname: Old Line State, Free State

State flower: Black-eyed Susan

State bird: Baltimore oriole

State tree: Wye oak

State fair: Late August–Labor Day, 1989 in Timonium (near Towson)

Time zone: Eastern

Interstate Highway System

The following alphabetical listing of Maryland towns in *Mobil Travel Guide* shows that these cities are within 10 miles (16 kilometers) of the indicated Interstate highways. A highway map should be checked, however, for the nearest exit.

> **INTERSTATE 70:** Baltimore, Columbia, Ellicott City, Frederick, Hagerstown.
>
> **INTERSTATE 81:** Hagerstown.
>
> **INTERSTATE 83:** Baltimore, Cockeysville, Towson.
>
> **INTERSTATE 95:** Aberdeen, Baltimore, College Park, Elkton, Havre de Grace, Laurel, Silver Spring, Towson.

Weather Statistics*

	WINTER	SPRING	SUMMER	FALL
Statewide	35°F (2°C)	54°F (12°C)	74°F (23°C)	56°F (13°C)
Eastern Shore	40°F (4°C)	55°F (13°C)	74°F (23°C)	59°F (15°C)
Western region	28°F (–2°C)	47°F (8°C)	66°F (18°C)	49°F (9°C)

*Average mean temperatures are listed for the entire state. Averages for specific regions are given if significant differences exist.

Visitor Information

A combined Maryland outdoor and travel guide, calendar of events, and Maryland highway map may be obtained from Maryland Office of Tourism, 45 Calvert St, Annapolis 21401, and a quarterly magazine, *Maryland*, from the Dept of Economic & Employment Development, Maryland Magazine, 45 Calvert St, Annapolis 21401.

There are several visitor centers in Maryland; visitors who stop by will find information and brochures helpful in planning trips to points of interest. Their locations are as follows: on I-95 (N & S) near Laurel; on I-70 (E & W) west of Frederick; on US 15 S in Emmitsburg; on I-95 N near North East; on US 48 E west of Friendsville; on US 13 N near Maryland-Virginia line; and in the State House, Annapolis. All visitor centers are open daily; closed Jan 1, Easter, Thanksgiving, Dec 25.

Room Rate Information

The following major city has higher room rates for two (double) than indicated on the cover of this Guide. However, the lodgings listed in this city offer a good value when compared to others of their type in the area.

Baltimore $65

Aberdeen

Pop: 11,533 **Elev:** 83 ft (25 m) **Area code:** 301 **Zip:** 21001

Motels

✓ ★**BEST WESTERN RED COACH MOTOR INN.** *783 W Bel Air Ave, at jct MD 22, I-95 exit 5.* 301/272-8500. 49 rms, 2 story. S $36–$48; D $38–$54; each addl $4; under 12 free. Crib free. TV. Pool. Free coffee. Cafe nearby. Ck-out 11 am. Cr cds: A, C, D, DS, MC, V.

[icons]

✓ ★★**COMFORT INN.** *(1700 Van Bibber Rd, Edgewood 21040) I-95 exit 4.* 301/679-0770. 104 rms, 2 story. July–Aug: S $38–$39; D $39–$44; each addl $2; suites $70–$74; under 16 free; lower rates rest of yr. Crib free. TV; in-rm movies. Heated pool; lifeguard. Free coffee. Cafe opp. Ck-out noon. Meeting rms. Sundries. Cr cds: A, C, D, DS, MC, V.

[icons]

Annapolis

Founded: 1649 **Pop:** 31,740 **Elev:** 57 ft (17 m) **Area code:** 301

Motels

✓ ★**ECONO LODGE.** *591 Revell Hwy (21401), 1 mi W of Chesapeake Bay Bridge on US 301, 50.* 301/974-4440. 74 rms, 2 story. Apr–mid-Nov: S $40–$53; D $50–$63; each addl $4; under 18 free; higher rates special events; lower rates rest of yr. Crib free. TV. Ck-out 11 am. Coin lndry. Cr cds: A, MC, V.

[icons]

✓ ★**THR-RIFT INN.** *2542 Riva Rd (21401), in Parole section of Annapolis.* 301/224-2800; res: 800/638-5179 (exc MD), 800/638-6323 (MD). 150 rms, 2 story, 9 kits. S $40–$46; D $44–$53; each addl $5; suites $60–$65; kit. units $65–$70; under 18 free; min stay required special events. Crib free. Free continental bkfst. Cafe nearby. Ck-out 11 am. Sundries. Refrigerators avail. Picnic tables, grills. Cr cds: A, C, D, MC, V.

[icons]

Baltimore

Settled: 1661 **Pop:** 786,775 **Elev:** 32 ft (10 m) **Area code:** 301

Motels

✓ ★★**CHRISTLEN.** *8733 Pulaski Hwy (US 40) (21237), I-695 exit 35 E.* 301/687-1740. 28 rms. S $32–$38; D $38–$42; each addl $5. Crib $5. TV; cable. Cafe adj open 24 hrs. Ck-out 11 am. Sundries. Refrigerators. Picnic tables, grill. Some antique furnishings. Cr cds: A, C, D, MC, V.

[icons]

✓ ★**COMFORT INN NORTHWEST.** *(10 Wooded Way, Pikesville 21208) 8 mi NW on MD 140 at I-695 exit 20.* 301/484-7700. 103 rms, 2–3 story. No elvtr. S $40–$49; D $45–$54; each addl $5; under 16 free; wkly, monthly rates. Crib free. TV; cable. Pool; wading pool, lifeguard. Free continental bkfst. Cafe adj 6:30 am–11:30 pm. Ck-out 11 am. Coin lndry. Meeting rms. Valet serv Mon–Fri. Sundries. Airport transportation. Cr cds: A, C, D, DS, ER, MC, V.

[icons]

★★**HOLIDAY INN-SOUTH.** *(6600 Ritchie Hwy, Glen Burnie 21061) S on MD 2, I-695 exit 3B; also Harbor Tunnel Thruway exit 14 S.* 301/761-8300. 100 rms, 3 story. S $54–$79; D $64–$94; each addl $15; under 18 free. Crib free. TV; cable. Pool; lifeguard. Cafe 6 am–2 pm, 5–10 pm; Sat, Sun from 7 am. Rm serv. Bar 4 pm–2 am. Ck-out noon. Meeting rms. Valet serv. Mall & shopping center opp. Cr cds: A, C, D, DS, MC, V.

✔★★**KNIGHTS INN-WEST.** *1654 Whitehead Ct (21207), 1 blk N of I-695, exit 17.* 301/265-7660. 135 units, 11 kits. S $37.50; D $40.50–$46.50; each addl $3; kit. units $49.50; under 18 free. Crib $3. TV; cable. Pool; lifeguard. Free coffee. Cafe adj open 24 hrs. Ck-out noon. Meeting rm. Sundries. Cr cds: A, C, D, MC, V.

✔★★**QUALITY INN WEST.** *5801 Baltimore Natl Pike (21228), on US 40, just E of I-695 exit 15A.* 301/744-5000. 217 rms, 2–3 story, 38 kits. No elvtr. S $44–$55; D $49–$59; each addl $5; kit. units $59; under 16 free. Crib free. TV; cable. Pool; lifeguard. Cafe 6:30 am–2 pm, 5–10 pm; Sun 7 am–10 pm. Rm serv. Bar 4 pm–midnight. Ck-out noon. Coin lndry. Meeting rms. Valet serv. Sundries. Cr cds: A, C, D, DS, ER, MC, V.

★★**SUSSE CHALET.** *4 Philadelphia Ct (21237), I-695 exit 34.* 301/574-8100. 132 rms, 5 story. S $39.70; D $43.70; each addl $3. Crib $2. TV; cable. Pool; lifeguard. Continental bkfst. Cafe nearby. Ck-out 11 am. Coin lndry. Valet serv. Sundries. Cr cds: A, C, D, MC, V.

Motor Hotels

✔★**COMFORT INN.** *24 W Franklin St (21201).* 301/727-2000. 194 rms, 9 story. S $49–$69; D $54–$74; each addl $10; suites $89–$169; under 16 free; wkend rates. Parking $5, in/out. TV; in-rm movies. Cafe 7 am–11 pm. Rm serv. Bar. Ck-out 11 am. Coin lndry. Meeting rms. Valet serv. Some in-rm whirlpools. Cr cds: A, C, D, DS, ER, MC, V. Ⓔ

✔★★**HOWARD JOHNSON.** *5701 Baltimore Natl Pike (21228), ½ mi E of I-695 exit 15A* 301/747-8900. 145 rms, 8 story. S $35–$50; D $40–$60; each addl $8; under 18 free. Crib free. TV; cable, in-rm movies. Pool; whirlpool, lifeguard. Free bkfst Mon–Fri. Cafe 6 am–11 pm. Ck-out noon. Coin lndry. Meeting rms. Valet serv. Sundries. Airport transportation. Racquetball privileges. Some balconies. Cr cds: A, C, D, DS, ER, MC, V.

QUALITY INN-BALTIMORE TRAVEL PLAZA. (Too new to be rated) *5625 O'Donnell St (21224), 5 blks S of I-95, exit 57.* 301/633-9500. 200 rms, 10 story. S $59–$74; D $54–$79; each addl $10; under 16 free. Crib $10. TV. Indoor pool; whirlpool, lifeguard. Cafe open 24 hrs. Bar; entertainment, dancing. Ck-out noon. Meeting rms. Bellhops. Valet serv. Sundries. Cr cds: A, C, D, DS, ER, MC, V. Ⓔ

Bowie

Pop: 33,695 **Elev:** 150 ft (46 m) **Area code:** 301

Motels

★**FOREST HILLS.** *(2901 Crain Hwy, Upper Marlboro 20772) 2½ mi N of MD 4 on US 301.* 301/627-3969 or -4057. 13 rms. S $34; D $37; each addl $3; under 12 free. Crib $3. TV. Free coffee in rms. Ck-out 11 am. Refrigerators avail. Cr cds: A, MC, V.

✔★★**QUALITY INN.** *(Box 730, 20715) 3 mi SE at jct US 50, 301, MD 3.* 301/464-2200. 111 rms, 2 story. S $48–$62; D $54–$68; each addl $6; under 16 free. Crib free. TV; cable. Pool; lifeguard. Free coffee in rms. Cafe 6:30 am–10 pm. Rm serv from 7 am. Bar 4 pm–1:30 am. Ck-out 11 am. Coin lndry. Meeting rm. Valet serv Mon–Fri. Cr cds: A, C, D, DS, ER, MC, V.

Cambridge

Founded: 1684 **Pop:** 11,703 **Elev:** 14 ft (4 m) **Area code:** 301 **Zip:** 21613

Motel

✔ ★**QUALITY INN.** *(Box 311) 1 mi E on US 50, 1 blk W of MD 343. 301/228-6900.* 60 rms, 2 story. S $35; D $48; each addl $6; under 16 free. Crib $1.50. TV. Pool. Cafe 7 am–9 pm; also dining rm. Bar 11 am–midnight. Ck-out noon. Cr cds: A, D, MC, V.

🐾 🏊 🛇 SC

Chesapeake Bay Bridge Area

Area code: 301

Motel

✔ ★**CHESAPEAKE.** *(US 50 & 301, Grasonville 21638) 8 mi E on US 50, 301. 301/827-7272.* 42 rms. S $31–$35; D $33–$41; each addl $4; under 10 free. Crib $4. TV; cable. Cafe 6 am–10 pm. Bar 5–11 pm. Ck-out 11 am. Cr cds: A, MC, V.

♿ 🛇 💲

College Park

Pop: 23,614 **Elev:** 190 ft (58 m) **Area code:** 301 **Zip:** 20740

Motels

★ ★**BEST WESTERN MARYLAND INN AND FUN DOME.** *8601 Baltimore Blvd. 301/474-2800.* 121 rms, 2 story. S $49–$59; D $54–$64; each addl $4. Crib $4. TV; cable. Indoor pool; lifeguard. Cafe 7 am–10 pm; Sun to 9 pm. Bar 11:30–1 am. Meeting rms. Valet serv. 18-hole golf privileges, greens fee $10.50, putting green, pro. Exercise equipt; weights, bicycles, whirlpool, sauna. Game rm. Cr cds: A, C, D, DS, MC, V.

🏌 🏊 🎿 🛇 SC

★**BEST WESTERN ROYAL PINE.** *9113 Baltimore Blvd. 301/345-4900.* 114 rms, 1–4 story. S $43–$53; D $47–$58; each addl $4; suites $75–$148; studio rm $49–$62. Crib $3. TV; cable. Pool; lifeguard. Free continental bkfst. Cafe adj 7 am–11 pm. Ck-out noon. Meeting rms. Valet serv. Airport transportation. Cr cds: A, C, D, DS, MC, V. Ⓔ Ⓕ

♿ 🏊 🅽 SC

✔ ★**COMFORT INN.** *9020 Baltimore Blvd. 301/441-8110.* 160 rms, 8 story. Apr–Oct: S $45–$55; D $55–$65; each addl $5; suite $125; under 18 free; higher rates Cherry Blossom Festival; lower rates rest of yr. Crib free. TV; cable, in-rm movies. Pool; lifeguard. Continental bkfst. Ck-out 11 am. Coin lndry. Meeting rms. Valet serv. Game rm. Cr cds: A, D, DS, ER, MC, V.

♿ 🏊 🛇 🅽 SC

✔ ★ ★**COURTYARD BY MARRIOTT.** *(8300 Corporate Dr, Landover 20785) ½ mi W of I-95 on US 50. 301/577-3373.* 152 rms, 2–4 story. S $48–$76; D $48–$87; each addl $8; suites $69–$92; under 12 free; wkly, wkend rates. Crib free. TV; cable. Indoor pool; lifeguard. Cafe 6:30 am–10 pm. Bar. Ck-out 1 pm. Coin lndry. Meeting rms. Valet serv. Exercise equipt; weights, bicycles, whirlpool. Many private patios, balconies. Cr cds: A, C, D, DS, MC, V. Ⓔ

♿ 🏊 🎿 🅽

✔ ★ ★**DAYS INN.** *(9023 Annapolis Rd, Lanham 20706) I-95 exit 20A, then 1 blk E, at jct MD 450. 301/459-6600.* 114 rms, 3 story. S $39–$69; D $39–$74; each addl $5; under 19 free; wkly, wkend rates. Crib free. TV; cable, in-rm movies. Cafe 6:30 am–11 pm. Bar 11–1 am. Ck-out noon. Meeting rms. Valet serv. Cr cds: A, C, D, DS, MC, V. Ⓔ Ⓕ

🐾 🏊 🛇 🅽 SC 💲

Cumberland

Settled: 1750 **Pop:** 25,933 **Elev:** 688 ft (209 m) **Area code:** 301 **Zip:** 21502

Motels

✔ ★ ★ ★**BEST WESTERN BRADDOCK MOTOR INN.** *(1268 National Hwy, La Vale 21502) 6 mi W on US 40 at jct MD 53; Natl Frwy exit 39 or 40. 301/729-3300.* 108 rms, 1–2 story. S $42–$72; D $48–$72; each addl $6; under 16 free. TV; cable. Indoor pool; poolside serv. Cafe 7 am–9 pm. Rm serv. Bar 4 pm–1 am. Ck-out 11 am. Sundries. Exercise rm; instructor, weights, bicycles, whirlpool, sauna. Game rm. Cr cds: A, C, D, DS, MC, V.

🏄 ➥ 🏄 🚫 🐾 sc

✔ ★ ★ ★**CONTINENTAL MOTOR INN.** *(Box 393A, RFD 5) 6 mi W on US 40 (Natl Frwy), exit 39 or 40. 301/729-2201.* 54 rms. S $35–$52.45; D, studio rms $41.95–$58; each addl $5; under 16 free. Crib $5. TV; cable. Heated pool. Cafe 6 am–9:30 pm. Rm serv. Bar 11 am–2 am; Sun 1 pm–midnight. Ck-out 11 am. Meeting rms. Sundries. Package store. Airport, RR station, bus depot transportation. Miniature golf. Lawn games. Balconies. On 25 wooded acres. Cr cds: A, C, D, DS, MC, V.

🏄 🏄 ➥ 🚫 🐾

★**DIPLOMAT.** *(Box 216, RR 6) 6½ mi S on US 220. 301/729-2311.* 15 rms, 1–2 story. S $24–$28; D $31–$41; each addl $4; under 10 free. Crib $3. TV; cable. Cafe nearby. Ck-out 11 am. Cr cds: A, C, D, MC, V.

🏄 🐾 sc

★**MARYLAND.** *(Rte 3) Bedford Rd, 3 mi N on US 220. 301/722-2836.* 12 units, 7 kits. S $25–$37; D $35–$53; each addl $4; kit. units $100–$169/wk. Crib $3. TV; cable. Pool. Cafe opp 7 am–8 pm. Ck-out 11 am. Cr cds: MC, V.

➥ 🐾

★**SLUMBERLAND.** *(1262 National Hwy, La Vale 21502) 4 mi W on US 40. 301/729-2880.* 25 rms, 1–2 story. June–Nov: S $31.95; D $35.95; each addl $4; under 12 free; lower rates rest of yr. Crib $4. TV; cable. Cafe nearby open 24 hrs. Ck-out 11 am. Picnic tables. Cr cds: A, MC, V.

🐾

Frederick

Settled: 1745 **Pop:** 28,086 **Elev:** 290 ft (88 m) **Area code:** 301 **Zip:** 21701

Motels

✔ ★ ★**BEST WESTERN RED HORSE MOTOR INN.** *998 W Patrick St (US 40). 301/662-0281.* 72 rms, 4 story. S $41–$52; D $51–$71; each addl $8; suites $62–$64; under 12 free. Crib $8. TV; cable. Cafe 6–11 am; Sat–Sun to noon. Dining rm 4:30–10:30 pm, Sun 4–9 pm. Bar 8 pm–2 am; entertainment, dancing Tu–Sat. Ck-out noon. City park opp. Cr cds: A, C, D, DS, MC, V.

🚫 sc

✔ ★**DAYS INN.** *5646 Buckeystown Pike. 301/694-6600.* 120 rms, 2 story. June–Aug: S, D $45–$55; under 18, $2; some lower rates rest of yr. Crib free. TV; in-rm movies. Pool. Playground. Cafe open 24 hrs. Ck-out noon. Meeting rms. Free local airport transportation. Cr cds: A, C, D, MC, V. Ⓓ Ⓔ

🏄 ➥ 🚫 sc 🅂

Gaithersburg

Pop: 60,000 **Elev:** 508 ft (155 m) **Area code:** 301

Motor Hotels

✔ ★ ★IMPERIAL INN. *(20260 Goldenrod Ln, Germantown 20874) N on I-270, MD 118 E exit. 301/428-1300.* 211 rms, 6 story. S $48–$55; D $54–$65; each addl $5; suites $60–$75; under 16 free; wkend rates. Crib free. TV; cable. Pool; sauna, lifeguard. Cafe 7–1 am; Fri, Sat to 2 am. Bar 11–1 am; entertainment, dancing. Ck-out noon. Meeting rms. Valet serv. 18-hole golf privileges, greens fee $12–$20, pro. Cr cds: A, C, D, DS, MC, V. Ⓓ Ⓔ

★ ★ ★MARRIOTT. *620 Lakeforest Blvd (20877), 1 blk E of I-270, exit 124 E. 301/977-8900.* 301 rms, 12 story. S $54–$112; D $54–$128; suites $250; under 18 free; wkend rates. Crib free. TV; cable, in-rm movies. Indoor/outdoor pool; lifeguard. Cafe 6:30 am–11 pm. Rm serv from 7 am. Bars 11–1 am; entertainment, dancing. Meeting rms. Bellhops. Valet serv Mon–Fri. Gift shop. Airport, city transportation. Tennis privileges. 18-hole golf privileges. Exercise equipt; weights, bicycles. Game rm. Rec rms. Refrigerators avail. Some private patios, balconies. Many amenities. Adj to Lake Forest shopping center. Cr cds: A, C, D, DS, MC, V. Ⓓ Ⓔ Ⓕ Ⓘ Ⓙ

Grantsville

Pop: 498 **Elev:** 2,300 ft (701 m) **Area code:** 301 **Zip:** 21536

Motor Hotel

✔ ★ ★HOLIDAY INN. *US 48 & 219 N, 3 mi E at US 48 exit 22. 301/895-5993.* 100 rms, 4 story. S $48–$64; D $54–$72; each addl $8; under 18 free; ski rates. Crib free. TV. Heated pool; whirlpool, sauna. Cafe 7 am–2 pm, 5–10 pm; Sun 7 am–10 pm. Rm serv. Bar; entertainment Fri-Sat, dancing exc Sun. Ck-out noon. Coin lndry. Downhill ski 18 mi; x-country ski 1 mi. Meeting rm. Bellhops. Sundries. Game rm. Cr cds: A, C, D, DS, MC, V.

Hagerstown

Settled: 1762 **Pop:** 34,132 **Elev:** 552 ft (168 m) **Area code:** 301 **Zip:** 21740

Motels

★DAYS INN. *(PO, Williamsport 21795) 4 mi SW at jct US 11, I-81. 301/582-3500.* 122 rms, 2 story. S $34; D $38; each addl $4; under 18, $2. Crib free. TV; cable. Pool. Playground. Cafe 6 am–9 pm. Ck-out noon. Gift shop. Cr cds: A, D, DS, MC, V.

✔ ★ ★HOLIDAY INN. *900 Dual Hwy (US 40). 301/739-9050.* 140 rms, 2 story. S $43–$58; D $50–$58; each addl $7; under 19 free; wkend rates. Crib free. TV; cable, in-rm movies. Pool; poolside serv. Cafe 6:30 am–2 pm, 5:30–10 pm. Rm serv. Bar 11:30–2 am; entertainment, DJ, dancing. Ck-out noon. Meeting rms. Bellhops. Cr cds: A, C, D, DS, MC, V. Ⓕ

★LUXURY BUDGET INN. *US 40E & Colonial Dr. 301/733-2700.* 84 rms, 4 story. S $28.99–$31.99; D $35.99–$38.99; each addl $4; suites $41.99; under 12 free. Crib $2. TV; cable. Free coffee in lobby. Cafe adj 6 am–8:30 pm. Ck-out 11 am. Cr cds: A, DS, MC, V. Ⓓ

★ ★ ★SHERATON INN. *1910 Dual Hwy (US 40). 301/790-3010.* 108 rms, 2 story. S $46–$56; D $52–$58; each addl $7; suites $127–$131; under 18 free. Crib free. TV; cable. Pool. Cafe 6:30 am–10 pm; Sun 7 am–9 pm. Rm serv. Bar 11–2 am; entertainment, dancing exc Sun. Ck-out noon. Meeting rms. Bellhops. Valet serv. Sundries. Beauty shop. Cr cds: A, C, D, DS, MC, V.

Motor Hotels

✔ ★ ★ ★**BEST WESTERN VENICE INN.** *431 Dual Hwy (US 40).* *301/733-0830.* 240 rms, 2–5 story. Apr–Oct: S $39–$48; D $44–$56; each addl $6; suites $75–$125; kits. $75; under 18 free; wkend rates; lower rates rest of yr. Crib $6. TV; cable, in-rm movies. Pool; whirlpools. Cafe 6 am–10:30 pm; Sun to 8:30 pm. Rm serv 7 am–10 pm. Bar; entertainment, dancing exc Sun. Ck-out noon. Meeting rms. Bellhops. Valet serv. Package store. Gift shop. Beauty shop. Golf opp. Cr cds: A, C, D, DS, MC, V. ⒹⒺⒿ

★ ★**HOWARD JOHNSON.** *107 Underpass Way.* *301/797-2500.* 165 units, 6 story. Apr–Oct: S $47–$53; D $52–$62; each addl $7; suites $61–$69; under 18 free; lower rates rest of yr. Crib free. TV. Indoor pool; lifeguard. Cafe 6:30 am–9 pm. Rm serv. Bar 11 am–11 pm. Ck-out noon. Meeting rms. Valet serv. Free airport transportation. Exercise equipt; weight machines, bicycles, whirlpool, sauna. Refrigerators. Cr cds: A, C, D, DS, MC, V. Ⓕ

✔ ★ ★ ★**RAMADA INN CONVENTION CENTER.** *901 Dual Hwy (US 40).* *301/733-5100.* 210 rms, 5 story. S $44–$47; D $49–$52; each addl $5; suites $85–$200; under 18 free. Crib free. TV; cable. Indoor pool. Cafe 6:30 am–10 pm. Rm serv. Bar 11–2 am; videos, dancing exc Sun. Ck-out noon. Coin lndry. Meeting rms. Bellhops. Shopping arcade. Barber, beauty shop. Indoor putting green, pro. Game rm. Cr cds: A, C, D, DS, MC, V.

Laurel

Pop: 12,103 **Elev:** 160 ft (49 m) **Area code:** 301

Motels

✔ ★**BUDGET HOST VALENCIA.** *10131 Washington Blvd (US 1) (20707).* *301/725-4200; res:* 800/835-7427, ext 631. 80 units, 1–2 story, 44 kits. S, D $38–$45; each addl $3; kit. units $45; under 18 free. Crib free. TV. Pool; lifeguard. Free coffee. Cafe nearby. Ck-out 11 am. Picnic tables. Cr cds: A, D, DS, MC, V.

✔ ★**ECONO LODGE.** *9750 Washington Blvd (US 1) (20707).* *301/776-8008.* 51 rms, 2 story. Apr–Sep: S $40–$45; D $45–$48; each addl $5; under 18 free; lower rates rest of yr. Crib free. TV; cable. Free coffee. Ck-out 11 am. Cr cds: A, D, MC, V.

Oakland (Garrett Co)

Settled: 1851 **Pop:** 1,994 **Elev:** 2,384 ft (727 m) **Area code:** 301 **Zip:** 21550

Motels

✔ ★ ★**ALPINE VILLAGE.** *(Star Rte 1) 7 mi N on US 219.* *301/387-5534.* 29 motel rms, 2 story, 8 kits., 14 kit. chalets. June–Sep: S $42–$58; D $47–$63; each addl $5; kit. units, studio rms $55; chalets for 1–6, $475–$650/wk; lower rates rest of yr. Crib $5. TV; cable. Heated pool; wading pool. Continental bkfst avail for motel rms. Cafe 5–10 pm; Sun from 4 pm. Bar 5 pm–midnight. Ck-out 11 am. Downhill/x-country ski 5 mi. On lake; private sand beach; dock. Some private patios. Picnic table, grills. Cr cds: A, D, MC, V.

★**LAKE BREEZ.** *(Star Rte 1) 9 mi N on US 219.* *301/387-5564.* 10 rms. May–Oct: S, D $48; each addl $4; MAP avail. Closed rest of yr. Crib free. TV. Pool privileges. Cafe adj 7 am–2 pm, 5–9:30 pm. Ck-out 11 am. Golf privileges, greens fee $9–$15. On lake; private beach, dock. Picnic tables. Cr cds: A, C, D, MC, V. Ⓓ

104   Maryland

★**LAKE SIDE MOTOR COURT.** *(Star Rte 1) 8 mi N on US 219. 301/387-5566.* 10 rms, 2 cottages. Mid-June–Labor Day: S, D $48–$68; each addl $4; cottages for 2–6, $345/wk; MAP avail; lower rates May–mid-June, after Labor Day–Oct. Closed rest of yr. TV. Pool privileges. Playground. Cafe adj 7 am–2 pm, 5–9:30 pm. Ck-out 11 am. Golf privileges, greens fee $9–$15. Overlooks lake; private beach; dock. Picnic area, grills. Cr cds: MC, V. ⓓ

✔ ★**TOWN.** *243 N 3d St (US 219). 301/334-3955.* 17 rms, 1 kit. June–Oct: S $25–$39; D $35–$51; each addl $5; kit. unit from $265/wk; lower rates rest of yr. TV; cable. Cafe nearby. Ck-out 11 am. Downhill/x-country ski 8 mi. Refrigerators. Cr cds: A, C, D, MC, V.

Ocean City

Founded: 1869 **Pop:** 6,631 **Elev:** 7 ft (3 m) **Area code:** 301 **Zip:** 21842

Motel

✔ ★ ★**SAHARA.** *(Box 540) 19th St at Boardwalk. 301/289-8101; res: 800/638-1600 (exc MD), 800/492-2310 (MD).* 113 rms, 3 story, 5 kits. No elvtr. Mid-Apr–Sep: S, D $38–$97; each addl $6; kit. units $48–$102. Closed rest of yr. Married couples, families only. Crib $6. TV. Pool. Cafe nearby. Ck-out 11 am. Some balconies. On beach. Cr cds: MC, V.

Motor Hotel

✔ ★ ★**HOLIDAY INN OCEAN FRONT.** *Oceanfront & 67th St. 301/524-1600.* 216 kit. units, 8 story. May–Sep: S, D $35–$144; each addl $5; suites $59–$174; under 12 free; higher rates hol wkends, July–Aug; lower rates rest of yr. Crib free. TV; cable. 2 pools, 1 indoor; wading pools, poolside serv, swim-up bar. Cafe 7 am–11 pm; dining rm 5–10 pm. Rm serv. Bar 5 pm–2 am. Ck-out 11 am. Free lndry. Meeting rms. Bellhops. Tennis. Exercise rm; instructor, weights, whirlpool, sauna. Game rm. Refrigerators. Balconies, picnic tables. On ocean. Cr cds: A, C, D, DS, MC, V.

Rockville

Pop: 43,811 **Elev:** 451 ft (137 m) **Area code:** 301

Motel

✔ ★**DAYS INN.** *16001 Shady Grove Rd (20850). 301/948-4300.* 190 rms, 2 story. S $41–$65; D $41–$70; each addl $5; under 18 free; wkend rates. Crib free. TV; cable. Pool; lifeguard. Playground. Cafe 6:30 am–9 pm; Sun 7 am–2:30 pm. Ck-out 11 am. Cr cds: A, C, D, DS, MC, V. ⓔ

Silver Spring

Pop: 72,893 **Elev:** 350 ft (107 m) **Area code:** 301

Motels

DAYS INN. (New owner, therefore not rated) *8040 13th St (20910). 301/588-4400.* 142 rms, 2 story. S $40–$55; D $45–$60; each addl $5; suites $60–$80; under 13 free. Crib free. TV. Pool; lifeguard. Cafe 6 am–2 pm, 5–9 pm. Bar. Ck-out 11 am. Meeting rms. Valet serv.

✔ ★**ECONO LODGE.** *7990 Georgia Ave (20910). 301/565-3444.* 130 rms, 6 story. S $41.95–$45.95; D $48.95–$52.95; each addl $4; under 18 free. Crib free. TV. Free coffee. Cafe opp 7 am–2:30 pm, 5–10 pm. Ck-out 11 am. Coin lndry. Valet serv. Cr cds: A, C, D, MC, V.

Hotel

★ ★**SHERATON INN-WASHINGTON NORTHWEST.** *8727 Colesville Rd (20910). 301/589-5200.* 287 rms, 12–14 story. Mar–May, Sep–Nov: S $52–$95; D $52–$120; each addl $10; under 18 free; wkly, wkend rates; higher rates Cherry Blossom season (Apr); lower rates rest of yr. Crib free. TV; cable. Cafe 7 am–11 pm. Bar 11–1 am; pianist Mon–Fri. Ck-out 1 pm. Meeting rms. Concierge. Gift shop. Drugstore. Balconies. Cr cds: A, C, D, DS, MC, V. Ⓓ Ⓔ Ⓕ Ⓘ

Towson

Pop: 51,083 **Elev:** 465 ft (142 m) **Area code:** 301 **Zip:** 21204

Motor Hotel

✔ ★**ECONO LODGE.** *8801 Loch Raven Blvd. 301/882-0900.* 180 rms, 5 story. S $37.75–$43.95; D $41.35–$48.95; each addl $4; under 16 free. Crib free. TV; cable. Cafe 7 am–10 pm. Rm serv. Bar 11–1 am. Ck-out 11 am. Coin lndry. Meeting rms. Sundries. Cr cds: A, C, D, MC, V.

Massachusetts

Population: 5,737,081	
Land area: 7,826 sq mi (20,269 sq km)	
Elevation: 0–3,491 ft (0–1,064 m)	
Highest point: Mt Greylock (Berkshire Co)	
Entered Union: Sixth of original 13 states (Feb 6, 1788)	
Capital: Boston	
Motto: *Ense petit placidam sub libertate quietem* (By the sword we seek peace, but peace only under liberty)	
Nickname: Bay State	
State flower: Mayflower	
State bird: Chickadee	
State tree: American elm	
Time zone: Eastern	

Interstate Highway System

The following alphabetical listing of Massachusetts towns in *Mobil Travel Guide* shows that these cities are within 10 miles (16 kilometers) of the indicated Interstate highways. A highway map should, however, be checked for the nearest exit.

INTERSTATE 90: Boston, Cambridge, Framingham, Great Barrington, Holyoke, Lee, Lenox, Natick, Newton, Pittsfield, Springfield, Stockbridge & West Stockbridge, Sturbridge, Sudbury Center, Waltham, Wellesley, Westfield, Worcester.

INTERSTATE 91: Amherst, Deerfield, Greenfield, Holyoke, Northampton, Springfield, Williamsburg.

INTERSTATE 93: Andover, Boston, Lawrence, Lowell, Methuen, Woburn.

INTERSTATE 95: Attleboro, Bedford, Boston, Burlington, Concord, Danvers, Dedham, Foxboro, Framingham, Lexington, Lynn, Lynnfield, Natick, Newton, Saugus, Sudbury Center, Waltham, Wellesley, Woburn.

Weather Statistics*

Statewide	WINTER 28°F (-2°C)	SPRING 52°F (11°C)	SUMMER 72°F (22°C)	FALL 52°F (11°C)

*Average mean temperatures are listed for the entire state. Averages for specific regions are given if significant differences exist.

Visitor Information

The Massachusetts Department of Commerce and Development, Division of Tourism, 100 Cambridge St, 13th Floor, Boston 02202, 617/727-3201, has brochures and maps.

There are many properties of the Society for the Preservation of New England Antiquities (SPNEA) located in Massachusetts and neighboring states. For complete information on these contact the SPNEA HQ, Harrison Gray Otis House, 141 Cambridge St, Boston 02114; 617/227-3956.

There are several visitor centers located in Massachusetts; they are located on the MA Turnpike (daily, 9 am–6 pm) at Charlton (eastbound & westbound), Lee (eastbound), and Natick (eastbound); also I-95 at Mansfield, between exits 5 and 6 (northbound); and at Plymouth on MA 3 (southbound). For weather information contact the National Weather Service in Boston, phone 617/567-4670. Massachusetts has many statewide fairs, though none is considered the official state fair. Contact the Massachusetts Dept of Agriculture, Division of Fairs, 100 Cambridge St, Boston 02202; phone 617/727-3037 for further information. For a "Free Spirit" vacation kit, calendar of events, and more, phone 800/942-MASS.

The Pequot Press, Old Chester Rd, Chester, CT 06412, has several interesting publications on New England.

Room Rate Information

The following resort areas have higher room rates for two (double) than indicated on the cover of this Guide. However, the lodgings listed in these cities offer a good value when compared to others of their type in the area.

Centerville	$70	Orleans	$70
Chatham	70	Provincetown	70
Dennis	65	Sandwich	60
Eastham	65	South Yarmouth	60
Falmouth	65	Springfield	65
Harwich	65	Truro & North Truro	60
Nantucket Island	65	Wellfleet	65

Amherst

Founded: 1759 **Pop:** 17,773 **Elev:** 320 ft (98 m) **Area code:** 413 **Zip:** 01002

Motel

 ✔ ★**UNIVERSITY MOTOR LODGE.** *345 N Pleasant St, between Amherst College and University of MA.* 413/256-8111. 20 rms, 2 story. S $42–$65; D $52–$65; each addl $7; under 18 free; higher rates special events. Crib free. TV; cable. Free coffee in rm. Cafe nearby. Ck-out 11 am. Downhill ski 18 mi; x-country ski 12 mi. Cr cds: A, C, D, MC, V.

Bedford

Pop: 13,513 **Elev:** 135 ft (41 m) **Area code:** 617 **Zip:** 01730

Motel

✔ ★**BEDFORD MOTEL.** *30 N Rd, 3 blks W on MA 4, 225.* 617/275-6300. 46 rms, 16 kits. S $46–$52; D $52–$58; each addl $5; kit. units $260/wk; under 12 free. Crib $5. TV. Pool. Cafe nearby. Ck-out 11 am. Coin lndry. Cr cds: A, DS, MC, V.

Boston

Founded: 1630 **Pop:** 562,994 **Elev:** 0–330 ft (0–101 m) **Area code:** 617

Motels

✔ ★**SUSSE CHALET.** *800 Morrissey Blvd (02122), in Dorchester section.* 617/287-9100. 177 rms, 2–3 story. S $41.70–$43.70; D $45.70–$48.70; each addl $3. Crib $3. TV. Pool; lifeguard. Cafe adj 6:30 am–11 pm. Ck-out 11 am. Coin lndry. Cr cds: A, C, D, MC, V. ⒹⒺⒻⒾ

✔ ★**SUSSE CHALET INN.** *900 Morrissey Blvd (02122), in Dorchester section.* 617/287-9200. 106 rms, 4 story. S $46.70–$48.70; D $50.70–$52.70; suite $94.70; each addl $3; under 5 free. Crib $3. TV; cable. Pool. Free coffee. Cafe adj 6:30 am–11 pm. Ck-out 11 am. Coin lndry. Meeting rms. Sundries. Cr cds: A, C, D, MC, V. ⒹⒺⒻⒾ

Brewster (Cape Cod)

Settled: 1656 **Pop:** 1,744 **Elev:** 39 ft (12 m) **Area code:** 508 **Zip:** 02631

Inn

 ★ ★OLD SEA PINES INN. *2553 Main St. 508/896-6114.* 14 rms, 3 story, 9 with bathrm, 9 A/C. No elvtr. No rm phones. July–Aug: S, D $36–$85; each addl $15; suite $80; lower rates Apr–June & Sep–late Nov. Closed rest of yr. Children over 9 yrs only exc in suite. Free full bkfst. Rm serv. Bkfst in bed avail 7:30–9:30 am. Serv bar 2–11 pm. Ck-out 11 am, ck-in 2 pm. Antiques; some handmade quilts; some fireplaces; front porch rockers. Former school; founded in 1907 as School of Charm and Personality for Young Women. On 3½ acres. Beach 1 mi. Cr cds: A, C, D, MC, V. Ⓓ Ⓕ Ⓘ

Centerville (Cape Cod)

Pop: 3,640 **Elev:** 40 ft (12 m) **Area code:** 508 **Zip:** 02632

Motel

★ ★TRADE WINDS INN. *(PO Box 107, Craigville Beach Rd, Craigville 02636)* 1 mi E. *508/775-0365.* 36 rms, 6 A/C, 2 story, 4 kits. Mid-June–Labor Day: S, D $70–$150; each addl $10; suites $135–$180; lower rates Apr–mid-June, Labor Day–Oct. Closed rest of yr. TV; cable. Ck-out 11 am. Meeting rms. Putting green. Balconies. Private beach opp. Cr cds: A, MC, V.

Chatham (Cape Cod)

Settled: 1656 **Pop:** 1,922 **Elev:** 46 ft (14 m) **Area code:** 508 **Zip:** 02633

Motel

★CHATHAM. *1487 Main St. 508/945-2630.* 22 rms. No A/C. July–mid-Sep: S, D $70–$80; each addl $5; lower rates mid-Apr–June, mid-Sep–Oct. Closed rest of yr. TV; cable, in-rm movies. Playground. Refrigerators. Cafe nearby. Ck-out 11 am. Lawn games. Picnic tables. In pine grove. Cr cds: MC, V.

Dennis (Cape Cod)

Settled: 1639 **Pop:** 900 **Elev:** 24 ft (7 m) **Area code:** 508 **Zip:** 02638

Motels

★DENNIS WEST. *(691 Main St, West Dennis 02670)* ½ mi E of West Dennis on MA 28. *508/394-7434.* 22 rms, 2 story. July–Labor Day: S $39–$52; D $47–$59; each addl $4–$8; lower rates rest of yr. Crib $4. TV; cable. Pool. Cafe adj 7 am–2 pm. Ck-out 11 am. Cr cds: A, DS, MC, V.

★DENNISPORT. *(Box 432, MA 28, Dennisport 02639)* On MA 28. *508/394-8531.* 22 rms, 2 story. July–Aug: S, D $50–$65; each addl $10; under 12 free; wkend rates; lower rates rest of yr. Crib free. TV; cable. Pool. Cafe nearby. Ck-out 11 am. Coin lndry. Refrigerators avail. Cr cds: A, MC, V.

★ ★HUNTSMAN. *(829 Main St, West Dennis 02670)* MA 28. *508/394-5415.* 27 units, 2 story, 9 kits. No rm phones. Mid-June–early Sep: S $46–$56; D $55–$62; each addl $6–$10; kit. units $59–$65; wkly rates; lower rates mid-Apr–mid-June, early Sep–Oct. Closed rest of yr. Crib

$3. TV. Pool. Free continental bkfst 8–10 am. Cafe adj 7 am–2 pm. Ck-out 11 am. Lawn games. Picnic tables, grills. Cr cds: MC, V.

★**SEA LORD.** *(Chase Ave & Inman Rd, Dennisport 02639) 1 mi S of MA 28. 508/398-6900.* 27 rms, 1–2 story. No A/C. Late June–Labor Day: S, D $65–$75; kit units $83–$92; each addl $5; lower rates May–late June, after Labor Day–Oct. Closed rest of yr. Crib $3. TV; cable. Pool. Free coffee. Ck-out 11 am. Some refrigerators. Balconies. Beach opp. Cr cds: MC, V.

✔ ★**SEA SHELL.** *(45 Chase Ave, Dennisport 02639) 1 mi S of MA 28. 508/398-8965.* 17 rms, 4 in guest house, 1–2 story, 5 kits. No A/C. Late June–Labor Day: S, D $45–$160; each addl $15; kit. units $75; lower rates rest of yr. Crib free. TV; cable. Free continental bkfst in season. Cafe adj 7 am–9:30 pm. Ck-out 11 am. Refrigerators. Balconies. Private beach; sun deck. Cr cds: A, C, D.

✔ ★**SESUIT HARBOR.** *(Box D, East Dennis 02641) 2 mi E on MA 6A. 508/385-3326.* 20 units, 17 baths, 1–2 story, 3 apts, 3 kits. No rm phones. Late June–mid-Sep: S, D $50–$65; each addl $10; apts $450–$500/wk; kits. $70; under 12, $6 addl; wkly rates; lower rates Apr–late June, mid-Sep–Oct. Closed rest of yr. Crib free. TV; cable. Pool. Cafe opp 7 am–2 pm. Ck-out 11 am. Some balconies. Picnic tables, grills. Cr cds: MC, V.

★**SHIFTING SANDS.** *(Box 5, Dennisport 02639) Chase Ave, 1 mi S of MA 28. 508/398-9145.* 23 rms, 1–2 story. No A/C. July–Aug: S, D $60–$80; each addl $10; lower rates June, Sep. Closed rest of yr. Over 7 yrs only. TV; cable. Cafe nearby. Ck-out 11 am. Refrigerators. Balconies. Private beach; sun deck. Cr cds: MC, V.

★**WIDOW'S WALK.** *(Box 991, Dennisport 01639) 396 Lower County Rd at Depot St , 1 mi S of MA 28. 508/398-6800.* 12 rms, 6 A/C, 11 kit. units. July–early Sep: S, D $65; each addl $8; kit. units $430/wk; lower rates Apr–late June, early Sep–Oct. Closed rest of yr. Crib free. TV; cable. Cafe opp 8 am–3 pm. Ck-out 10 am. Some private patios. Beach 2 blks. Cr cds: MC, V.

Eastham (Cape Cod)

Settled: 1644 **Pop:** 1,100 **Elev:** 48 ft (15 m) **Area code:** 508 **Zip:** 02642

Motels

★**ASPINET.** *(Box 505) 1 mi E of Orleans Circle on US 6. 508/255-2835.* 5 cottages, 5 kits., 3 A/C. No rm phones. Mid-June–Labor Day: D $55–$79; each addl $12; kits. $400/wk; 4-rm kit. cottages $590/wk; lower rates May–mid-June, Labor Day–Oct; Nov–mid-Dec open wkends. Closed rest of yr. TV; cable. Playground. Cafe nearby 7 am–10 pm. Ck-out 10 am. Picnic tables, grills. Cr cds: MC, V. ⓘ

✔ ★★**BLUE DOLPHIN INN.** *(Drawer S, N Eastham 02651) 3 mi N of Natl Seashore entrance on US 6. 508/255-1159; res: 800/654-0504 (exc MA), 800/334-3251 (MA).* 50 rms. Mid-June–early Sep: S, D $67; each addl $5; under 12 free; lower rates Apr–mid-June, early Sep–Oct. Closed rest of yr. Crib $5. TV; cable, in-rm movies. Pool; poolside serv. Cafe 6–1 am. Rm serv. Bar to 1 am; entertainment Fri, Sat in season. Ck-out 11 am. Tennis. Lawn games. Bicycles avail. Refrigerators. Private patios. On 7 wooded acres. Closed caption TV decoders for the hearing impaired. Cr cds: A, MC, V. Ⓔ

✔ ★★**CAPTAIN'S QUARTERS.** *(Box Y, US 6, North Eastham 02651) Approx 2 mi N on US 6. 508/255-5686; res: 800/327-7769 (MA).* 75 rms. Mid-June–Labor Day: S, D $65–$80; each addl $7; lower rates mid-Apr–mid-June, Labor Day–mid-Nov. Closed rest of yr. TV; cable, in-rm movies. Heated pool. Free continental bkfst. Cafe nearby. Ck-out 11 am. Meeting rms. Tennis. Health club privileges. Lawn games. Refrigerators. Picnic tables, grills. Near beach. Cr cds: A, C, D, DS, MC, V.

✔ ★CRANBERRY COTTAGES. *(RR 1, Box 146) ¾ mi N of Orleans Rotary on US 6.* 508/255-0602. 14 cottages, 7 kits. No A/C. Late June–Labor Day: S, D $48–$59; each addl $12–$20; 2-bedrm kit. cottages for 1–4, $525–$625/wk; each addl $75/wk; lower rates rest of yr. Crib $5–$9. TV; cable. Ck-out 10 am. Some refrigerators. Grill. Cape Cod cottages in shady grove.

★MIDWAY MOTEL & COTTAGES. *(Box 174, N Eastham 02651) On US 6, 2½ mi N of Eastham Visitor Center.* 508/255-3117. 11 units, 3 kits. No A/C. Late June–Labor Day: S, D $60–$68; studio rms $65; 1-bedrm cottage $460/wk; 3-bedrm cottage $540/wk; lower rates after Labor Day–Oct, Mar–late June. Closed rest of yr. TV; cable, in-rm movies. Playground. Free coffee. Cafe nearby. Ck-out 11 am. Lawn games. Refrigerators. Cr cds: A, MC, V.

✔ ★★VIKING SHORES RESORT MOTOR LODGE. *(Box AO, N Eastham 02651) 3 mi N on US 6 at jct Nauset Rd.* 508/255-3200; res: 800/742-4128 (MA), 800/242-2131 (New England). 40 units. Mid-June–Labor Day: S, D $59–$84; each addl $5; under 16 free; lower rates mid-Feb–mid-June, after Labor Day–early Nov. Closed rest of yr. Crib $5. TV; cable, in-rm movies. Pool. Free continental bkfst. Ck-out 11 am. Tennis. Bicycle rentals. Lawn games. Refrigerators, private patios. Picnic tables, grills. Shuttle to beach. Cr cds: A, DS, MC, V.

Inn

★PENNY HOUSE. *(Box 238, Rte 6, North Eastham 02651) ½ mi N of Visitors' Center on MA 6.* 508/255-6632. 12 rms, shared bathrms, 2 story. No elvtr. July–Aug: D $65–$70; lower rates rest of yr. Children over 12 yrs only. Free full bkfst 8–10 am. Ck-out 11 am, ck-in 2 pm. Lawn games. Picnic tables. Former sea captain's house (1751); antiques. Beach 1½ mi. Cr cds: A, MC, V.

Falmouth (Cape Cod)

Settled: ca 1660 **Pop:** 5,720 **Elev:** 10 ft (3 m) **Area code:** 508

Motel

✔ ★MARINER. *555 Main St (MA 28) (02540).* 508/548-1331. 30 rms. Late June–Labor Day: S, D $65–$75; each addl $4–$8; lower rates Apr–late June, after Labor Day–late Nov. Closed rest of yr. TV. Pool. Free morning coffee. Cafe nearby. Ck-out 11 am. Lawn games. Picnic tables, grills. Cr cds: A, C, D, DS, MC, V.

Inns

✔ ★CAPT. TOM LAWRENCE HOUSE. *75 Locust St (02540).* 508/540-1445. 6 rms, 4 baths, 2 story. No A/C. No rm phones. Mid-June–mid-Oct: S $45–$65; D $65–$79; each addl $15. Children over 12 yrs only. Closed rest of yr. TV in sitting rm. Free full bkfst; complimentary tea. Ck-out 11 am, ck-in 3 pm. Free airport, RR station, bus depot transportation. Bicycle rentals. Island ferry tickets avail. Antiques, handmade quilts. Picnic tables. Whaling captain's home (1861). Cr cds: MC, V. Ⓓ

✔ ★★ELM ARCH INN. *Elm Arch Way (02540), ¼ blk S of MA 28.* 508/548-0133. 24 rms, 20 with heat, 6 A/C, 12 baths, 2 story. No rm phones. Mid-June–mid-Oct: D $45–$60; each addl $8; lower rates rest of yr. Crib $8. TV in lobby. Pool. Free morning coffee in season. Cafe nearby. Ck-out 11 am. Small colonial inn built in 1810; screened terrace. In town.

Great Barrington

Settled: 1726 **Pop:** 3,150 **Elev:** 721 ft (220 m) **Area code:** 413 **Zip:** 01230

Motel

(Rates may be higher during Berkshire Music Festival; Fair week)

✔ ★**LANTERN HOUSE.** *(Box 97) Stockbridge Rd, 1¼ mi N on US 7, 11 mi SW of MA Tpke exit 2.* 413/528-2350. 14 rms. S, D $46–$80; each addl $3–$5; wkly rates. Crib free. TV; cable. Pool. Cafe nearby. Ck-out 11 am. Free bus depot transportation. Downhill/x-country ski 1¼ mi. Lawn games. Picnic tables. On 3 acres. Antique shop. Cr cds: MC, V.

⊟ ⚡ ⇌ SC

Greenfield

Settled: 1686 **Pop:** 14,198 **Elev:** 250 ft (76 m) **Area code:** 413 **Zip:** 01301

Motel

✔ ★★**CANDLE LIGHT.** *208 Mohawk Trail (MA 2), at I-91 exit 26.* 413/772-0101; *res: 800/241-3848 (exc MA).* 64 rms, 4 kit. units. May–Oct: S $34–$68; D $45–$76; each addl $10; suites $76–$121; kit. units $59–$89; under 12 free; wkly rates, ski plan; lower rates rest of yr. Crib $5. TV; cable, in-rm movies. Pool. Cafe adj 11 am–10 pm. Ck-out 11 am. Meeting rms. Bellhops. Free bus depot transportation. Tennis. Downhillski 15 mi; x-country ski on site. Some refrigerators. Scenic setting on 12 acres. Cr cds: A, C, D, DS, ER, MC, V. ⓓ ⓔ

🏊 ⊟ ⚡ ⚒ ⇌ SC $

Harwich (Cape Cod)

Settled: ca 1670 **Pop:** 4,399 **Elev:** 55 ft (17 m) **Area code:** 508 **Zip:** 02645

Motels

✔ ★**HANDKERCHIEF SHOALS.** *(MA 28, South Harwich 02661) On MA 28 at Deep Hole Rd.* 508/432-2200. 26 rms. No A/C. Late June–Labor Day: S, D $58–$65; each addl $5; lower rates May–late June, after Labor Day–Oct. Closed rest of yr. Crib free. TV; cable. Pool. Cafe nearby. Ck-out 11 am. Lawn games. Refrigerators. Cr cds: MC, V.

⇌ 🚫

★**MOBY DICK.** *(767 Main St, South Harwich 02661) ¾ mi E of Harwich Port on MA 28.* 508/432-1434. 24 rms, 2 A/C, 11 kits. Mid-June–early Sep: D $60–$75; each addl $10; kit. units $72–$85; cottage with kit. for 4, $775/wk; lower rates Apr–mid-June, after Labor Day–Oct. Closed rest of yr. Crib $10. TV; cable. Pool. Playground. Cafe opp 7 am–noon. Ck-out 10 am. Lawn games. Refrigerators. Library. Picnic tables, gas grill. Cr cds: A, DS, MC, V.

⇌ 🚫

★**SALT MEADOW.** *(Box 484, West Harwich 02671) 1½ mi E on MA 28.* 508/432-2101. 16 rms. No A/C. Late June–Labor Day: D $60; each addl $8; lower rates Apr–late June, after Labor Day–Oct. Closed rest of yr. TV; cable. Pool. Cafe nearby. Ck-out 11 am. Cr cds: A, MC, V. ⓕ

⇌ 🚫

✔ ★★**SEADAR INN BY THE SEA.** *(Bank St & Braddock Lane, Harwich Port 02646) 2 blks S of MA 28.* 508/432-0264. 20 rms, 1–2 story, 1 kit. apt. No A/C. Late June–Labor Day: D $55–$90; each addl $8; 2-bedrm kit. apt $1,000/wk; lower rates May–late June, after Labor Day–mid-Oct. Closed rest of yr. TV in some rms, lobby; cable. Free continental bkfst. Cafe nearby. Ck-out 11 am. Bellhops. Lawn games. Picnic tables, grill. Private beach opp. Main bldg old Colonial house (1789); Early Amer decor; some rms with bay windows, full ocean view. Cr cd: A.

⇌ 🚫

✔ ★**TROY COURT.** *(28 Sea St, Harwich Port 02646) 1 blk S of MA 28. 508/432-1275.* 23 rms, 1–2 story. No A/C. Mid-June–Labor Day: S, D $62–$70; each addl $10; lower rates rest of yr. Children over 12 yrs only. TV in lobby; cable. Free continental bkfst. Cafe nearby. Ck-out 11 am. Lawn games. Early Amer decor; porches, ocean view. Extensive grounds, attractive landscaping. Beach ½ blk.

Inn

✔ ★**COUNTRY INN ACRES.** *(86 Sisson Rd, Harwich Port 02646) 1 mi SW from jct MA 124, 39. 508/432-2769.* 17 rms, 2 story. 2 A/C. Late May–mid-Oct: D $60–$70; each addl $12.50; lower rates rest of yr. TV in lobby; cable. Pool. Free continental bkfst. Cafe (public by res) 5:30–8:30 pm. No rm serv. Bar. Ck-out 11 am, ck-in 1–4 pm. Tennis. Built 1780. Early Amer decor. Old-fashioned garden; quiet surroundings. Cr cds: A, MC, V.

Holyoke

Settled: 1745 **Pop:** 44,678 **Elev:** 270 ft (82 m) **Area code:** 413 **Zip:** 01040

Inn

✔ ★ ★**YANKEE PEDLAR INN.** *1866 Northhampton (US 5) at jct US 202. 413/532-9494.* 47 rms in 5 houses, 3 story. No elvtr. S $40–$45; D $50–$55; each addl $53–$63. Crib $5. TV; cable. Free continental bkfst. Cafe 7 am–midnight. Bar 11–1 am; entertainment. Ck-out noon. Meeting rms. Some refrigerators. Cr cds: A, C, D, MC, V. Ⓔ Ⓕ

Hyannis (Cape Cod)

Settled: 1639 **Pop:** 9,118 **Elev:** 19 ft (6 m) **Area code:** 508 **Zip:** 02601

Motels

✔ ★**COUNTRY LAKE.** *(MA 132) Iyanough Rd, 2½ mi NW on MA 132, ¾ mi S of exit 6. 508/362-6455.* 20 rms, 5 kits. (no ovens). Late June–early Sep: S, D $52–$65; each addl $4–$10; kit. units $60–$75; 3-night package off-season; lower rates early Sep–Oct, mid-Mar–late June. Closed rest of yr. Crib free. TV; cable. Heated pool. Coffee in office. Cafe nearby. Ck-out 11 am. Free bus depot transportation. Refrigerators avail. Picnic tables, grills. On lake; boats. Cr cds: A, C, D, MC, V.

✔ ★ ★**HYANNIS REGENCY INN.** *MA 132, 2 mi NW on MA 132, 2 mi S of exit 6 off US 6. 508/775-1153.* 196 units, 2 story. Late June–Labor Day: S, D $45.95–$99.95; each addl $5; suites $65.95–$135. Crib free. TV; cable. Indoor pool; lifeguard, poolside serv. Cafe 7 am–9 pm. Rm serv. Bar noon–1 am. Ck-out 11 am. Meeting rms. Concierge (in season). Exercise rm; instructor, weights, bicycles, whirlpool, steam rm, sauna. Game rm. Some refrigerators. Some private patios. Cr cds: A, C, D, MC, V.

Lee

Founded: 1777 **Pop:** 2,140 **Elev:** 1,000 ft (305 m) **Area code:** 413 **Zip:** 01238

Motels

★**LEE MOTOR INN.** *(Box 426) 2 mi SW on MA 102, MA Tpke exit 2. 413/243-0501.* 24 rms. S $32–$110; D $36–$110; each addl $5; under 12 free, wkly rates. Crib $5. TV; cable. Free coffee in rms. Ck-out 11 am. Picnic tables. Cr cds: A, C, D, DS, MC, V.

✔ ★ ★**PILGRIM.** *On US 20, ¼ mi N of MA Tpke exit 2. 413/243-1328.* 27 rms, 2 story. July–Aug: S $38–$116; D $53–$132; each addl $5–$15; under 12 free; wkly rates off-season;

lower rates rest of yr. Crib free. TV; cable. Pool. Cafe adj 6:30 am–midnight. Ck-out 11 am. Coin lndry. Downhill ski 15 mi; x-country ski 5 mi. Balconies. Picnic tables, grills. Cr cds: A, C, D, MC, V. ⓓ

🏊 ➳ SC

Inn

✔ ★★MORGAN HOUSE. *33 Main St. 413/243-0181.* 13 rms, 12 shared bathrms, 3 story. No rm phones. No elvtr. July–Oct: S, D $42.28–$89.85; each addl $10; suites $96–$160; lower rates rest of yr. Crib $8. Free continental bkfst. Cafe 11:30 am–2:30 pm, 5–9:30 pm; Fri, Sat to 10 pm; Sun noon–9:30 pm. Bar 11–1:30 am. Ck-out 11 am, ck-in 1 pm. Former stagecoach inn (1853); antiques; country-style decor; library. Cr cds: A, C, D, MC, V.

Lenox

Settled: ca 1750 **Pop:** 2,668 **Elev:** 1,200 ft (366 m) **Area code:** 413 **Zip:** 01240

Motels

(Rates are generally higher during Berkshire Music Festival)

✔ ★LENOX. *(PO Box 713) US 7, 20, 4 mi NE. 413/499-0324.* 17 rms. July–Aug: S $34–$110; D $38–$110; each addl $7–$8; under 12 free; wkly rates off-season; higher rates foliage season; lower rates Nov–May. Crib $5. TV; cable. Pool. Free coffee in rms. Cafe nearby. Ck-out 11 am. Downhill ski 1 mi. Sundries. Picnic tables. Cr cds: A, C, D, DS, MC, V.

🏊 ➳ 🚫 SC

★SUSSE CHALET. *(Box 622) 444 Pittsfield-Lenox Rd (US 7, 20). 413/637-3560.* 59 rms, 2 story. June–late Oct: S, D $50–$70; each addl $5–$10; higher rates July–Aug wkends (2-day min); lower rates Nov–May. Crib $3. TV; cable. Pool. Cafe 7–10 am. Ck-out 11 am. Coin lndry. Downhill ski 3 mi. Cr cds: A, C, D, MC, V.

🏊 ➳ 🚫 🚫 SC

Martha's Vineyard

Settled: 1642 **Pop:** 7,500 **Elev:** 0–311 ft (0–95 m) **Area code:** 508

Inns

✔ ★★EDGARTOWN INN. *(Box 1211, Edgartown 02539) 56 N Water St. 508/627-4794.* 12 rms in inn, 10 rms in 2 annexes, 1–2 story. No A/C. Late May–late Sep; annex D $50–$85; inn S, D $70–$135; each addl $10; lower rates Oct, Apr–late-May. Closed rest of yr. Crib $10. TV in lobby. Cafe 8–11 am. Ck-out 11 am. Inn since 1800; colonial furnishings & antiques in rms. Beach 1 blk. Ⓕ

✔ ★SHIRETOWN INN. *(Box 921, Edgartown 02539) N Water St. 508/627-3353; res: 800/541-0090 (exc MA), 800/541-0004 (MA).* 35 units in 4 bldgs, 1–3 story. No A/C. No elvtr. May–Oct: S, D $55–$132; each addl $10; suites $100–$145; guest houses $650–$850/wk; under 12 free; lower rates May–mid-June, mid-Sep–mid-Oct. Closed rest of yr. Crib $10. Free continental bkfst in season. Cafe 6–10 pm. No rm serv. Bar 4–11 pm. Ck-out 11 am, ck-in 1 pm. Bellhops. Balconies. Sun deck. Cr cds: A, MC, V.

Nantucket Island

Settled: 1659 **Pop:** 3,229 **Elev:** 0–108 ft (0–33 m) **Area code:** 508 **Zip:** 02554

Inns

★CARRIAGE HOUSE. *5 Ray's Ct. 508/228-0326.* 7 rms, 2 story. No A/C. Mid-June–Labor Day: S, D $65–$100; each addl $15; lower rates rest of yr. TV in lobby; cable. Free continental bkfst. Cafe nearby. Ck-out 11 am. In converted 1865 carriage house. Victorian decor. Patio.

🚫

✔ ★**SHIPS INN.** *13 Fair St. 508/228-0040.* 12 rms, 10 with bathrm. No A/C. Mid-June–Oct: S $20–$37; D $55–$90; each addl $10–$15; lower rates mid-Mar–mid-June, Nov–mid-Dec. Children over 2 yrs only. Closed rest of yr. Free continental bkfst in season. Cafe 6–9:15 pm. Ck-out 11 am. Built in 1812 by a sea captain; many original furnishings. Cr cds: A, MC, V. Ⓔ

Newburyport

Settled: 1635 **Pop:** 15,900 **Elev:** 37 ft (11 m) **Area code:** 508 **Zip:** 01950

Inn

★★**MORRILL PLACE.** *209 High St. 508/462-2808.* 9 rms, 3 story, 7 share baths. No A/C. No elvtr. S, D $55–$70; each addl $10; EP; wkly rates. TV rm; cable. Free continental bkfst 8–10 am. Cafe nearby. Ck-out noon, ck-in 4 pm. Tennis privileges. 18-hole golf privileges, pro. Built in 1806. Once owned by law partner of Daniel Webster; Webster was frequent visitor. Formal front parlor and library.

Orleans (Cape Cod)

Settled: 1693 **Pop:** 1,811 **Elev:** 60 ft (18 m) **Area code:** 508 **Zip:** 02653

Motels

★★**OLDE TAVERN MOTEL & INN.** *(Box 943) On MA 6A. 508/255-1565.* 29 rms. Late June–early Sep: S, D $70–$95; each addl $9; lower rates Apr–mid-June, early Sep–Dec. Closed rest of yr. Crib free. TV; cable, in-rm movies. Heated pool. Free continental bkfst. Cafe adj. Ck-out 11 am. Refrigerators. 18 deck rms. Main bldg is a restored tavern visited by Thoreau in 1849, Daniel Webster and other personalities of the day. Cr cds: A, DS, MC, V.

★**PACKET LANDING/SEA BREEZE.** *(Box 457, East Orleans 02643) 5 Nauset Beach Rd. 508/255-1550.* 35 units, 2 story, 3 kits. No rm phones. Late June–early Sep: S, D $66–$76; each addl $8; kit. units $525–$575/wk; under 4 free; wkly rates; lower rates mid-Apr–late June, early Sep–Oct. Closed rest of yr. Crib $4. TV; cable, in-rm movies. Pool. Continental bkfst. Cafe adj 5 am–10 pm. Ck-out 10 am. Refrigerators. Picnic tables, grills. Sun deck. Near Nauset Beach. Cr cds: MC, V. Ⓓ

✔ ★**RIDGEWOOD MOTEL & COTTAGES.** *(Box 82, S Orleans 02662) At jct MA 28, 39. 508/255-0473.* 12 rms, 6 kit. cottages, 1–2 bedrm. No A/C. Late June–Labor Day: S, D $60–$66; each addl $4; cottages $350–$435/wk; lower rates rest of yr. Crib avail. TV; cable. Pool. Free continental bkfst. Ck-out 11 am; cottages 10 am. Lawn games. Refrigerators. Picnic tables, grills. Cr cds: MC, V.

★**SEASHORE PARK MOTOR INN.** *(Box 175) 24 Canal Rd at US 6. 508/255-2500.* 62 rms, 2 story, 24 kits. Mid-June–early Sep: S, D $68–$88; each addl $10; each addl 5–15 yrs $5; under 5 free; kit. units $88; lower rates Apr–June, after Labor Day–Oct. Closed rest of yr. Crib $5. TV; cable. 2 pools, 1 indoor; whirlpool, sauna. Free morning coffee. Cafe adj 7 am–midnight. Ck-out 11 am. Private patios, balconies. Sun deck. Cr cds: A, MC, V.

Pittsfield

Settled: 1743 **Pop:** 51,974 **Elev:** 1,039 ft (317 m) **Area code:** 413 **Zip:** 01201

Motel

(Rates may be higher during Berkshire Music Festival)

✔ ★**HEART OF THE BERKSHIRES.** *970 W Housatonic St, on US 20. 413/443-1255.* 16 rms. July–Aug: S $40–$45; D $45–$55; each addl $5; wkly, ski rates; higher rates music festival; lower rates rest of yr. Crib $5. TV; cable. Pool; wading pool. Free coffee in rms. Cafe nearby. Ck-out 11 am. Downhill ski 2 mi; x-country ski 1 mi. Picnic tables, grills. On river. Cr cds: A, C, D, MC, V.

Plymouth

Settled: 1620 **Pop:** 7,232 **Elev:** 50 ft (15 m) **Area code:** 508 **Zip:** 02360

Motels

★**COLD SPRING.** *188 Court St. 508/746-2222.* 31 rms. Late Mar–late Nov: S, D $49–$63; each addl $5. Closed Dec–mid-Mar. Crib $5. TV. Free continental bkfst. Cafe nearby 7 am–11 pm. Ck-out 11 am. Picnic tables, grills. Cr cds: A, DS, MC, V.

✔ ★**SLEEPY PILGRIM.** *182 Court St. 508/746-1962.* 12 rms. Mid-June–late Oct: S $50; D $52–$57; each addl $6; lower rates late Oct–Thanksgiving, Apr–mid-June. Closed rest of yr. Crib $5. TV. Free coffee. Cafe nearby. Ck-out 10 am. Picnic tables, grills. Cr cds: MC, V.

Provincetown (Cape Cod)

Settled: ca 1700 **Pop:** 3,372 **Elev:** 40 ft (12 m) **Area code:** 508 **Zip:** 02657

Motels

★**BLUE SEA.** *(Box 537) 1¾ mi E on MA 6A. 508/487-1041.* 40 units, 1–2 story. No rm phones. July–Aug: S, D $68–$89; each addl $5; kit. units $520–$720/wk; under 5 free; lower rates Sep–Oct, late Apr–June. Closed rest of yr. Crib $5. TV. Indoor pool. Cafe nearby. Ck-out 11 am. Refrigerators. Balconies. Picnic tables, grills. On ocean; swimming beach. Cr cds: A, C, D, MC, V.

✔ ★**EAST HARBOUR.** *(MA 6A, N Truro 02652) 2½ mi E on MA 6A. 508/487-0505.* 8 rms, 7 kit. cottages. No A/C. Late June–Labor Day (2-day min): S, D $52–$68; cottages to 4, $550–$975/wk; lower rates mid-May–late June, after Labor Day–late Oct. Closed rest of yr. TV; cable. Free coffee. Cafe nearby. Ck-out 10 am. Picnic tables, grills. On beach; sun deck. Cr cds: A, MC, V.

✔ ★★**MASTHEAD MOTEL AND COTTAGES.** *(Box 577) 31 Commercial St. 508/487-0523.* 10 rms, 4 cottages, 7 apts, most A/C, 2 share bath, 2 story, 13 kits. (oven in 10). July–Labor Day, motel rms: S, D $55–$135; each addl $15; efficiency apts $750–$890/wk; kit. cottages (1-wk min) $875–$1500/wk; under 12 free up to two children; lower rates rest of yr. Crib free. TV; cable. Cafe nearby. Ck-out 11 am, cottages 10 am. Refrigerators. 400-ft sun deck on water. Picnic tables; grills. On private beach. In-shore & deep water moorings & launch serv. Cr cds: A, C, D, MC, V.

✔ ★**SHIP'S BELL.** *586 Commercial St. 508/487-1674.* 23 units, 2 story. 8 kits. No rm phones. July–Aug: D $42–$63; each addl $10; kits. $416–$720/wk; lower rates May–June, Sep–Oct. Closed rest of yr. Cafe adj 7 am–11 pm. Ck-out 10 am. Tennis privileges. Grills. Opp beach. Cr cds: MC, V.

★★**TIDES MOTOR INN.** *(Box 617) Beach Point Rd, 1½ mi E on MA 6A. 508/487-1045.* 64 rms, 2 story. No A/C. July–Labor Day: S, D $69–$79; each addl $8; suites $85; wkly rates; lower rates mid-May–June, after Labor Day–mid-Oct. Closed rest of yr. TV; cable, in-rm movies. Heated pool in season. Cafe 7:30–11 am. Ck-out 11 am. Coin Indry. Lawn games. All beach units with porch or balcony. Private beach. Cr cds: A, C, D, DS, MC, V.

Inns

★★**BRADFORD GARDENS.** *178 Bradford St (MA 6A). 508/487-1616.* 8 rms, 1–2 story, 4 cottages. No A/C. S, D $69–$99; each addl $15; cottages $70–$140. TV. Free full bkfst. Cafe nearby. No rm serv. Ck-out 11 am. Beach 1 blk. 9 fireplaces. Built 1820. Cr cds: A, MC, V.
Ⓕ

✔★**SOMERSET HOUSE.** *378 Commercial St. 508/487-0383.* 12 rms, 1 apt, 10 with bath, 2–3 story. No A/C. Late June–Labor Day: S $45–$70; D $50–$80; each addl $10; apt $650 wk; lower rates rest of yr. Cafe nearby. Opp beach. Restored 1850s home. Cr cds: A, MC, V.

Salem

Settled: 1626 **Pop:** 38,220 **Elev:** 9 ft (3 m) **Area code:** 508 **Zip:** 01970

Inn

✔★**CAP'N JACK'S WATERFRONT INN.** *(253 Humphrey St, Swampscott 01907) 6½ mi S on MA 1 to MA 129 in downtown Swampscott. 508/595-7910.* 33 rms, 21 A/C, 3 story, 5 kits. No elvtr. Memorial Day–Oct: S $36–$70; D $42–$76; each addl $6; kit. units $395–$550/wk; lower rates rest of yr. Crib $6. TV. Pool; whirlpool. Free coffee. Cafe nearby. Ck-out 11 am. Refrigerators. Built in 1835. On ocean. Cr cds: MC, V.

Sandwich (Cape Cod)

Settled: 1637 **Pop:** 1,784 **Elev:** 20 ft (6 m) **Area code:** 508 **Zip:** 02563

Motels

✔★**COUNTRY ACRES.** *(Box 307) 1 mi E on MA 6A. 508/888-2878.* 17 rms, 1 kit. cottage. Late June–Labor Day: S, D $48–$56; each addl $5; cottage $365/wk; lower rates rest of yr. Crib $3. TV; cable. Pool. Ck-out 11 am. Lawn games. Refrigerators avail. Cr cds: A, C, D, DS, MC, V.

✔★**OLD COLONY.** *(Box 429, East Sandwich 02537) 3½ mi E on MA 6A. 508/888-9716.* 10 rms. Mid-June–Labor Day: S, D $52–$64; each addl $8; lower rates rest of yr. TV; cable, in-rm movies. Pool. Free juice, coffee. Cafe nearby 6 am–midnight. Ck-out 11 am. Picnic tables. Cr cds: A, C, D, DS, MC, V.

✔★**SANDY NECK MOTEL.** *(669 MA 6A, East Sandwich) 5½ mi E. 508/362-3992.* 12 rms, 1 kit. unit. Mid-June–Labor Day: S, D $59–$70; each addl $7; kit. unit $80; lower rates rest of yr. Closed Jan–Feb. Crib free. TV; cable, in-rm movies. Free coffee. Cafe nearby. Ck-out 11 am. Refrigerators. Cr cds: A, C, MC, V.

Saugus

Settled: 1630 **Pop:** 24,746 **Elev:** 21 ft (6 m) **Area code:** 617 **Zip:** 01906

Motels

✔ ★**CHISHOLM'S.** *1314 Broadway. 617/233-5100.* 43 rms. June–Oct: S $42–$54; D $42–$68; each addl $5; wkly rates; lower rates rest of yr. TV; cable. Free coffee in rm. Cafe nearby. Ck-out 11 am. Sundries. Some in-rm whirlpools, steam baths. Cr cds: A, C, D, MC, V. ⓔ ⓓ

✔ ★**COLONIAL TRAVELER.** *1753 Broadway. 617/233-6700; res: 800/322-8029.* 24 rms, 1–2 story. S $45; D $51; each addl $5; children under 12 $2. Crib $5. TV; cable, in-rm movies. Free continental bkfst. Cafe 7–10:15 am. Ck-out 11 am. Cr cds: A, C, D, MC, V.

South Yarmouth (Cape Cod)

Pop: 7,525 **Elev:** 20 ft (6 m) **Area code:** 508 **Zip:** 02664

Motels

✔ ★**AMERICANA HOLIDAY.** *(99 Main, West Yarmouth 02673) 3½ mi W on MA 28. 508/775-5511; res: 800/445-4497.* 154 rms, 2 story. Late June–Labor Day: S, D $50–$64; each addl $5; suites $85–$95; package plans off-season; lower rates Mar–late June, after Labor Day–Nov. Closed rest of yr. Crib free. TV; cable, in-rm movies. 3 pools, 1 indoor. Playground. Free coffee. Cafe nearby. Ck-out 11 am. Putting green. Exercise equipt; weights, bicycles, whirlpool, steam rm, sauna. Game rm. Lawn games. 48 large family units. Cr cds: MC, V.

★**BASS RIVER.** *(891 MA 28, Bass River 02664) ½ mi W. 508/398-2488.* 20 rms, 4 kits. (no ovens). Late June–Labor Day: S, D $54–$60; each addl $6; suites $66–$78; kit. units $56–$60; lower rates rest of yr. Crib $4. TV; cable. Pool. Cafe nearby. Ck-out 11 am. Lawn games. Refrigerators. Picnic tables. Cr cds: A, MC, V.

✔ ★★**BEACH 'N TOWNE.** *MA 28, ¼ mi W of Bass River Bridge. 508/398-2311.* 21 rms. Late June–Labor Day: S, D $56–$60; each addl $6; lower rates rest of yr. Crib free. TV; cable. Pool. Playground. Cafe nearby. Ck-out 11 am. Lawn games. Refrigerators. Picnic tables, grills. Library. Cr cds: A, MC, V.

✔ ★**CAPE COD IRISH VILLAGE.** *(MA 28, West Yarmouth 02673) 512 Main St, ½ mi W. 508/771-0100.* 88 rms, 5 kits., 1–2 story. Late June–Labor Day; S, D $55–$65; each addl $10; kit. units $95; wkly, off-season rates; lower rates rest of yr. Crib free. TV; cable. 2 pools, 1 indoor; whirlpool, sauna. Cafe 8 am–noon, 5–10 pm. Bar 3 pm–1 am; Irish music. Ck-out 11 am. Meeting rms. Tennis. Game rm. Lawn games. Picnic tables; grills. Irish gift shop. Cr cds: MC, V.

★**CAPE SOJOURN.** *(149 Main St, West Yarmouth 02673) 3½ mi W on MA 28. 508/ 775-3825.* 66 rms, 2 story. June 25–Sep 5: S $46–$56; D $59–$69; each addl $5; lower rates Apr–late June, Sep 6–Oct. Closed rest of yr. Crib $5. TV; cable, in-rm movies. 2 pools, 1 indoor; whirlpool, wading pool. Cafe nearby. Ck-out 11 am. Rec rm. Cr cds: A, MC, V.

★**CAPE TRAVELER.** *(MA 28, West Yarmouth 02673) 2 mi W on MA 28. 508/775-1225.* 29 rms. Mid-June–early Sep: S, D $50–$64; each addl $8; lower rates Feb–mid–June, early Sep–Nov. Closed rest of yr. Crib $6. TV; cable. Heated pool. Playground. Cafe nearby. Ck-out 11 am. Rec rm. Lawn games. Sun deck. Some refrigerators. Picnic tables, grills. Cr cds: A, MC, V.

✔ ★★**CAVALIER MOTOR LODGE & RESORT.** *(881 Main St, Bass River 02664) ½ mi W on MA 28. 508/394-6575.* 64 rms, 46 A/C, 1–2 story. Late June–early Sep: S, D $58–$66; each addl $7; kit. units $475–$695; lower rates Mar–late June, Labor Day–Oct. Closed rest of yr. TV; cable, in-rm movies. Indoor/outdoor pool; wading pool, whirlpool, sauna, hot tub. Cafe 6 am–1 pm in season. Putting green. Lawn games. Cr cds: A, MC, V.

✔ ★ ★**HUNTERS GREEN.** *(MA 28, West Yarmouth 02673) 2 mi W on MA 28. 508/771-1169; res: 800/637-8370 (exc MA), 800/334-3220 (MA).* 74 rms, 2 story. Late June–Labor Day: S, D $52–$60; each addl $6; package plans; lower rates Apr–late June, after Labor Day–Oct. Closed rest of yr. Crib free. TV; cable, in-rm movies. Indoor/outdoor pool; whirlpool. Cafe nearby. Ck-out 11 am. Lawn games. Picnic tables. Cr cds: MC, V.

✔ ★ ★**MARINER MOTOR LODGE.** *(573 Main St, West Yarmouth 02673). 508/771-7887; res: 800/262-9666 (MA).* 100 rms, 2 story. S, D $28–$75; each addl $5. Crib $5. TV; cable, in-rm movies. 2 heated pools, 1 indoor; whirlpool, sauna. Continental bkfst off-season. Cafe opp 7 am–4 pm. Ck-out 11 am. Meeting rm. Game rm. Ocean 1 mi. Cr cds: A, DS, MC, V.

Springfield

Settled: 1636 **Pop:** 152,319 **Elev:** 70 ft (21 m) **Area code:** 413

Motels

(Higher rates Exposition wk)

✔ ★**BEST WESTERN-CHICOPEE MOTOR LODGE.** *(463 Memorial Dr, Chicopee 01020) At MA Tpke exit 5. 413/592-6171.* 107 rms, 2 story. S $40–$54; D $45–$60; each addl $8; under 12 free. Crib $8. TV. Pool. Cafe adj open 24 hrs. Ck-out 11 am. Downhill/x-country ski 8 mi. Game rm. Cr cds: A, C, D, DS, MC, V. Ⓔ Ⓕ

✔ ★ ★**COMFORT INN.** *(450 Memorial Dr, Chicopee 01020) Off I-90 exit 5. 413/739-7311.* 100 units, 3 story, 14 suites. S $43–$53; D $50–$60; each addl $7; suites $53–$60; under 16 free. Crib free. TV; cable, in-rm movies. Cafe 7 am–11 pm. Bar from 11 am; entertainment Fri–Sun. Ck-out 11 am. Meeting rms. Exercise equipt; weights, bicycles. Cr cds: A, C, D, DS, MC, V. Ⓔ Ⓕ

★ ★**RAMADA INN.** *(357 Burnett Rd, Chicopee 01020) 5 mi N, just off I-291, MA Tpke exit 6. 413/592-9101.* 124 rms, 1–2 story. S $49–$62; D $56–$90; each addl $10; under 17 free; wkend rates; higher rates special events. Crib free. TV; cable. Pool. Playground. Cafes 6:30–2 pm, 5–9 pm. Bar 11–2 am. Ck-out noon. Meeting rms. Bellhops. Valet serv. Sundries. Downhill/x-country ski 10 mi. Cr cds: A, C, D, DS, MC, V.

✔ ★**SUSSE CHALET MOTOR LODGE.** *(Johnnycake Hollow Rd, Chicopee 01020) Just off MA Tpke exit 6 & I-291E. 413/592-5141.* 88 rms, 2 story. S $33.70; D $37.70; each addl $4. Crib $2. TV. Pool. Cafe opp 7 am–11 pm. Ck-out 11 am. Coin lndry. Downhill/x-country ski 8 mi. Cr cds: A, D, MC, V.

Motor Hotel

★ ★ ★**HOWARD JOHNSON.** *(1150 Riverdale St, West Springfield 01089) 5 mi N on US 5, ¼ mi SE of I-91 exit 13B, I-90 exit 4. 413/739-7261.* 112 rms, 5 story. Mid-May–mid-Oct: S $58–$80; D $61–$80; each addl $8; under 18 free; lower rates rest of yr. Crib free. TV. Pool; whirlpool, steam rm. Cafe 6:30 am–11 pm. Bar noon–midnight. Ck-out noon. Meeting rms. Valet serv. Downhill/x-country ski 7 mi. Private patios, balconies. Cr cds: A, C, D, DS, ER, MC, V.

Sturbridge

Settled: ca 1729 **Pop:** 1,891 **Elev:** 619 ft (189 m) **Area code:** 508 **Zip:** 01566

Motels

✔ ★**BAY PATH.** *US 20 W, off I-90 exit 9, I-84 exit 20W.* 508/347-2324. 53 units, 7 suites. June–Oct: S, D $45–$60; each addl $5; suites $65–$75; wkly rates; lower rates rest of yr. Crib $5. TV; cable. Pool. Ck-out 11 am. Coin lndry. 18-hole golf privileges 6 mi, greens fee $10, pro. Some refrigerators. Cr cds: MC, V.

✔ ★**STURBRIDGE COACH MOTOR LODGE.** *US 20; W of MA Tpke exit 9.* 508/347-7327. 54 rms, 2 story. May–Oct: S $42–$52; D $54–$72; each addl $5; higher rates special events; lower rates rest of yr. Crib $5. TV. Pool. Coffee in lobby. Cafe nearby. Ck-out 11 am. Spacious grounds. Old Sturbridge Village opp. Cr cds: A, MC, V.

Truro & North Truro (Cape Cod)

Settled: Truro: ca 1700 **Pop:** Truro: 500; N Truro: 700 **Elev:** 20 ft (6 m) **Area code:** 508
Zip: Truro: 02666; N Truro: 02652

Motels

✔ ★**ANCHORAGE.** *(MA 6A, North Truro) 2 mi E on MA 6A at Beach Point.* 508/487-0168. 10 apts, 2 rms, 8 cottages. No A/C. Late June–Labor Day: S, D $39; each addl $10; kit. units $490/wkly; cottages to 6, $525–$650/wkly; daily rates; lower rates mid-Apr–late June, after Labor Day–Oct. Closed rest of yr. Crib free. TV. Ck-out 10 am. Private beach; sun deck. Ⓕ

★**KALMAR VILLAGE.** *(Box 745, MA 6A, North Truro 02652)* 508/487-0585. 12 rms, 36 kit. cottages. No A/C. July–Labor Day: S, D $55–$60; each addl $7; cottages $565–$755/wk; each addl $70/wk; lower rates mid-May–June, after Labor Day–late Sep. Closed rest of yr. Crib free. TV; cable. Pool. Cafe nearby. Ck-out 11 am. Coin lndry. Picnic tables, grills. On private beach. Cr cds: MC, V. Ⓕ

★**SEA GULL.** *(Box 126, North Truro) 2½ mi E of Provincetown on MA 6A.* 508/487-9070. 26 rms, 5 kit. apts, 4 with 2 bedrms. No A/C. Late June–Labor Day: S, D $58–$68; each addl $5; cottages $600/wk; each addl $50/wk; lower rates Apr–late June & after Labor Day–Oct. Closed rest of yr. TV. Cafe nearby. Ck-out 10:30 am. Sun deck; private beach. Picnic tables, grills. Cr cds: A, DS, MC, V.

Wellfleet (Cape Cod)

Settled: ca 1724 **Pop:** 1,950 **Elev:** 50 ft (15 m) **Area code:** 508 **Zip:** 02667

Motels

★**EVEN'TIDE.** *(Box 41, South Wellfleet 02663) 5 mi S on US 6.* 508/349-3410; res: 800/368-0007 (MA). 31 units, 2 story, 8 suites, 3 kits. No rm phones. Mid-July–mid-Sep (2-night min wkends): S, D $64–$80; each addl $7–$10; suites $70–$85; kit. units (3-night min) $78; wkly rates; lower rates rest of yr. Crib $5–$15. TV. Indoor pool. Playground. Free coffee in rms. Ck-out 11 am. Coin lndry. Meeting rms. Refrigerators. Picnic tables, grills. Cr cds: A, C, D, DS, MC, V. Ⓕ

✔ ★**OCEAN PINES.** *(Box 604, South Wellfleet 02663) 5 mi S on US 6.* 508/349-2774. 7 air-cooled motel rms, 7 cottages. No rm phones. July–Labor Day: S $50; D $56; each addl $5; cottages $300–$400/wk; lower rates Apr–June, Labor Day–mid-Nov. Closed rest of yr. Crib $8. 7 color TV, 7 B/W. Ck-out 10 am. Refrigerators. Picnic tables, grills. Cape Cod Bay 1 blk. Cr cds: MC, V.

★★**WELLFLEET MOTEL & LODGE.** *(Box 606, South Wellfleet 02663) 5 mi SE on MA 6. 508/349-3535; res: 800/852-2900 (MA).* 65 rms, 1–2 story. Late June–Labor Day: S, D $62–$95; each addl $7; suites $90–$130; lower rates rest of yr. Crib $5. TV. Indoor pool; whirlpool. Playground. Free coffee in rm. Cafe 7 am–noon. Bar. Ck-out 11 am. Meeting rm. Picnic tables, grills. Cr cds: A, C, D, MC, V.

Inn

✔★**HOLDEN INN.** *On Wellfleet Bay, on road to the pier. 508/349-3450.* 25 rms, 11 with bath, 4 A/C. 2 story. No rm phones. Mid-Apr–Oct 12: S $35; D $48–$55. Closed rest of yr. Children over 14 yrs only. Cafe nearby. No rm serv. Ck-out 10 am, ck-in 2 pm. Picnic tables. Built 1840.

Williamstown

Settled: 1749 **Pop:** 4,798 **Elev:** 638 ft (194 m) **Area code:** 413 **Zip:** 01267

Motels

✔★★**ELWAL PINES MOTOR INN.** *811 Cold Spring Rd (US 7, MA 2). 413/458-8161.* 12 rms. May–Nov: S $35–$45; D $45–$60; each addl $5; higher rates college events; lower rates Apr. Closed Nov–Mar. Crib free. TV; cable. Pool. Cafe adj 11:30 am–10 pm. Ck-out 11 am. Lawn games. Downhill/x-country ski 6 mi. Picnic tables, grills. Spacious wooded grounds with pond. Cr cds: A, DS, MC, V. ⒺⒺ

✔★★**NORTHSIDE.** *45 North St, at jct US 7, MA 2. 413/458-8107.* 34 rms, 2 story. May–Nov: S, D $48–$52; each addl $5; suites $52; lower rates rest of yr. Crib free. TV; cable. Pool. Playground. Full bkfst 7:30–10:30 am (June–Nov). Ck-out 11 am. Sundries. Downhill/x-country ski 6 mi. Cr cds: A, D, MC, V.

Woburn

Settled: 1640 **Pop:** 36,626 **Elev:** 100 ft (30 m) **Area code:** 617 **Zip:** 01801

Motor Hotel

✔★★**SUSSE CHALET.** *285 Mishawum Rd. 617/938-7575.* 125 rms, 5 story. S $42.70–$44.70; D $46.70–$48.70; each addl $3; under 3 free. Crib $2. TV; cable. Pool. Cafe adj 11–1 am. Ck-out 11 am. RR station transportation. Cr cds: A, D, MC, V. Ⓔ

Worcester

Settled: 1673 **Pop:** 161,799 **Elev:** 480 ft (146 m) **Area code:** 508

Motel

✔★**DAYS INN-DAYS LODGE.** *50 Oriol Dr (01605). 508/852-2800.* 114 units, 3 story. S $50–$60; D $54–$64; each addl $5; suites $58–$73; under 18, $2. Crib free. TV; cable. Pool. Playground. Free continental bkfst. Cafe nearby. Ck-out noon. Coin lndry. Sundries. Lighted tennis. Downhill/x-country ski 19 mi. Game rm. Balconies. Picnic tables. Cr cds: A, C, D, MC, V.

Michigan

Population: 9,262,070

Land area: 56,954 sq mi (147,520 sq km)

Elevation: 570–1,980 ft (174–604 m)

Highest point: Mt Curwood (Baraga Co)

Entered Union: January 26, 1837 (26th state)

Capital: Lansing

Motto: If you seek a pleasant peninsula, look about you

Nickname: Wolverine State

State flower: Apple blossom

State bird: Robin

State tree: White pine

State fair: August 25–September 4 1989, in Detroit

Time zone: Eastern (except four counties on the Wisconsin border of the upper peninsula which are in the Central Time Zone. These counties are: Menominee, Dickinson, Iron and Gogebic).

Interstate Highway System

The following alphabetical listing of Michigan towns in *Mobil Travel Guide* shows that these cities are within 10 miles (16 kilometers) of the indicated Interstate highways. A highway map should, however, be checked for the nearest exit.

INTERSTATE 69: Coldwater, Flint, Lansing, Marshall, Owosso, Port Huron.

INTERSTATE 75: Bay City, Birmingham, Bloomfield Hills, Cheboygan, Dearborn, Detroit, Flint, Frankenmuth, Gaylord, Grayling, Holly, Mackinaw City, Monroe, Pontiac, Saginaw, St Ignace, Sault Ste Marie, West Branch.

INTERSTATE 94: Albion, Ann Arbor, Battle Creek, Bridgman, Dearborn, Detroit, Jackson, Kalamazoo, Marshall, Mount Clemens, Port Huron, St Clair, St Joseph, Ypsilanti.

INTERSTATE 96: Brighton, Detroit, Grand Haven, Grand Rapids, Lansing, Muskegon.

Weather Statistics*

	WINTER	SPRING	SUMMER	FALL
Alpena	20°F (-7°C)	39°F (4°C)	64°F (18°C)	46°F (8°C)
Detroit	26°F (-3°C)	47°F (8°C)	70°F (21°C)	62°F (17°C)
Lansing	24°F (-4°C)	46°F (8°C)	69°F (21°C)	50°F (10°C)
Marquette	15°F (-9°C)	27°F (-2°C)	62°F (17°C)	43°F (6°C)
Muskegon	25°F (-4°C)	44°F (7°C)	68°F (20°C)	51°F (11°C)
Sault Ste Marie	16°F (-9°C)	37°F (3°C)	62°F (17°C)	44°F (7°C)

*Average mean temperatures are listed for the entire state. Averages for specific regions (or cities representing specific regions) are given if significant differences exist.

Visitor Information

The Travel Bureau, Michigan Dept of Commerce, Box 30226, Lansing 48909; phone 517/373-1195, or 800/5432-YES, distributes publications including seasonal travel planners, calendars of events; charter boat directories, campground directories and accomodations directories.

A 24-hr, toll-free conditions report line gives current seasonal conditions of fishing, fall color, skiing, snowmobiling. Phone 800/292-5404 (MI) or 800/248-5708 (NE quadrant of US and SD).

There are 11 travel information centers in Michigan; visitors who stop will find information and brochures most helpful in planning stops to points of interest. Their locations are as follows: in Clare off US 27; in Coldwater off I-69; in Dundee off US 23; in Iron Mountain off US 2; in Ironwood off US 2; in Mackinaw City off I-75; in Menominee off US 41/MI 35; in Monroe off I-75; in New Buffalo off I-94; in Port Huron off I-94; and in Sault Ste Marie off I-75. (Daily)

Room Rate Information

The following resort area has higher room rates for two (double) than indicated on the cover of this Guide. However, the lodging listed in this resort area offers a good value when compared to others of its type in the area.

    Mackinac Island   **$65**

Alpena

Pop: 12,214 **Elev:** 593 ft (181 m) **Area code:** 517 **Zip:** 49707

Motels

✔ ★★**BEST WESTERN.** *1286 MI 32. 517/356-9087.* 35 rms, 1–2 story. June–Aug: S $32; D $34–$43; each addl $5; under 12 free; lower rates rest of yr. Crib $2. TV; cable. Indoor pool. Cafe 6 am–9 pm. Rm serv. Bar. Ck-out 11 am. Meeting rms. Sundries. Game rm. Cr cds: A, C, D, DS, MC, V.

✔ ★★**FLETCHER'S.** *1001 US 23N. 517/354-4191.* 88 rms, 64 A/C, 2 story. June–Oct: S $38–$43; D $45–$51; each addl $5; suites $55; kit. units $52; under 16 free; wkly rates; lower rates rest of yr. Crib $3. TV; cable. Indoor pool in season; sauna. Cafe 6 am–11 pm; Sat–Mon from 7 am. Rm serv. Bar 11–2 am; Sun from noon. Ck-out noon. Meeting rms. Bellhops. Free airport, bus depot transportation. Tennis. Nature trail. Many refrigerators. Grills. Some balconies. Cr cds: A, C, D, MC, V.

Ann Arbor

Settled: 1823 **Pop:** 107,966 **Elev:** 840 ft (256 m) **Area code:** 313

Motels

★**BEST WESTERN WOLVERINE INN.** *3505 S State St (48108). 313/665-3500.* 119 rms, 2 story. S $36.95–$40.95; D $42.95–$46.95; each addl $6; higher rates football wkends; under 12 free. Crib free. TV. Free continental bkfst Mon–Fri. Cafe adj 11 am–10 pm; Sat, Sun 8 am–11 pm. Ck-out 11 am; Sun, hols noon. Meeting rms. Valet serv. X-country ski 10 mi. Whirlpool. Sauna. Cr cds: A, C, D, DS, MC, V.

✔ ★★**HAMPTON INN-NORTH.** *2300 Green Rd (48105). 313/996-4444.* 130 units, 4 story. S $44; D $49; suites $75–$95; under 18 free. Crib free. TV; cable. Indoor pool. Free continental bkfst. Cafe nearby. Ck-out noon. Meeting rms. Bellhops. Valet serv. X-country ski 3 mi. Exercise equipt; bicycles, rowing machines, whirlpool. Refrigerators in suites. Cr cds: A, C, D, DS, MC, V.

✔ ★★**HOWARD JOHNSON.** *2380 Carpenter Rd (48108). 313/971-0700.* 128 rms, 2 story. S, D, studio rms $45–$56; each addl $5; suites $90–$112; under 18 free; wkend rates. Crib free. TV; in-rm movies. Indoor pool; whirlpool, sauna. Free continental bkfst. Ck-out noon. Meeting rms. Bellhops. Valet serv. Sundries. X-country ski 2 mi. Game rm. Lawn games. Sun deck. Some refrigerators. Private patios, balconies. Cr cds: A, C, D, ER, MC, V. ⅅ Ⓔ

✔★**KNIGHTS INN.** *3764 S State St (48108).* *313/665-9900.* 109 rms, 12 kits. S $31.50–$32.50; D $37–$38; each addl $3; studio rms $33.50–$41.50; under 18 free. Crib $3. TV; satellite. Pool. Free coffee. Cafe adj 6 am–11 pm. Ck-out noon. Meeting rm. X-country ski 4 mi. Cr cds: A, C, D, MC, V.

[icons]

Battle Creek

Settled: 1831 **Pop:** 35,724 **Elev:** 830 ft (253 m) **Area code:** 616

Motels

✔★★**HOWARD JOHNSON.** *2590 Capital Ave SW (49015).* *616/965-3201.* 86 rms, 2 story. May–mid-Sep: S $41–$53; D $48–$60; each addl $7; under 14 free; lower rates rest of yr. Crib free. TV; cable. Heated pool. Cafe opp 5 am–10 pm. Ck-out noon. Meeting rms. X-country ski 4 mi. Private patios, balconies. Picnic tables. Cr cds: A, C, D, DS, ER, MC, V. Ⓔ

[icons]

✔★**REGAL 8 INN.** *4775 Beckley Rd (49017).* *616/979-1141.* 77 rms, 2 story. S $21.88; D $26.88–$31.88; suites $36.88. Crib free. TV; cable. Indoor pool. Cafe adj open 24 hrs. Ck-out 1 pm. X-country ski 10 mi. Picnic tables. Cr cds: A, C, D, DS, MC, V.

[icons]

Cadillac

Settled: 1871 **Pop:** 10,199 **Elev:** 1,328 ft (404 m) **Area code:** 616 **Zip:** 49601

Motels

★★**BILL OLIVER'S CABERFAE MOTOR INN.** *(Box 266) 865 S Lake Mitchell Dr (MI 55).* *616/775-2458.* 66 rms. May–mid-Oct, Dec 26–mid-Mar: D $49–$57; each addl $3; studio rms $61–$71; lower rates rest of yr. Crib $3. TV; cable, in-rm movies. Indoor pool; sauna. Playground. Cafe 7 am–10 pm; Mon from 11:30 am; Sat from 8 am; Sun 8 am–6 pm. Rm serv. Bar 11 am–midnight. Ck-out 11 am. Tennis. Golf privileges. Downhill ski 12 mi; x-country ski on site. Game rm. Lawn games. Picnic tables, grills. Cr cds: A, C, D, MC, V.

[icons]

★**BUDGET HOST PINE KNOLL.** *8072 Mackinaw Trail.* *616/775-9471.* 16 rms. S $30–$45; D $40–$60; each addl $5. Crib $5. TV; cable, in-rm movies. Indoor pool; sauna. Playground. Cafe nearby. Ck-out 11 am. Meeting rm. Downhill ski 15 mi; x-country ski adj. Game rm. Picnic tables, grill. 27-hole golf adj. Cr cds: A, C, D, DS, MC, V.

[icons]

✔★★**CADILLAC SANDS MOTOR INN.** *On MI 115, jct MI 55.* *616/775-2407.* 55 rms, 2 story. S $39.50–$49.50; D $49.50–$79.50; each addl $5; under 2 free. Crib $2. TV; cable. Indoor pool. Cafe. Bar 4 pm–2:30 am; entertainment, dancing Wed, Fri, Sat. Ck-out 11 am. Meeting rm. Golf privileges, putting green. Downhill ski 13 mi; x-country ski 3½ mi. Game rm. Lawn games. Some private patios, balconies. Private beach; dockage. Cr cds: A, DS, MC, V.

[icons]

★**MAPLE HILL.** *US 131S.* *616/775-0164.* 23 rms, 1–2 story. S $28; D $32; each addl $4; suites $34–$45. Crib $4. TV; cable, in-rm movies. Playground. Cafe nearby. Ck-out 11 am. Downhill ski 15 mi; x-country ski 2 mi. Picnic table, grill. Cr cds: MC, V.

[icons]

✔★**SOUTH SHORE.** *1246 Sunnyside Dr (MI 55).* *616/775-7641.* 15 rms, 5 kits. May–mid-Sep, Oct, hunting season, Christmas wk: S $38; D $42; each addl $5; kit. units $40–$56; under 6 free; lower rates rest of yr. Crib $5. TV; cable. Free coffee. Cafe nearby. Ck-out 11 am. Downhill ski 15 mi; x-country ski 3 mi. Lawn games. Private beach. Boats; launch, dock. Picnic tables. Cr cds: DS, MC, V.

[icons]

Charlevoix

Pop: 3,296 **Elev:** 599 ft (183 m) **Area code:** 616 **Zip:** 49720

Motels

★**CAPRI.** *(RR 1) 1 mi S on US 31, jct MI 66. 616/547-2545.* 18 rms, 1 kit. July–early Sep, ski wkends: S, D $45–$70; each addl $2–$5; kit. unit $75; under 12 free; wkly rates off-season; lower rates rest of yr. Crib free. TV; cable, in-rm movies. Cafe opp 5:30 am–9 pm. Ck-out 10 am. Downhill/x-country ski 2 mi. Cr cds: DS, MC, V.

✔ ★**VILLA MODERNE.** *1415 S Bridge St (US 31). 616/547-2578.* 20 rms. June–Aug: S $38–$58; D $48–$68; wkly rates; lower rates rest of yr. Crib free. TV; cable, in-rm movies. Cafe adj 5 am–8 pm. Ck-out 11 am. Free airport, bus depot transportation. Downhill/x-country ski 2 mi. Cr cds: DS, MC, V.

✔ ★ ★ ★**WEATHERVANE TERRACE.** *111 Pine River Lane, just N of bridge. 616/547-9955; res: 800/552-0025 (MI).* 68 rms, 2–3 story. S, D $35–$79; suites $55–$140; kit. units $45–$95; under 12 free; wkly, ski rates; higher rates Venetian Festival, Art Fair, Dec 25–Jan 1. TV; cable, in-rm movies. Heated pool; hot tub. Free coffee in rms. Cafe adj 11 am–midnight in season. Ck-out 11 am. Valet serv. Meeting rms. Downhill/x-country ski 1 mi. Game rm. Refrigerators, wet bars; some fireplaces, in-rm whirlpools. Many balconies. Sun deck overlooks 2 lakes, river. Cr cds: A, D, MC, V.

Cheboygan

Founded: 1871 **Pop:** 5,106 **Elev:** 600 ft (183 m) **Area code:** 616 **Zip:** 49721

Motels

★ ★**BEST WESTERN RIVER TERRACE.** *847 S Main St (US 27). 616/627-5688.* 29 rms, 19 A/C, 2 story. Mid-June–Oct: S, D $54–$68; each addl $5; ski plans; higher rates hol wkends; lower rates rest of yr. Crib $5. TV; cable. Cafe adj 6 am–midnight. Ck-out 11 am. X-country ski 5 mi. Spacious grounds, excellent view of river. Cr cds: A, C, D, DS, MC, V.

✔ ★ ★**CONTINENTAL INN.** *613 N Main St (US 23). 616/627-7164.* 42 rms, 2 story. Mid-June–early Sep: S $36–$48; D $42–$62; each addl $5; suites $75–$115; under 10 free; higher rates hol wkends; lower rates rest of yr. Crib $5. TV; cable. Heated pool. Cafe 7 am–10 pm. Ck-out 11 am. X-country ski 5 mi. Cr cds: A, C, D, MC, V.

Copper Harbor

Pop: 25 **Elev:** 621 ft (189 m) **Area code:** 906 **Zip:** 49918

Motels

★**BELLA VISTA.** *(Box 26) Just off jct US 41, MI 26. 906/289-4213.* 20 rms, 1–2 story, 8 kit. cottages. No A/C. May–Oct: D $36–$40; each addl $3; cottages for 2–5, $34–$50. Closed rest of yr. TV; satellite. Cafe nearby. Ck-out 10 am. Picnic tables. Glass doors in most rms open onto terrace overlooking harbor. On Lake Superior. Cr cds: MC, V.

✔ ★ ★ ★**KEWEENAW MOUNTAIN LODGE.** *1½ mi S on US 41. 906/289-4403.* 42 units, 34 cottages. No A/C. Mid-May–mid-Oct: D $40; 2-bedrm unit for 1–4, $52. Closed rest of yr. TV. Cafe 8 am–9 pm. Snacks. Bar noon–10 pm. Ck-out 11 am. Meeting rms. Tennis. 9-hole golf, greens fee $6. Lawn games. Fireplace in some units. Hiking trails. On Keweenaw Peninsula near Lake Superior. Cr cds: MC, V.

★**NORLAND.** *2 mi E on US 41, just beyond entrance to Ft Wilkins State Park. 906/ 289-4815.* 8 rms, 4 kits. No A/C. Mid-May–mid-Oct: D $27–$30; each addl $3; kit. units $2 addl; wkly rates. Closed rest of yr. TV, some B/W; satellite. Cafe nearby. Ck-out 10 am. Boat, canoe. Large, screened picnic shelter; grill. Refrigerators. Rustic; on lake in forest area. ⓓ

Dearborn

Settled: 1763 **Pop:** 90,660 **Elev:** 605 ft (184 m) **Area code:** 313

Motel

✔ ★★**FAIRLANE INN.** *21430 Michigan Ave (US 12) (48124) at Brady St. 313/565-0800.* 100 rms, 2 story. S $42–$48; D $50–$55; each addl $6; studio rms $50–$65; family, wkend rates. Crib free. TV; cable, in-rm movies. Heated pool; poolside serv, lifeguard. Free continental bkfst. Ck-out noon. Meeting rms. Bellhops. Valet serv. Downhill ski 14 mi; x-country ski 2 mi. Refrigerators. Near Henry Ford Museum & Greenfield Village. Cr cds: A, C, D, MC, V. ⓓ Ⓔ Ⓕ ⓘ

Detroit

Founded: 1701 **Pop:** 1,203,339 **Elev:** 600 ft (183 m) **Area code:** 313

Motels

✔ ★★**BEST WESTERN COACH & LANTERN MOTOR INN.** *(25255 Grand River Ave, Redford 48240) 18 mi NW on MI 5. 313/533-4020.* 70 rms, 2 story. S $40–$50; D $45–$55; each addl $5; under 12 free. Crib free. TV; cable, in-rm movies. Heated pool. Free continental bkfst. Cafe nearby. Ck-out 11 am. Downhill ski 15 mi; x-country ski 10 mi. Colonial decor; fireplace in lobby. Cr cds: A, C, D, DS, MC, V.

★**BUDGETEL.** *(9000 Wickham Rd, Romulus 48174). 313/722-6000.* 102 rms, 3 story. S $34.95–$39.95; D $39.95–$42.95; each addl $5; under 18 free. Crib free. TV; satellite, in-rm movies. Cafe opp 6 am–2 pm, 5:30–11 pm. Ck-out noon. Coin lndry. Meeting rms. Valet serv. Cr cds: A, C, D, DS, MC, V.

★**ENVOY INN.** *(8300 Chicago Rd, Warren 48093) N on MI 53. 313/826-9300; res: 800/227-7378.* 120 rms, 3 story. S $30.95–$35.95; D $32.95–$37.95; each addl $5; under 18 free. Crib free. TV; cable. Cafe nearby. Ck-out noon. Downhill/x-country ski 19 mi. Some refrigerators. Cr cds: A, C, D, DS, MC, V.

✔ ★★**FAIRFIELD INN BY MARRIOTT.** *(31119 Flynn Dr, Romulus 48174) I-94E at Merriman Rd exit N. 313/728-2322; res: 800/228-2800.* 133 rms, 3 story. S $33.95–$39.95; D $36.50–$45.50; each addl $6; under 18 free. Crib free. TV; cable. Heated pool. Free coffee. Cafe adj 6 am–10 pm. Ck-out noon. Meeting rm. Cr cds: A, C, D, DS, MC, V. ⓓ Ⓕ

★**RED ROOF INN.** *(26300 Dequindre Rd, Warren 48091) 313/573-4300.* 137 rms, 2 story. S $31.95–$36.95; D $37.95–$42.95; 3 or more $41.95; under 18 free. Crib free. TV; cable, in-rm movies. Free coffee. Cafe nearby. Ck-out noon. Downhill, x-country ski 15 mi. Cr cds: A, C, D, DS, MC, V.

★**TRAVELODGE.** *(27650 Northwestern, Southfield 48034) 19 mi NW, 1 blk N of I-696 exit Telegraph Rd (N). 313/353-6777.* 112 rms, 2 story. S $43; D $49; each addl $4; under 18 free. Crib free. TV. Free continental bkfst. Cafe nearby. Ck-out noon. Meeting rms. Valet serv. Downhill/x-country ski 15 mi. Cr cds: A, C, D, DS, ER, MC, V.

Escanaba

Settled: 1830 **Pop:** 14,355 **Elev:** 598 ft (182 m) **Area code:** 906 **Zip:** 49829

Motels

✔ ★ ★ **BEST WESTERN PIONEER MOTOR INN.** 2635 Ludington St. 906/786-0602. 72 rms, 2 story. S $35–$60; D $40–$70; each addl $5. Crib $5. TV; cable. Indoor pool. Cafe 7 am–2 pm, 5–10 pm. Bar 5 pm–2 am. Ck-out 11 am. Meeting rms. Sundries. Downhill/x-country ski 7 mi. Health club privileges. Many balconies. Cr cds: A, C, D, DS, MC, V.

★ **HIAWATHA.** 2400 Ludington St. 906/786-1341. 28 rms, 2 kits. June–Sep: D $36–$42; each addl $2; kit. unit for 4–6, $40–$60; lower rates rest of yr. Crib $2; under 12 free. TV; cable, in-rm movies. Free morning coffee. Cafe nearby. Ck-out 11 am. Downhill/x-country ski 7 mi. Some refrigerators. Cr cds: A, C, D, DS, MC, V.

✔ ★ ★ **TERRACE BAY INN.** (Box 453) 4½ mi N, ½ blk E of US 2, 41, MI 35. 906/786-7554. 71 rms, 1–2 story. S $34–$45; D $40–$60; each addl $5; package rates. Crib $2. TV; cable. 2 heated pools; sauna. Cafe 7–10 am (summer only), 5–10 pm. Bar 5 pm–midnight. Ck-out 11 am. Tennis. Golf, driving range. Downhill ski 5 mi; x-country ski 7 mi. Lawn games. Game rm. Meeting rms. Sundries. Private patios, balconies. Overlooks Little Bay de Noc. Cr cds: A, C, D, MC, V.

Farmington

Pop: 11,022 **Elev:** 750 ft (229 m) **Area code:** 313

Motels

★ **ENVOY INN.** (38300 Grand River Ave, Farmington Hills 48018) I-96 W to Grand River exit. 313/471-0590. 110 rms, 2 story. S $30.95–$32.95; D $37.95; each addl $5; under 18 free. Crib free. TV; cable. Cafe nearby. Ck-out noon. Cr cds: A, C, D, DS, MC, V.

✔ ★ ★ **KNIGHTS INN.** (37527 Grand River Rd, Farmington Hills 48024) Near jct I-96 & 10 Mile Rd. 313/477-3200. 112 rms, 1 story. 12 kits. S $31.50–$33.50; D $37–$39; each addl $3; kit. units $41.50–$47; under 18 free; wkly rates. Crib $3. TV; cable. Pool. Cafe nearby. Ck-out noon. Meeting rm. Cr cds: A, C, D, MC, V. ⒹⒻ

★ **RED ROOF INN.** (24300 Sinacola Ct, Farmington Hills 48018) 3 mi W. 313/478-8640. 109 rms. S $29.95–$31.95; D $34.95–$36.95; 3 or more $38.95; under 18 free. Crib free. TV; in-rm movies. Cafe adj open 24 hrs. Ck-out noon. Cr cds: A, C, D, DS, MC, V.

Inn

✔ ★ ★ ★ **BOTSFORD INN.** 28000 Grand River Ave (I-96 Business) (48024). 313/474-4800. 75 rms. S $35–$55; D $50–$70; each addl $5; studio rms $50–$75; suites, kit. units $90–$130; under 12 free. Crib $5. TV; cable, in-rm movies. Coffee in rms. Free full bkfst. Cafe 7 am–10 pm exc Mon; Sun 10 am–8 pm. Bar 11 am–midnight. Ck-out 1 pm. Meeting rms. Bellhops. Valet serv. Tennis. Early Amer, Victorian furnishings; many antiques. Built in 1836; restored by Henry Ford. Cr cds: A, C, D, MC, V. ⒹⒺⒻ

Flint

Settled: 1819 **Pop:** 159,611 **Elev:** 750 ft (228 m) **Area code:** 313

Motels

✔★**BEST WESTERN.** *G-4380 W Pierson Rd (48504). 313/733-7570.* 74 rms, 1–2 story 2 kits. June–Labor Day: S $41–$52; D, studio rms $45–$61; each addl $5; family rates. Crib $3. TV; satellite. Cafe opp open 24 hrs. Ck-out 11 am. Meeting rm. Downhill ski 20 mi. Exercise equipt; weights, bicycles, whirlpool, steam rm, sauna. Some in-rm whirlpools, steam baths. Cr cds: A, C, D, DS, MC, V.

★**L-K COUNTRY HEARTH INN.** *(G-2435 W Grand Blanc Rd, Grand Blanc 48439) 6 mi SW at US 23 exit 88. 313/655-4681.* 42 rms, 1–2 story. S $35–$39; D $45–$69; kit. units $45–$55; each addl $6; under 18 free. Crib free. TV. Free continental bkfst. Cafe nearby. Ck-out noon. Downhill ski 10 mi. Cr cds: A, C, D, DS, ER, MC, V.

★**SCENIC INN.** *(G-8308 S Saginaw Rd, Grand Blanc 48439) 8 mi S on MI 54, 3 mi N of I-75 Grand Blanc exit. 313/694-6611.* 16 rms. S $31–$33; D $36–$38; suites $47–$51; each addl $2; wkly rates off-season. Crib $4. TV; cable. Pool. Cafe 7 am–10 pm. Rm serv. Bar. Ck-out 11 am. Free transportation to airport, RR station, bus depot. Downhill ski 6 mi; x-country ski adj. Lawn games. Some refrigerators. Grills. Cr cds: A, C, D, DS, MC, V.

Motor Hotels

★★**BEST WESTERN MR. GIBBY'S INN.** *G-3129 Miller Rd (48507), jct US 23, I-75. 313/235-8561.* 110 rms, 1–2 story. S $46–$53; D $52–$59; each addl $6; under 12 free. Crib free. TV; cable, in-rm movies. Heated pool; whirlpool, poolside serv (in summer). Playground. Free full bkfst Mon–Fri. Cafe 6:30 am–10 pm; Sun 10 am–8 pm. Bar to 2 am; entertainment, dancing. Ck-out noon. Meeting rms. Valet serv. Sundries. Free airport transportation. Tennis privileges. Exercise trail. Some in-rm steam baths. Private patios, balconies. Cr cds: A, C, D, MC, V.

✔★★**HOWARD JOHNSON EAST.** *932 S Center Rd (48503) at Court St. 313/744-0200.* 176 rms, 2 story. S $43–$53; D $46–$53; each addl $4; under 18 free; wkend rates. Crib free. TV; satellite. Indoor pool; whirlpool. Bar 11–2 am. Ck-out noon. Coin lndry. Meeting rms. Valet serv. Free airport, RR station, bus depot transportation. Tennis. Some in-rm steam baths. Private patios, balconies. Cr cds: A, C, D, DS, MC, V.

Grand Haven

Settled: 1834 **Pop:** 11,763 **Elev:** 590 ft (180 m) **Area code:** 616 **Zip:** 49417

Motels

(Rates may be higher during tulip time and the Coast Guard Festival)

✔★**FOUNTAIN INN.** *1010 S Beacon Blvd (US 31). 616/846-1800.* 47 rms, 2 story. Mid-May–Labor Day: S $35–$45; D $45–$50; each addl $5; higher rates special events; lower rates rest of yr. Crib $5. TV; cable. Free continental bkfst. Free coffee in rms. Cafe nearby. Ck-out 11 am. X-country ski 8 mi. Cr cds: A, MC, V.

★**SOUTH SHORE.** *805 S Beacon Blvd (US 31). 616/842-7720.* 19 rms. May–Labor Day: S $30–$42; D $34–$53; each addl $4; family rates; higher rates special events; lower rates rest of yr. Crib free. TV; cable. Cafe nearby. Ck-out 10 am. X-country ski 7 mi. Cr cds: A, MC, V.

Grand Rapids

Settled: 1826 **Pop:** 181,843 **Elev:** 657 ft (200 m) **Area code:** 616

Motels

(Rates may be higher during tulip festival, mid-May)

★**EXEL INN.** *4855 28th St SE (MI 11) (49508).* 616/957-3000. 111 rms, 2 story. S $28.95–$33.95; D $35.95–$43.95; each addl $4; under 18 free. Crib free. TV; cable, in-rm movies. Cafe opp 6 am–10 pm. Ck-out noon. Downhill ski 15 mi; x-country ski 4 mi. Cr cds: A, C, D, DS, MC, V.

🏃 🏊 🐾 🐕 ⊘ SC

✔ ★**HAMPTON INN.** *4981 28th St SE (49508).* 616/956-9304. 120 rms, 2 story. S $38–$49; D $42–$53; each addl $4; under 18 free. Crib free. TV; cable. Heated pool. Free continental bkfst. Cafe opp 6 am–11 pm; wkends open 24 hrs. Ck-out noon. Valet serv. Downhill ski 15 mi; x-country ski 4 mi. Exercise equipt; weights machines, bicycles. Cr cds: A, C, D, DS, MC, V. Ⓔ

🏃 🐾 🏊 🐕 ⊘ 🐕 SC

✔ ★**HOWARD JOHNSON.** *35 28th St SW (49508) 1½ blks E of US 131 at Division Ave.* 616/452-5141. 104 rms, 2 story. S $45–$50; D $47–$62; each addl $4; under 18 free; wknd rates. Crib free. TV; cable. Indoor pool; whirlpool. Cafe 6:30 am–11 pm. Ck-out noon. Meeting rms. Bellhops. Valet Serv. Sundries. Downhill ski 15 mi; x-country ski 3 mi. Beamed ceilings. Private patios, balconies. Cr cds: A, C, D, DS, MC, V.

🏃 🐾 🐾 🏊 ⊘ 🐕 SC

★**RED ROOF INN.** *5131 28th St SE (MI 11) (49508).* 616/942-0800. 107 rms, 2 story. S $29.95; D $31.95; each addl $6; under 18 free. Crib free. TV. Free coffee in lobby. Cafe adj 6 am–11 pm; Sun 8 am–10 pm. Ck-out noon. Downhill ski 15 mi; x-country ski 5 mi. Cr cds: A, C, D, DS, MC, V.

🐾 🐾 ⊘ 🐕 SC

★**RIVIERA.** *4350 Remembrance Rd NW (49504).* 616/453-2404. 25 rms. May–Sep: S $30; D $34; each addl $3; suites $55; under 5 free; higher rates special events; lower rates rest of yr. Crib $2. TV. Free coffee. Cafe nearby. Ck-out noon. Sundries. Downhill ski 20 mi; x-country ski 8 mi. Lawn games. Cr cds: A, MC, V.

🐾 SC $

✔ ★**SWAN INN.** *(5182 Alpine Ave NW, Comstock Park 49321) 7 mi NW on MI 37.* 616/784-1224. 40 rms, 1–2 story, 4 kits. S $26–$32; D, kit. units $35–$45; each addl $2; wkly rates; under 12 free; higher rates conventions. Crib free. TV; satellite. Heated pool. Cafe 6:30 am–10:30 pm; Sun 8 am–4 pm. Rm serv. Ck-out noon. Meeting rms. Downhill/x-country ski 12 mi. Cr cds: A, C, D, MC, V.

🏃 🐾 🏊 🐕 SC

✔ ★★**TRAVELODGE.** *65 28th St SW (MI 11) (49508).* 616/452-1461. 58 rms, 2 story. S $36–$39; D $46; each addl $5; under 18 free; wknd rates exc summer, tulip festival. Crib free. TV; cable. Heated pool. Free continental bkfst. Cafe adj 6 am–11 pm. Ck-out noon. Bellhops. Valet serv. Downhill ski 15 mi; x-country ski 3 mi. Balconies. Cr cds: A, C, D, DS, ER, MC, V.

🐾 🏊 ⊘ SC $

Grayling

Pop: 1,792 **Elev:** 1,137 ft (347 m) **Area code:** 517 **Zip:** 49738

Motels

★★**HOSPITALITY HOUSE.** *I-75 Business Loop.* 517/348-8900; res: 800/722-4151 *(MI).* 56 rms, 1-2 story. Memorial Day–Labor Day, wkends, Christmas wk: S, D $52–$80; each addl $5; honeymoon suite $100; under 12 free; wkly rates; lower rates rest of yr. Crib $5. TV; cable, in-rm movies. Indoor pool; whirlpool. Cafe 6 am–2 pm. Rm serv. Ck-out 11 am. Valet serv.

Free airport, bus depot transportation. Downhill/x-country ski 3 mi. Game rm. Picnic tables, grills. Cr cds: A, C, D, DS, MC, V.

♿⛷➡⊘

✔ ★NORTH COUNTRY LODGE. *(Box 290) ¾ mi N on old US 27, I-75 Business. 517/ 348-8471.* 23 rms, 8 kits. Mid-June–Labor Day, winter wkends, Christmas wk: S $34; D $35–$45; each addl $2; kit. units $39–$50; family, wkly rates; lower rates rest of yr. Crib free. TV; cable. Cafe adj 6 am–9 pm. Ck-out 11 am. Free airport, bus depot transportation. Downhill/x-country ski 3 mi. Cr cds: A, C, D, DS, MC, V.

♿⚭➡➲⊘

Holland

Founded: 1847 **Pop:** 26,281 **Elev:** 610 ft (186 m) **Area code:** 616 **Zip:** 49423

Motels

★BLUE MILL INN. *409 US 31 at 16th St (US 31). 616/392-7073.* 81 rms, 2 story. Mid-June–Labor Day: S $27.95–$35.95; D $35.95–$44.95; each addl $6; under 12 free; higher rates tulip festival; lower rates rest of yr. Crib $2. TV. Cafe adj 6 am–11 pm. Ck-out noon. X-country ski 2 mi. Cr cds: A, MC, V.

♿⚭➡➲ⓈⓈⓄ

✔ ★★COMFORT INN. *422 E 32d St. 616/392-1000.* 71 units, 2 story. Mid-Apr–Labor Day: S $42.95–$47.95; D $46.95–$53.95; suites $65–$75; under 16 free; higher rates Tulip Festival; wkly rates; ski packages; lower rates rest of yr. Crib $2. TV; cable. Heated pool; whirlpool. Cafe opp open 24 hrs. Ck-out noon. Meeting rm. Valet serv. X-country ski 3 mi. Health club & racquetball privileges. Refrigerators in suites. Cr cds: A, C, D, DS, ER, MC, V.

♿➲➡⊘ⓈⓄ

Houghton

Settled: 1843 **Pop:** 7,512 **Elev:** 607 ft (185 m) **Area code:** 906 **Zip:** 49931

Motels

✔ ★★BEST WESTERN KING'S INN. *215 Shelden Ave (US 41) downtown. 906/482-5000.* 65 rms, 5 story. S $42–$64; D $48–$70; each addl $6; under 12 free; higher rates Feb Winter Carnival, May & Nov graduations. Crib $4. TV; cable. Indoor pool; whirlpool, sauna. Cafe opp 6 am–midnight. Ck-out 11 am. Meeting rms. Downhill ski 1 mi; x-country ski 2 mi. Some in-rm whirlpools. Cr cds: A, C, D, MC, V.

♿➲ⓒⓄ

★CHIPPEWA. *(Rte 1, Box 3, Chassell 49916) 7 mi SE on US 41. 906/523-4611.* 15 rms, 7 kits. June–mid-Oct: S $28–$34; D $28–$36; kit. units for 2–6, $36–$66; lower rates rest of yr. Crib $2. TV; cable. Cafe 7 am–8 pm; Sun from 8 am. Ck-out 10 am. Meeting rms. Downhill ski 8½ mi; x-country ski 2 mi. Dockage. Picnic tables. Rms overlook bay of Portage Lake. City park adj with beach, playground picnic area, boat launch. Cr cds: DS, MC, V.

➡➲

✔ ★VACATIONLAND. *2 mi SE on US 41. 906/482-5351.* 24 rms, 1–2 story. July–Labor Day: S $32–$49; D $36–$49; family rates; lower rates rest of yr. Crib $2. TV; cable. Heated pool; sauna. Free coffee. Continental bkfst. Cafe nearby. Ck-out 11 am. Sundries. 18-hole golf adj. Downhill ski 5 mi; x-country ski 3 mi. Picnic tables. Beach, boat launching ramp opp. Cr cds: A, C, D, DS, MC, V.

➡➲➡ⓒⓄ

Houghton Lake

Pop: 2,449 **Elev:** 1,162 ft (354 m) **Area code:** 517 **Zip:** 48629

Motels

(Rates may be higher during Tip-Up-Town USA Ice Festival)

★ ★ ★HOLIDAY INN. *9285 M 55, US 27 (48629) 1 blk E of US 27, MI 55 exit. 517/422-5175.* 101 rms, 2 story. S $44–$73; D $54–$83; each addl $6; suite $77–$87; under 19 free; higher rates: wkends, hols, deer season. Crib free. TV; satellite, in-rm movies. Indoor pool; whirlpool, sauna. Playground. Cafe 7 am–10 pm. Rm serv. Bar 4 pm–2 am; Sun to 10 pm; entertainment, dancing (in season) exc Sun. Ck-out noon. Coin lndry. Meeting rms. Sundries. X-country ski 17 mi. Game rm. Cr cds: A, C, D, DS, MC, V.

🏨 ❄ 🛏 ⚡ 🏊 🐾 SC $

★REDWOOD MOTOR LODGE. *(8097 N Harrison Rd, Roscommon 48653) 8 mi N on Old US 27. 517/821-6343.* 30 rms, 23 A/C, 7 kits. Memorial Day–Labor Day: S, D $49–$65; each addl $5; kit. units $60–$150; lower rates rest of yr. Crib $2. TV. Pool. Playground. Game rm. Ck-out 10 am. Sundries. Lawn games. Downhill ski 13 mi; x-country ski 7 mi. Picnic tables, grill. Sun deck. Cr cds: MC, V.

🏊 ⚡ 🐾

★ ★VAL HALLA. *9869 Old US 27. 517/422-5137.* 12 rms, 2 kits. No A/C. Memorial Day wkend–Labor Day: S, D $40–$45; each addl $5; 2-bedrm kit. apts $400/wkly; some lower rates rest of yr. Crib $1. TV. Heated pool; wading pool. Cafe nearby. Ck-out 11 am. Free airport, bus depot transportation. Putting green. Downhill ski 17 mi; x-country ski 12 mi. Lawn games. Private patios. Picnic table, grills. Cr cds: MC, V.

🏨 🏊 ⚡ 🐾 🚶 ⚡ SC

★VENTURE INN. *8939 Old US 27, at jct MI 55. 517/422-5591.* 12 rms. Mid-June–Labor Day: S $36; D $42; each addl $5; higher rates hols; lower rates rest of yr. Crib $2. TV. Pool. Free coffee in rms. Cafe opp open 24 hrs. Ck-out 11 am. Downhill ski 20 mi; x-country ski 15 mi.

🏨 ⚡ 🐾 ⚡

✔ ★WAY NORTH. *9052 N Old US 27, 1 blk N of MI 55. 517/422-5523.* 13 rms, 3 kits. 8 A/C. Memorial Day–Labor Day: S $32–$44; D $38–$48; each addl $2; kit. units $250/wk; lower rates rest of yr. Crib $3. TV; satellite. Heated pool. Free coffee in rms. Cafe adj open 24 hrs. Ck-out 11 am. Free airport, bus depot transportation. Downhill ski 20 mi; x-country ski 14 mi. Dock. Lawn games. Cr cds: DS, MC, V.

❄ 🏊 ⚡ 🐾

Cottage Colony

✔ ★ ★SHEA'S LAKEFRONT LODGE. *(Box 357, Prudenville 48651) 8 mi E of US 27 on MI 55. 517/366-5910.* 34 rms in 2 lodges, 2 story, 5 kit. cottages. No A/C. Memorial Day–Labor Day, mid-Dec–Feb, lodges: S $32.50; D $35.50; suites $51; kit. cottages $50–$60; family, wkly rates; lower rates rest of yr. Crib $2. TV, some B/W; cable. Playground. Child's program. Continental bkfst. Cafe nearby. Ck-out 11 am. Free bus depot transportation. Game rm. 18-hole golf privileges. Private sand beach; paddleboats, canoes, rowboats, motorboats; dockage. Downhill ski 20 mi; x-country 16 mi. Snowmobile trails. Lawn games. Picnic tables, grills. In wooded area on Houghton Lake. Cr cds: A, C, D, DS, MC, V.

🏊 ⚡ 🎣 🐾

Iron Mountain

Settled: 1878 **Pop:** 8,341 **Elev:** 1,138 ft (347 m) **Area code:** 906 **Zip:** 49801

Motels

★ ★BEST WESTERN EXECUTIVE INN. *1518 S Stephenson Ave (US 2). 906/774-2040.* 45 rms, 2 story. June–Sep: S $46; D $52; each addl $4; suites $67. Crib $5. TV; cable. Indoor pool. Free continental bkfst. Cafe opp 6 am–10 pm. Ck-out 11 am. Downhill/x-country ski 3 mi. Cr cds: A, C, D, DS, MC, V.

⚡ 🐾 ⚡ SC

✓ ★**HOLIDAY.** *1609 S Stephenson Ave (US 2). 906/774-6220.* 68 rms, 2 story. S $30–$36; D $38–$45; each addl $3; suites $63. Crib $4. TV; cable, in-rm movies. Heated pool. Cafe adj 6 am–9 pm; Sat from 8 am; Sun 8 am–noon. Ck-out noon. Meeting rm. Downhill/x-country ski 2 mi. Rec rm. Cr cds: A, C, D, DS, MC, V.

★**LAKE ANTOINE.** *1½ mi N on US 2. 906/774-6797.* 22 rms, 3 kits. S $34; D $32–$40; each addl $3; kit. units $5 addl. Crib $2. TV; cable, in-rm movies. Heated pool. Cafe nearby. Ck-out 11 am. Putting green. Downhill/x-country ski 1 mi. Cr cds: A, MC, V.

✓ ★**TIMBERS MOTOR LODGE.** *200 S Stephenson Ave. 906/774-7600.* 52 rms, 2 story. S $29–$39; D $39–$48; each addl $3; suites $49–$61. Crib $4. TV; cable, in-rm movies. Cafe adj 6 am–10 pm. Ck-out noon. Meeting rms. Dwonhill/x-country ski 1½ mi. Exercise equip; weights, bicycles, whirlpool, sauna. Game rm. Cr cds: A, C, D, DS, MC, V.

Ironwood

Settled: 1885 **Pop:** 7,741 **Elev:** 1,503 ft (458 m) **Area code:** 906 **Zip:** 49938

Motels

★**ARMATA.** *124 W Cloverland Dr (US 2). 906/932-4421.* 12 rms, 1 kit. cottage. July–Labor Day, Dec–Apr: D $22–$25; each addl $3; cottage for 2–7, $24–$48; lower rates rest of yr. Crib $2. TV; cable, in-rm movies. Cafe nearby. Ck-out 11 am. Dwonhill ski 5 mi; x-country ski 2 mi. Grill. Cr cds: DS, MC, V. ⊕

✓ ★**BEST WESTERN CLOVERLAND.** *447 W Cloverland Dr (US 2). 906/932-1260.* 16 rms, 2 story. S $30–$35; D $35–$42; each addl $3; suites for 2–6, $50–$65. TV; cable, in-rm movies. Playground. Free coffee in rms. Cafe nearby. Ck-out 11 am. Coin lndry. Downhill ski 6 mi; x-country ski 4 mi. Cr cds: A, C, D, DS, MC, V.

★**CEDARS.** *¼ mi E of jct US 51, 2. 906/932-4376.* 20 rms, 2 story. D $20–$40; each addl $7; higher rates winter wkends. Crib $2. TV; cable. Playground. Cafe nearby. Ck-out 10:30 am. Downhill ski 6 mi. Picnic tables; grill.

✓ ★**SANDPIPER.** *1200 Cloverland Dr (US 2). 906/932-2000.* 29 rms. S $22; D $24–$28; higher rates winter wkends. Crib $4. TV; cable, in-rm movies. Sauna. Cafe opp 7 am–11 pm. Ck-out 10 am. Downhill ski 4 mi; x-country ski 2 mi. Cr cds: C, D, DS, MC, V. ⊕ ⊕ ⊕

✓ ★**TOWNE HOUSE MOTOR INN.** *215 S Suffolk, downtown. 906/932-2101.* 19 rms, 2 story. S $26.50–$28.50; D $32.50–$34.50; each addl $10; under 12 free; higher rates: winter wkends, late Dec. Crib $6. TV; cable. Cafe 11 am–2 pm, 4–9 pm exc Sun. Bar 4 pm–1 am exc Sun. Ck-out 11 am. Meeting rms. Downhill/x-country ski 7 mi. Cr cds: A, C, D, DS, MC, V.

Jackson

Founded: 1829 **Pop:** 39,739 **Elev:** 960 ft (293 m) **Area code:** 517

Motels

★**JACKSON.** *2505 Spring Arbor Rd (49203), 3 blks W of Cascades. 517/784-0571.* 12 rms, 4 kits. S $23; D $27; each addl $2; kit. units $22–$25; under 10 free. Crib $1. TV; cable. Cafe nearby. Ck-out 11 am. X-country ski ¼ mi. Picnic tables. Cr cds: MC, V.

✔ ★KNIGHTS INN. *830 Royal Dr (49202). 517/789-7186.* 96 units, 11 kits. S $28.50–$30.50; D $34–$36; each addl $3; kit. units $38.50–$44; under 18 free. Crib $3. TV; satellite. Pool. Coffee. Cafe adj 6 am–10 pm; Fri, Sat open 24 hrs. Ck-out noon. Meeting rm. Downhill/x-country ski 5 mi. Cr cds: A, C, D, MC, V. Ⓓ Ⓔ Ⓕ

♿ 🐾 🏃 🏊 🚭 🅰 sc

Kalamazoo

Settled: 1829 **Pop:** 79,722 **Elev:** 780 ft (238 m) **Area code:** 616

Motels

✔ ★ ★HOWARD JOHNSON. *1912 E Kilgore Rd (49002). 616/382-2303.* 70 rms, 2 story. S $42–$55; D $48–$61; each addl $6; under 18 free; higher rates tulip festival, air show. Crib free. TV; cable, in-rm movies. Pool. Cafe open 24 hrs. Bar 5 pm–midnight. Ck-out noon. Coin lndry. Meeting rms. Sundries. Free airport transportation. Downhill/x-country ski 15 mi. Private patios, balconies. Cr cds: A, C, D, DS, MC, V.

♿ 🐾 🏃 🏊 🚭 🅰 sc

✔ ★KNIGHTS INN. *3704 Van Rick Rd (49002). 616/344-9255.* 104 rms. S $28.50–$29.50; D $35–$36; each addl $3; kit. unit $38.50–$44; under 18 free. Crib $3. TV; satellite. Pool. Cafe opp 6 am–11 pm; Thurs–Sat, open 24 hrs. Ck-out noon. Downhill /x-country ski 15 mi. Cr cds: A, C, D, MC, V.

♿ 🐾 🏃 🏊 🚭 🅰 sc

✔ ★ ★LA QUINTA. *3750 Easy St (49002). 616/388-3551.* 122 rms, 2 story. S $40; D $45; each addl $5; under 18 free; wkend rates. Crib free. TV; cable, in-rm movies. Heated pool. Cafe adj 6 am–11 pm. Ck-out 1 pm. Meeting rms. Valet serv. Airport, RR station, bus depot transportation. Downhill/x-country ski 15 mi. Cr cds: A, C, D, DS, MC, V.

♿ 🐾 🏃 🏊 🚭 🅰 sc

★RED ROOF INN-WEST. *5425 W Michigan (49009). 616/375-7400.* 109 rms, 2 story. S $29.95–$35.95; D $31.95–$37.95; 3 or more $39.95; under 18 free. Crib free. TV; cable, in-rm movies. Free coffee. Cafe nearby. Ck-out noon. Downhill ski 20 mi; x-country ski 5 mi. Picnic tables. Cr cds: A, C, D, DS, MC, V.

♿ 🐾 🏃 🚭 🅰 sc

Lansing & East Lansing

Settled: 1847 **Pop:** Lansing, 130,414; East Lansing, 51,392 **Elev:** 860 ft (262 m) **Area code:** 517

Motels

★ ★BEST WESTERN OF FOWLERVILLE. *(950 S Fowlerville Rd, Fowlerville 48836) 517/223-9165.* 60 rms, 2 story. June–mid-Sep: S $46–$48; D $50; each addl $6; suites $62–$68; under 12 free; lower rates rest of yr. Crib free. TV. Indoor pool. Cafe opp open 24 hrs. Ck-out 11 am. Coin lndry. Valet serv. Downhill ski 20 mi. Refrigerators. Cr cds: A, C, D, DS, MC, V.

♿ 🛏 🏃 🚭 🅰 sc Ⓢ

★ ★COMFORT INN. *(2209 University Park Dr, Okemos 48864) E via I-96, Okemos Rd exit N. 517/349-8700.* 128 rms, 2 story. S $45–$75; D $51–$75; each addl $6; under 16 free. Crib $6. TV; cable, in-rm movies. Heated pool. Free continental bkfst. Cafe adj 6 am–midnight. Ck-out 11 am. Meeting rm. X-country ski 5 mi. Exercise equipt; weights, bicycles, whirlpool, steam rm, sauna, hot tub. Cr cds: A, C, D, DS, MC, V. Ⓓ

♿ 🏃 🚭 🅰 sc

✔ ★ ★HOWARD JOHNSON. *6741 S Cedar St (48910). 517/694-0454.* 100 rms, 2 story. S $39.50; D $46.50; each addl $7.50; studio rms $39.50–$46.50; under 18 free. Crib free. TV; cable. Heated pool. Playground. Meeting rms. Bellhops. Valet serv. Sundries. X-country ski 5 mi. Private patios, balconies. Cr cds: A, C, D, DS, MC, V. Ⓔ Ⓕ

♿ 🏃 🚭 🅰 sc

✔ ★★KNIGHTS INN. *1100 Ramada Dr (48911) at I-96 Cedar St exit. 517/394-7200.* 106 rms, 12 kit. units. S $28.50; D $34–$35; each addl $3; kit. units $38.50–$44; under 18 free. Crib $3. TV; in-rm movies. Pool. Cafe adj 6 am–midnight. Ck-out noon. Meeting rm. X-country ski 5 mi. Cr cds: A, C, D, MC, V.

🏙️ 🛁 ⛷️ 🐾 🚫 🚫 SC

★RED ROOF INN-EAST. *3615 Dunckel Rd (48910). 517/332-2575.* 81 rms, 2 story. S $29.95–$35.95; D $31.95–$39.95; each addl $2; under 18 free. Crib free. TV. Cafe opp 7 am–11 pm. Ck-out noon. X-country ski 5 mi. Movies. Cr cds: A, C, D, DS, MC, V.

🏙️ 🛁 🐾 🚫 🚫 SC

✔ ★★UNIVERSITY INN. *(1100 Trowbridge Rd, East Lansing 48823) At jct I-496, I-69, US 127. 517/351-5500; res: 800/221-8466 (exc MI).* 170 rms, 2 story, 9 kit. units (no equipt). S $34.50; D $39.50; each addl $3; suites, kit. units $47; under 12 free. Crib free. TV; cable. Heated pool. Playground. Cafe 11 am–11 pm. Bar to 2 am. Ck-out noon. Valet serv. Meeting rms. Free airport, RR station, bus depot transportation. X-country ski 2 mi. Cr cds: A, C, D, DS, MC, V.

🛁 ⛷️ 🐾 🚫 🚫 SC

Ludington

Settled: 1880 **Pop:** 8,937 **Elev:** 610 ft (186 m) **Area code:** 616 **Zip:** 49431

Motels

★FOUR SEASONS. *717 E Ludington Ave (US 10). 616/843-3448.* 32 rms. Mid-June–mid-Oct: S, D $42–$82; higher rates hols, festivals, fairs; lower rates rest of yr. Crib $5. TV; cable, in-rm movies. Cafe nearby. Ck-out 11 am. X-country ski 6 mi. Cr cds: MC, V.

🛁 🐾 🚫 🚫

✔ ★NADER'S LAKE SHORE MOTOR LODGE. *612 N Lakeshore Dr. 616/843-8757.* 23 rms, 2 kits. No A/C. Mid-June–early Sep: S $42; D $48–$53; each addl $4; kit. units $40–$44; lower rates May–mid-June, early Sep–Oct. Closed rest of yr. Crib free. TV; cable. Heated pool. Cafe nearby. Ck-out 11 am. Free airport, car ferry transportation. X-country ski 4 mi. Lawn games. Private patios. Picnic tables. Beach 1 blk. Cr cds: MC, V.

🛁 🐾 🐾 🚫

✔ ★★VIKING ARMS. *930 E Ludington Ave (US 10). 616/843-3441.* 45 rms. Mid-May–mid-Oct: S $32–$80; D $35–$125; each addl $4; family, ski rates; higher rates hols, festivals, fairs; lower rates rest of yr. Crib $2. TV; cable, in-rm movies. Heated pool; whirlpool. Cafe nearby. Ck-out 11 am. Airport, ferry dock transportation. X-country ski 7 mi. Some in-rm whirlpools. Cr cds: MC, V.

🏙️ 🛁 ⛷️ 🐾 🚫 🚫

Mackinac Island

(By ferry from St Ignace and Mackinaw City. By air from Pellston and Detroit.) **Pop:** 479 **Elev:** 600–925 ft (183–282 m) **Area code:** 906 **Zip:** 49757

Hotel

★CHIPPEWA. *Main St, downtown. 906/847-3341.* 75 rms, 4 story. Mid-May–mid-Oct: S, D $65–$170; each addl $10. Closed rest of yr. Crib free. B/W TV (fee). Heated pool. Cafe 7–11 am, noon–3 pm, 5:30–9:30 pm. Bar noon–1 am. Ck-out 11 am. Victorian decor. Overlooks Straits of Mackinac and the yacht marina. Cr cds: A, MC, V.

🐾 🚫

Mackinaw City

Settled: 1681 **Pop:** 820 **Elev:** 590 ft (180 m) **Area code:** 616 **Zip:** 49701

134 Michigan

Motels

✔ ★★**AFFORDABLE INNS OF AMERICA.** *206 Nicolet St. 616/436-8961.* 47 rms, 2 story. Mid-June–Labor Day: D $38.50–$68.50; each addl $6; higher rates hol wkends; lower rates rest of yr. Crib $4. TV; cable. Heated pool. Cafe adj 8 am–11 pm. Ck-out 10 am. X-country ski 5 mi. Cr cds: A, MC, V.

⚒ 🛏 🍽 🐾 🚫

✔ ★★**ANCHOR INNS.** *138 Old US 31. 616/436-5553.* 32 rms, 2 story. July–early Sep: S, D $38–$58; each addl $4; suites $68–$88; higher rates: July 4, Labor Day; lower rates early Sep–mid-Oct, May–June. Closed rest of yr. Crib $5. TV; cable, in-rm movies. Heated pool; whirlpool. Playground. Coffee in rms. Cafe nearby. Ck-out 10 am. Picnic tables. Cr cds: A, DS, MC, V. ⓓ

🐾 🚫

★★**BEACHCOMBER.** *1011 S Huron (US 23). 616/436-8451.* 12 rms, 1 kit. cottage. July–early Sep: D $38–$52; each addl $3; kit. cottage $70–$80. higher rates: July 4, Labor Day wkends; lower rates May–June, early Sep–mid-Oct. Closed rest of yr. Crib $3. TV; cable, in-rm movies. Playground. Cafe nearby. Ck-out 10 am. Picnic tables. On lake; private beach. Cr cds: MC, V.

🍽 🐾 🚫

★★**BEL-AIRE.** *(Box 298) ½ mi S on US 23, Old US 31. 616/436-5733.* 34 rms. July–early Sep: S, D $40–$60; each addl $3; suites $60–$80; family, wkly rates; higher rates: July 4, Labor Day wkend, special events; lower rates mid-May–June, after Labor Day–mid-Oct. Closed rest of yr. Crib $3. TV; cable, in-rm movies. 2 pools, 1 indoor. Playground. Cafe nearby. Ck-out 10 am. Valet serv. Picnic tables. Cr cds: A, MC, V. ⓓ

🍽 🐾 🚫

✔ ★**BELL'S MELODY.** *1067 S Huron St (US 23). 616/436-5463.* 26 rms. July–early Sep: S $28–$42; D $36–$73; each addl $2; family, wkly rates off-season; higher rates hol wkends; lower rates late Apr–June, early Sep–mid-Oct. Closed rest of yr. Crib free. TV; cable, in rm-movies. Indoor/outdoor pool; whirlpool. Playground. Free continental bkfst off-season. Free coffee. Cafe nearby. Ck-out 10 am. Tennis. Private beach on Lake Huron; sailboats, canoes, moorage. Lawn games. Private patios. Picnic tables, grills. View of Mackinac Bridge, lake. Cr cds: DS, MC, V. Ⓔ Ⓕ

🍽 🔍 🐾

✔ ★★**CARRIAGE INN.** *601 N Huron St. 616/436-5252.* 16 rms, 2 story. July–early Sep: D $45–$65; each addl $3–$5; higher rates hol wkends; lower rates rest of yr. Closed Jan. Crib $3. TV; cable. Heated pool. Playground. Free coffee. Cafe nearby. Ck-out 11 am. X-country ski 5 mi. Lawn games. Opp Lake Huron. Cr cds: A, DS, MC, V.

🍽 🐾 🐾 🚫 SC

✔ ★★**ECONO LODGE.** *412 Nicolet St. 616/436-5026.* 32 rms, 1-2 story. Mid-June–early Sep: S $38.95–$58.95; D $52.95–$68.95; each addl $5; suites $100; under 18 free; higher rates hol wkends; lower rates rest of yr. Crib free. TV; cable. Cafe adj 7:30 am–10:30 pm; off-season to 10 pm. Ck-out 11 am. X-country ski 5 mi. Cr cds: MC, V.

🐾 🛏 🐾 🚫 SC

✔ ★★**FRIENDSHIP INN-STARLITE.** *(Box 758) ½ mi SE on Old US 31, 1 blk W of US 23. 616/436-5959; res: 800/453-4511.* 33 rms. July–early Sep: S $54–$56; D $54–$64; each addl $3; family rates; higher rates Labor Day wkend; lower rates May–June, early Sep–Oct. Closed rest of yr. Crib $3. TV; cable. Heated pool. Playground. Coffee in rms. Cafe nearby. Ck-out 10 am. Sundries. Lawn games. Refrigerators. Cr cds: A, C, D, DS, MC, V.

⚒ 🛏 🐾 🚫

✔ ★★**NORTH STAR.** *(Box 705) 1001 S Huron St (US 23). 616/436-5565.* 33 units. July–early Sep: D $42–$60; each addl $3; suites $75–$80; higher rates Labor Day wkend; lower rates May–June, early Sep–Oct. Closed rest of yr. Crib $3. TV; cable, in-rm movies. Indoor pool; whirlpool. Cafe nearby. Ck-out 10 am. Picnic tables. Sun deck. Private beach on Lake Huron. Cr cds: MC, V.

🍽 🐾 🚫

★**NORTHWINDS.** *1055 S Huron St (US 23). 616/436-5463.* 18 rms. July–early Sep: S $28–$42; D $36–$73; each addl $2; family rates; wkly rates off-season; higher rates hol wkends; lower rates late Apr–June, early Sep–late Oct. Closed rest of yr. Crib free. TV. Playground. Free coffee. Cafe nearby. Ck-out 10 am. Tennis privileges. Canoes, sailboats, dock. Picnic tables, grill. On lake, private beach. Cr cds: MC, V. Ⓔ Ⓕ

⚫ 🔍 🐟

✔ ★**VAGABOND.** *(Box 911) 925 S Huron St (US 23). 616/436-8621.* 14 rms, 6 cottages, 17 A/C, 1–2 story. July–early Sep: S $38–$50; D $40–$58; each addl $3; higher rates hol wkends; lower rates May–June, Sep–Oct. Closed rest of yr. Crib $3. TV; cable. Playground. Free coffee. Cafe opp 7 am–11 pm. Ck-out 10 am. Lawn games. Some refrigerators. Picnic area, grill. Beach. Cr cds: MC, V.

⚫ 🐟 🔍 Ⓢ

Manistee

Pop: 7,566 **Elev:** 600 ft (183 m) **Area code:** 616 **Zip:** 49660

Motels

★ ★**BELLA VISTA MOTOR LODGE.** *(US 31, Bear Lake 49614) 16 mi N on US 31. 616/864-3000.* 20 rms. No A/C. July–Oct, all wkends: S $45–$63; D $53–$74; each addl $3–$4; lower rates rest of yr; wkly, ski, fishing, hunting rates. TV; satellite. Pool. Cafe adj 6:30–1 am. Ck-out 10 am. Sundries. Downhill /x-country ski 15 mi. Picnic tables. Early Amer decor. Cr cds: MC, V. Ⓔ

🏊 ⚫ 🐟 🔍

✔ ★ ★**HILLSIDE.** *1570 US 31S. 616/723-2584.* 28 rms. Mid-June–Sep: S $35–$55; D $45–$65; each addl $3; higher rates: forest festival, hols; lower rates rest of yr. Crib $5. TV; cable, in-rm movies. Heated pool. Playground. Cafe opp 6 am–midnight. Ck-out 10 am–noon. Meeting rms. Airport, bus depot transportation. 18-hole golf privileges. X-country ski 3 mi. Exercise equipt; weights, bicycles. Lawn games. Picnic tables, grills. Cr cds: A, D, DS, MC, V. Ⓘ

🏋 🏃 🐟 🚶 🔆 ⊙ 🔍

✔ ★**SUNSET.** *1599 US 31S. 616/723-6401 , -6440.* 20 rms. July–Sep: S $36–$49; D $50–$58; each addl $4; snowmobile package plan; higher rates hol wkends; lower rates rest of yr. Crib free. TV; cable, in-rm movies. Heated pool; whirlpool. Playground. Cafe adj 5 am–10 pm. Ck-out 11 am. Free airport transportation. X-country ski 3 mi. Refrigerators. Cr cds: A, C, D, DS, MC, V.

⚫ 🏋 🔍 SC

Manistique

Pop: 3,962 **Elev:** 600 ft (183 m) **Area code:** 906 **Zip:** 49854

Motels

✔ ★ ★**BEACHCOMBER.** *(Box 3) 1 mi E on US 2. 906/341-2567.* 20 rms. No A/C. Mid-June–Labor Day: D $34–$45; each addl $4; lower rates rest of yr. Crib $4. TV; cable, in-rm movies. Coffee in rm. Cafe adj 6:30 am–9 pm. Ck-out 11 am. Airport transportation. X-country ski 15 mi. Lake Michigan opp. Cr cds: A, C, D, MC, V.

⚫ 🏋 🐟 🔍

✔ ★ ★**BEST WESTERN BREAKERS.** *(Box 322) 2 mi E on US 2. 906/341-2410.* 20 rms. No A/C. Mid-June–early Sep: S $38–$42; D $38–$46; each addl $3; studio rms $48–$60; lower rates rest of yr. Crib $2. TV; cable, in-rm movies. Free coffee in rms. Cafe adj 7 am–9 pm. Ck-out 11 am. X-country ski on site. Overlooks Lake Michigan; Driftwood Beach opp. Cr cds: A, C, D, DS, MC, V.

⚫ 🏋 🔍

✔ ★ ★**MANISTIQUE MOTOR INN.** *(Rte 1) 3½ mi E on US 2. 906/341-2552.* 26 rms. No A/C. Mid-June–Labor Day: D $36–$44; each addl $3; suites $50–$74; lower rates rest of yr. Crib $3. TV; cable, in-rm movies. Heated pool. Playground. Cafe adj 11 am–10 pm. Bar adj. Ck-out 11 am. Free airport, bus depot transportation. X-country ski on site. Snowmobile trails. Lawn games. Cr cds: A, C, D, DS, MC, V.

★**MAPLE LEAF.** *(Box 184) 1¼ mi E on US 2. 906/341-6014.* 13 rms. July–Labor Day: D $32–$36; lower rates rest of yr. TV; cable, in-rm movies. Cafe nearby. Ck-out 10 am. X-country ski 10 mi. Lake Michigan opp. Cr cds: A, C, D, MC, V.

Marquette

Settled: 1849 **Pop:** 23,288 **Elev:** 628 ft (191 m) **Area code:** 906 **Zip:** 49855

Motels

✔ ★ ★**BEST WESTERN EDGEWATER.** *1¾ mi SE on US 41, MI 28. 906/225-1305.* 49 rms, 1–2 story. Mid-June–mid-Oct: D $40.60–$48.60; each addl $3; lower rates rest of yr. Crib $3. TV; cable, in-rm movies. Cafe 7 am–9:30 pm; Fri, Sat to 10 pm. Bar 11:30 am–midnight. Ck-out 11 am. Meeting rm. Downhill/x-country ski 5 mi. Opp Lake Superior. Cr cds: A, C, D, DS, MC, V. Ⓓ

★**CEDAR MOTOR INN.** *2523 US 41W. 906/228-2280.* 44 rms, 1–2 story, 2 kits. Mid-June–mid-Oct: S, D $29–$42; each addl $2; kit. units (1–4 persons) $42; lower rates rest of yr. Crib $3. TV; cable, in-rm movies. Indoor pool; sauna. Cafe nearby. Ck-out 11 am. Meeting rm. Downhill ski 5 mi; x-country ski 3 mi. Sun deck. Cr cds: A, DS, MC, V.

★**IMPERIAL.** *2493 US 41W. 906/228-7430.* 43 rms, 2 story. S $28–$32; D $32–$40; each addl $4. Crib $4. TV; cable, in-rm movies. Indoor pool; sauna. Cafe nearby. Ck-out 11 am. Downhill ski 5 mi; x-country ski 3 mi. Game rm. Balconies. Picnic tables. Cr cds: A, D, DS, MC, V.

✔ ★ ★ ★**TIROLER HOF.** *150 Carp River Hills (MI 28), US 41. 906/226-7516.* 44 rms, 2 story. 24 A/C. May–Oct: S, D $40–$44; each addl $3; suites $56–$58; studio rms $42–$44; lower rates rest of yr. Crib avail. TV; cable. Sauna. Playground. Cafe 7:30–10 am, 5:30–9 pm. Ck-out 11 am. Coin lndry. Meeting rm. Downhill/x-country ski 1½ mi. Rec rm. Private patios, balconies. Picnic tables, grills. Pond; boat. Overlooks Lake Superior; on 15 acres. Cr cds: A, DS, MC, V. Ⓓ Ⓘ

★**VILLAGE INN OF MARQUETTE.** *1301 N 3d St. 906/226-9400.* 40 units, 3 story, 8 kits. June–Sep: S $36–$40; D $40–$44; each addl $4; suites $49.50–$70; kit. units $42–$48; under 18 free; wkly rates; ski packages; lower rates rest of yr. Crib $5. TV; cable. Ck-out noon. Coin lndry. Metting rms. Valet serv. Free airport, bus depot transportation. Downhill ski 5 mi; x-country ski 1 mi. Some refrigerators. Cr cds: A, C, D, DS, MC, V. Ⓔ Ⓕ

Munising

Pop: 3,083 **Elev:** 620 ft (189 m) **Area code:** 906 **Zip:** 49862

Motels

★**ALGER FALLS.** *(Box 967, Rte 1) 2 mi E on MI 28, 94. 906/387-3536.* 17 rms. No A/C. July–Labor Day: S $32–$35; D $32–$38; kit. cottages $42–$50; lower rates rest of yr. Crib $4. TV; cable. Playground. Cafe nearby. Ck-out 10 am. Downhill ski 2 mi; x-country ski 3 mi. Snowmobile trails; free guides Dec–mid-Apr. Rec rm. Picnic tables. Wooded area. Cr cds: MC, V.

★ ★**BEST WESTERN.** *Box 310, 3 mi E on MI 28. 906/387-4864.* 50 rms, 2 story. Mid-June–Aug: S, D $50–$60; each addl $5–$7; lower rates rest of yr. Crib $4. TV; cable, in-rm movies. Heated pool. Playground. Cafe 7 am–10 pm; off season to 9 pm. Ck-out 11 am. Meeting rm. Downhill ski 3 mi; x-country ski on site. Snowmobile trails. Game rm. Rec bldg. Picnic tables, grills. Cr cds: A, C, D, DS, MC, V.

🚳🚳🏂🚭🏃🚭🚭

✔ ★★NORTHERN. *(Box 403) 5 blks SE on MI 28. 906/387-2493.* 46 rms. No A/C. July–Sep: S, D $44–$56; suite $78–$83; lower rates rest of yr. Crib free. TV; cable, in-rm movies. Cafe adj 7 am–10 pm. Ck-out 11 am. Downhill/x-country ski 1 mi. Cr cds: A, C, D, DS, MC, V.

♿🚭🏂

✔ ★SUNSET RESORT. *(Box 471, Rte 1) 1 mi E on H 58. 906/387-4574.* 16 units, 1–3-rm, 6 kits. No A/C. June–Labor Day: S, D $34–$39; kit. units $5 addl; lower rates rest of yr. Crib $1. TV; cable. Playground. Free morning coffee. Cafe nearby. Ck-out 11 am. Downhill/x-country ski 1 mi. Lawn games. Picnic tables, grills. Private beach on Lake Superior. Docking facilities. Cr cds: MC, V.

🚳🏂🚭🚭

★VACATIONER. *(Box 308) 5 blks SE on MI 28. 906/387-3400.* 20 rms. No A/C. July–Labor Day: S, D $38–$45; each addl $4; lower rates rest of yr. Crib free. TV; cable, in-rm movies. Cafe opp 7 am–10 pm. Ck-out noon. Downhill ski ¼ mi; x-country ski 6 mi. Picnic tables, grills. Cr cds: A, C, D, MC, V.

🏂🚭

Muskegon

Settled: 1810 **Pop:** 40,823 **Elev:** 625 ft (190 m) **Area code:** 616

Motels

★BEL-AIRE. *4240 Airline Rd (49444), jct US 31, I-96 exit 1A. 616/733-2196.* 16 rms. S $24–$32; D $34–$42; each addl $4–$5; under 16 free; wkly rates; higher rates special events. Crib $3. TV; cable. Cafe nearby. Ck-out 11 am. Free airport, bus depot transportation. X-country ski 11 mi. Cr cds: A, MC, V.

🏂sc

★CORNER HOUSE MOTOR INN. *3350 Glade St (49444). 616/733-1056.* 23 rms, 2 story, 5 kits. S, kit. units $34–$37; D $40–$46.50; each addl $4; under 5 free. Crib $5. TV; cable. Cafe 11–2 am. Bar. Ck-out 11 am. X-country ski 5 mi. Cr cds: A, C, D, MC, V.

🏂🚭🚭

✔ ★DAYS INN. *150 Seaway Dr (49444). 616/739-9429.* 152 rms, 2 story. June–Labor Day: S $39–$47; D $41–$52; each addl $5; under 19, $1; higher rates tulip festival; lower rates rest of yr. Crib free. TV; cable. Indoor pool; whirlpool. Cafe adj 6 am–10 pm; Sun to 8 pm. Ck-out noon. Valet serv. Sundries. X-country ski 5 mi. Cr cds: A, C, D, DS, MC, V.

♿🏂🚭🚭sc🅂

✔ ★★★HOLIDAY INN. *Seaway Dr at Hoyt St (49444). 616/733-2601.* 199 rms, 2 story. S $44; D $49; each addl $5–$8; family rates. Crib free. TV; cable. Heated pool; poolside serv. Playground. Cafe 6:30 am–10 pm; Sat 7 am–11 pm; Sun from 7 am. Rm serv. Bar 11–1 am. Ck-out noon. Coin lndry. Meeting rms. Bellhops. Valet serv. Sundries. X-country ski 5 mi. Cr cds: A, C, D, DS, MC, V.

♿🚭🏂🚳🚭🚭sc

✔ ★★SEAWAY. *631 Norton Ave (49441). 616/733-1220.* 29 rms, 2 story. S $36–$39; D $40–$49; each addl $5; suites $60–$80; under 14 free; wkly rates off-season; higher rates tulip festival. Crib free. TV; cable. Heated pool. Free continental bkfst. Cafe nearby. Ck-out 11 am. X-country ski 3 mi. Cr cds: A, C, D, DS, MC, V.

🚳🏂🚭🚭🚭sc

Newberry

Pop: 2,334 **Elev:** 788 ft (240 m) **Area code:** 906 **Zip:** 49868

Motels

✔ ★BEST WESTERN VILLAGE INN. *S Newberry Ave (MI 123), 2½ mi N of jct MI 28.* *906/293-5114.* 20 rms. S $32; D $35–$42; each addl $4. Crib $5. TV; cable. Cafe 6 am–10 pm. Rm serv. Bar 4 pm–11 pm. Ck-out 11 am. Meeting rms. Sundries. Game rm. Cr cds: A, C, D, MC, V.

✔ ★ ★COMFORT INN. *Jct MI 28, 123.* *906/293-3218.* 32 rms, 2 story. Mid-June–Oct: S $38–$46; D $44–$50; each addl $4; under 16 free; lower rates rest of yr. Crib free. TV; cable, in-rm movies. Cafe opp 6 am–midnight; off-season 7 am–11 pm. Rm serv. Ck-out 10 am. Coin lndry. Meeting rm. Valet serv. X-country ski ¾ mi. Game rm. Some in-rm whirlpools. Cr cds: A, C, D, DS, ER, MC, V.

★MANOR. *(Rte 1, Box 979) S Newberry Ave (MI 123), 3 mi N of jct MI 28.* *906/293-5000.* 12 rms. Mid-June–mid Sep: S, D $34–$44; each addl $2; suites $48–$54; family rates; lower rates May–mid-June, mid-Sep–Oct. Closed rest of yr. Crib $3. TV; cable. Playground. Cafe nearby. Ck-out 10 am. Lawn games. Grills. Cr cds: MC, V.

Plymouth

Pop: 9,986 **Elev:** 730 ft (223 m) **Area code:** 313 **Zip:** 48170

Motels

✔ ★ ★FAIRFIELD INN BY MARRIOTT. *(5700 Haggerty Rd, Canton 48187) I-94 W to I-275 N, exit Ford Rd W.* *313/981-2440; RES: 800/228-2800.* 133 rms, 3 story. S $33.95; D $36.50; each add $6; under 18 free. Crib free. TV; cable, in-rm movies. Heated pool. Free coffee. Cafe adj 5:30 am–10 pm; Fri, Sat open 24 hrs. Ck-out noon. Meeting rm. Cr cds: A, C, D, DS, MC, V. Ⓔ

★RED ROOF INN. *39700 Ann Arbor Rd at I-275 exit 28.* *313/459-3300.* 109 rms, 2 story. S $30.95–$32.95; D $35.95–$37.95; 3 or more $39.95; under 19 free. Crib free. TV; cable. Cafe opp open 24 hrs. Ck-out noon. Cr cds: A, C, D, DS, MC, V.

Hotel

✔ ★ ★MAYFLOWER. *827 W Ann Arbor Trail.* *313/453-1620.* 100 rms. S $40–$72; D $50–$91; each addl $10; under 10 free; wkend rates. Crib $4. TV. Free full bkfst, Sun brunch. Cafe 6:30 am–10 pm; Sun 10 am–8 pm. Bar 11–1 am. Ck-out 1 pm. Meeting rms. Some refrigerators, whirlpools. Colonial atmosphere. Family-owned. Cr cds: A, C, D, DS, MC, V. Ⓔ Ⓕ Ⓙ

Port Austin

Pop: 883 **Elev:** 600 ft (183 m) **Area code:** 517 **Zip:** 48467

Motels

✔ ★CASTAWAYS MOTOR INN & BEACH RESORT. *1404 Port Austin Rd.* *517/738-5101.* 36 rms, 10 kit. cottages, 28 A/C, 1–2 story. Many rm phones. June–Labor Day: S $32; D $35–$55; each addl $3, kit. cottages $60–$80; under 18 free; MAP; wkly, ski, getaway plans; lower rates rest of yr. Crib free. TV. Heated pool. Playground. Cafe 8 am–10 pm. Bar to 2 am; entertainment, dancing Wed–Fri. Ck-out 11 am. Sundries, gift shop. Free dock transportation. X-country ski 1 mi. Game rm. Lawn games. Balconies. Picnic tables, grills. 200-ft beach. On Lake Huron, Saginaw Bay. Cr cds: MC, V.

★**SUN 'N SAND.** *891 Port Austin Rd. 517/738-7513.* 16 rms, 4 kits. No A/C. June–Aug: S $39; D $42; each addl $3; kit. units $49; under 12 free; lower rates rest of yr. Crib free. TV; cable. Heated pool. Playground. Morning coffee in lobby. Cafe nearby. Ck-out 11 am. X-country ski 1½ mi. Lawn games. Picnic tables, grill. Beach opp. Cr cds: MC, V.

⊗ ⊜ ⊅ ⊁ SC

Port Huron

Pop: 33,981 **Elev:** 600 ft (183 m) **Area code:** 313 **Zip:** 48060

Motels

✔ ★★**COLONIAL MOTOR INN.** *2908 Pine Grove Ave (MI 25) at N end of I-94. 313/984-1522.* 107 rms, 2 story, 34 kits. June–mid-Sep: S $36.50–$52.75; D $39.75–$58.75; each addl $5; family, wkly rates; lower rates rest of yr. Crib free. TV; cable. Heated pool; whirlpool. Playground. Free continental bkfst. Cafe adj 6 am–11 pm. Ck-out noon. Meeting rms. Bellhops. Valet serv. Sundries. Tennis. Game rm. Lawn games. Cr cds: A, C, D, DS, MC, V.

⊞ ⊗ ⊗ ⊁ ⊘ SC

✔ ★**ECONO LODGE.** *1720 Hancock St, at Blue Water Bridge. 313/984-2661; res: 800/446-6900.* 100 rms, 2 story. S $36.75–$37.75; D $45.75–$46.75; each addl $5; under 12 free. Crib free. TV. 2 pools, 1 indoor; whirlpool, sauna. Playground. Free continental bkfst. Bar. Ck-out noon. Meeting rms. Valet serv. Game rm. Cr cds: A, C, D, DS, MC, V.

⊗ ⊁ ⊘ SC

★★**KNIGHTS INN.** *2160 Water St. 313/982-1022.* 105 units. June–Sep: S $37.50–$43; D $38.50–$44; each addl $3; kit units $47.50; under 18 free; lower rates rest of yr. Crib $3. TV; cable. Heated pool. Cafe nearby. Ck-out noon. View of river. Cr cds: A, D, MC, V.

⊞ ⊜ ⊅ ⊁ ⊘ SC

Saginaw

Settled: 1816 **Pop:** 77,508 **Elev:** 595 ft (181 m) **Area code:** 517

Motels

✔ ★★**BEST WESTERN.** *3325 Davenport Ave (48602) at Morson St. 517/793-2080.* 117 rms, 2 story. May–Sep: S $45–$55; D $50–$60; each addl $4; suites $50–$65; under 18 free; lower rates rest of yr. Crib free. TV; cable. Heated pool. Free full bkfst. Cafe 6 am–2 pm, 5–10 pm. Rm serv. Bar 3 pm–midnight; Sat 5–10:30 pm. Ck-out noon. Coin lndry. Meeting rms. Bellhops. Valet serv. Airport transportation. Downhill/x-country ski 10 mi. Health club privileges. Some refrigerators. Cr cds: A, C, D, DS, MC, V. Ⓔ

⊞ ⊁ ⊅ ⊘ SC

★**SUPER 8.** *4848 Town Centre Rd (48603). 517/791-3003.* 62 units, 2–3 story. S $26; D $32; each addl $1.50; suites $38; under 12 free. Crib free. TV; cable. Cafe nearby. Ck-out 11 am. Cr cds: A, C, D, DS, MC, V.

⊞ ⊛ ⊘ SC

Motor Hotel

✔ ★★**FLORENTINE INN.** *400 Johnson St (48607). 517/755-1161; res: 800/323-8909 (exc MI), 800/321-8119 (MI).* 178 rms, 8 story. S $39.95–$47; D $39.95–$53; each addl $6; suites $75–$100; under 18 free; wkend, plans. Crib free. TV; in-rm movies. Indoor pool; whirlpool, sauna. Cafe 7 am–2 pm, 5–9 pm; Sun to 2:30 pm. Rm serv. Bar 11:30 am–midnight; Fri, Sat to 1 am. Ck-out noon. Meeting rms. Bellhops. Valet serv. Cr cds: A, C, D, MC, V.

⊞ ⊅ ⊘ SC

St Ignace

Pop: 2,632 **Elev:** 600 ft (183 m) **Area code:** 906 **Zip:** 49781

Motels

✔ ★★**BELLE ISLE.** *1030 N State St (I-75 Business). 906/643-8060.* 47 rms. Late June–Labor Day: D $44–$58; each addl $4; lower rates May–late June, after Labor Day–mid-Oct. Closed rest of yr. Crib $3. TV; cable, in-rm movies. Indoor pool; whirlpool. Playground. Cafe adj 6:30 am–10 pm. Ck-out 10 am. Sun deck, balconies. Picnic tables, grills. Lake opp. Cr cds: A, C, D, DS, MC, V.

🛁🏊🚫

✔ ★★**CHALET NORTH.** *1140 N State St (I-75 Business). 906/643-9141.* 70 rms. 52 A/C. June–Labor Day: D $40–$60; each addl $4; lower rates May–June, after Labor Day–mid-Oct. Closed rest of yr. Crib free. TV; cable, in-rm movies. Heated pool; sauna. Playground. Free in-rm coffee. Cafe nearby. Ck-out 10 am. Free airport transportation. Game rm. Volleyball. Beach opp. Picnic tables, grills. Nature trail. Cr cds: A, C, D, DS, MC, V.

🏊🚫🆂🅲

✔ ★**COLLINS.** *US 2W, 1 blk E of I-75. 906/643-8511.* 50 rms, 1–2 story. July–Sep: S $50–$65; D $55–$70; each addl $5; lower rates rest of yr. Crib $3. TV; cable, in-rm movies. Indoor pool; whirlpool. Playground. Cafe adj 7 am–10 pm. Ck-out 10 am. Downhill/x-country ski 5 mi. Game rm. Lawn games. Picnic tables. Cr cds: MC, V.

🏊🚫

★**DRIFTWOOD.** *590 N State St (I-75 Business). 906/643-7744.* 22 rms. 20 A/C. Mid-June–Labor Day: D $40–$52; each addl $4; lower rates mid-Apr–mid-June, after Labor Day–Oct. Closed rest of yr. Crib free. TV; cable, in-rm movies. Cafe 7 am–10 pm. Bar 11–2 am. Ck-out 10 am. Meeting rms. Free airport transportation. Opp ferry. Cr cds: DS, MC, V.

★**GOLDEN ANCHOR.** *700 N State St (I-75 Business). 906/643-9666.* 21 rms, 2 story, 1 kit. unit (no equipt). Mid-June–Labor Day: D $48; each addl $3; suite $60–$80; kit. units for 8, $70–$80; lower rates rest of yr. Crib $3. TV; cable, in-rm movies. Ck-out 10 am. Downhill/x-country ski 5 mi. Some refrigerators. Sun deck Overlooks Moran Bay. Ferry 1 blk. Cr cds: A, C, D, MC, V.

♿🚫

★★**THUNDERBIRD.** *10 S State (I-75 Business). 906/643-8900.* 34 rms, 2 story. Mid-June–Labor Day: D $52–$58; lower rates May–mid-June, after Labor Day–Oct. Closed rest of yr. Crib $4. TV; cable, in-rm movies. Cafe nearby. Ck-out 10 am. Tennis adj. Mackinac Island Ferry opp. Cr cds: MC, V.

♿🚫

✔ ★★**TRADEWINDS.** *1190 N State St (I-75 Business). 906/643-9388.* 25 rms. Late June–early Sep: D $48–$55; each addl $4; lower rates mid-May–late June, mid-Sep–Oct. Closed rest of yr. Crib $2. TV; cable, in-rm movies. Heated pool. Playground. Coffee in rms. Cafe adj 7 am–10 pm. Ck-out 11 am. Free airport, bus depot transportation. Picnic tables, grill. Opp Lake Huron. Cr cds: MC, V.

St Joseph

Pop: 9,622 **Elev:** 630 ft (192 m) **Area code:** 616 **Zip:** 49085

Motels

✔ ★**BEST WESTERN GOLDEN LINK LODGE.** *2723 Niles Ave (MI 63). 616/983-6321.* 36 rms, 2 story, 2 kit. May–Oct: S $27–$29; D $38–$49; each addl $3; suite $38–$52; kit. units $38–$45; under 12 free; wkly rates off-season; lower rates rest of yr. Crib $3. TV; cable, in-rm movies. Heated pool. Cafe adj open 24 hrs. Ck-out noon. X-country ski 5 mi. Cr cds: A, C, D, DS, MC, V.

🅿♿🏊🚫🆂🅲

★★★**HOWARD JOHNSON.** *(2699 MI 139S, Benton Harbor 49022) 3 mi SE on MI 139, at I-94 exit 28. 616/925-7021.* 120 rms, 2 story. S $48–$56; D $53–$75; each addl $5; under 18 free; wkend rates; higher rates: festivals, May. Crib free. TV; cable. Indoor pool. Cafe open 24 hrs. Rm serv 8 am–9 pm. Bar 4 pm–1 am. Ck-out noon. Coin lndry. Meeting rms. Bellhops. Valet serv.

Sundries. X-country ski 20 mi. Exercise equipt; weights, bicycles, whirlpool, sauna. Game rm. Rec rm. Lawn games. Private patios, balconies. Cr cds: A, C, D, DS, MC, V.

🏊 🏖 🏋 🎿 🎯 🚫 🐾 SC

Saugatuck

Pop: 1,079 **Elev:** 600 ft (183 m) **Area code:** 616 **Zip:** 49453

Motel

(Rates may be higher during Tulip Festival)

✔ ★**SHANGRAI-LA.** *Blue Star Hwy (A-2). 616/857-1453.* 20 rms. May–early Sep: S $35–$50; D $40–$55; each addl $5; lower rates rest of yr. Crib $3. TV. Pool. Cafe nearby. Ck-out 11 am. Sundries. Free airport, bus depot transportation. X-country ski 4 mi. Lawn games. Refrigerators. Picnic tables, grill. Cr cds: A, MC, V.

🏖 🏋 🎿 🚫

Inn

★**TWIN GABLES COUNTRY INN.** *900 Lake St. 616/857-4346.* 13 rms, 2 story. No rm phones. May–Oct: S, D $50–$89; Nov–Apr: S, D $34–68; each addl $10–$15; under 3 free; wkly rates. Crib $3. TV in lobby. Heated pool; hot tub. Free continental bkfst. Ck-in 3 pm. Free airport, RR station, bus depot transportation. X-country ski 3 mi. Bicycles. Picnic tables, grills. Fireplace in lobby, embossed tin ceilings and walls; antiques. Near lake. Cr cds: MC, V. ⓕ ①

♿ 🏖 🏋 🎿

Sault Ste Marie

Settled: 1668 **Pop:** 14,448 **Elev:** 613 ft (187 m) **Area code:** 906 **Zip:** 49783

Motels

✔ ★**BAMBI.** *1801 Ashmun St (I-75 Business). 906/632-7881.* 28 rms. Mid-June–Labor Day: D $36–$50; lower rates mid-May–mid-June, after Labor Day–mid-Oct. Closed rest of yr. Crib $3. TV; cable, in-rm movies. Heated pool. Playground. Coffee in rms. Cafe adj 6–3 am. Ck-out 11 am. Airport, bus depot transportation. Picnic tables, grill. Cr cds: DS, MC, V.

🐾 🎿 🚫

✔ ★★**BEST WESTERN COLONIAL INN.** *(Box 659) 2½ mi S on I-75 Business. 906/632-2170.* 58 rms, 2 story. Mid-June–Labor Day: D $51–$55; lower rates March–June, Labor Day–Nov. Closed rest of yr. Crib free. TV; cable. Indoor pool; sauna. Cafe nearby. Ck-out 11 am. Game rm. Refrigerators. Cr cds: A, C, D, DS, MC, V.

🎿 🚫 🐾 SC

★**DORAL.** *518 E Portage Ave. 906/632-6621.* 20 rms, 2 story. Mid-June–Oct: S $48; D $52; each addl $5; suites $55–$65; under 12 free; lower rates mid-Apr–mid-June. Closed rest of yr. Crib $2.50. TV; cable. Heated pool; whirlpool, sauna. Cafe nearby. Ck-out 11 am. Game rm. Lawn games. Picnic tables. Cr cds: A, C, D, DS, MC, V.

🏖 🎿 🚫 🐾

★★**LA FRANCE TERRACE.** *1608 Ashmun St (I-75 Business). 906/632-7823.* 30 rms, 15 A/C. July–Oct: D $42–$46; each addl $5; lower rates mid-May–June. Closed rest of yr. Crib $3. TV; cable. Heated pool. Playground. Cafe nearby. Ck-out 11 am. Picnic tables. Cr cds: A, C, D, DS, MC, V.

🐾 🎿 🚫

✔ ★**SKYLINE.** *2601 I-75 Business. 906/632-3393.* 24 rms, 2 story. July–mid-Oct: D $48–$55; each addl $5; lower rates rest of yr. Crib $5. TV; cable, in-rm movies. Free continental bkfst. Cafe nearby. Ck-out 11 am. Valet serv. X-country ski 1½ mi. Cr cds: A, C, D, DS, MC, V.

🏋

★**SNO-WHITE.** *3295 I-75 Business. 906/632-7413.* 14 rms. No A/C. Late June–Oct: S $32; D $34–$42; lower rates May–late June. Closed rest of yr. Crib $3. TV; cable. Coffee in rm. Cafe opp 6 am–10 pm. Ck-out 11 am. Some refrigerators. Picnic tables. Cr cds: DS, MC, V.

South Haven

Pop: 5,943 **Elev:** 618 ft (188 m) **Area code:** 616 **Zip:** 49090

Motels

✔ ★★**HOLLY INN.** *09817 MI 140 (I-196 Business). 616/637-5141; res: 800/527-9122 (MI).* 60 rms. S $32–$50; D $40–$54; each addl $5; suites $45–$100; family, ski, golf rates; higher rates: tulip festival, some hols. Crib free. TV; in-rm movies. Playground. Indoor pool. Free coffee in rms. Cafe adj open 24 hrs. Ck-out 11 am. Valet serv. Free local airport, bus depot, marina transportation. Downhill ski 20 mi; x-country ski 5 mi. Exercise rm; instructor, weights, bicycles, sauna. Raquetball. Lawn games. Cr cds: A, C, D, DS, MC, V.

★**LAKE BLUFF.** *76648 11th Ave. 616/637-8531.* 46 rms, 17 kits. May–Labor Day: S, D $38–$62; kit. units $53–$74; family, wkly, ski rates. Crib free. TV; cable, in-rm movies. Heated pool; wading pool, sauna, hot tub. Cafe nearby. Ck-out 11 am. Free airport, bus depot transportation. X-country ski 2 mi. Lawn games. Rec rm. Picnic tables, grills. On Lake Michigan. Cr cds: A, MC, V.

Sturgis

Pop: 9,468 **Elev:** 920 ft (280 m) **Area code:** 616 **Zip:** 49091

Motels

✔ ★★★**HOLIDAY INN.** *(Box 626) 1300 S Centerville Rd (MI 66). 616/651-7881.* 81 rms, 2 story. S $44–$49; D $52–$57; each addl $6; under 18 free. Crib free. TV; cable. Heated pool. Cafe 6:30 am–2 pm, 5–10 pm. Rm serv. Bar 4 pm–2 am. Ck-out noon. Coin lndry. Meeting rms. Valet serv. Cr cds: A, C, D, DS, MC, V.

★**MAPLE CREST.** *1203 E Chicago Rd (US 12). 616/651-8190.* 12 rms, 5 kits. May–Sep: S $22–$30; D $24–$38; each addl $3; wkly rates off-season; lower rates rest of yr. TV; cable. Cafe nearby. Ck-out 11 am. Free airport transportation. Lawn games. Cr cds: C, D, MC, V.

Traverse City

Settled: 1847 **Pop:** 15,516 **Elev:** 600 ft (183 m) **Area code:** 616 **Zip:** 49684

Motels

★**BRIAR HILL.** *461 Munson Ave (US 31). 616/947-5525.* 20 rms. Mid-June–early Sep: D $55–$70; each addl $5; lower rates rest of yr. Crib free. TV; cable, in-rm movies. Cafe opp 6 am–midnight. Ck-out 10:30 am. Downhill ski 3½ mi; x-country ski 6½ mi. Beach 1 blk. Cr cds: DS, MC, V.

✔ ★**KNIGHTS INN.** *618 E Front St. 616/929-0410.* 94 units, 21 kit. units. June–Aug: S $44.50–$46.50; D $52–$54; each addl $3; kit. units $54.50–$62; under 18 free; lower rates rest of yr. Crib $3. TV; cable. Heated pool. Ck-out 11 am. Meeting rm. Downhill ski 5 mi; x-country ski 8 mi. Opp beach. Cr cds: A, C, D, MC, V.

Minnesota

Population: 4,075,970

Land area: 79,548 sq mi (206,029 sq km)

Elevation: 602–2,301 ft (182–701 m)

Highest point: Eagle Mt (Cook Co)

Entered Union: May 11, 1858 (32d state)

Capital: St Paul

Motto: *L'Etoile du Nord* (Star of the North)

Nicknames: Gopher State, North Star State

State flower: Pink and white ladyslipper

State bird: Common loon

State tree: Norway pine

State fair: August 24–September 4, 1989 in St Paul

Time zone: Central

Interstate Highway System

The following alphabetical listing of Minnesota towns in *Mobil Travel Guide* shows that these cities are within 10 miles (16 kilometers) of the indicated Interstate highways. A highway map should be checked, however, for the nearest exit.

INTERSTATE 35: Albert Lea, Cloquet, Duluth, Faribault, Hinckley, Lakeville, Minneapolis, Mora, Northfield, Owatonna, St Paul.

INTERSTATE 90: Albert Lea, Austin, Blue Earth, Fairmont, Jackson, Luverne, Rochester, Spring Valley, Winona, Worthington.

INTERSTATE 94: Alexandria, Anoka, Elk River, Fergus Falls, Minneapolis, Moorhead, St Cloud, St Paul, Sauk Centre.

Weather Statistics*

	WINTER	SPRING	SUMMER	FALL
Northern	7°F (-14°C)	36°F (2°C)	63°F (17°C)	41°F (5°C)
Southern	16°F (-9°C)	43°F (6°C)	69°F (20°C)	47°F (8°C)

*Average mean temperatures are listed for the entire state. Averages for specific regions are given if significant differences exist.

Visitor Information

Minnesota travel information is available free from the Minnesota Travel Information Center, 375 Jackson St, 250 Skyway, St Paul 55101. Phone 612/296-5029, toll free 800/328-1461 or, in Minnesota, 800/652-9747 for information on special events, recreational activities and places of interest. Also available are: *Minnesota Explorer,* a free newspaper with events and attraction information, including a calendar of events for each season; *Canoeing, Hiking, Backpacking, Biking, and Fishing*; a state map and directories to restaurants, accommodations and campgrounds, as well as tourism region publications.

Whitman's Travel Guide to Minnesota (Nodin Press, Minneapolis, 1977) provides both general information about the state and car and walking tours of various regions and cities.

There are ten travel information centers at entry points to Minnesota; visitors will find the information provided at these stops very helpful in planning their trip through the area. Their locations are as follows: northbound I-35 at Iowa border in Glenville; US 53 south of Eveleth; I-90 at South Dakota border in Beaver Creek; I-90 at Wisconsin border in La Crescent; US 2, 10 mi east of North Dakota border in Crookston (May–Oct); US 61 at Canadian border in Grand Portage (May–Sep); US 53 in International Falls; I-94 at North Dakota border in Moorhead; I-94 at Wisconsin border in Lakeland; I-35 and US 2 in Duluth.

Albert Lea

Settled: 1855 **Pop:** 19,200 **Elev:** 1,299 ft (396 m) **Area code:** 507 **Zip:** 56007

Motels

★**BEL-AIRE.** *US 69S, 1 blk S of jct US 16, MN 13. 507/373-3983.* 46 rms, 1–2 story. S $26; D $33–$38; each addl $4. Crib $2. TV; cable. Pool. Cafe opp 6 am–10 pm. Ck-out 11 am. Sundries. X-country ski 3 mi. Cr cds: A, C, D, DS, MC, V.

🦽 ⛷ 🐕 Ⓝ SC

✔ ★ ★**BEST WESTERN ALBERT LEA INN.** *2301 E Main St, S of jct I-35, I-90. 507/373-8291.* 124 rms, 3 story. S $42–$52; D $47–$59; each addl $5; under 18 free. Crib free. TV. Indoor pool; whirlpool. Cafe 7 am–2 pm, 5–10 pm; Sat 6:30 am–2:30 pm, 5–10 pm. Bar 11–1 am exc Sun; entertainment, dancing. Ck-out 11 am. Coin lndry. Meeting rms. Sundries. X-country ski 1 mi. Game rm. Cr cds: A, C, D, DS, MC, V.

🦽 🦽 ⛷ 🐕 Ⓝ Ⓝ SC

✔ ★ ★**HOLIDAY INN.** *2306 E Main St, S of jct I-35, I-90. 507/373-6471.* 129 rms, 2 story. S $42–$50; D $49–$59; each addl $5; under 20 free. Crib free. TV. Indoor pool; poolside serv. Cafe 6:30 am–9 pm; dining rm 11 am–2 pm, 5–9 pm. Rm serv. Bar 5 pm–12:30 am. Ck-out noon. Coin lndry. Meeting rms. Sundries. X-country ski 1 mi. Snowmobile trails. Cr cds: A, C, D, DS, MC, V.

🦽 🦽 ⛷ 🐕 Ⓝ SC

Alexandria

Settled: 1866 **Pop:** 7,608 **Elev:** 1,400 ft (427 m) **Area code:** 612 **Zip:** 56308

Motels

✔ ★**DAYS INN.** *3 mi S on MN 29 at I-94. 612/762-1171.* 60 rms, 2 story. S $19–$40; D $19–$50; each addl $5; under 18 free. Crib $3. TV; cable. Free continental bkfst. Cafe adj open 24 hrs. Ck-out noon. Sundries. Cr cds: A, C, D, MC, V.

🦽 🐕 Ⓝ SC Ⓢ

✔ ★ ★**PARK INN ALEXANDRIA.** *(Box 459) MN 29 & jct I-94. 612/763-6577.* 149 rms, 2 story. S $43; D $53–$63; each addl $4; under 16 free. Crib free. TV; satellite. Indoor pool; sauna, hot tub. Cafe 6 am–10 pm; Sun from 7 am. Rm serv. Bar 11–1 am; entertainment, dancing exc Sun. Ck-out noon. Coin lndry. Meeting rms. Valet serv. Sundries. Rec rm. Cr cds: A, D, DS, MC, V.

🦽 🐕 Ⓝ SC

★**SUPER 8.** *4620 MN 29S. 612/763-6552.* 41 rms, 2 story. S $24.88–$30.88; D $32.88–$34.88; each addl $2; under 12 free. Crib $2. TV; cable. Cafe nearby. Ck-out 11 am. Meeting rms. Snowmobile trails. Game rm. Cr cds: A, C, D, DS, MC, V.

🦽 🦽 Ⓝ

Bemidji

Settled: 1894 **Pop:** 10,949 **Elev:** 1,350 ft (411 m) **Area code:** 218 **Zip:** 56601

Motels

✔ ★**DAYS INN.** *2420 Paul Bunyan Dr NW, 2½ mi NW at jct US 2 & 71N. 218/751-0390.* 58 rms, 2 story. S $29–$34; D $32–$37; each addl $1–$3. Crib free. TV; cable. Free continental bkfst. Cafe adj open 24 hrs. Ck-out noon. Free airport, bus depot transportation. Downhill ski 12 mi; x-country ski 4 mi. Cr cds: A, C, D, DS, MC, V.

✔ ★**EDGEWATER.** *1015 Paul Bunyan Dr NE (MN 197), ¾ mi E on MN 197, on Lake Bemidji.* 218/751-3600; res: 800/328-5552 (exc MN), 800/642-3896 (MN). 73 rms, 7 kits. Mid-May–mid-Sep: D $35–$55; suites $50–$135; lower rates rest of yr. Crib $4. TV; cable, in-rm movies. Whirlpool, steam rm, sauna. Playground. Cafe opp 5 am–11 pm. Ck-out 11 am. Free airport, bus depot transportation. Sand beach, dock; boat, canoe, paddleboat. Downhill ski 16 mi; x-country ski 6 mi. Snowmobile trail adj. Cr cds: A, C, D, DS, MC, V.

★**SUPER 8.** *1815 Paul Bunyan Dr NW.* 218/751-8481. 101 rms, 2 story. S $27.88; D $34.88–$37.88; each addl $2; suites $54.88; under 12 free. Crib free. TV; cable. Whirlpool, sauna. Free coffee, juice. Cafe nearby. Ck-out 11 am. Downhill ski 15 mi; x-country ski 5 mi. Cr cds: A, D, DS, MC, V.

Brainerd

Founded: 1870 **Pop:** 11,489 **Elev:** 1,231 ft (375 m) **Area code:** 218 **Zip:** 56401

Motels

✔ ★**DAYS INN.** *(Box 364) 2 mi W of town at jct MN 210, MN 371.* 218/829-0391. 60 rms, 2 story. Apr–Sep: S $42–$47; D $47–$57; lower rates rest of yr. Crib free. TV; cable; in-rm movies. Free continental bkfst. Cafe adj open 24 hrs. Ck-out noon. Downhill ski 15 mi; x-country ski 1 mi. Cr cds: A, C, D, DS, MC, V.

✔ ★ ★**PAUL BUNYAN.** *(Box 2566, Baxter 56425) 2 mi W at jct MN 210, MN 371.* 218/829-3571. 36 rms. Memorial Day wknd–Labor Day: S, D $36–$51; lower rates rest of yr. Crib $1. TV; cable, in-rm movies. Indoor pool; whirlpool, sauna. Free coffee. Cafe adj open 24 hrs. Ck-out noon. Meeting rm. Sundries. Downhill ski 15 mi; x-country ski 1 mi. Picnic tables. Paul Bunyan Amusement Park adj. Cr cds: A, DS, MC, V.

✔ ★**RIVER VIEW.** *324 W Washington St.* 218/829-8771. 70 rms. May–Sep: D $36–$42; suites $50–$56; under 12 free; lower rates rest of yr. Crib avail. TV; cable, in-rm movies. Heated pool; sauna. Complimentary continental bkfst. Cafe adj open 24 hrs. Ck-out 11 am. Meeting rm. Downhill ski 15 mi; x-country ski 1 mi. Cr cds: A, C, D, MC, V.

Detroit Lakes

Pop: 7,106 **Elev:** 1,365 ft (428 m) **Area code:** 218 **Zip:** 56501

Motels

✔ ★ ★**BEST WESTERN HOLLAND.** *1 mi E on US 10.* 218/847-4483. 56 rms, 1–2 story. D $40–$56; each addl $5; suites $47–$70; family rates. Crib free. TV; cable, in-rm movies. Indoor pool; whirlpool, wading pool, sauna. Cafe adj open 24 hrs. Ck-out 11 am. Coin lndry. Meeting rms. Putting green. Downhill/x-country ski 5 mi. Game rm. Wet bars. Refrigerators. Some bathrm phones, balconies. Snowmobile trails opp. Cr cds: A, C, D, DS, ER, MC, V.

★**CASTAWAY.** *US 10E, 2 mi E on US 10.* 218/847-4449. 15 rms, 2 levels, 3 kits. June–Labor Day: S $30–$35; D $40–$50; kit. units $50–$70; lower rates rest of yr. Crib free. TV; cable, in-rm movies. Playground. Free coffee, tea in rms. Cafe nearby. Ck-out 11 am. Coin lndry. Grocery. Downhill/x-country ski 2 mi. Lawn games. On lake, private beach; boats, motors. Also 9 cabins, 5 A/C, 7 kits. Cr cds: A, C, D, DS, MC, V.

Duluth

Founded: 1856 **Pop:** 92,811 **Elev:** 620 ft (188 m) **Area code:** 218

Motels

★**ALLYNDALE.** *510 N 66th Ave W (55807), I-35 Cody St (251A) N or Central Ave (252) S exits, near Spirit Mountain Recreation Area.* 218/628-1061; res: 800/341-8000. 21 rms. S $30–$32; D $34–$37; family rates. Crib $3. TV; cable. Playground. Free coffee, tea. Cafe nearby. Ck-out 11 am. Downhill/x-country ski 1½ mi. Picnic tables. Cr cds: A, C, D, DS, MC, V.

✔★**BEST WESTERN DOWNTOWNER.** *131 W 2d St (55802), 2 blks NE on US 61 Bypass, MN 194, 23.* 218/727-6851. 46 rms, 2 story. Late May–early Sep: S $33–$39; D $38–$56; each addl $4; under 12 free; lower rates rest of yr. Crib free. TV; cable, in-rm movies. Continental bkfst; free coffee. Cafe nearby. Ck-out noon. Downhill/x-country ski 8 mi. Cr cds: A, C, D, DS, MC, V.

✔★**DAYS INN.** *909 Cottonwood Ave (55811), Miller Hill Mall opp.* 218/727-3110. 85 rms, 2–3 story. No elvtr. S, D $34–$49; each addl $3. Crib $3. TV; cable. Free continental bkfst. Cafe opp open 24 hrs. Ck-out noon. Cr cds: A, C, D, MC, V.

✔★**PRIME RATE.** *2610 Miller Trunk Hwy (55811).* 218/722-5522. 67 rms, 2 story. S $27; D $38–$46; each addl $4; family rates. Crib free. TV; in-rm movies. Free continental bkfst. Cafe nearby. Ck-out noon. Meeting rm. Game rm. Cr cds: A, D, MC, V.

★**VIKING.** *2511 London Rd (55812), 2 mi NE on US 61.* 218/728-3691. 30 rms, 2 story. June–Oct: D $39.50–$59.50; lower rates rest of yr. Crib $3. TV; cable, in-rm movies. Free coffee in rms. Cafe nearby. Ck-out 11 am. Downhill ski 6 mi; x-country ski 2 mi. View of Lake Superior from some rms. Cr cds: A, C, D, DS, MC, V.

Elk River

Pop: 6,785 **Elev:** 924 ft (275 m) **Area code:** 612 **Zip:** 55330

Motels

✔★★**BEST WESTERN SILVER FOX INN.** *(I-94 & MN 25, Monticello 55362)* 612/295-4000. 72 rms, 2 story. S $31; D $38–$42; each addl $3; suites $52; under 16 free. Crib free. TV; in-rm movies. Cafe 6 am–10 pm; Sat, Sun 7 am–11 pm. Rm serv. Bar. Ck-out noon. Meeting rm. Sundries. Whirlpool, sauna. Cr cds: A, C, D, DS, MC, V.

★★**COMFORT INN.** *(200 E Oakwood Dr, Monticello 55362)* I-94 & MN 25. 612/295-1111. 33 units, 2 story. S $32; D $39–$44; suites $62–$69; under 16 free. Crib free. TV; cable. Free continental bkfst. Rm serv. Bar. Ck-out noon. Coin lndry. Meeting rms. Some refrigerators. Cr cds: A, C, D, DS, ER, MC, V.

✔★★**KEMETHESE.** *17291 US 10 NW.* 612/441-2424. 43 units, 1–2 story. S $26–$40; D $34–$40; each addl $4; suites $53–$63. Crib free. TV; cable. Heated pool. Free continental bkfst. Cafe 10 am–10 pm. Ck-out 11 am. Meeting rms. Sundries. Cr cds: A, C, D, DS, MC, V.

Fergus Falls

Settled: 1857 **Pop:** 12,519 **Elev:** 1,196 ft (365 m) **Area code:** 218 **Zip:** 56537

Motels

✔ ★ ★ ★ **HOLIDAY INN.** *(Box 103) On MN 210 at jct I-94. 218/739-2211.* 100 rms, 2 story. S $42–$66; D $52–$66; each addl $4; under 19 free. Crib free. TV; cable. Indoor pool; whirlpool, sauna. Cafe 7 am–10 pm. Rm serv. Bar; entertainment, dancing exc Sun. Ck-out noon. Coin lndry. Meeting rms. Bellhops. Valet serv. Sundries. Free airport, bus depot transportation. Downhill/x-country ski 2 mi. Solardome. Rec rm. Game rm. Balconies. Cr cds: A, C, D, DS, MC, V.

♿ 🐕 ⛷ 🏊 🚭 📶 SC

★ **TRAVEL HOST.** *610 Western Ave. 218/739-3311; res: 800/346-4974 (exc MN).* 59 rms, 2 story. S $25.90; D $29.90–$34.90; each addl $1; under 12 free. Crib $1.50. TV; cable, in-rm movies. Free coffee. Cafe adj open 24 hrs. Ck-out 11 am. Sundries. Downhill/x-country ski 2 mi. Bus depot adj. Cr cds: A, C, D, DS, MC, V.

🐕 ⛷ 🚭 📶 SC

Grand Marais

Pop: 1,289 **Elev:** 688 ft (210 m) **Area code:** 218 **Zip:** 55604

Motels

★ ★ **BEST WESTERN SUPERIOR INN.** *(Box 456) 1st Ave E, 1 blk E, just off US 61. 218/387-2240.* 20 rms, 2 story. Mid-June–mid-Oct: D $55–$66; lower rates rest of yr. Crib free. TV; cable, in-rm movies. Free coffee 7:30–11:30 am. Cafe nearby. Ck-out 11 am. Downhill ski 12 mi; x-country ski ½ mi. Refrigerators. Balconies. Cr cds: A, C, D, DS, MC, V.

♿ 🛏 ⛷

★ **HARBOR INN.** *On US 61. 218/387-1191.* 10 rms, 2 story. No A/C. S $36–$42; D $47–$53; each addl $6. Crib free. TV; cable. Cafe 6 am–9 pm; Sun from 7 am. Ck-out 11 am. Downhill ski 18 mi; x-country ski 1 mi. Balconies. Overlooks Lake Superior. Cr cds: ER, MC, V.

🐕 🛏 ⛷ 🏊

★ **LAMPLIGHTER.** *(Box 667) 1 mi SW on US 61. 218/387-2633; res: 800/247-6020 (MN).* 17 rms. No A/C. Mid-June–mid-Oct: S $30–$36; D $35–$42; each addl $6; lower rates rest of yr. Crib $3. TV; cable, in-rm movies. Cafe nearby. Ck-out 11 am. Downhill ski 20 mi; x-country ski on site. Cr cds: A, C, D, DS, MC, V.

🐕 ⛷

✔ ★ ★ **NANIBOUJOU LODGE.** *(Rte 1, Box 505) 15 mi NE on US 61. 218/387-2688.* 29 rms, 2 story. No A/C. Mid-May–mid-Oct: S $31–$42; D $37–$63; suites $59–$72. Closed rest of yr. Crib avail. Cafe 8–10:30 am, 11:30 am–2:30 pm, 5:30–8:30 pm. Ck-out 10:30 am. Sundries. Lawn games. Hiking trails. Movies. On Lake Superior. Cr cds: A, D, MC, V.

🛏

✔ ★ ★ **SHORELINE.** *20 S Broadway (Box 667) 2 blks S of US 61. 218/387-2633; res: 800/247-6020 (MN).* 30 rms, 2 story. No A/C. Mid-June–mid-Oct: S $39–$56; D $46–$62; each addl $6; lower rates rest of yr. Crib $3. TV; cable, free in-rm movies. Cafe nearby. Ck-out 11 am. Downhill ski 20 mi; x-country 3 mi. Rocky private beach on Lake Superior. Cr cds: A, C, D, DS, MC, V.

🛏 ⛷ 🏊 🚭

★ **SPRUCEGLEN INN.** *(Box 667) 3 blks NE on US 61. 218/387-2633; res: 800/247-6020 (MN).* 13 rms. No A/C. May–Oct: S $28; D $46; lower rates rest of yr. TV; cable, in-rm movies. Cafe nearby. Ck-out 11 am. Downhill ski 20 mi; x-country 5 mi. Picnic tables. Cr cds: A, C, D, DS, MC, V.

🐕 ⛷

Grand Rapids

Settled: 1877 **Pop:** 7,934 **Elev:** 1,290 ft (393 m) **Area code:** 218 **Zip:** 55744

Motels

✔ ★ ★ BEST WESTERN RAINBOW INN. *1300 E US 169, 1 mi E. 218/326-9655.* 80 rms, 2 story. S $39–$46.95; D $47–$54.95; each addl $5; suites $52–$59.95; under 12 free. Crib free. TV; cable, in-rm movies. Indoor pool; whirlpool, sauna, hot tub. Cafe 6 am–10 pm; Fri, Sat to 11 pm. Rm serv. Bar 11–1 am. Ck-out noon. Meeting rms. Sundries. Package store. Airport, bus depot transportation. Downhill/x-country ski 10 mi. Game rm. Cr cds: A, C, D, MC, V.

★ HOLIDAY VILLAGE. *6 blks E at jct US 2, 169. 218/326-3457; res: 800/356-3194.* 34 rms, 1–2 story. D $34–$44; each addl $4. Crib $3. TV; cable, in-rm movies. Heated pool. Playground. Cafe adj open 24 hrs. Ck-out 11 am. Downhill/x-country ski 9 mi. Picnic tables; grills. Cr cds: A, D, DS, MC, V.

✔ ★ ★ SAWMILL INN. *2301 S Pokegama Ave, 1½ mi S on US 169. 218/326-8501; res: 800/235-6455 (MN).* 125 rms, 2 story. S $39–$42; D $49–$52; each addl $4; suites $60–$70; under 12 free. Crib free. TV; cable, in-rm movies. Indoor pool; whirlpool, sauna, poolside serv. Cafe 6:30 am–10 pm; Fri, Sat to 11 pm. Rm serv. Bar 11–1 am; entertainment, dancing Tu–Sat. Ck-out noon. Coin lndry. Meeting rms. Valet serv. Sundries. Free airport, bus depot transportation. Downhill/x-country ski 7 mi. Game rm. Cr cds: A, C, D, DS, MC, V.

★ SUPER 8. *(Box 335) 1902 S Pokegama Ave. 218/327-1108.* 41 rms, 2 story. May–Sep: S $26.88; D $34.88–$37.88; each addl $3; family rates; lower rates rest of yr. Crib $2. TV; cable, in-rm movies. Cafe nearby. Ck-out 11 am. Valet serv. Free airport, bus depot transportation. Downhill/x-country ski 7 mi. Cr cds: A, C, D, DS, MC, V.

Hastings

Settled: 1850 **Pop:** 12,827 **Elev:** 726 ft (221 m) **Area code:** 612 **Zip:** 55033

Motels

★ AMERICINN. *2400 Vermillion. 612/437-8877.* 27 rms, 2 story. S $29.90–$33.90; D $35.90–$39.90; each addl $6; under 12 free. Crib free. TV; cable. Cafe nearby. Ck-out noon. Meeting rms. Cr cds: A, C, D, DS, MC, V. ·

✔ ★ HASTINGS INN. *1520 Vermillion St. 612/437-3155.* 43 rms, 2 kits. (no equipt). S $29–$34; D $36–$40; each addl $2–$4; family units to 8, $54–$59. Crib free. TV; satellite. Indoor pool; sauna. Free continental bkfst 7–11 am. Cafe nearby. Ck-out 11 am. Sundries. Downhill ski 6 mi; x-country ski 1 mi. Game rm. Sun deck. Cr cds: A, C, D, DS, MC, V.

Inn

✔ ★ ★ THORWOOD. *649 W 3d St. 612/437-3297.* 9 rms, 3 story. No elvtr. S $39–$119; D $45–$125; each addl $15; under 12 free. TV avail. Free full bkfst. Ck-out 1 pm, ck-in 4 pm. Downhill ski 6 mi; x-country ski 3 mi. Some in-rm whirlpools. Historic home built 1880; antiques, Victrolas, feather comforters, marble fireplaces. Cr cds: A, MC, V.

Hinckley

Pop: 963 **Elev:** 1,030 ft (314 m) **Area code:** 612 **Zip:** 55037

Motels

★ ★ AMERICINN. *(Box 338) Jct I-35, MN 48. 612/384-7451.* 29 rms, 2 story. S $35.90–$55.90; D $41.90–$61.90; each addl $6; under 12 free. Crib free. TV; satellite. Whirlpool;

sauna. Free coffee, donuts. Cafe adj open 24 hrs. Ck-out noon. X-country ski 15 mi. Snowmobile trails leading from premises. Large fieldstone fireplace in lobby. Cr cds: A, C, D, MC, V.

✔ ★ ★**BEST WESTERN CASSIDY'S GOLD PINE INN.** *At jct MN 48, I-35. 612/384-6112.* 48 rms, 1–2 story. May–Nov: S $32–$45; D $38–$51; each addl $6; under 12 free; lower rates rest of yr. Crib $1.50. TV. Free continental bkfst. Cafe 6 am–11 pm. Ck-out 11 am. Municipal tennis courts nearby. X-country ski 15 mi. Cr cds: A, C, D, DS, MC, V.

International Falls

Pop: 5,611 **Elev:** 1,124 ft (343 m) **Area code:** 218 **Zip:** 56649

Motels

✔ ★**DAYS INN.** *(Drawer O, South Intl Falls 56679) 1¾ mi S on US 53. 218/283-9441.* 60 rms, 2 story. Mid-May–Sep: S $34; D $39; lower rates rest of yr. Crib $3. TV; cable. Free continental bkfst. Cafe adj open 24 hrs. Ck-out noon. Cr cds: A, C, D, MC, V.

★**FALLS.** *(Box 72) 1½ mi S on US 53. 218/283-8434.* 28 rms, 1–2 story. S $27.90–$39.90; D $29.90–$45.90; each addl $4; family rates. Crib $4. TV; cable, in-rm movies. Free coffee. Cafe nearby. Ck-out 11 am. Free airport transportation. Cr cds: A, MC, V.

★**FRANK YOUSO'S NORTHLAND MOTOR COURT.** *(Box 1046) 1¼ mi S on US 53. 218/283-2503.* 8 rms, 5 kits. Mid-June–mid-Sep: D $26–$33; each addl $2; kit. units $2 addl; lower rates Apr–mid-June, mid-Sep–Oct. Closed rest of yr. Crib $1. TV; cable. Cafe nearby. Ck-out 11 am. Cr cds: MC, V.

★**INTERNATIONAL MOTOR LODGE.** *1 mi W on US 71, MN 11. 218/283-2577.* 29 rms, 2 story. S $23; D $29–$31. Crib free. TV; cable. Free coffee in rms. Cafe opp 7 am–11 pm. Ck-out 11 am. Cr cds: A, DS, MC, V.

★**VOYAGEURS.** *1200 3d Ave, ¼ mi S on US 53. 218/283-9424.* 25 rms, 1–2 story. Mid-May–mid-Sep: S $24; D $28–$32; each addl $2; family rates; lower rates rest of yr. Crib $3. TV; cable. Free coffee in am. Cafe nearby. Ck-out 11 am. Cr cds: MC, V.

Itasca State Park

(28 mi N of Park Rapids on US 71)

Resort

✔ ★**DOUGLAS LODGE.** *(Lake Itasca 56460) 2 mi W of jct US 71, MN 200, on Park Rd. 612/266-3656.* 36 rms in lodge, annexes, 9 A/C, 27 baths, 2 story, 18 (1–3) bedrm cabins, 6 with kit., central shower area. Memorial Day wkend–early Oct, lodge, annexes: S $20–$28; D $26–$39; each addl $6; cabins: D $42; 3-bedrm family units for 4, $62; kit. cabins (no maid serv): D $39; $35/day for 2–14 days; family rates. Closed rest of yr. Crib avail. Playground. Cafe 8 am–8 pm. Box lunches. Ck-out 11 am; ck-in 4 pm. Grocery 2 mi. Coin lndry 8 mi. Meeting rms. Sand beach 3 mi; lifeguard; boats, canoes. Hiking trails & naturalist program. Bicycles. Some cabins with fireplace, screened porch. In center of park. State park sticker required for entry to park & lodge. Launch tours on Lake Itasca. Cr cds: MC, V.

Le Sueur

Pop: 3,763 **Elev:** 800 ft (244 m) **Area code:** 612 **Zip:** 56058

Motel

★**COACHLIGHT.** *(Box 199, Rte 2) 2 mi NW on MN 93, just off US 169. 612/665-3341.* 13 rms. S $20–$24; D $25–$34; each addl $2; under 12 free. Crib $1. TV. Playground. Free coffee in rms. Cafe nearby; supper club adj 11 am–2 pm, 5:30–11 pm; Sun 4–10 pm; closed Mon. Setups, beer. Ck-out noon. Sundries. X-country ski 1 mi. Cr cds: A, MC, V.

Mankato

Founded: 1852 **Pop:** 28,651 **Elev:** 785 ft (239 m) **Area code:** 507 **Zip:** 56001

Motels

★**BUDGETEL.** *111 W Lind Court. 507/345-8800.* 66 rms, 2 story. S $26.95–$29.95; D $31.95–$34.95; under 18 free. Crib free. TV; cable. Cafe adj 7 am–11 pm. Ck-out noon. Meeting rm. Valet serv. Sundries. Downhill ski 6 mi; x-country ski 2 mi. Whirlpool, sauna. Cr cds: A, C, D, DS, MC, V.

★**CLIFF KYES.** *1727 Riverfront Dr, 1 ½ mi N on MN 22. 507/388-1638.* 16 rms. S $19–$23; D $23–$27; each addl $3. Crib free. TV; cable. Free coffee in rms. Cafe nearby. Ck-out 11:30 am. Valet serv. Downhill ski 5 mi; x-country ski 1 mi. Municipal pool nearby. Cr cds: A, D, MC, V.

Motor Hotels

✔ ★ ★**BEST WESTERN GARDEN INN.** *(1111 Range St, N Mankato) 1 mi N, just off US 169. 507/625-9333.* 147 rms, 2 story. S $42; D $53; each addl $6; under 19 free. Crib free. TV; cable. Indoor pool; whirlpool. Cafe 6 am–10 pm. Rm serv. Bar. Ck-out noon. Coin lndry. Meeting rms. Sundries. Putting green. Downhill ski 6 mi; x-country ski 1 mi. Rec rm. Cr cds: A, D, DS, MC, V.

✔ ★ ★ ★**HOLIDAY INN DOWNTOWN.** *101 Main St, 6 blks S on US 169. 507/345-1234.* 151 rms, 4 story. S $44–$54; D $49–$66; each addl $5; suites $70–$79; under 19 free. Crib free. TV; cable. Indoor pool; whirlpool, poolside serv. Cafe 7 am–10 pm; Sat to 11 pm. Rm serv. Bar 11:30–1 am; entertainment. Ck-out noon. Coin lndry. Meeting rms. Valet serv. Sundries. Putting green. Downhill ski 4 mi; x-country ski 1 mi. Rec rm. Cr cds: A, C, D, DS, MC, V.

Minneapolis

Settled: 1847 **Pop:** 370,951 **Elev:** 687–980 ft (209–299 m) **Area code:** 612

Motels

★**AMERICINN OF ROGERS.** *(Box 13, Rogers 55374) Jct I-94 & MN 101. 612/428-4346.* 30 rms, 2 story. S $27.90–$40.90; D $33.90–$40.90; each addl $4; under 13 free. Crib free. TV; satellite. Free coffee, continental bkfst. Cafe adj open 24 hrs. Ck-out 11 am. Meeting rms. Cr cds: A, C, D, DS, MC, V.

★**AQUA CITY.** *5739 Lyndale Ave S (55419). 612/861-6061.* 37 rms, 8 kit. units, 1–2 story. S $29–$39; D $34–$42; each addl $4. Crib free. TV. Pool; wading pool. Cafe nearby. Ck-out 11 am. X-country ski ½ mi. Game rm. Cr cds: A, C, D, DS, MC, V.

★ ★**BEST WESTERN AMERICAN INN.** *3924 Excelsior Blvd (55416). 612/927-7731.* 36 rms, 2 story. S $42; D $43–$51; each addl $5; suites $56; under 17 free. Crib free. TV; cable, in-rm movies. Free coffee, doughnuts. Cafe nearby. Ck-out noon. X-country ski 1 mi. Some refrigerators. Sun deck. Cr cds: A, C, D, DS, MC, V.

[icons]

★**BOULEVARD.** 5637 Lyndale Ave S (55419), just off I-35W, MN 190 exit. 612/861-6011. 35 rms. Apr–Oct: S $26–$36; D $32–$40; each addl $3–$5; lower rates rest of yr. Crib $4–$5. TV; cable. Pool. Cafe 7:30 am–2:30 pm, 5–8 pm. Ck-out 11 am. X-country ski ½ mi. Cr cds: A, C, D, DS, MC, V.

[icons]

★**BUDGETEL INN.** (7815 Nicollet Ave S, Bloomington 55420) 612/881-7311; res: 800/428-3488. 194 rms, 2 story. S $29.95–$37.95, D $34.95–$42.95; each addl $5; under 19 free. Crib free. TV; cable. Cafe adj 6 am–11 pm. Ck-out noon. Meeting rms. Downhill ski 10 mi; x-country ski ½ mi. Cr cds: A, C, D, DS, MC, V.

[icons]

★**DAYS INN.** 2407 University Ave SE (55414), ¼ mi N of I-94, on University of Minnesota campus. 612/623-3999; res: 800/325-2525. 130 rms, 6 story. S $41–$47; D $47–$53; each addl $6; suites $68–$110; under 16 free. Crib free. TV. Free continental bkfst 6–10 am. Cafe opp open 24 hrs. Ck-out 11 am. Coin lndry. Meeting rms. X-country ski ½ mi. Some refrigerators. Cr cds: A, C, D, DS, MC, V.

[icons]

★**DAYS INN.** 6300 Wayzata Blvd (55416). 612/546-6277. 102 units. S $36–$39; D $38–$50; under 5 free. Crib $3. TV. Free continental bkfst 6:30–9:30 am. Cafe nearby. Ck-out noon. Valet serv. Sundries. Airport transportation. X-county ski 1 mi. Cr cds: A, C, D, DS, MC, V.

[icons]

★**EXEL INN.** 2701 E 78th St (55420), just off I-494 exit 24th Ave. 612/854-7200; res: 800/356-8013. 205 rms, 2 story. S $32.95; D $34.95–$39.95; under 18 free. Crib free. TV; in-rm movies. Cafe adj. Free coffee in lobby. Ck-out noon. Sundries. Free airport transportation. Downhill ski 10 mi; x-country ski 2 mi. Cr cds: A, C, D, DS, MC, V.

[icons]

✔ ★★**HAMPTON INN EDEN PRAIRIE.** (7740 Flying Cloud Dr, Eden Prairie 55344) SW via I-494 at jct US 169. 612/942-9000. 124 rms, 3 story. S $32.95; D $37.95; each addl $5; under 18 free. Crib free. TV; in-rm movies. Continental bkfst. Cafe nearby. Ck-out noon. Valet serv. Cr cds: A, C, D, DS, MC, V.

[icons]

✔ ★★**HOWARD JOHNSON.** 7801 Normandale Rd (55435), SW at jct MN 100, I-494 Normandale Rd exit. 612/835-7400. 146 rms, 2 story. S $48; D $51–$57; each addl $8; under 18 free. Crib free. TV; cable. Indoor pool. Cafe open 6–12:30 am. Bar 11–1 am. Ck-out noon. Coin lndry. Meeting rm. Valet serv. Sundries. Free airport transportation. Downhill/x-country ski 2 mi. Game rm. Private patios, balconies. Cr cds: A, C, D, DS, ER, MC, V.

[icons]

★**THRIFTY SCOT.** (6445 James Circle, Brooklyn Center 55430) NE corner I-94/694 & Shingle Creek Pkwy Interchange exit 34. 612/566-9810. 103 rms, 2 story. S $28–$31; D $33–$36; each addl $5; under 18 free. Crib free. TV; satellite. Free continental bkfst. Cafe adj. Ck-out noon. Valet serv. Cr cds: A, C, D, MC, V.

[icons]

Motor Hotels

✔ ★★**HAMPTON INN RICHFIELD.** (7745 Lyndale Ave, Richfield 55423) S on I-35E. 612/861-1000. 149 rms, 5 story. S $36–$45; D $40–$50; under 19 free. Crib free. TV; cable. Indoor pool; whirlpool. Free coffee. Continental bkfst. Cafe nearby. Ck-out noon. Meeting rms. Bellhops. Valet serv. Some refrigerators. Cr cds: A, C, D, DS, MC, V.

[icons]

✔ ★★**HOPKINS HOUSE.** (1501 MN 7, Hopkins 55343) 9 mi W on MN 7. 612/935-7711. 162 rms, 7 story. S, D $49.95–$82; suites $79–$125; wkly, wkend rates. Crib free. TV. Indoor pool; whirlpool, sauna. Cafe 6:30 am–10 pm; Sat, Sun from 8:30 am. Rm serv. Bar 11–1 am;

entertainment, dancing exc Sun, Mon. Ck-out 12:30 pm. Meeting rms. Valet serv. Airport transportation. X-country ski 1 mi. Putting green. Game rm. Cr cds: A, C, D, DS, MC, V.

Owatonna

Pop: 18,632 **Elev:** 1,154 ft (352 m) **Area code:** 507 **Zip:** 55060

Motels

★**BEST WESTERN COUNTRY HEARTH.** *745 State Ave. 1 mi N on US 14 at jct I-35 Owatonna-Waseca exit 42. 507/451-8712.* 27 rms, 2 story. S $28.90; D $31.90–$34.90; each addl $4. Crib $4. TV; cable. Cafe adj open 24 hrs. Ck-out 11 am. Meeting rm. X-country ski 1 mi. Cr cds: A, DS, MC, V.

✔ ★**OWATONNA INN.** *Vine & Oak Sts. 507/451-4620; res: 800/346-3552 (exc MN), 800/662-5708 (MN).* 54 rms, 2 story. S $25–$32; D $30–$37; each addl $4; family rates. Crib free. TV; cable. Cafe 6:30 am–10 pm, Sun 10 am–9 pm. Bar 11:30–1 am; wkend entertainment, dancing. Ck-out noon. Meeting rms. X-country ski 1 mi. Cr cds: A, C, D, DS, MC, V.

✔ ★ ★**WESTERN INN.** *(Box 609) 1212 I-35N, 1 mi NW at jct US 14, I-35. 507/455-0606.* 120 rms, 2 story. S $35; D $40; each addl $5; under 16 free. Crib free. TV; cable. Indoor pool; whirlpool, sauna. Cafe 6 am–2 pm, 5:30–10 pm. Rm serv. Bar 4 pm–1 am. Ck-out noon. Coin lndry. Sundries. Free airport transportation. X-country ski 1 mi. Cr cds: A, C, D, DS, MC, V. Ⓓ

Park Rapids

Founded: 1880 **Pop:** 2,976 **Elev:** 1,440 ft (439 m) **Area code:** 218 **Zip:** 56470

Motels

✔ ★**PARK TERRACE.** *US 71 N, on Fish Hook River. 218/732-3344.* 20 rms, 1–2 story. S $26–$36; D $45. TV; cable, in-rm movies. Cafe 11 am–2 pm, 5–10 pm; Sat from 5 pm. Bar 11 am–2 pm, 5–11 pm. Ck-out 11 am. Airport, bus depot transportation. 18-hole golf privileges nearby; greens fee. X-country ski ½ mi. Snowmobile, bicycle trails. Some refrigerators. On beach. Cr cds: A, MC, V.

★**SUPER 8.** *(Box 388) MN 34E. 218/732-9704.* 38 rms, 2 story. S $26.88; D $34.88–$37.88; each addl $3. Crib $2. TV; cable, in-rm movies. Free morning coffee. Cafe nearby. Ck-out 11 am. Free airport, bus depot transportation. X-country ski 2 & 9 mi. Rec rm. Cr cds: A, C, D, DS, MC, V.

Resort

✔ ★ ★**VACATIONAIRE.** *(HCO5, Box 181) Island Lake Dr, 9½ mi N on US 41, then ¾ mi NE on County 89, on Island Lake. 218/732-5270.* 12 A/C lodge rms, 4 kits., 1–2 story; 16 (1–4 bedrm) kit. cottages. S $28; D $45; suites for 4–6, $68–$74; cottages for 2–8 (2-day min) $55–$168 each; each addl $8; EP; wkly, family rates. Crib avail. TV; color in lodge rms, lobby. Indoor pool; sauna. Playground. Cafe 5–10 pm; mid-May–mid-Sep 8–10 am, noon–2 pm, 5–10 pm. Box lunches, snacks. Bar 8–1 am. Ck-out 11 am; ck-in 4 pm. Coin lndry summer only. Grocery, package store 9 mi. Free local airport, bus depot transportation. Tennis. Private beach; waterskiing; launching ramp, dock. Boats, motors, canoe, sailboats, pontoon boat, water bike. X-country ski on site. Skating. Snowmobile trails. Occasional entertainment. Rec rm. Fireplace. 373 acres. Cr cds: A, DS, MC, V.

Red Wing

Founded: 1836 **Pop:** 13,736 **Elev:** 720 ft (219 m) **Area code:** 612 **Zip:** 55066

Motels

✔ ★**RED CARPET INN.** *235 Withers Harbor Dr. 612/388-1502.* 37 rms, 2 story. S $31–$35; D $36–$42; each addl $4; suites $74–$79. Crib $2. TV; satellite, in-rm movies. Heated pool; whirlpool. Cafe adj 6 am–midnight. Ck-out 11 am. Miniature golf adj. Downhill ski 12 mi; x-country ski 1 mi. Cr cds: A, C, D, DS, MC, V.

★**STERLING.** *1½ mi E on US 61, 63. 612/388-3568; res: 800/341-8000.* 43 rms. S $26–$36; D $34–$40; each addl $3. Crib free. TV; cable. Free coffee in rms. Cafe nearby. Ck-out 11 am. Downhill ski 7 mi; x-country ski 1 mi. Municipal park, pool opp. Cr cds: A, C, D, MC, V.

Rochester

Settled: 1854 **Pop:** 57,890 **Elev:** 1,297 ft (394 m) **Area code:** 507

Motels

★**AMERICINN OF STEWARTVILLE.** *(1700 2d Ave NW, Stewartville 55976) S on US 63, 1 mi S of I-90. 507/533-4747.* 29 rms. S $28.90–$40.90; D $33.90–$45.90; each addl $5; under 12 free. Crib free. TV; cable. Cafe nearby. Ck-out noon. Airport transportation. Cr cds: A, C, D, DS, MC, V.

✔ ★**BEST WESTERN FIFTH AVENUE.** *20 5th Ave NW (55901), near clinic. 507/289-3987.* 90 kit. units, 4 story. S $39–$45; D $45–$55; each addl $5; under 16 free. Crib free. TV; cable. Indoor pool. Free continental bkfst. Cafe nearby. Ck-out noon. Sundries. X-country ski 1 mi. Game rm. Cr cds: A, C, D, DS, MC, V.

✔ ★**CENTER TOWNE TRAVEL INN.** *116 SW 5th St (55901), near clinic. 507/289-1628.* 58 rms, 2 story. S $26–$33; D $33–$39; each addl $4; under 16 free. Crib free. TV; cable. Indoor pool; sauna. Free continental bkfst. Cafe nearby. Ck-out noon. Coin lndry. Sundries. X-country ski 2 mi. Cr cds: A, C, D, DS, MC, V.

★**COMFORT INN.** *111 28th St (55901). 507/286-1001.* 129 rms. S $31; D $41; each addl $5; under 16 free. Crib $5. TV; cable. Free continental breakfast. Cafe nearby. Ck-out noon. Free airport, bus depot, Mayo Clinic transportation. X-country ski 2 mi. Cr cds: A, C, D, DS, ER, MC, V. ⓔ

✔ ★**DAYS INN.** *6 First Ave NW (55901). 507/282-3801.* 74 units, 5 story, 14 kits. S $35–$45; D $41–$55; under 18 free. Crib free. TV; cable. Cafe 6 am–10 pm. Rm serv. Ck-out noon. Coin lndry. Cr cds: A, C, D, DS, MC, V.

★**ECONO LODGE.** *519 3d Ave SW (55902), near clinic. 507/288-1855.* 62 rms, 2 story, 6 kits. S $32–$36; D $36–$42; each addl $4; kit. units $38; under 19 free. Crib free. TV; cable. Free coffee in rms. Cafe nearby. Ck-out noon. Coin lndry. Sundries. X-country ski 1 mi. City park opp. Cr cds: A, C, D, MC, V.

✔ ★★**HOLIDAY INN-SOUTH.** *1630 S Broadway (55903). 507/288-1844.* 200 rms, 2 story, 3 kits. S $37–$55; D $43–$59; each addl $5; kit. units $49–$62. Crib free. TV; cable. Indoor pool. Cafe 6 am–10 pm; Fri, Sat to 11 pm. Rm serv. Bar 11:30–1 am. Ck-out 2 pm, noon Sat.

Meeting rms. Coin lndry. Valet serv. Sundries. Free airport, bus depot transportation. X-country ski 1 mi. Rec rm. Cr cds: A, C, D, DS, MC, V.

🖑 🕹 🏋 🏊 🚫 🐾

✔ ★★HOWARD JOHNSON. *435 16th Ave NW (55901), US 52 exit 5th St.* 507/288-9090. 115 rms, 20 kit. units, 3 story. S $35–$74; D $42–$74; each addl $8; under 18 free. Crib free. TV; cable. Heated pool. Cafe opp. Ck-out noon. Coin lndry. Meeting rms. Valet serv. Sundries. Free clinic transportation. X-country ski 1 mi. Cr cds: A, C, D, DS, MC, V.

🏋 🏊 🚫 🐾 SC

✔ ★★RAMADA INN. *1625 S Broadway (55901).* 507/281-2211. 163 rms, 5 story. S, D $38–$65; each addl $5; under 17 free. Crib free. TV; cable. Indoor pool; whirlpool, sauna, poolside serv. Cafe 6 am–10 pm. Rm serv. Bar noon–midnight. Ck-out 1 pm. Coin lndry. Meeting rms. Valet serv. Hospital, clinic transportation. X-country ski 1 mi. Some private patios. Cr cds: A, C, D, DS, MC, V.

🖑 🏋 🏊 🚫 🐾

✔ ★RED CARPET INN. *2214 S Broadway (55901).* 507/282-7448. 46 rms, 2 story, 6 kits. S $23.95–$25.95; D $26.95–$28.95; each addl $3; kit. units $21.95–$24.95; under 14 free. Crib $3. TV; cable. Indoor pool. Free coffee in lobby. Cafe nearby. Ck-out noon. Coin lndry. Meeting rm. Sundries. X-country ski 1 mi. Cr cds: A, DS, MC, V.

🏋 🏊 🐾 SC

★RODEWAY INN. *1850 S Broadway (55904).* 507/282-9905. 62 rms. S $25.95–$29.95; D $31.95–$33.95; each addl $3; under 13 free. Crib free. TV; cable. Ck-out noon. Meeting rms. Cr cds: A, DS, MC, V.

🖑 🚫 🐾 SC 💲

St Cloud

Founded: 1856 **Pop:** 42,566 **Elev:** 1,041 ft (318 m) **Area code:** 612 **Zip:** 56301

Motels

★AMERICINN OF AVON. *(PO Box 9, 304 Blattner Dr, Avon 56310) 15 mi NW on I-94 exit 153.* 612/356-2211. 27 units, 1–2 story. S $26.90–$40.90; D $32.50–$42.50; each addl $4.50; under 12 free. Crib free. TV; cable. Continental bkfst. Cafe opp 8 am–10 pm. Ck-out 11 am. Cr cds: A, C, D, DS, MC, V.

🖑 🕹

✔ ★★BUDGETEL INN. *70 S 37th Ave.* 612/253-4444. 91 units, 2 story. S $29–$36; D $36–$43; each addl $4; suites $55–$60; under 18 free. Crib free. TV; cable. Whirlpool, sauna. Cafe nearby. Ck-out noon. Meeting rms. Cr cds: A, C, D, DS, MC, V.

🖑 🚫 SC

★GATEWAY. *310 Lincoln Ave SE.* 612/252-4050. 35 rms, 2 story. S $20–$24; D $24–$30; each addl $4; under 12 free. Crib $3. TV; satellite. Ck-out 11 am. Downhill ski 18 mi; x-country ski 8 mi. Sundries. Cr cds: A, DS, MC, V.

🏋 💲

★TRAVEL HOUSE. *3820 Roosevelt Rd, County Rd 75 & I-94.* 612/253-3338. 28 rms, 2 story. S $24.95–$28.95; D $26.95–$31.95; each addl $2; suite $101. Crib $4. TV; in-rm movies. Continental bkfst. Bar noon–1 am. Ck-out noon. Meeting rms. Racquetball, health club privileges. Lawn games. Refrigerators. Cr cds: A, C, D, MC, V.

🖑 🕹 🚫 💲

★TRAVEL WISE. *US 10S, jct MN 23.* 612/253-0500; res: 800/341-8000. 80 rms, 2 story. S $25–$31; D $31–$34; each addl $5; under 19 free. Crib $2. TV; satellite. Ck-out 11 am. Valet serv. Sundries. Downhill ski 10 mi; x-country ski 1 mi. Rec rm. Cr cds: A, C, D, DS, MC, V.

🖑 🕹 🏋 🚫 SC 💲

Motor Hotels

✔ ★★BEST WESTERN AMERICANNA INN. *520 S US 10, S of jct US 10, MN 23.* 612/252-8700. 64 rms, 2 story. S $35.95–$38; D $42.95–$55; each addl $5; suites for 2–6, $64.95–$69.95; under 19 free. Crib $1. TV; cable, in-rm movies. Indoor pool; whirlpool, sauna. Free in-rm coffee. Cafe 6:30 am–10 pm; Sun to 9 pm. Bar 10:30–1 am; entertainment. Ck-out 11 am; Sun 2 pm. Meeting rms. Valet serv. Sundries. Cr cds: A, C, D, DS, MC, V.

🐾 ➡️ SC

✔ ★★BEST WESTERN SUNWOOD INN. *1 Sunwood Dr.* 612/253-0606; res: 800/253-0606. 230 rms, 6 story. S $45–$68; D $48–$72; each addl $7; suites $95–$140; under 18 free. Crib free. TV; cable. Indoor pool; wading pool, whirlpool, sauna. Cafe 6:30 am–10 pm; Fri, Sat to 11 pm. Bar 11–1 am; Sun to midnight. Ck-out noon. Coin lndry. Meeting rms. Valet serv. Sundries. Game rm. Poolside rms. Cr cds: A, C, D, DS, MC, V.

♿ ➡️ ⊘ SC

St Paul

Settled: 1840 **Pop:** 270,230 **Elev:** 874 ft (266 m) **Area code:** 612

Motels

★AMERICINN OF FOREST LAKE. *(1291 W Broadway, Forest Lake 55025) 20 mi N on I-35.* 612/464-1930; res: 800/634-3444 (exc MN), 800/426-7070 (MN). 29 rms, 2 story. S $30.90–$42.90; D $36.90–$48.90; each addl $6; under 12 free. Crib free. TV; cable, in-rm movies. Free coffee. Continental bkfst. Cafe adj 6 am–11 pm. Ck-out 11 am. Health club privileges. Cr cds: A, DS, MC, V.

♿ 🐾 ⊘ 🅽 SC

✔ ★★BEST WESTERN DROVER'S INN. *(701 S Concord St, S St Paul 55075)* 612/455-3600. 84 rms, 4 story. S $45.90; D $51.90; each addl $6; under 12 free. Crib free. TV; cable, in-rm movies. Cafe 6:30 am–10 pm; Sun from 8 am. Rm serv to 9 pm. Bar 11–1 am; entertainment, dancing Fri, Sat. Ck-out noon. Meeting rms. Valet serv. Sundries. Airport, bus depot transportation. Whirlpool, sauna. Cr cds: A, C, D, DS, MC, V.

♿ ⊘ 🅽 SC

★★BEST WESTERN YANKEE SQUARE INN. *(3450 Washington Dr, Eagan 55122) Adj Yankee Square Shopping Center.* 612/452-0100. 109 rms, 3 story, 1 kit. S $44.50; D $51.50; each addl $6; suites $73; kit. unit $120; under 12 free; wkend rates. Crib free. TV; in-rm movies. Continental bkfst. Ck-out 11:30 am. Meeting rms. Bellhops. Airport transportation. Downhill ski 10 mi; x-country ski 5 mi. Health club privileges. Whirlpool, sauna. Cr cds: A, C, D, DS, MC, V.

♿ ➡️ ⊘ 🅽 SC

✔ ★★DAYS INN NORTH. *1780 E County Road D (55109), adj to Maplewood Mall.* 612/770-2811. 117 rms, 2 story. Mid-May–mid-Sep: S $49–$52; D $54–$57; each addl $5; under 16 free; lower rates rest of yr. Crib free. TV; cable, in-rm movies. Indoor pool; whirlpool, sauna. Cafe 7 am–2 pm, 5–10 pm. Rm serv. Bar 4 pm–1 am; entertainment Wed–Sat. Ck-out noon. Coin lndry. Meeting rms. Valet serv. Sundries. Game rm. Cr cds: A, C, D, DS, MC, V.

♿ 🐾 ➡️ ⊘ 🅽 SC $

★NORTHRIDGE EMERALD INN. *1125 Red Fox Rd (55112).* 612/484-6557. 66 rms, 3 story. S $29; D $32–$35; each addl $1; suites $49; under 16 free. Crib free. TV; satellite, in-rm movies. Free coffee. Ck-out 11 am. Sundries. Cr cds: A, C, D, MC, V.

♿ ⊘ 🅽 SC

★RED ROOF INN. *(1806 Wooddale Dr, Woodbury 55125) I-494 at Valley Creek Road.* 612/738-7160. 109 units, 2 story. S $27.95–$29.95; D $33.95–$35.95; each addl $2; under 18 free. Crib free. TV; in-rm movies. Free coffee. Cafe nearby. Ck-out noon. Downhill ski 15 mi; x-country ski 3 mi. Cr cds: A, D, DS, MC, V.

♿ 🐾 ⊘ 🅽 SC

✔ ★★SUNWOOD INN BANDANA SQUARE. *1010 Bandana Blvd W (55108).* 612/647-1637. 109 rms, 2 story. S $50–$55; D $52–$57; suite $85–$110. Crib free. TV; cable. Indoor pool; wading pool, whirlpool, sauna. Free continental bkfst. Cafe adj 6:30 am–10 pm. Ck-out 11 am.

Meeting rms. Valet serv. Free RR station, bus depot transportation. Downhill ski 15 mi; x-country ski 1 mi. Health club privileges. Some refrigerators. Motel built within exterior structure of old railroad repair bldg; old track runs through lobby. Shopping center adj; connected by skywalk. Cr cds: A, C, D, DS, MC, V. ⓓ

🦽 ♿ ➡ ⊘ 🚫 SC

Stillwater

Settled: 1839 **Pop:** 12,290 **Elev:** 700 ft (213 m) **Area code:** 612 **Zip:** 55082

Motel

✔ ★**STILLWATER INN.** *1750 Frontage Rd W, near St Croix Mall. 612/430-1300.* 61 rms, 2 story. S $33.50–$39.50; D $43–$58; each addl $6; under 14 free. Crib free. TV; satellite. Free continental bkfst, coffee. Cafe nearby. Ck-out 11 am. Downhill ski 20 mi; x-country ski 2 mi. Picnic table. Cr cds: A, D, DS, MC, V.

🦽 ♿ ♨ ⊘ 🚫 SC

Inn

★★**AFTON HOUSE.** *(St Croix Trail, Afton 55001) 1 blk from St Croix River. 612/436-8883.* 12 rms, 2 story. D $50–$100; AP avail; mid-wk rates. Crib free. TV. Cafe 7 am–10 pm; Sat to 11 pm; Sun 10 am–10 pm. Rm serv. Ck-out noon, ck-in 2 pm. Downhill/x-country ski 2 mi. Some fireplaces. Some balconies. Historic inn (1867); some antiques. Cr cds: A, MC, V.

🍽 ♨ ⊘ 🚫 SC

Thief River Falls

Pop: 9,105 **Elev:** 1,133 ft (345 m) **Area code:** 218 **Zip:** 56701

Motels

✔ ★★**BEST WESTERN.** *MN 32S, ½ mi S. 218/681-7555.* 78 rms. S, studio rms $36–$38; D $44–$51; each addl $3; under 18 free. Crib free. TV; cable. Indoor pool; whirlpool; sauna. Cafe 6 am–10 pm. Rm serv. Bar 3 pm–1 am; entertainment. Ck-out noon. Meeting rms. Sundries. Airport transportation. X-country ski 3 mi. Game rm. Refrigerators, poolside rms. Cr cds: A, C, D, DS, MC, V.

🦽 ♿ ♨ ➡ ⊘ 🚫 SC

★**TRAVEL HOST.** *US 59S, 1½ mi SE. 218/681-6205.* 43 rms. S $22–$26; D $27–$32; each addl $3; under 16 free. Crib $1. TV; cable, in-rm movies. Free continental bkfst. Cafe adj 6 am–11 pm. Ck-out 11:30 am. Meeting rms. X-country ski 1½ mi. Cr cds: A, D, DS, MC, V.

🦽 ♨ ⊘ 🚫 SC

Winona

Settled: 1851 **Pop:** 25,075 **Elev:** 666 ft (203 m) **Area code:** 507 **Zip:** 55987

Motels

★**BUDGET HOST WESTGATE.** *1501 Service Dr. 507/454-2980.* 62 rms, 1–2 story, 14 kits. S $26–$38; D $32–$44; kit. suites $52–$71. Crib $4. TV; cable. Free coffee in rms. Cafe nearby. Ck-out 11 am. Meeting rms. X-country ski 1 mi. Cr cds: A, C, D, DS, MC, V.

♨ 🚫

✔ ★**DAYS INN.** *420 Cottonwood Dr. 507/454-6930.* 58 rms, 2 story. S $33–$35; D $38–$40; each addl $5; under 18 free. Crib free. TV; cable. Free continental bkfst. Cafe nearby. Ck-out noon. X-country ski 1 mi. Cr cds: A, C, D, DS, MC, V.

🦽 ♿ ♨ ⊘ 🚫 SC 💲

★★HOLIDAY INN. *956 Mankato Ave, 2 mi SE at jct US 14, 61, MN 43. 507/454-4390.* 112 rms, 2 story. S $45-$55; D $51-$61; each addl $6; family rates. Crib free. TV; cable. Indoor pool; whirlpool. Free coffee in rms. Cafes 6:30 am-10 pm. Rm serv. Bar 11:30-1 am; Sun from 5 pm. Ck-out 11 am. Meeting rms. Valet serv. Sundries. X-country ski 1 mi. Cr cds: A, C, D, DS, MC, V.

New Hampshire

Population: 920,610

Land area: 8,992 sq mi (23,289 sq km)

Elevation: 0–6,288 ft (0–1,917 m)

Highest point: Mount Washington

Entered Union: Ninth of original 13 states (June 21, 1788)

Capital: Concord

Motto: Live free or die

Nickname: Granite State

State flower: Purple lilac

State bird: Purple finch

State tree: White birch

Time zone: Eastern

Interstate Highway System

The following alphabetical listing of New Hampshire towns in *Mobil Travel Guide* shows that these cities are within 10 miles (16 kilometers) of the indicated Interstate highways. A highway map should, however, be checked for the nearest exit.

INTERSTATE 89: Concord, Hanover, New London, Plainfield, Sunapee.

INTERSTATE 91 (in Vermont): Claremont, Hanover.

INTERSTATE 93: Concord, Franconia, Franconia Notch State Park, Franklin, Holderness, Laconia, Lincoln/North Woodstock, Littleton, Manchester, Meredith, Plymouth, Salem.

INTERSTATE 95: Exeter, Hampton Beach, Portsmouth, Rye & Rye Beach.

Weather Statistics*

	WINTER	SPRING	SUMMER	FALL
Statewide	20°F (-5°C)	55°F (13°C)	70°F (21°C)	49°F (9°C)
Northern Mountains	5°F (-15°C)	34°F (1°C)	49°F (9°C)	31°F (-.6°C)

*Average mean temperatures are listed for the entire state. Averages for specific regions are given if significant differences exist.

Visitor Information

New Hampshire Vacation Center, 105 Loudon Rd, PO Box 856, Concord 03301; 603/271-2343, publishes a large number of helpful bulletins and pamphlets, including "Events and Attractions."

League of New Hampshire Craftsmen Foundation offers the Visual Arts Map, a statewide guide to more than 90 galleries, museums, historic sites, craft shops and craftsmen's studios. Send stamped, self-addressed, business-size envelope to 205 N Main St, Concord 03301.

For information about events, foliage and ski conditions phone 800/258-3608 from New England (except NH) and New York or 603/224-2525 (NH).

For road condition information contact Hooksett Division Five Highway Office, Hooksett 03106; 603/485-9526 or -5767.

There are several welcome centers in New Hampshire; visitors who stop by will find information and brochures most helpful in planning stops at points of interest. Open daily: on the Everett Turnpike at Hooksett (2) and Nashua; on I-93 at Canterbury, Salem and Sanborton Boulder; on I-89 at Lebanon, Springfield and Sutton; on I-95 at Seabrook; and on NH 16 at North Conway.

Open Memorial Day–Columbus Day: on NH 9 at Antrim; on US 3 at Colebrook; on US 4 at Epsom; on NH 25 at Rumney; and on US 2 at Shelburne.

Room Rate Information

The following resort area has higher room rates for two (double) than indicated on the cover of this Guide. However, the lodgings listed in this area offer a good value when compared to others of their type in the area.

Jackson $70

Bartlett

Pop: 1,566 **Elev:** 681 ft (208 m) **Area code:** 603 **Zip:** 03812

Motels

★★ATTITASH MOUNTAIN VILLAGE. *(US 302) 2¼ mi S on US 302. 603/374-6501.* 225 rms, 2 story. S, D $50–$70; each addl $15–$20; studio rms $85–$130; 2–3 bedrm units for 2–8, $110–$275; efficiency units for 2–4, $55–$110; ski season 2-day min; hol wks 3-night min; mid-wk ski package plan. Crib $15. TV; cable. Indoor pool; whirlpool, sauna. Cafe 5–10 pm. Bar 11:30 am–11 pm. Ck-out 11 am. Coin lndry. Meeting rms. Tennis. Downhill ski ¼ mi; x-country ski on site. Ice-skating. Game rm. Refrigerators. Private patios; many balconies. Picnic tables. Cr cds: A, DS, MC, V.

✔★NORTH COLONY. *(Box 1) 1½ mi S on US 302. 603/374-6679.* 14 rms, 2 kits. July–late Oct, ski hol wks: S, D $44–$57; each addl $4; lower rates rest of yr. Crib avail. TV; cable. Pool. Playground. Cafe adj 6 am–9 pm. Ck-out 10 am. Downhill ski 1 mi; x-country ski 5 mi. Lawn games. Picnic tables, grills; screened porches. Cr cds: MC, V.

Franconia

Pop: 743 **Elev:** 971 ft (296 m) **Area code:** 603 **Zip:** 03580

Motels

✔★★GALE RIVER. *½ mi N on NH 18; I-93 exit 38. 603/823-5655; res: 800/255-7989.* 10 rms, 3 1–5 bedrm kit. cottages. No A/C. July–mid-Oct, hol ski wks: S, D $51–$74; each addl $5; cottages $79–$125 (5-day min); ski package plans, wkly rates (cottages); higher rates: wkends, foliage season; lower rates rest of yr. Crib free. TV; in-rm movies. Heated pool; hot tub. Playground. Free coffee in rms. Ck-out 11 am. Downhill ski 4 mi. Lawn games. Picnic tables, grills. 1851 farm house. Cr cds: A, DS, MC, V.

✔★★RAYNOR'S MOTOR LODGE. *At jct NH 18, 142, I-93 exits 37, 38. 603/823-9586; res: 800/634-8187.* 30 rms, 7 A/C in motel; 1 kit. cottage. S, D $36–$70; each addl $5; kit. cottage for 4–6 (no maid serv) $95–$120; ski, golf package plans. Crib $5. TV. Heated pool. Free coffee in rms. Cafe adj from 7:30 am. Bar. Ck-out 11 am. Downhill ski 2½ mi; x-country ski 2 mi. Bicycles. Shuffleboard. Some refrigerators. Rms vary. Picnic tables, grill. Cr cds: A, MC, V. ⑩ Ⓕ

★★STONYBROOK MOTOR LODGE. *1¼ mi S on NH 18. 603/823-8192.* 24 rms. Late June–mid-Oct, hol wks: S, D $48–$60; each addl $5; under 10 free; lower rates rest of yr. Crib free. TV. 2 heated pools. Playground. In-rm coffee. Ck-out 11 am. Downhill/x-country ski 2 mi. Rec rm. Lawn games. Picnic tables, grills. Hiking trails. Pond; canoes. Cr cds: A, C, D, MC, V.

Inns

✔★★FRANCONIA INN. *Easton Rd, 2⅛ mi W on NH 116. 603/823-5542.* 32 rms, 28 with bath, 3 story. No A/C. No elvtr. No phones. S $50–$80; D $55–$85; each addl $10; suites

$100–$120; family rates; package plans; wkend rates. Closed Apr–mid-May, late Oct–mid-Dec. Crib $5. TV in lounge; satellite. Pool; hot tub. Cafe 8–10 am, 6–9 pm. Rm serv with hrs. Bar from 4 pm. Box lunches. Ck-out 11 am. Tennis; pro. Downhill ski 3 mi; x-country ski. Tandem bicycles. Trail rides. Soaring center. Game rm. Rec rm. Library. Cr cds: A, MC, V.

★ ★SUNSET HILL HOUSE. *(PO, Sugar Hill 03585) 2¼ mi W on NH 117, then ½ mi W on Sunset Rd.* 603/823-5522. 35 rms, 4 A/C, 33 baths, 3 story. No elvtr. No rm phones. MAP: S $72–$83; D $53–$67/person; family rates. Crib $4. TV in lounge. Heated pool; whirlpool, poolside serv (summer). Cafe 7:30–9:30 am, noon–2 pm, 6:30–9 pm. Box lunches. Bar from 5 pm; entertainment in ski season. Ck-out 1 pm. Meeting rm. Beauty shop. Airport, bus depot transportation. Tennis. Golf, greens fee $4–$6, putting green. Downhill ski 4 mi; x-country ski opp. Rec rm in ski season. Lawn games. Cr cds: A, MC, V. ⓕ

Gorham

Settled: 1805 **Pop:** 2,180 **Elev:** 801 ft (244 m) **Area code:** 603 **Zip:** 03581

Motels

✔ ★GORHAM MOTOR INN. *324 Main St.* 603/466-3381. 39 rms. S $32–$40; D $36–$60; each addl $4–$5. Crib $5. TV; cable, in-rm movies. Heated pool. Cafe adj 7 am–9 pm. Bar 11 am–midnight. Ck-out 11 am. Downhill/x-country ski 8 mi. Cr cds: A, MC, V. ⓕ

★ ★TOURIST VILLAGE. *130 Main St, on US 2, NH 16.* 603/466-3312. 61 motel rms, 7 lodge rms, 1–2 story. July–Labor Day, mid-Sep–Oct: S, D $46–$58; each addl $6; lower rates rest of yr. Crib $4. TV; cable. Heated pool. Cafe nearby. Ck-out 11 am. Downhill ski 9 mi; x-country ski 7 mi. Cr cds: A, DS, MC, V. ⓕ

✔ ★ ★ ★TOWN & COUNTRY MOTOR INN. *½ mi E on US 2.* 603/466-3315. 160 rms, 2 story. June–Oct: S $38–$52; D $44–$66; each addl $6; suites $66–$80; lower rates rest of yr. Crib $5. TV; cable. Indoor/outdoor pool. Cafe 6–10:30 am, 5:30–10 pm; Sun 6–10:30 am, noon–9 pm. Bar 4:30 pm–1 am; entertainment, dancing exc Sun. Ck-out 11 am. Meeting rms. Sundries. Bus depot transportation. Golf privileges, putting green. Exercise equipt; weights, bicycles, sauna. Game rm. Some steam baths. Private patios, balconies. Cr cds: A, D, DS, MC, V. ⓕ

Hampton Beach

Settled: 1638 **Pop:** 500 **Elev:** 56 ft (17 m) **Area code:** 603 **Zip:** 03842

Motels

✔ ★BEST WESTERN SEABROOK. *(Box 1209, Seabrook 03874) On NH 107, ¼ mi W of I-95.* 603/474-3078. 163 rms, 2 story. Mid-June–Sep: S $41–$54; D $45–$58; each addl $4; under 12 free; lower rates rest of yr. Crib free. TV. Free continental bkfst. Cafe opp 11 am–9:30 pm. Ck-out 11 am. Picnic tables. Cr cds: A, C, D, DS, MC, V.

★PINE HAVEN. *(183 Lafayette Rd, North Hampton 03862) 4 mi N on US 1.* 603/964-8187. 19 rms, 4 kits. (no oven). Mid-June–mid-Oct (3-day min hols, wkends): S $46–$50; D $54–$58; each addl $3–$5; kit. units $59–$65; lower rates rest of yr. Crib $3. TV. Free coffee in rms. Cafe nearby. Ck-out 10 am. Refrigerators avail for 1-wk stays. Cr cds: A, MC, V. ⓓ

★SEASCAPE. *(955 Ocean Blvd, Hampton 03842) 3 mi N on NH 1A, opp ocean.* 603/926-9153. 19 rms, 1–2 story. Late June–Labor Day: D $50–$74; each addl $6; some lower rates rest of yr. Crib free. TV; cable. Free coffee. Cafe adj. Ck-out 11 am. Some refrigerators. Rms vary. Cr cds: MC, V. Ⓕ

Hanover

Settled: 1765 **Pop:** 6,861 **Elev:** 531 ft (162 m) **Area code:** 603 **Zip:** 03755

Motels

(Rates may be higher during Dartmouth events, foliage season)

✔ ★★**CHIEFTAIN.** *2 mi N on NH 10. 603/643-2550.* 22 rms, 1–2 story. May–Oct: S $45–$50; D $50–$55; each addl $5; lower rates rest of yr. TV. Pool. Continental bkfst 8–10 am in season. Ck-out 11 am. Picnic tables. View of Connecticut River. Cr cds: A, C, D, MC, V.

✔ ★★**HIGBEA.** *(NH 120, Lebanon 03766) 4 mi S on NH 120; ½ mi N of I-89 exit 18. 603/448-5070.* 48 rms, 2 story. S $43; D $49–$57; each addl $5; studio rm $45–$53; under 12 free; wkly rates. Crib free. TV; cable. Free continental bkfst. Cafe adj 7 am–10 pm; bar. Ck-out 11 am. Downhill ski 5 mi; x-country ski 4 mi. Game rm. Picnic tables. Cr cds: A, C, D, MC, V.

★**SUNSET.** *(NH 10, West Lebanon 03784) 2½ mi NW of I-89 exit 19 on NH 10. 603/298-8721.* 18 rms. S $42–$63; D $53–$74; each addl $4. Crib free. TV; cable. Free continental bkfst in lobby. Ck-out 11 am. Lawn games. Picnic tables. Cr cds: A, D, DS, MC, V.

Jackson

Settled: 1790 **Pop:** 642 **Elev:** 971 ft (296 m) **Area code:** 603 **Zip:** 03846

Motels

✔ ★★**COVERED BRIDGE.** *(Box V) ½ blk W on NH 16 at jct NH 16A. 603/383-9151.* 26 rms, 2 levels, 5 kit. apts. Mid-June–mid-Oct, ski season: S, D $52–$66; each addl $2–$5; kit. apts (maid serv avail) for 2–4, $375–$495/wk; ski, golf, tennis package plans; lower rates rest of yr. Crib free. TV; cable. Heated pool; whirlpool, sauna. Playground. Continental bkfst. Ck-out 11 am. Free bus depot transportation. Clay-court tennis. Downhill ski 1 mi; x-country ski. Lawn games. Fireplace in some apts. Some balconies. Picnic tables, grill. Trout stream. Cr cds: A, DS, ER, MC, V.

✔ ★**LINDERHOF.** *(Box 126, Glen 03838) 2 mi S on NH 16. 603/383-4334.* 33 rms, 2 story. Jan–Mar, July–Oct: S $52–$68; D $62–$78; chalets & condominiums $120–$225; each addl $5; under 12 free; higher rates hols; lower rates rest of yr. Crib $5. TV; cable. Pool. Cafe (seasonal) 7:30–11 am. Ck-out 11 am. Balconies. Downhill ski 3 mi; x-country ski 2 mi. Fishing, horseback riding nearby. Cr cds: A, MC, V. Ⓕ

Hotel

★★**WENTWORTH RESORT HOTEL.** *NH 16A. 603/383-9700.* 60 rms, 3 story. No elvtr. S, D $65–$135; each addl $10; suites $150; under 12 free; golf package plans; wkly rates; higher rates hol wks. TV; cable. Pool. Cafe 8 am–10 pm. No rm serv. Bar 5 pm–1 am; entertainment wkends. Ck-out 11 am. Meeting rms. Airport, bus depot transportation. Tennis. 18-hole golf, greens fee $15, pro. Downhill ski 2 mi; x-country ski on site. Lawn games. Private patios. View of river. Cr cds: A, MC, V. Ⓓ Ⓕ Ⓘ

Inns

✔ ★★**DANA PLACE.** *(Box L) 5 mi N on NH 16. 603/383-6822.* 13 inn rms, 10 baths, 3 story. No elvtr. EP: S, D $35–$80; MAP: S, D $70–$135; Bed & Bkfst: S, D $40–$95; wkly rates; ski packages. Crib avail. TV rm. Indoor pool; whirlpool. Cafe 8–10 am, 6–9 pm. Box lunches (winter). Bar 4–11 pm; pianist wkends in season. Ck-out 11 am. Tennis. Downhill ski 5 mi; x-country ski on site. Hiking trails. Cr cds: A, MC, V.

★★**WHITNEYS' VILLAGE INN.** *(Box W, NH 16B) At Black Mt. 603/383-6886.* 37 rms in inn, motel, cottages, 31 baths. No A/C. No rm phones. MAP: S $69; D $59–$74/person; 3 or more, $30–$45/person; suites $59–$69; family rates; ski package plans. Serv charge 15%. Crib avail. TV in rec rm. Dining rm (public by res) 8–9:30 am, 6–9 pm. Box lunches, Wed eve cookouts (in season). Bar from 5 pm; entertainment (ski wkends). Ck-out 11 am. Meeting rms. Free bus depot transportation. Tennis. Downhill ski on site; x-country ski 4 mi. Hiking trails. Ice-skating. Game rm. Rec rm. Lawn games. Some refrigerators. Picnic tables. Early Amer decor. Cr cds: MC, V.

Jefferson

Settled: 1772 **Pop:** 100 **Elev:** 1,384 ft (422 m) **Area code:** 603 **Zip:** 03583

Motels

✔ ★**EVERGREEN.** *W on US 2. 603/586-4449.* 18 rms. July–mid-Oct: D $40–$51; each addl $5; lower rates May, June. Closed rest of yr. Crib free. TV. Pool. Cafe 8 am–8 pm; hrs vary off-season. Ck-out 11 am. Picnic area. Camping, trailer facilities. Cr cds: A, MC, V. Ⓕ

✔ ★**MORSE LODGE AND MOTEL.** *(39 Portland St, Lancaster 03584) 7 mi NW on US 2. 603/788-2096.* 8 motel rms; 10 rms, 5 baths in 2–3 story lodge. No A/C. Mid-June–mid-Oct, motel: S, D $33–$40; each addl $5. All yr, lodge: S, D $35–$40; alpine ski package. Crib free. B/W cable TV in motel rms; color in lobby. Playground. Cafe 8–9:30 am, 6–7:30 pm. Ck-out 11 am. Gift shop. X-country ski on site. Snowmobiling. Lawn games. Picnic tables. Rms vary. Cr cds: MC, V.

Lincoln/North Woodstock Area

Pop: Lincoln, 950; N Woodstock, 600 **Elev:** Lincoln, 811 ft (247 m); N Woodstock, 738 ft (225 m) **Area code:** 603 **Zip:** Lincoln, 03251; N Woodstock, 03262

Motels

✔ ★★**DRUMMER BOY.** *(RFD 1, Lincoln 03251) 3 mi N on US 3, I-93 exit 33. 603/745-3661.* 53 rms, 8 kits.; 2 kit. cottages. May–Oct: D $54–$74; each addl $5; suites $68–$90; kit. units $10 addl; cottages for 2–4, $66–$90; varied lower rates rest of yr. Crib $5. TV; cable. 2 heated pools, 1 outdoor. Playground. Cafe nearby. Ck-out 11 am. Coin lndry. Meeting rm. Sundries. Downhill/x-country ski 3 mi. Exercise equipt; weight machines, bicycle, whirlpool, sauna. Game rm. Patios, balconies. Picnic tables, grill. Cr cds: A, DS, MC, V.

✔ ★**KANCAMAGUS MOTOR LODGE.** *(Box 505, Lincoln 03251) 2 mi E on NH 112, I-93 exit 32. 603/745-3365.* 34 rms, 2 story. Late June–mid-Oct, hol ski wks & wkends: S, D $52–$60; each addl $5; under 12, $2; ski package plans; lower rates rest of yr. Crib free. TV; cable. Heated pool. Cafe 7–11 am; closed Apr & Nov. Ck-out 11 am. Coin lndry. Downhill/x-country ski 2 mi. Lawn games. In-rm steam baths. Balconies. Cr cds: A, MC, V.

★**MOUNT COOLIDGE.** *(Box 275, N Woodstock 03262) 3 mi N on US 3, ¼ mi N of I-93 exit 33. 603/745-8052.* 18 rms, 2 cottages. July–Labor Day, fall foliage season: S, D $38–$48; each addl $4; 3-bedrm cottages for 5, $60; lower rates mid-May–June. Closed rest of yr. Crib free. TV; cable. Cafe adj 7:30 am–8:30 pm; closed mid-Oct–mid-May. Ck-out 11 am. On mountain stream. Cr cds: A, MC, V.

✔ ★★**RED DOORS.** *(RFD 1, Box 109A, Lincoln 03251) I-93 exit 33. 603/745-2267; res: 800/527-7596 (exc NH).* 30 rms. May–Oct, hol ski wks & wkends: S, D $53–$66; each addl $5; under 3 free; lower rates rest of yr. Crib $5. TV; free in-rm movies. Heated pool. Playground. Free coffee in rms. Cafe opp (mid-June–mid-Oct) 7:30 am–8:30 pm. Ck-out 10 am. Coin lndry. Downhill/x-country ski 10 mi. Game rm. Lawn games. Picnic tables, grills. Cr cds: A, C, D, DS, MC, V.

✔ ★★★**WOODWARD'S MOTOR INN.** *(US 3, Lincoln 03251) 1 mi N of I-93 exit 33. 603/745-8141.* 80 rms, 1–2 story, 2 cottages. S, D $53–$74; each addl $5; 2-bedrm cottages for 3–6, $61–$85; 2-rm units avail; MAP, ski package plan. Crib free. TV; cable. 2 pools, 1 indoor; whirlpool, sauna. Playground. Cafe 7:30–11 am, 5–9 pm. Bar 5 pm–midnight; entertainment wkends, dancing winter wkends. Ck-out 11 am. Coin lndry. Meeting rm. Tennis. Racquetball. Game rm. Lawn games. Some balconies. Duck pond. Cr cds: A, C, D, DS, MC, V.

Littleton

Chartered: 1784 **Pop:** 4,480 **Elev:** 822 ft (251 m) **Area code:** 603 **Zip:** 03561

Motels

✔ ★★**LITTLETON.** *187 Main St, on US 302, NH 10, 18, 116. 603/444-5780.* 19 rms, 1 kit. (no oven). May–early Sep: S $36–$45; D $45–$53; each addl $5; 2-rm kit. unit $55–$63; higher rates foliage season. Closed mid-Oct–Apr. TV; cable. Heated pool. Playground. Cafe nearby. Ck-out 11 am. Picnic tables, grills. On hillside back from hwy. Cr cds: A, ER, MC, V.

★**MAPLE LEAF.** *297 W Main St, ¾ mi W on NH 18. 603/444-5105.* 21 rms, 5 kits. July–mid-Oct: S, D $36–$47; each addl $2–$5; wkly rates; lower rates rest of yr. Crib $3. TV; cable, in-rm movies. Heated pool. Cafe nearby. Ck-out 11 am. Downhill ski 10 mi. Some rm phones. Picnic tables, grills. Cr cds: A, MC, V.

✔ ★★**WAYSIDE INN.** *(Box 480, Bethlehem 03574) On US 302, 7 mi E of I-93 exit 40. 603/869-3364.* 13 rms in motel, 2 story; 23 rms, most with bath, in 3-story inn. No A/C. No elvtr. June–late Oct, Dec–late Feb: D $38–$46; each addl $10; golf, ski package plans; lower rates rest of yr. TV in motel rms, living rm of inn. Cafe 8–10 am, 6–9 pm exc Mon. Bar from 4:30 pm. Ck-out 11 am. 18-hole golf privileges. Downhill/x-country ski 8 mi. Snowmobile trails. Lawn games. Balconies in motel. Built 1825 as four-rm homestead by family of Franklin Pierce, 14th US President. On Ammonoosuc River; natural sand beach. Cr cds: A, C, D, MC, V.

Inn

✔ ★★**BEAL HOUSE INN.** *247 W Main St, I-93 exits 41–43. 603/444-2661.* 12 rms, 11 baths, 2 story. No A/C. S $40–$75; D $45–$90; wkend rates. Crib $10. Free continental bkfst. Ck-out 11 am, ck-in 3 pm. Downhill/x-country ski 10 mi. Picnic tables. Antique shop. Historic farmhouse (1833). Cr cds: A, C, D, MC, V.

Manchester

Settled: 1722 **Pop:** 90,936 **Elev:** 225 ft (69 m) **Area code:** 603

Motels

✔ ★**HILL-BROOK.** *(250 NH 101, Bedford 03102) 4 mi SW on NH 101; Everett Tpke Bedford exit. 603/472-3788.* 17 rms, 5 kits. (no ovens). S $36–$42; D $42–$46; each addl $4; wkly rates. Crib $3. TV; cable. Bkfst 7–10 am. Cafe nearby. Rm serv. Ck-out 11 am. Picnic table, grill. On hillside. Cr cds: A, DS, MC, V.

✔ ★**SUSSE CHALET INN.** *860 S Porter (03103). 603/625-2020.* 102 rms, 4 story. S $38.70; D $42.70; each addl $3. Crib $2. TV; satellite. Pool. Continental bkfst. Cafe opp 6 am–11 pm. Ck-out 11 am. Valet serv. Sundries. Cr cds: A, C, D, MC, V.

Nashua

Settled: 1656 **Pop:** 67,865 **Elev:** 169 ft (52 m) **Area code:** 603

Motels

✔ ★★**BEST WESTERN HALLMARK.** *220 Daniel Webster Hwy (03060), E of Everett Tpke exit 1. 603/888-1200.* 81 rms, 13 kits. (no ovens). S $44–$51; D $51–$58; each addl $4; kit. units $49–$56. Crib $8. TV. Pool. Free continental bkfst. Cafe nearby. Ck-out 11 am. Coin lndry. Sundries. Airport transportation. Cr cds: A, C, D, DS, MC, V. Ⓓ Ⓔ Ⓘ

✔ ★**RED ROOF INN.** *77 Spit Brook Rd (03063), US 3 exit 1. 603/888-1893.* 116 rms, 3 story. Apr–Oct: S $36.95–$42.95; D $38.95–$46.95; each addl $6; under 18 free; lower rates rest of yr. Crib free. TV; satellite, in-rm movies. Free coffee. Ck-out noon. Meeting rms. Cr cds: A, C, D, DS, MC, V. Ⓔ

✔ ★**SUSSE CHALET.** *(Box 3478, 03061) 2 Progress Ave, W of Everett Tpke exit 5E. 603/889-4151.* 81 rms, 2 story. S $34.70–$43.70; D $37.70–$48.70; each addl $3. Crib $2. TV. Pool. Cafe nearby. Ck-out 11 am. Coin lndry. Valet serv. Sundries. Picnic tables. Cr cds: A, D, MC, V.

North Conway

Settled: 1764 **Pop:** 2,104 **Elev:** 531 ft (162 m) **Area code:** 603 **Zip:** 03860

Motels

✔ ★**ATTITASH VALLEY.** *(PO, Glen 03838) 8 mi N on US 302, 2 mi W of jct NH 16. 603/383-4239.* 24 rms in motel, cottages, 16 A/C, 8 kits. (oven in 6). Mid-June–Oct, mid-Dec–mid-Apr, wkends: S, D $39–$54; kit. units, apts for 2–6, $42–$60; wkly rates; lower rates rest of yr. Crib free. TV; cable. Playground. Free coffee in rms. Cafe 5–9:30 pm; mid-June–Oct, mid-Dec–mid-Apr, wkends. Bar 4 pm–midnight. Ck-out 10 am. Downhill/x-country ski 2 mi. Lawn games. Picnic tables, grill. On river. Rms vary. Cr cds: A, ER, MC, V.

✔ ★★**GREEN GRANITE MOTEL & CONFERENCE CENTER.** *(Box 3127, US 302 & NH 16). 603/356-6901.* 89 rms, 2 story. S, D $44–$108; each addl $6; kit. units $54–$185; family, wkly rates; package plans. Crib free. TV; cable. Pool. Playground. Free continental bkfst. Meeting rms. Sundries. Bus depot transportation. Downhill ski 4 mi; x-country ski 7 mi. Private patios, balconies. Picnic tables, grills. Near beach. Cr cds: A, MC, V. Ⓔ Ⓕ

✔ ★★**MERRILL FARM.** *(RFD Box 151) 2 mi S on NH 16. 603/447-3866; res: 800/445-1017 (exc NH).* 43 rms, 6 suites, 2-3 story; 11 cottages, 7 with kits. No elvtr. D $52–$115; each addl $10; suites $84–$126; kit. cottages $73–$115; cottages without kit. $52–$94; under 17 free; ski plans; wkend rates. Crib $10. TV; cable. Pool. Free continental bkfst. Cafe nearby. Ck-out 11 am. Coin lndry. Meeting rms. Bus depot transportation. Downhill ski 3 mi; x-country ski 4 mi. Game rm. Rec rm. Lawn games. Some in-rm steam baths, refrigerators, fireplaces. Picnic tables, grills. Converted farmhouse and cottages on Saco River. Cr cds: A, D, DS, MC, V.

✔ ★★**OLD FIELD HOUSE MOTOR LODGE.** *(Box 1, NH 16A, Intervale 03845) 3½ mi N on NH 16A. 603/356-5478.* 17 rms, 2 story, 1 kit. S, D $50–$80; each addl $10; suites $74–$86; kit. unit (3-day min) $78–$90. Crib free. TV; cable. Heated pool. Free continental bkfst in season. Cafe opp from 8 am. Ck-out 11 am. Coin lndry. Meeting rms. Downhill ski 3 mi; x-country ski on site. Rec rm. Lawn games; basketball. Some rm phones, refrigerators. Cr cds: A, MC, V. Ⓕ

Inns

✔ ★★**THE FOREST.** *(Box 37, Intervale 03845) 3¼ mi N on NH 16A. 603/356-9772.* 13 rms, 1–3 story. No A/C. No elvtr. No rm phones. S $37–$48; D $44–$80; family, mid-wk summer rates; mid-wk ski package plan. TV rm; cable. Heated pool. Cafe 8–9 am, dinner 6:30 pm. Ck-out 11 am, ck-in 2 pm. Downhill ski 4 mi; x-country ski on site. Hiking trails. Lawn games. Cr cds: MC, V.

★★★**STONEHURST MANOR.** *(Box 1937) 1 mi N on US 302, NH 16, on Bigelow estate. 603/356-3113.* 25 rms, 3 story. No elvtr. No rm phones. S, D $53–$143; each addl $10; suites $111–$190; under 12 free; MAP avail; higher rates special events. TV; cable. Pool. Cafe 8–10 am (summer, fall & if inn full; guests only); dining rm 6–10 pm. Bar from 5 pm. Ck-out 11 am, ck-in 2 pm. Bellhops. Tennis. Downhill ski 3 mi; x-country ski 6 mi. Hiking. Lawn games. Hot tub. Some fireplaces, balconies. Cr cds: A, MC, V. Ⓓ Ⓕ

Resort

★**PURITY SPRING RESORT.** *(NH 153, East Madison 03849) 9 mi S on NH 153. 603/367-8896.* 30 rms, 10 A/C, 26 baths; 6 (2-bedrm) cottages. AP: S $62–$70; D $51–$59/person; each addl $19–$34; EP, MAP avail; ski packages; wkly rates. Crib $4. TV in lobby. Playground. Cafe 8–9:30 am, noon–1:30 pm, 6–7:30 pm; closed Apr, Nov. Bar 5–11 pm. Ck-out 11 am, ck-in 1 pm. Coin lndry. Grocery, package store 9 mi. Sports dir. Tennis, pro. Beach, waterskiing, boats, rowboats, canoes, sailboats. Downhill ski ½ mi; tobogganing. Lawn games. Rec rm. Game rm. Fish clean & store. Picnic tables. Cr cds: A, MC, V. Ⓕ

Portsmouth

Settled: 1630 **Pop:** 26,254 **Elev:** 21 ft (6 m) **Area code:** 603 **Zip:** 03801

Motel

✔ ★**PORTSMOUTH INN.** *383 Woodbury Ave, off I-95 exits 6N, 5S. 603/431-2500.* 60 rms, 4 story. July–Aug: S $28.75–$83.75; D $39.75–$91.75; each addl $5; under 10 free; lower rates rest of yr. Crib free. TV; cable. Cafe adj 6:30 am–10:30 pm. Ck-out 11 am. Valet serv. Cr cds: A, C, D, MC, V.

Salem

Pop: 24,124 **Elev:** 131 ft (40 m) **Area code:** 603 **Zip:** 03079

Motels

★**BEST WESTERN PARK VIEW.** *109 S Broadway St, at I-93 exit 1. 603/898-5632.* 58 rms, 28 kits. May–Dec: S $44–$54; D, kit. units (4-night min) $54; each addl $8; under 12 free;

wkly rates; lower rates rest of yr. Crib free. TV; cable. Free continental bkfst. Cafe nearby. Ck-out 11 am. Coin lndry. Many refrigerators. Cr cds: A, C, D, DS, MC, V.

⊘ ⊗

★**RED ROOF INN.** *15 Red Roof Ln, just off I-93 exit 2. 603/898-6422.* 108 rms, 2 story. S $36.95; D $36.95–$46.95; each addl $2; under 18 free. Crib free. TV; satellite. Free coffee. Cafe nearby. Ck-out noon. Valet serv. Cr cds: A, C, D, DS, MC, V.

🖰 🖰 ⊘ ⊗ SC

✔ ★★**SALEM INN.** *Keewaydin Dr, just W of I-93 exit 2. 603/893-5511; res: 800/447-2536 (exc NH).* 118 rms, 6 story. June–Oct: S $44–$60; D $46–$65; each addl $7; under 14 free; wkly rates; higher rates hol wkends, fall foliage; lower rates rest of yr. Crib free. TV; cable. Pool; poolside serv. Cafe 6 am–11 pm. Rm serv. Bar 11–1 am; entertainment, dancing Wed–Sat. Ck-out 11 am. Meeting rms. Bellhops. Valet serv. Sundries. Some refrigerators. Picnic tables. Cr cds: A, C, D, DS, ER, MC, V. Ⓓ Ⓔ Ⓕ Ⓘ Ⓙ

🖰 🖰 ⊘ ⊗ SC

✔ ★**SUSSE CHALET.** *6 Keewaydin Dr, off I-93 exit 2. 603/893-4722.* 105 rms, 4 story. S $38.70; D $42.70; each addl $4–$7. Crib $2. TV; cable. Pool. Continental bkfst. Cafe opp 6 am–11 pm. Ck-out 11 am. Coin lndry. Meeting rms. Valet serv. Boston airport transportation. Cr cds: A, C, D, MC, V.

🖰 🖰 ⊘ ⊗

Sunapee

Pop: 700 **Elev:** 1,008 ft (307 m) **Area code:** 603 **Zip:** 03782

Motel

✔ ★★**MT SUNAPEE.** *(Mt Sunapee 03772) 4 mi S on NH 103 at jct NH 103B, just E of state park entrance. 603/763-5592.* 22 rms, 11 kits. Dec–Mar: S $48–$73; D $53–$74; each addl $7.50; suites, kit. units $63–$74; wkly rates; mid-wk ski package plan; lower rates rest of yr. Crib free. TV; cable. Pool. Playground. Free coffee in rms. Ck-out 11 am. Downhill ski ½ mi; x-country ski 8 mi. Game rm. Lawn games. Many refrigerators. Picnic tables, grills. Cr cds: A, C, D, MC, V. Ⓕ

🖰 🖰 🖰 🖰

Twin Mountain

Pop: 200 **Elev:** 1,442 ft (440 m) **Area code:** 603 **Zip:** 03595

Motels

✔ ★★**CHARLMONT MOTOR INN.** *On US 3, ½ mi S of jct US 302. 603/846-5549.* 40 rms, 1–2 story. No A/C. June–mid-Oct: S $34; D $49–$53; each addl $5; suites $70–$80; lower rates rest of yr. Crib $5. TV; satellite. Playground. Cafe 7–10 am, 5–9 pm; hrs vary off-season. Bar from 5 pm. Ck-out 11 am. Coin lndry. Tennis. Downhill/x-country ski 5 mi. Lawn games. Some balconies. Cr cds: A, MC, V.

🖰 🖰

✔ ★★**FOUR SEASONS MOTOR INN.** *(Box 157) US 3, I-93 exit 35. 603/846-5708; res: 800/228-5708.* 24 rms, 13 A/C, 2 story. Phones avail. S $38; D $38–$54; each addl $5; studio rms $54; under 12 free; ski plans. Crib free. TV. Pool. Playground. Cafe nearby. Ck-out 11 am. Meeting rms. Sundries. Free airport transportation. Downhill/x-country ski 7 mi. Game rm. Lawn games. Many balconies. Picnic tables, grills. Cr cds: MC, V.

🖰 🖰 🖰 🖰 ⊘ SC

New Jersey

Population: 7,365,011	
Land area: 7,468 sq mi (19,342 sq km)	
Elevation: 0–1,803 ft (0–550 m)	
Highest point: High Point Mountain (Sussex Co)	
Entered Union: Third of original 13 states (December 18, 1787)	
Capital: Trenton	
Motto: Liberty and Prosperity	
Nickname: Garden State	
State flower: Purple violet	
State bird: Eastern goldfinch	
State tree: Red oak	
State fair: Early Aug, 1989 in Cherry Hill	
Time zone: Eastern	

Interstate Highway System

The following alphabetical listing of New Jersey towns in *Mobil Travel Guide* shows that these cities are within 10 miles (16 kilometers) of the indicated Interstate highways. A highway map should be checked, however, for the nearest exit.

INTERSTATE 78: Clinton, Plainfield, Scotch Plains, Somerville, Union, Watchung.

INTERSTATE 80: Fort Lee, Hackensack, Hackettstown, Lake Hopatcong, Paramus, Parsippany, Ridgefield Park, Rockaway, Saddle Brook, Wayne.

INTERSTATE 95: Elizabeth, Fort Lee, Newark, Ridgefield Park, Trenton, Woodbridge.

Weather Statistics*

	WINTER	SPRING	SUMMER	FALL
Atlantic City	34°F (1°C)	57°F (14°C)	73°F (23°C)	52°F (11°C)
Newark	33°F (0.6°C)	57°F (14°C)	74°F (23°C)	52°F (11°C)
Trenton	33°F (0.6°C)	57°F (14°C)	74°F (23°C)	52°F (11°C)

*Average mean temperatures are listed for the entire state. Averages for specific regions (or cities representing specific regions) are given if significant differences exist.

Visitor Information

The State Division of Travel and Tourism, CN-826, Trenton 08625, phone 609/292-2470 or 800/537-7397, publishes a variety of material of interest to travelers. Also, *New Jersey, A Guide to Its Present and Past* (Hastings House, New York, new rev ed, 1977), one of the American Guide Series, is excellent on historical and general information to the date of publication. Other helpful and informative publications are: *New Jersey, America's Main Road* (Doubleday, New York, 1976) by John T. Cunningham; Michaela M. Mole's *Away We Go: The Favorite Family Field Trip Guide for New Jersey and Neighboring Regions* (Rutgers University Press, New Brunswick, NJ, 1976). There are also periodicals which may be of interest to travelers: *New Jersey Monthly* (write Subscription Dept, Box 936, Farmingdale, NY 11737); *New Jersey Outdoors* (write CN-402, Trenton 08625).

There are 50 welcome centers in New Jersey; visitors who stop by will find information and brochures most helpful in planning trips to points of interest. For a publication which shows the locations of the centers contact the State Division of Travel and Tourism.

Room Rate Information

The following major cities and resort area have higher room rates for two (double) than indicated on the cover of this Guide. However, the lodgings listed in these cities offer a good value when compared to others of their type in the area.

Atlantic City	$75	Wildwood Crest	$75
Newark	70		

Atlantic City

Settled: 1852 **Pop:** 40,199 **Elev:** 8 ft (2 m) **Area code:** 609

Motels

(Includes Absecon, Pleasantville, West Atlantic City)

★★**COMFORT INN VICTORIAN.** *(1175 Black Horse Pike, Pleasantville 08232) 609/646-8880.* 117 rms, 2 story. May–Sep: S, D $70–$120; each addl $6; under 16 free; lower rates rest of yr. Crib $6. TV; cable. Heated pool; lifeguard. Free continental bkfst. Ck-out noon. Meeting rms. Cr cds: A, C, D, DS, MC, V.

✔ ★★**COMFORT INN WEST.** *(Black Horse Pike at Dover Pl, West Atlantic City 08232) 609/645-1818.* 198 rms, 3 story. Mid-June–mid-Sep: S, D $59–$100; each addl $10–$15; suites $110–$150; under 16 free; higher rates hols; lower rates rest of yr. Crib free. TV; cable. Heated pool; lifeguard. Cafe 7–11 am. Ck-out noon. Meeting rm. Casino transportation. Cr cds: A, C, D, DS, ER, MC, V.

★★**WHITTIER INN.** *(Black Horse Pike, Pleasantville 08232) Garden State Pkwy exit 37. 609/484-1500; res: 800/237-9682.* 196 units, 4 story. Mid-June–mid-Sep: S, D $75–$125; each addl $6; under 12 free; lower rates rest of yr. Crib free. TV; cable. Heated pool; lifeguard. Free continental bkfst. Coin lndry. Meeting rms. Valet serv. Sundries. Free casino transportation. Cr cds: A, C, D, DS, MC, V. Ⓔ

Motor Hotel

★★**COMFORT INN NORTH.** *(405 E Absecon Blvd, Absecon 08201) W on US 30. 609/646-5000.* 200 rms, 6 story. Mid-June–mid-Sep: S, D $70–$90; each addl $15; suites $120–$145; under 16 free; casino package plans; higher rates hols; lower rates rest of yr. Crib free. TV; cable. Heated pool; lifeguard. Cafe 7–11 am. Ck-out noon. Meeting rms. Casino transportation. Cr cds: A, C, D, DS, ER, MC, V.

Hotels

✔ ★★**HOWARD JOHNSON.** *(539 Absecon Blvd, Absecon 08201) 4 mi W on US 30. 609/641-7272.* 208 units, 7 story. Mid-June–mid-Sep: S, D $45–$95; each addl $12; suites $95–$170; under 18 free; higher rates hols; lower rates rest of yr. Crib free. TV; cable. Cafe 7 am–9 pm. Serv bar. Ck-out noon. Meeting rms. Free airport transportation. Refrigerators avail. Sun deck. Cr cds: A, C, D, DS, MC, V.

★★★**RESORTS INTERNATIONAL CASINO HOTEL.** *N Carolina Ave at Boardwalk (08404). 609/344-6000; res: 800/438-7424 (exc NJ).* 696 rms, 15 story. July–Labor Day: S, D $75–$170; each addl $10; under 12 free; lower rates rest of yr. Crib free. TV; cable. 2 pools, 1 indoor/outdoor. Cafes open 24 hrs; dining rm 6 pm–midnight exc Sun, Mon. Bars; entertainment. Ck-out noon. Convention facilities. Concierge. Shopping arcade. Valet parking. Exercise rm; instructor, weights, bicycles, whirlpool, steam rm, sauna. Game rm. Bathrm phones. Some balconies. First casino. Cr cds: A, C, D, MC, V. Ⓓ Ⓔ Ⓕ Ⓘ Ⓙ

Cape May

Settled: 1631 **Pop:** 4,853 **Elev:** 14 ft (4 m) **Area code:** 609 **Zip:** 08204

Motor Hotel

✔ ★★★**MONTREAL.** *Beach & Madison Aves. 609/884-7011.* 70 units, 4 story, 42 kits. Mid-June–mid-Sep: S, D, suites $50–$90; each addl $4–$7; kit. units $60–$100; lower rates Mar–mid-June, mid-Sep–Dec. Closed rest of yr. Crib free. TV; in-rm movies. Heated pool; wading pool, sauna, poolside serv, lifeguard. Cafe 8 am–11 pm. Rm serv. Bar from 11 am. Ck-out 11 am. Coin lndry. Valet serv. Package store. Airport transportation. Putting green, miniature golf. Game rm. Refrigerators. Balconies. Picnic tables, grills. On ocean. Cr cds: A, MC, V. ⑩

Cherry Hill

Pop: 68,785 **Area code:** 609

Motels

✔ ★**BEL-AIR MOTOR LODGE.** *(NJ 73, Maple Shade 08052)* On NJ 73, ¼ mi W of I-295, ¾ mi W of NJ Tpke exit 4. *609/235-4500; res: 800/257-0435 (exc NJ).* 66 rms, 2 story, 10 kits. S $28.95–$34.95; D $31.95–$39.95; each addl $4; kit. units $40–$45. Crib $5. TV; cable. Pool; lifeguard. Free continental bkfst. Cafe nearby. Ck-out 11 am. Coin lndry. Valet serv. Sundries. Refrigerators. Cr cds: A, D, MC, V.

★★**BEST WESTERN MONTICELLO MOTOR LODGE.** *(Black Horse Pike, Bellmawr 08031)* At NJ Tpke exit 3. *609/931-0700.* 141 rms, 2 story. S $49; D $54; each addl $6; under 12 free. Crib $5. TV; cable. Pool; lifeguard. Cafe 6 am–10 pm. Bar to 2 am. Ck-out noon. Coin lndry. Meeting rms. Valet serv. Gift shop. Exercise rm; instructor, weights, bicycles, whirlpool. Many refrigerators. Cr cds: A, C, D, DS, MC, V.

✔ ★★**BUDGET MOTOR LODGE.** *(Mount Laurel 08054)* NJ 73 at NJ Tpke exit 4. *609/235-7400.* 206 rms, 2 story. S $35.95–$38.95; D $42.95; each addl $4; under 12 free. Crib avail. TV. Pool; lifeguard. Cafe 6:30 am–10 pm. Rm serv. Bar 11–1 am; dancing. Coin lndry. Meeting rms. Valet serv. Game rm. Some refrigerators. Cr cds: A, C, D, MC, V.

✔ ★★**KINGSWAY MOTOR LODGE.** *(Maple Shade 08052)* At jct NJ 73, I-295, ½ mi W of NJ Tpke exit 4. *609/235-3550; res: 800/257-0435 (exc NJ).* 106 rms, 3 story. S $34.95–$37.95; D $39.95–$42.95; each addl $4. Crib $5. TV; cable. Pool; lifeguard. Free continental bkfst. Cafes adj open 24 hrs. Ck-out 11 am. Coin lndry. Meeting rms. Valet serv. Sundries. Many refrigerators. Picnic tables. Cr cds: A, D, MC, V.

★★**LANDMARK INN MOTOR LODGE.** *(Maple Shade 08052)* At jct NJ 73, 38, ½ mi N of I-295, 1 mi N of NJ Tpke exit 4. *609/235-6400.* 163 rms, 3 story. S $45–$58; D $48–$62; each addl $3; suites $130–$150; under 18 free. Crib free. TV. Pool; wading pool, sauna, lifeguard. Playground. Cafe 6:30 am–10 pm; Sat, Sun 8:30 am–noon, 5–10 pm. Rm serv. Bar; entertainment, dancing Wed–Sat. Ck-out noon. Coin lndry. Meeting rms. Valet serv. Sundries. Refrigerators avail. Private patios, balconies. Cr cds: A, D, DS, MC, V.

★**McINTOSH INN.** *(NJ 73 & Church Rd, Mount Laurel 08054)* On NJ 73, ¼ mi E of NJ Tpke exit 4. *609/234-7194.* 93 rms, 2 story. S $29.95; D $35.95; each addl $3. Crib $3. TV. Cafe adj open 24 hrs. Ck-out 11 am. Valet serv. Cr cds: A, MC, V.

✔ ★RED CARPET INN. *(Mount Laurel 08054) On NJ 73 just E of NJ Tpke exit 4. 609/ 235-5610.* 70 rms, 2 story. S $36–$40; D $40–$44. TV; cable. Pool. Free continental bkfst. Cafe nearby. Ck-out 11 am. Meeting rm. Cr cds: A, C, D, MC, V.

Flemington

Settled: 1738 **Pop:** 4,132 **Elev:** 160 ft (49 m) **Area code:** 201 **Zip:** 08822

Motels

★ ★BEL AIR INN. *On US 202, ½ mi S of jct NJ 31. 201/782-7472.* 104 rms, 2 story, 24 kits. S, D $52–$65; each addl $8; suites $75–$120; kit. units $5 addl. Crib $8. TV. Pool. Cafe 6:30 am–midnight. Bar 9 am–midnight. Ck-out 11 am. Coin lndry. Meeting rms. Some in-rm steam baths. Cr cds: A, MC, V.

✔ ★FLEMINGTON TRAVEL INN. *(Box 14) On US 202, 1½ mi N of circle. 201/782-2883.* 42 rms, 1–2 story. S $36–$42; D $42–$48; each addl $4. Crib $4. TV. Pool. Free coffee in rms. Cafe 11:30 am–10 pm. Ck-out 11 am. Meeting rms. Refrigerators avail. Cr cds: A, MC, V.
Ⓔ

Hightstown

Pop: 4,581 **Elev:** 84 ft (26 m) **Area code:** 609 **Zip:** 08520

Motel

✔ ★ ★TOWN HOUSE. *¼ mi E on NJ 33 at NJ Tpke exit 8. 609/448-2400; res: 800/922-0622 (exc NJ).* 104 rms, 1–2 story. S $50–$90; D $55–$95; each addl $8; suites, studio rms $75–$140; under 12 free; package plans. Crib free. TV; in-rm movies. Pool; wading pool, lifeguard. Free continental bkfst. Cafe 7 am–10 pm. Bar 11–2 am; entertainment, dancing Wed, Fri & Sat. Ck-out 1 pm. Meeting rms. Sundries. Bicycle rentals. Refrigerators; whirlpool in some suites. Cr cds: A, C, D, DS, ER, MC, V.

Long Beach Island

Area code: 609

Motel

✔ ★SANDPIPER. *(Boulevard at 10th St, Ship Bottom 08008) 1 blk S of NJ 72. 609/ 494-6909.* 20 rms. Mid-June–Labor Day: S, D $42–$79; each addl $5; lower rates Apr–mid-June, after Labor Day–Nov. Closed rest of yr. TV; cable. Cafe nearby. Ck-out 11 am. Refrigerators. Ocean 1 blk. Cr cds: A, MC, V.

Mount Holly

Settled: 1676 **Pop:** 10,818 **Elev:** 52 ft (16 m) **Area code:** 609 **Zip:** 08060

Motel

✔ ★ ★ ★HOWARD JOHNSON. *(Box 73) On NJ 541 at NJ Tpke exit 5. 609/267-6550.* 138 rms, 2 story. S $50–$80; D $55–$85; each addl $6; under 12 free. Crib free. TV. Pool; lifeguard. Playground. Cafe 6 am–11 pm. Bar from 5 pm. Ck-out noon. Meeting rms. Airport transportation. Exercise equipt; bicycles, treadmills, whirlpool, sauna. Private patios. Cr cds: A, C, D, DS, ER, MC, V. Ⓕ

Newark

Settled: 1666 **Pop:** 329,248 **Elev:** 146 ft (45 m) **Area code:** 201

Motel

✔ ★**FRANKLIN INN.** *50 Port St (07114). 201/344-1500; res: 800/447-6363.* 171 rms, 3 story, 4 kits. S $59.95–$75.95; D $65.95–$81.95; each addl $6; suites $79.95; kit. units $81.95; under 18 free; wkend rates. Crib free. TV; cable. Free continental bkfst. Bar 11–1:30 am; Sun to 10 pm. Ck-out noon. Coin lndry. Meeting rms. Free airport transportation. Exercise equipt; weights, bicycles. Cr cds: A, C, D, DS, MC, V. Ⓔ Ⓕ Ⓘ

New Brunswick

Settled: 1681 **Pop:** 41,442 **Elev:** 42 ft (13 m) **Area code:** 201

Motels

✔ ★★**FRANKLIN INN.** *(244 NJ 18, East Brunswick 08816) At Edgeboro Rd. 201/390-4545; res: 800/447-6363.* 114 units, 2 story. S $45.95; D $51.95; each addl $6; under 18 free; wkend rates. Crib free. TV; in-rm movies. Free continental bkfst 6:30–9:30 am. Cafe opp. Ck-out noon. Valet serv. Health club privileges. Picnic tables. Cr cds: A, C, D, DS, MC, V. Ⓔ

Ⓝ Ⓢ

★**McINTOSH INN.** *(764 NJ 18, East Brunswick 08816) 6 mi E on NJ 18, 4 mi NE of NJ Tpke exit 9. 201/238-4900.* 103 rms, 2 story. S $33.95–$36.95; D $39.95–$42.95; each addl $3. Crib $3. TV. Cafe adj open 24 hrs. Ck-out 11 am. Cr cds: A, MC, V. Ⓔ

✔ ★**TRAVELODGE AT SOMERSET.** *(1850 Easton Ave, Somerset 08873) At jct Easton Ave & I-287 exit 6. 201/469-5050.* 121 rms, 2 story. S $40–$49.95; D $45–$55; each addl $8; under 10 free; wkend rates. Crib $8. TV. Indoor pool; sauna, lifeguard. Free continental bkfst. Cafe 7 am–10 pm; Sun 10:30 am–3 pm, 6–10 pm. Bar 11:30 am–midnight; Fri, Sat to 3 am. Ck-out noon. Meeting rms. Sundries. Cr cds: A, C, D, DS, MC, V. Ⓔ Ⓘ

Ocean City

Pop: 13,949 **Elev:** 4 ft (1 m) **Area code:** 609 **Zip:** 08226

Motels

✔ ★★**FORUM.** *(Box 448) 8th St, Ocean to Atlantic. 609/399-8700.* 58 rms, 2–3 story. July–Aug (3-day min): S, D $46–$96; each addl $8–$10; some wkend rates; lower rates Apr–May, Sep–Oct. Closed rest of yr. Crib avail. TV. Heated pool; wading pool, poolside serv, lifeguard. Cafe 8 am–2 pm. Rm serv. Ck-out noon. Coin lndry. Game rm. Rec rm. Refrigerators. Picnic tables. Sun deck. Cr cds: MC, V.

✔ ★★**PAVILION MOTOR LODGE.** *Beach Block at 8th St. 609/399-8080.* 76 rms, 2–3 story, 8 kits. July–Labor Day: S, D $55–$90; each addl $8; kit. units $65–$145; family, wkly rates; lower rates Mar–June, Sep–Nov. Closed rest of yr. Crib avail. TV. Heated pool; wading pool, poolside serv, lifeguard. Cafe 7 am–9 pm. Rm serv. Ck-out 11 am. Coin lndry. Meeting rm. Sun deck. Cr cds: A, C, D, DS, MC, V. Ⓕ Ⓘ

Parsippany

Pop: 7,488 **Elev:** 282 ft (86 m) **Area code:** 201 **Zip:** 07054

Motel

★★**TOMAC MOTOR LODGE.** *(Morris Plains 07950) On NJ 10, ½ mi W of US 202. 201/ 539-7000.* 72 rms, 2 story. S, D $55; each addl $5; 2 children under 16 free. Crib $3. TV; in-rm movies. Pool; lifeguard. Cafe 6:30 am–2 pm. Rm serv. Ck-out 11 am. Coin lndry. Meeting rms. Sundries. Refrigerators. Cr cds: A, DS, MC, V.

Princeton

Settled: 1685 **Pop:** 12,035 **Elev:** 215 ft (66 m) **Area code:** 609

Motels

 ★**McINTOSH INN.** *(3270 Brunswick Pike, Lawrenceville 08648) ¼ mi N of jct I-295. 609/896-3700.* 116 rms, 4 story. S $35.95; D $41.95; each addl $3. Crib $3. TV. Cafe opp open 24 hrs. Ck-out 11 am. Cr cds: A, MC, V.

✔★**RED ROOF INN.** *(3203 Brunswick Pike, Lawrenceville 08648) at jct I-295 & US 1N. 609/896-3388.* 109 rms, 2 story. S $37.95; D $45.95; each addl $2; under 18 free. Crib free. TV; cable, in-rm movies. Free coffee. Ck-out noon. Cr cds: A, C, D, DS, MC, V.

Vineland

Pop: 53,753 **Elev:** 106 ft (32 m) **Area code:** 609 **Zip:** 08360

Motels

✔★**BUENA VISTA.** *(Buena 08310) 6 mi NE at jct US 40, NJ 54, 9 mi SW of Atlantic City Expy exit 28. 609/697-1400.* 44 rms, 7 kits. Mid-June–mid-Sep, hols: S $35–$70; D $40–$85; each addl $5–$10; kit. units $45–$75; some wkend rates; lower rates rest of yr. Crib $5–$10. TV; in-rm movies. Pool; lifeguard. Cafe nearby. Bar 11–2 am. Ck-out 11 am. Meeting rms. Cr cds: A, C, D, MC, V. ①

★**CIRCLE PLAZA.** *62 S Delsea Dr. 609/691-6685.* 40 rms, 2 story. S $32; D $35; each addl $4.25. Crib avail. TV. Cafe opp open 24 hrs. Ck-out 11 am. Cr cds: A, D, MC, V.

Wildwood Crest

Pop: 4,149 **Elev:** 8 ft (2 m) **Area code:** 609 **Zip:** 08260

Motel

(Rates quoted may be for advance reservation only; holiday rates may be higher)

★★**MADRID RESORT.** *Miami Ave, on beach. 609/729-1600.* 54 rms, 5 story, 24 kits. July–Labor Day: S, D $75–$105; each addl $10; suites $120; kit. units to 4, $125; higher rates wkends; lower rates mid-May–June, after Labor Day–Sep. Closed rest of yr. Crib avail. TV. Heated pool; wading pool; lifeguard. Cafe 7 am–8 pm. Ck-out 11 am. Coin lndry. Sundries. Rec rm. Sun deck. Refrigerators. Balconies. All oceanfront rms. Cr cds: A, MC, V. Ⓔ Ⓕ ①

New York

Population: 17,558,072	

Population: 17,558,072

Land area: 47,379 sq mi (122,711 sq km)

Elevation: 0–5,344 ft (0–1,629 m)

Highest point: Mount Marcy (Essex Co)

Entered Union: Eleventh of original 13 states (July 26, 1788)

Capital: Albany

Motto: Excelsior (Ever upward)

Nickname: Empire State

State flower: Rose

State bird: Bluebird

State tree: Sugar maple

State fair: August 25–September 4, 1989 in Syracuse

Time zone: Eastern

Interstate Highway System

The following alphabetical listing of New York towns in *Mobil Travel Guide* shows that these cities are within 10 miles (16 kilometers) of the indicated Interstate highways. A highway map should, however, be checked for the nearest exit.

INTERSTATE 81: Alexandria Bay, Binghamton, Clayton, Cortland, Syracuse, Watertown

INTERSTATE 84: Brewster, Fishkill, Middletown, Newburgh, Port Jervis

INTERSTATE 87: Albany, Ausable Chasm, Bolton Landing, Catskill, Diamond Point, Glens Falls, Hartsdale, Hudson, Kingston, Lake George Village, Lake Luzerne, Mohonk Lake, Monroe, Newburgh, New Paltz, New York City, Nyack, Plattsburgh, Poughkeepsie, Rouses Point, Saratoga Springs, Saugerties, Schroon Lake, Spring Valley, Stony Point, Tarrytown, Troy, Warrensburg, Woodstock, Yonkers

INTERSTATE 88: Bainbridge, Binghamton, Oneonta

INTERSTATE 90: Albany, Amsterdam, Auburn, Batavia, Buffalo, Canaan, Canajoharie, Canandaigua, Canastota, Clinton, Dunkirk, Fultonville, Geneva, Gloversville, Herkimer, Ilion, Johnstown, Oneida, Palmyra, Rochester, Rome, Schenectady, Seneca Falls, Syracuse, Troy, Utica, Victor, Waterloo, Weedsport, Westfield

INTERSTATE 95: Mamaroneck, Port Chester, White Plains

Weather Statistics*

	WINTER	SPRING	SUMMER	FALL
Albany	29°F (-2°C)	34°F (1°C)	66°F (19°C)	61°F (16°C)
Buffalo	25°F (-4°C)	44°F (7°C)	68°F (20°C)	51°F (10°C)

*Average mean temperatures are listed for the entire state. Averages for specific areas are given if significant differences exist.

Visitor Information

Ski New York and the *I Love New York* series of guides (covering upstate New York, Long Island and New York City) may be obtained from the State Department of Economic Development,

Division of Tourism, One Commerce Plaza, Albany 12245; 518/474-4116 or toll-free, 800/CALL NYS.

Room Rate Information

The following resort areas have higher room rates for two (double) than indicated on the cover of this Guide. However, the lodgings listed in these cities offer a good value when compared to others of their type in the area.

Corning	$65	Ithaca	$65
East Hampton, L.I.	65	Southampton, L.I.	80
Greenport, L.I.	80		

Albany

Settled: 1624 **Pop:** 101,727 **Elev:** 150 ft (46 m) **Area code:** 518

Motels

(Rates may be higher Saratoga racing season)

✔ ★ **AMBASSADOR MOTOR INN.** *1600 Central Ave (12205), I-87 exit 2W.* 518/456-8982; *res: 800/950-STAY.* 56 rms, 2 story. S $30–$32; D $32–$44; each addl $4–$5; some wkend rates; higher rates special events & Aug. Crib $4–$5. TV; cable, in-rm movies. Free continental bkfst. Cafe nearby. Ck-out 11 am. Valet serv. Sundries. Cr cds: A, C, D, DS, MC, V.

★ **BEST VALUE INN.** *1579 Central Ave (12205), I-90 exit 24, I-87 exit 2 W.* 518/869-8471. 60 rms, 2 story. S $30; D $34–$40; each addl $4; under 4 free; some wkend rates; higher rates Aug. Crib $4. TV; cable. Free continental bkfst 7–9 am. Cafe adj 10–1 am. Ck-out 11 am. Cr cds: A, C, D, DS, MC, V. Ⓕ

✔ ★ ★ **BLUE SPRUCE.** *(PO, Valatie 12184) 16 mi SE on US 9, 3 mi S of I-90 exit B1.* 518/758-9711. 29 rms, 1–2 story, 7 kits. Mid-June–Labor Day: S $30–$44; D $39–$48; each addl $2; suites $52–$64; studio rms, kit. units $46–$54; under 12, $1; wkly rates; higher rates wkends; lower rates rest of yr. Crib $3. TV. Pool; wading pool. Playground. Bkfst 7–11 am. Cafe nearby. Ck-out 11 am. Coin lndry. Lawn games. Refrigerators. Balconies. Picnic tables, grill. Cr cds: A, MC, V. Ⓓ Ⓕ Ⓘ

✔ ★ ★ **DAYS INN.** *16 Wolf Rd (12205).* 518/459-3600. 168 rms, 3 story. S $36–$44; D $44–$59; higher rates Aug. Crib free. TV; cable. Pool; lifeguard. Playground. Free coffee. Cafe adj 6 am–11 pm. Rm serv. Ck-out noon. Meeting rms. Valet serv. Game rm. Cr cds: A, C, D, MC, V.

★ **FORT CRAILO.** *(110 Columbia Tpke, Rensselaer 12144) I-87 exit 23 on Rte 9 & 20.* 518/472-1360. 28 rms, 2 kits. S $28; D $32–$38; kit. units $140/wk; lower rates winter. Crib free. TV; cable. Cafe adj. Ck-out 11 am. RR station, bus depot transportation. Picnic tables, grills. Cr cds: MC, V.

sc

★ **SUSSE CHALET.** *(44 Wolf Rd, Colonie 12205) I-87 exit 2E.* 518/459-5670. 97 rms, 2 story. S $38.70; D $42.70; each addl $3. Crib $2. TV; cable. Pool. Cafe nearby. Ck-out 11 am. Coin lndry. Valet serv. Health club privileges. Miniature golf. Cr cds: A, C, D, MC, V.

✔ ★ **TRAVELODGE.** *1230 Western Ave (12203), I-90 exit 24.* 518/489-4423. 75 rms, 2 story. S $35–$39; D $42–$56; each addl $4; under 18 free. Crib free. TV; cable. Pool. Cafe adj open 24 hrs. Ck-out noon. Sundries. Private patios, balconies. Cr cds: A, C, D, DS, ER, MC, V.

Alexandria Bay (Thousand Islands)

Pop: 1,265 **Elev:** 284 ft (87 m) **Area code:** 315 **Zip:** 13607

Motels

✔ ★ ★**NORTH STAR.** *(Box 605) On NY 12, just E of jct NY 26. 315/482-9332.* 18 rms. May–mid-Oct: S $34–$56; D $46–$66; each addl $5; lower rates rest of yr. Crib $5. TV. Pool. Playground. Cafe 7 am–9 pm. Ck-out 11 am. Putting green. Lawn games. Some refrigerators. Picnic tables, grill. Boat launch, dock. Cr cds: A, MC, V.

★ ★**PINE TREE POINT.** *(Box 68) 1 mi NE of NY 12, on St Lawrence. 315/482-9911.* 83 rms in lodge, chalets. July–Labor Day: S, D $47–$89; each addl $5; suites $110; under 12 free; lower rates May–June, after Labor Day–mid-Oct. Closed rest of yr. Crib $5. TV. Pool. Cafe 7:30–11 am, noon–2 pm, 6–10 pm. Rm serv. Bar noon–1 am; entertainment, dancing. Ck-out noon. Meeting rms. Sundries. Gift shop. Golf privileges. Rec rm. Lawn games. Most rms with balcony. Launching ramp; dockage. Cr cds: A, C, D, DS, MC, V.

★**PINEHURST.** *(Box 57) Pinehurst Rd, 3 mi SW on NY 12, 1 mi NE of I-81 exit 50N. 315/482-9452.* 23 motel rms, 19 A/C, 29 cottages, 20 with kit. Mid-June–Labor Day: S, D $44–$50; each addl $4; kit. units $32–$95; cottages for 2–5, $28–$50; wkly rates; lower rates mid-May–mid-June, rest of Sep. Closed rest of yr. Crib $4. TV; B/W in cottages. Pool. Playground. Cafe nearby. Ck-out 11 am. Grocery. Sundries. Lawn games. Picnic tables, grills. Boathouse. Dockage; launching ramp. Cr cds: A, MC, V.

✔ ★**ROCK LEDGE.** *(RR Box 28) ¼ mi W on NY 12. 315/482-2191.* 14 A/C rms in motel, 6 cottages. Mid-June–mid-Sep: S $30–$36; D $40–$44; each addl $3–$5; cottages to 6, $24–$60; lower rates mid-May–mid-June, rest of Sep. Closed rest of yr. Crib free. TV; cable. Playground. Cafe nearby. Ck-out 11 am. Lawn games. Picnic tables. Cr cds: MC, V.

Amsterdam

Settled: 1785 **Pop:** 21,872 **Elev:** 450 ft (137 m) **Area code:** 518 **Zip:** 12010

Motels

★**VALLEY VIEW.** *Jct NY 5S & NY 30, I-90 Thrwy exit 27. 518/842-5637.* 60 rms, 2 story. July–Aug: S $39.50; D $46.50; each addl $4; under 17 free; wkly rates; lower rates rest of yr. Crib free. TV; cable. Cafe 5:30 am–1 pm, 4–9 pm. Bar; entertainment, dancing wkends. Ck-out 11 am. Coin lndry. Meeting rms. Sundries. Airport, RR station transportation. Some refrigerators. Cr cds: A, MC, V.

✔ ★**WINDSOR.** *(RD 4) 2½ mi N on NY 30; N of I-90 exit 27. 518/843-0243.* 36 rms. S, D $32–$36; each addl $4; higher rates Saratoga races. Crib free. TV; cable. Pool. Playground. Bkfst avail 7–11 am. Ck-out 11 am. Gift shop. Downhill/x-country ski 20 mi. Petting zoo in season. Cr cds: A, MC, V.

Avon

Pop: 3,006 **Elev:** 651 ft (198 m) **Area code:** 716 **Zip:** 14414

Motels

★**CREST HILL.** *6110 Avon-Lima Rd, I-390 exit 10. 716/226-3450.* 15 rms. No A/C. S $26–$28; D $32–$40; each addl $4–$6; under 3 free; higher rates special events. Crib free. TV. Cafe opp 6 am–10 pm. Ck-out 11 am. Cr cds: MC, V.

★STRATFORD. *6076 Avon-Lima Rd, I-390 exit 10. 716/226-9908.* 17 rms. S $28–$32; D $34–$40; each addl $4–$6; higher rates special events. Crib free. TV. Cafe opp 6 am–10 pm. Ck-out 11 am. Cr cds: MC, V.

Inn

✔ ★★AVON. *55 E Main St. 716/226-8181.* 16 rms, 2 story. No rm phones. May–Sep: S $29–$42; D $34–$42; suites $42; kit. units $37; children free; wkly rates, package plans; lower rates rest of yr. Closed 1 wk Feb. B/W TV. Playground. Cafe 11:30 am–2 pm, 5–9 pm; Fri, Sat to 10 pm; Sun 10 am–7 pm. Rm serv. Ck-out noon, ck-in 3 pm. Historic inn (1820); antiques; fireplace. Gazebo & fountain in rear. Cr cds: A, C, D, MC, V.

Batavia

Founded: 1801 **Pop:** 16,703 **Elev:** 895 ft (273 m) **Area code:** 716 **Zip:** 14020

Motels

✔ ★MISTER DAVID. *8212 Park Rd, just off NY 98, W of I-90 exit 48. 716/343-2311.* 20 rms, 2 story. May–Oct: S $32–$45; D $34–$65; each addl $3–$5; under 12 free; lower rates rest of yr. Crib $5. TV. Pool. Playground. Cafe adj 7 am–9 pm. Ck-out 11 am. Airport transportation. Picnic tables, grill. Cr cds: A, MC, V. Ⓔ

✔ ★PARK-OAK. *Park Rd & Oak St, I-90 exit 48. 716/343-7921.* 20 rms, 2 story. S $30–$35; D $32–$48; each addl $5; higher rates special events. Crib $4. TV. Free continental bkfst. Cafe adj 6:30 am–9 pm. Ck-out 11 am. Cr cds: A, MC, V.

Binghamton

Settled: 1787 **Pop:** 55,860 **Elev:** 860 ft (262 m) **Area code:** 607

Motels

✔ ★★BEST WESTERN OF JOHNSON CITY. *(569 Harry L Dr, Johnson City 13790)* N of NY 17 exit 70N. 607/729-9194. 103 rms, 4 story. S $44–$46; D $52–$54; each addl $5–$8; under 13 free; higher rates special events. Crib $8. TV; cable, in-rm movies. Free coffee. Cafe adj 6 am–midnight. Bar 5 pm–1 am. Ck-out noon. Meeting rms. X-country ski 4 mi. Health club privileges. Some wet bars. Regional Mall adj. Cr cds: A, C, D, DS, MC, V.

✔ ★FIRESIDE MOTOR LODGE. *1156 Front St (13905), I-81 exit 6N. 607/722-5353; res: 800/345-9843.* 65 rms, 2 story. S $35–$65; D $45–$75; each addl $5; kit. suites $60–$80; under 12 free. Crib $5. TV; cable. Free continental bkfst. Cafe adj 7 am–11 pm. Ck-out 11 am. Coin lndry. Meeting rm. Cr cds: A, C, D, DS, MC, V. ⒻⒾ

★★HOWARD JOHNSON-NORTH. *700 Front St (13905), jct I-88 & NY 17. 607/724-1341.* 106 rms, 2 story. June–Oct: S $47–$60; D $54–$67; each addl $8; higher rates special events; lower rates rest of yr. Crib free. TV; cable. Heated pool; lifeguard. Free continental bkfst Mon–Fri. Cafe adj open 24 hrs. Ck-out noon. Meeting rms. Valet serv. X-country ski 5 mi. Balconies. Cr cds: A, C, D, DS, ER, MC, V.

✔ ★★PARK PLAZA INN. *(581 Harry L Dr, Johnson City 13790)* W on NY 17, exit 70N. 607/770-9333. 62 units, 4 story. S $44–$50; D $52–$57; each addl $8; suites $49–$57; under 13 free; higher rates college graduation. TV; cable. Indoor pool. Cafe adj. Meeting rms. Valet serv.

Airport transportation. Exercise equipt; weights, bicycles, whirlpool, steam rm, sauna. Cr cds: A, C, D, DS, MC, V.

🚹 🏊 🏃 🚫 🐾 SC

✔ ★ ★**PARKWAY.** *(Box 363, Vestal 13850) 900 Vestal Pkwy E, NY 17 exit 67S, NY 434 E, right turn.* 607/785-3311. 58 rms, 10 kits. S $28–$35; D $32–$40; each addl $8–$10; kit. units $28–$40; family, wkly, wkend rates; higher rates graduation. Crib $5–$8. TV; cable. Pool. Free continental bkfst. Cafe adj. Bar 11–1 am. Ck-out 11 am. Valet serv. Some refrigerators. Cr cds: A, C, D, DS, MC, V. ①

🚹 🏊 🚫 🐾 SC

Buffalo

Pop: 357,870 **Elev:** 600 ft (183 m) **Area code:** 716

Motels

✔ ★**AIRWAYS.** *(4230 Genesee St, Cheektowaga 14225) I-90 exit 51 E.* 716/632-8400. 150 rms, 2 story. S $34.50–$41.50; D $39.50–$47.50; each addl $5; under 12 free; package plan. Crib free. TV; in-rm movies. Heated pool; poolside serv, lifeguard. In-rm coffee. Cafe 5 am–midnight. Rm serv. Bar 11–3 am. Ck-out noon. Coin lndry. Meeting rms. Bellhops. Valet serv. Sundries. Airport transportation. Rec rm. Lawn games. Cr cds: A, C, D, DS, MC, V.

🏊 🏊 🐾 SC

★ ★**BUFFALO SOUTH MOTOR INN.** *(4344 Mile Strip Rd, Blasdell 14219) I-90 exit 56.* 716/825-7530. 127 units, 40 kits. (no equipt). S $23.95; D $30–$34; each addl $5; kit. units Sep–May for monthly, wkly rates; higher rates special events. Crib free. TV. Pool; wading pool, lifeguard. Playground. Cafe 6 am–10 pm. Bar noon–midnight. Ck-out noon. Coin lndry. Cr cds: A, MC, V.

🏊 🐾

★**ELLICOTT PARK COURT.** *(2740 Niagara Falls Blvd, Tonawanda 14150) I-90 exit 50.* 716/693-6412. 14 rms, 4 kits. Memorial Day–Labor Day: S $35; D $39; each addl $4; kit. units $10 addl; higher rates hols, special events; lower rates rest of yr. Crib free. TV; cable, in-rm movies. Free coffee in rms. Cafe nearby. Ck-out 11 am. Whirlpool. Some refrigerators. Picnic tables. Cr cds: A, MC, V.

🐾

✔ ★ ★**HAMPTON INN.** *(10 Flint Rd, Amherst 14226) I-290 to exit 5B, left at Flint Rd.* 716/689-4414. 117 rms, 4 story. S $43–$47; D $48–$52; under 18 free. Crib free. TV; cable. Pool; lifeguard. Free continental bkfst. Cafe opp open 24 hrs. Ck-out noon. Meeting rm. Airport, RR station transportation. Cr cds: A, C, D, MC, V.

🚹 🏊 🚫 🐾 SC

★**HERITAGE HOUSE MOTOR INN.** *(8261 Main St, Williamsville 14221)* 716/633-4900. 57 rms, 2 story, 9 kits. S $28.95; D $32.95; each addl $4; kit. units $125–$225/wk; monthly rates. Crib free. TV; cable. Free continental bkfst. Cafe nearby. Ck-out noon. Meeting rms. Cr cds: A, C, D, DS, MC, V.

🏊 🚫

✔ ★ ★**HOWARD JOHNSON.** *(6700 Transit Rd, Williamsville 14221) On NY 78 at I-90 exit 49.* 716/634-7500. 80 rms, 2 story. S $49–$62; D $53–$94; each addl $8; under 18 free. Crib free. TV; in-rm movies. Pool; lifeguard. Cafe adj open 24 hrs. Ck-out noon. Valet serv. Private patios, balconies. Cr cds: A, C, D, DS, MC, V.

🚹 🏊 🚫 SC

★**JOURNEY'S END.** *(4400 Maple Rd, Amherst 14226) NE via I-290, exit 5B.* 716/834-2231; res: 800/668-4200 (NY). 96 rms. S $34.88–$36.88; D $41.88–$43.88; each addl $4. Crib free. TV; cable. Continental bkfst. Cafe nearby. Ck-out 11 am. Valet serv. Cr cds: A, C, D, MC, V.

🚹 🏊 🚫 🐾 SC

✔ ★**LUXURY BUDGET INN.** *(4630 Genesee St, Cheektowaga 14225)* 716/631-8966. 84 rms, 4 story. S $31.99; D $37.99–$40.99; each addl $4; under 12 free. Crib $2. TV; cable, in-rm movies. Free continental bkfst in lobby. Cafe nearby. Ck-out 11 am. Valet serv. Airport transportation. Cr cds: A, D, DS, MC, V.

🔲 🚫 🔲

★**RED ROOF INN-AMHERST.** *(42 Flint Rd, Amherst 14226) NE on I-290, Millersport exit to Flint Rd.* 716/689-7474. 109 rms. S $31.95–$39.95; D $37.95–$41.95; each addl $6; under 18 free. Crib free. TV; cable, in-rm movies. Free coffee. Cafe nearby. Ck-out noon. Valet serv. Cr cds: A, D, DS, MC, V.

🔲 🔲 🚫 🔲 SC

✔ ★★**VILLAGE HAVEN.** *(9370 Main St, Clarence 14031) I-90 exit 49.* 716/759-6845. 27 rms, 7 kits. Late May–early Sep: S $26–$38; D $32–$42; each addl $4; kit. units $3 addl; wkly rates off-season; higher rates hols; lower rates rest of yr. Crib $4. TV. Pool; lifeguard. Playground. Free coffee. Free continental bkfst in season. Cafe nearby. Ck-out 11 am. Some refrigerators. Picnic tables. Cr cds: A, MC, V.

🔲 SC

★**WILLIAMSVILLE INN.** *(5447 Main St, Williamsville 14221) I-90 exit 50.* 716/634-1111. 99 rms, 2 story. S $35–$40; D $36–$44; each addl $4; under 12 free. Crib free. TV; cable, in-rm movies. Cafe 6:30 am–midnight. Rm serv. Bar 11–4 am. Ck-out noon. Coin lndry. Meeting rm. Valet serv. Free airport transportation. Cr cds: A, C, D, MC, V.

🔲 🔲 🚫

Motor Hotels

✔ ★★**BEST WESTERN INN DOWNTOWN.** *510 Delaware Ave (14202), I-190 exit N-9 Niagara St.* 716/886-8333. 60 rms, 5 story. S $47–$56; D $52–$61; each addl $5–$7; suites $54–$73; under 12 free. Crib $5. TV; cable. Cafe adj 7 am–midnight. Ck-out noon. Meeting rm. Valet serv. Health club privileges. Wet bar in suites. Cr cds: A, C, D, MC, V. ①

🚫 🔲 SC

✔ ★★**LORD AMHERST.** *(5000 Main St, Amherst 14226) I-90 exit 50 to I-290 exit Main St, NY 5W.* 716/839-2200. 101 rms, 2 story, 4 kits. May–Sep: S $39–$45; D $48–$55; each addl $7–$12; suites $85–$120; kit. units $56–$95; under 18 free; some wknd rates; lower rates rest of yr. Crib free. TV. Heated pool; lifeguard. Cafe 7 am–9 pm. Bar 11 am–midnight. Ck-out 1 pm. Coin lndry. Meeting rms. Valet serv. Airport transportation. Game rm. Colonial decor. Cr cds: A, C, D, MC, V. Ⓕ

🔲 🔲 🚫 🔲 SC

Canandaigua

Pop: 10,419 **Elev:** 767 ft (234 m) **Area code:** 716

Motels

★**BUDGET HOST-HERITAGE.** *(RD 1; 14424) 2 mi E on US 20 (NY 5), 7 mi S of I-90 exit 44.* 716/394-6170; *res:* 800/835-7427, ext 44. 16 rms. Apr–Dec: S $32; D $32–$36; each addl $4; lower rates rest of yr. Crib $3. TV; cable, in-rm movies. Free continental bkfst. Cafe nearby. Ck-out 11 am. Downhill ski 12 mi. Picnic tables, grill. Cr cds: MC, V. Ⓕ

🔲 🔲 SC

✔ ★★**ECONO LODGE.** *170 Eastern Blvd (14424).* 716/394-9000. 65 rms, 2 story. Apr–Oct: S $39.95; D $43.95; each addl $5; under 12 free; lower rates rest of yr. Crib free. TV; cable. Cafe adj open 24 hrs. Ck-out 11 am. Meeting rms. Downhill ski 12 mi. Opp lake. Cr cds: A, D, DS, MC, V.

🔲 🔲 🔲 🔲 🚫 🔲 SC

✔ ★★**KELLOGG'S PAN-TREE INN.** *130 Lake Shore Dr (14424), I-90 exit 43 or 44.* 716/394-3909. 15 rms. Late June–Labor Day: S $40; D $44; each addl $4; lower rates May–late June, after Labor Day–mid-Oct. Closed rest of yr. Crib $4. TV; cable. Cafe 7 am–7:30 pm; Sun from 8 am. Ck-out 11 am. Private patios. Opp park; swimming beach; boats at marina. Cr cds: MC, V.

🔲 🔲 🔲 🔲

Catskill

Settled: 1662 **Pop:** 4,718 **Elev:** 47 ft (14 m) **Area code:** 518 **Zip:** 12414

Motels

✔ ★★**CARL'S RIP VAN WINKLE.** *(Box 45, Star Rte 1) On Old NY 23B, ¼ mi W of I-87 exit 21. 518/943-3303.* 41 rms, 21 cabin units, 6 kits. July–Aug: S, D $36–$50; each addl $5; kit. units to 4, $350–$375/wk; lower rates mid-Apr–June, Sep–Oct. Closed rest of yr. Crib $5. TV; cable. Pool; wading pool. Playground. Cafe nearby. Ck-out 11 am. Lawn games. Some refrigerators; fireplace in some cabins. Picnic tables, grill. On 160 wooded acres. Cr cds: A, MC, V.

🏊

★**CATSKILL MOTOR LODGE.** *On NY 23B at I-87 exit 21. 518/943-5800.* 74 rms, 2 story, 4 kits. S $40; D $45; each addl $4; kit. units $70–$75; higher rates summer wkends. Crib $4. TV; cable. Pool; wading pool. Playground. Cafe 7 am–11 pm. Bar noon–2 am. Ck-out 11 am. Meeting rms. Downhill/x-country ski 15 mi. Cr cds: A, C, D, MC, V.

🛗 ⚓ 🏊 🚫

✔ ★★**RED RANCH.** *(Box 216, RD 1) On NY 32, ½ mi S of jct NY 23A. 518/678-3380.* 39 rms, 2 story, 4 kits. No rm phones. July–Labor Day: S, D $38–$60; kit. units to 6, $55–$80; wkly rates; ski plans; higher rates Hunter Mt festivals, hol wkends; lower rates rest of yr. Crib $5. TV; cable. Pool; wading pool. Playground. Cafe adj 7:30 am–9:30 pm. Ck-out 11 am. Downhill/x-country ski 10 mi. Game rm. Lawn games. Refrigerators avail. Picnic tables. Cr cds: A, C, D, DS, MC, V. Ⓓ

♿ ⚓ 🏊 🚫

Resort

✔ ★★**WOLFF'S MAPLE BREEZE.** *(Box 96, RD 1) Cauterskill Rd, 2 mi E of NY 32. 518/943-3648.* 42 rms, 1–2 story. July–Aug, MAP: S, D $43–$50; suites $50–$60; wkly: $285/person; family rates; lower rates May–June, Sep–Nov. Closed rest of yr. Crib free. TV. Pool; lifeguard. Playground. Cafe (public by res) 8:30–10 am, 5:30–6:30 pm. Snack bar. Bar; entertainment, dancing. Ck-out 11 am. Coin lndry, grocery, package store 3 mi. Tennis. Boats, rowboats. Game rm. Lawn games. Spacious grounds. Two lakes. Ⓓ

🔍 🏊 🚫

Clayton (Thousand Islands)

Pop: 1,816 **Elev:** 260 ft (79 m) **Area code:** 315 **Zip:** 13624

Motels

★**BERTRAND'S.** *(Box 129) 229 James St. 315/686-3641.* 28 rms, 1–2 story, 5 kits. July–Labor Day: S $36; D $50; each addl $6; kit. units $8–$12 addl; family, wkly rates off-season; lower rates Apr–June, early Sep–Nov. Closed Dec–Mar. Crib free. TV; cable. Cafe opp 6 am–10 pm. Ck-out noon. Sundries. Picnic tables, grills. Island tours. Fish clean and store. Cr cds: A, C, D, MC, V.

 SC

★**BUCCANEER.** *(Box 332, Cape Vincent 13618) W on NY 12E, 1 blk off Seaway Trail on Point St. 315/654-2975.* 10 rms, 2 story. S, D $55–$65; under 12 free. Crib free. TV; in-rm movies. Free continental bkfst. Cafe nearby. Ck-out 11 am. On river. Cr cds: MC, V.

🏊 🚫

★**C-WAY INN.** *(RD 1, Box 270) 3 mi S on NY 12. 315/686-4214.* 44 units, 2 story, 4 suites. No rm phones. May–early Nov: S $36; D $50–$65; each addl $4; suites $70–$75; kit. units $60; under 16 free; golf package plans; higher rates wkends July–Aug. Closed mid-Nov–Apr. TV; cable. Pool. Free coffee. Cafe opp 6 am–10 pm. Ck-out 11 am. Meeting rms. Fishing guides. Picnic tables. Cr cds: A, MC, V.

🏊 🏊 🚫

✔ ★★**FAIR WIND LODGE.** *(Box 276, RD 12E) 2½ mi SW on NY 12 E, on St Lawrence Seaway. 315/686-5251.* 10 rms, 8 cottages, 6 with kit. No A/C. Mid-May–mid-Oct: S, D $42–$48; each addl $4; kit. cottages for 2, $275/wk, each addl $10. Closed rest of yr. Crib free. TV. Heated pool. Cafe nearby. Ck-out 10 am. Picnic tables, grills. 45-ft dock. Cr cds: MC, V. ⒺⒻ

⊜⊯

✔ ★★**WEST WINDS.** *(Box 56, RD 2) 2 mi on NY 12 E, on shore of St Lawrence Seaway. 315/686-3352; off-season: 607/625-2963.* 20 units, 4 kits., 4 kit. cottages. No A/C. Mid-June–Labor Day: S $34–$40; D $39–$48; each addl $5; suites $80; kit. cottages for 4–6, $290–$475/wk; lower rates mid-May–mid-June & rest of Sep. Closed rest of yr. Crib $5. TV. Pool. Free coffee. Cafe nearby. Ck-out 10 am. Boats; dockage. Game rm. Picnic tables. On 5 acres. Cr cds: MC, V.

⊜⊯⊛

Cooperstown

Founded: 1786 **Pop:** 2,342 **Elev:** 1,264 ft (386 m) **Area code:** 607 **Zip:** 13326

Motels

★**AALSMEER.** *(Box 790, RD 2) 7½ mi N on NY 80, on Otsego Lake. 607/547-8819.* 8 rms, 10 cottages. Late June–Labor Day, hols: S, D $55–$58; each addl $5 (no charge for 2d addl spring & fall); cottages $390/wk; lower rates after Labor Day–Oct, mid-May–late June. Closed rest of yr. Crib free. TV; cable. Playground. Free coffee. Ck-out 11 am. X-country ski 6 mi. Refrigerators. Beach; dock. Boat livery nearby. Cr cds: MC, V. Ⓕ

⊕⊜⊯⊯

★**BAY SIDE MOTOR INN.** *(Box 788, RD 2) 7 mi N on NY 80, on Otsego Lake. 607/547-2371.* 15 A/C rms in motel, 1–2 story, 10 kit. cottages. Late June–Labor Day: S, D $52–$67; each addl $5; kit. cottages $325–$525/wk; lower rates rest of yr. Crib free. TV; cable. Continental bkfst. Cafe. Ck-out 11 am. 9-hole golf privileges. X-country ski 6 mi. Picnic tables, grills. Sand beach, lake swimming. Boat rentals; dockage nearby. Cr cds: A, MC, V.

⊜⊯⚓⊗⊛⊗

Corning

Settled: 1833 **Pop:** 12,953 **Elev:** 937 ft (286 m) **Area code:** 607 **Zip:** 14830

Motels

✔ ★★★**BEST WESTERN LODGE ON THE GREEN.** *(Box 150, Painted Post 14870) 3 mi W on US 15, NY 417, Gang Mills exit. 607/962-2456.* 135 rms, 1–2 story. May–Oct: S $50–$75; D $60–$80; each addl $5; lower rates rest of yr. Crib free. TV; cable. Heated pool; lifeguard. Cafe 7 am–2 pm, 5:30–9:30 pm. Bar. Ck-out noon. Meeting rms. Airport transportation. Lawn games. Some balconies. Spacious grounds. Cr cds: A, C, D, DS, MC, V. Ⓕ

⊕⊜⊛⊗⊛sc

✔ ★★★**HOLIDAY INN.** *(304 S Hamilton St, Painted Post 14870) Just S of jct US 15, NY 417 Gang Mills exit. 607/962-5021.* 105 rms, 2 story. S $53–$63; D $62–$72; each addl $5; under 12 free. Crib free. TV; cable, in-rm movies. Pool; wading pool, lifeguard. Cafe 7 am–2 pm, 5–10 pm. Rm serv. Bar; entertainment, dancing Fri, Sat. Ck-out noon. Coin lndry. Meeting rms. Bellhops. Sundries. Barber, beauty shop. Cr cds: A, C, D, DS, ER, MC, V.

⊕⊜⊗⊛sc

★**PIERRI'S CRYSTAL CITY.** *52 Ferris St. 607/936-9370.* 40 rms, 2 story. June–Oct: S $49; D $54; each addl $5; under 13 free; lower rates rest of yr. Crib free. TV; cable, in-rm movies. Playground. Cafe nearby. Ck-out 11 am. Valet serv. Cr cds: A, D, MC, V.

⊕⊗⊛sc

★**STILES.** *(RD 2, Box 10, Painted Post 14870) Victory Hwy, 4 mi N on NY 415; ½ mi W of NY 17 exit 42. 607/962-5221.* 15 rms. May–Nov: S $27–$30; D $32–$42; each addl $4;

family rates; wkly rates Dec–Apr; lower rates rest of yr. Crib $1. TV; cable. Playground. Free coffee in rm. Ck-out 10:30 am. Picnic tables. Country surroundings. Gazebo. Cr cds: MC, V.

Inn

✔ ★★★ROSEWOOD. *134 E First St. 607/962-3253.* 6 rms, 2 story, 4 with bathrm, 2 A/C. S $50–$70; D $60–$90; 12 and older, $15; under 12, $10; off-season rates. Crib free. Some TV. Free full bkfst. Ck-out 11 am, ck-in 3 pm. Restored Victorian home (1855); antiques, hand-made quilts. Rms individually decorated. Fireplace in parlor. 4 blks to public swimming. Cr cds: D, MC, V.

Dunkirk

Pop: 15,310 **Elev:** 598 ft (182 m) **Area code:** 716 **Zip:** 14048

Motels

★DUNKIRK. *310 W Lake Shore Dr, I-90 exit 59. 716/366-2200.* 45 units, 7 kits. May–Oct: S $29; D $35–$37; each addl $3; kit. units $50–$60; lower rates rest of yr. Crib $1. TV; cable. Pool; wading pool, lifeguard. Cafe adj 6:30 am–10 pm. Ck-out 11 am. Cr cds: A, MC, V.

✔ ★★HOLIDAY INN. *(10455 Bennett Rd, Fredonia 14063) ¼ mi S, I-90 exit 59. 716/673-1351.* 133 rms, 2 story. Late May–Sep: S $42; D $45–$59; each addl $5; under 12 free; ski rates; special plans; lower rates rest of yr. Crib free. TV. Pool; wading pool, poolside serv, lifeguard. Cafe 6 am–2 pm, 5–10 pm. Rm serv. Bar noon–2 am; entertainment exc Sun. Ck-out noon. Meeting rms. Bellhops. Valet serv. Sundries. Downhill/x-country ski 20 mi. Cr cds: A, DS, MC, V.

Ⓔ Ⓕ

✔ ★★QUALITY INN VINEYARD. *Vineyard Dr, 2 mi S, just off NY 60 at I-90 exit 59. 716/366-4400.* 39 rms. Early June–late Oct: S $36–$38; D $42–$45; each addl $4; suite $65; under 16 free; some lower rates rest of yr. Crib $3. TV. Pool; wading pool, lifeguard. Playground. Cafe 7–1 am; Sun to 11 pm; dining rm 11:30 am–2 pm, 5–10 pm. Bar 9–1 am; Sun noon–10 pm. Ck-out noon. Meeting rms. Sundries. Free airport, bus depot transportation. Cr cds: A, C, D, DS, MC, V.

★SOUTHSHORE. *5040 W Lake Shore Drive, I-90 exit 59, on lake. 716/366-2822.* 9 A/C units in motel, 8 kits., 12 kit. cottages. July–Aug: D, kit. units, kit. cottages $32–$65; each addl $5; wkly rates; lower rates rest of yr. Crib free. TV. Heated pool. Playground. Ck-out 10 am. Coin lndry. Lawn games. Refrigerators. Picnic tables, grill. Cr cds: MC, V.

East Hampton, L. I.

Settled: 1648 **Pop:** 1,886 **Elev:** 36 ft (11 m) **Area code:** 516 **Zip:** 11937

Motel

★★DUTCH. *488 Montauk Hwy. 516/324-4550.* 24 kit. units. Late June–Labor Day: S, D $62–$135; each addl $15; suites $100–$148; lower rates rest of yr. Crib free. TV; cable. Heated pool; whirlpool, lifeguard. Cafe nearby. Ck-out noon. Lawn games. Free beach passes. Private patios. Picnic tables, grills. Cr cds: A, C, D, MC, V.

Elmira

Settled: 1788 **Pop:** 35,327 **Elev:** 859 ft (262 m) **Area code:** 607

Motels

✔ ★ ★**BEST WESTERN MARSHALL MANOR.** *(Box 238, Horseheads 14845) Watkins Rd, on NY 14, 4 mi N of NY 17 exit 52N. 607/739-3891.* 40 rms. S $32–$40; D $38–$56; each addl $5; under 12 free; higher rates special events. Crib $2. TV; cable. Pool. Free coffee in rms. Cafe 7 am–9 pm; Sat, Sun 9 am–10 pm. Bar 11–1 am. Ck-out 11 am. Cr cds: A, C, D, DS, MC, V.

★**COACHMAN MOTOR LODGE.** *908 Pennsylvania Ave (NY 14) (14904). 607/733-5526.* 18 kit. units, 2 story. S $44–$46; D $54–$56; under 18 free; each addl $5. Crib free. TV; cable. Cafe nearby. Ck-out noon. Coin lndry. Sundries. Some balconies. Cr cds: A, C, D, DS, MC, V.

Endicott

Settled: 1795 **Pop:** 14,457 **Elev:** 840 ft (256 m) **Area code:** 607 **Zip:** 13760

Motels

✔ ★ ★**BEST WESTERN HOMESTEAD.** *749 W Main St. 607/754-1533.* 62 rms, 2 story, S $38–$42; D $42–$50; each addl $7; kit. units $55–$85; higher rates Broome County Open, college graduation wkend. Crib $2. TV; cable, in-rm movies. Cafe 6:30 am–2 pm; dining rm 5:30–10 pm; Sat to 10:30 pm; Sun 4–9 pm. Bar 4 pm–1 am exc Sun. Ck-out noon. Valet serv. Airport transportation. Health club privileges. Refrigerator $3. Balconies. Cr cds: A, C, D, DS, MC, V. ⑩

✔ ★**ENDICOTT INN.** *214 Washington Ave. 607/754-6000; res: 800/223-0888.* 57 rms, 3 story. S $39; D $48; each addl $5; under 12 free; wkly, ski rates. Crib $5. TV; cable. Free full bkfst. Cafe 6:30 am–10 pm. Bar 4 pm–1 am; entertainment, dancing Fri. Ck-out 11 am. Meeting rms. Valet serv. Sundries. Some refrigerators. 1 blk from river. Cr cds: A, C, D, DS, MC, V.

Geneseo

Pop: 6,746 **Elev:** 800 ft (244 m) **Area code:** 716 **Zip:** 14454

Motel

✔ ★ ★**GENESEO INN.** *4242 Lakeville Rd. 716/243-0500.* 76 rms, 1–2 story. S $34.95; D $44.95; each addl $3; under 18 free; ski plan. Crib free. TV; cable. Pool. Cafe 7–10 am, 11:30 am–3 pm, 5–9 pm; Sat from 8 am; Sun 8–11 am, noon–8 pm. Rm serv. Bar 11–2 am. Ck-out noon. Coin lndry. Meeting rms. Valet serv. Sundries. X-country ski 6 mi. Cr cds: A, D, DS, MC, V.

Glens Falls

Settled: 1763 **Pop:** 15,897 **Elev:** 340 ft (104 m) **Area code:** 518 **Zip:** 12801

Motel

✔ ★ ★**LANDMARK.** *(Box 376) 5½ mi S on US 9, 1 mi N of I-87 exit 17N. 518/793-3441; res: 800/453-4511 (exc NY).* 67 rms. July–Aug: S $34–$70; D $42–$80; each addl $3–$5; higher rates hols; lower rates rest of yr. Crib $3–$5. TV; cable. Pool. Playground. Cafe adj open 24 hrs in season. Ck-out 11 am. Meeting rm. Free airport, bus depot transportation. Putting green. Downhill ski 6 mi; x-country ski 3 mi. Snowmobiling. Ice-skating. Rec rm. Lawn games. Picnic tables, grills. Cr cds: A, C, D, DS, MC, V. ⑩ Ⓕ

Greenport, L. I.

Pop: 2,273 **Elev:** 10 ft (3 m) **Area code:** 516 **Zip:** 11944

Motel

★SUNSET. *North Rd, 1¼ mi NW on County Rd, on L. I. Sound. 516/477-1776.* 19 units, 1–2 story, 15 kits. Mid-June–mid-Sep, Memorial Day wkend (3-day min; hol wkends 4-day min): D $80–$110; each addl $10; kit. units $95–$110; lower rates mid-Apr–mid-June, mid-Sep–mid-Nov. Closed rest of yr. Crib free. TV; cable. Cafe nearby. Ck-out 11 am. Tennis privileges. Lawn games. Porches. Picnic tables, grills. Private beach. Cr cds: MC, V.

Hague (Lake George Area)

Pop: 766 **Elev:** 328 ft (100 m) **Area code:** 518 **Zip:** 12836

Motel

✔ ★ ★TROUT HOUSE VILLAGE. *(Box 42) Lake Shore Dr, 1 blk N on NY 9N, opp lake. 518/543-6088.* 9 rms in motel, lodge, 4 kits.; 3 kit. cottages; 9 kit. chalets, 1–3 story. No A/C. Mid-June–mid-Sep: S, D $43–$69; each addl $6; kit. units to 4, $70–$175; $350–$890/wk; ski rates; lower rates rest of yr. Crib free. TV; cable. Free coffee in some rms. Cafe off-season (res) 7:30–9:30 am, 7–7:30 pm. Ck-out 11 am. Airport, RR station, bus depot transportation. Putting green. X-country ski 2 mi. Rec rm. Lawn games. Picnic tables, grill. Some fireplaces. Bicycles. X-country ski rentals. 400-ft beach. Canoes, rowboats, kayaks, sailboats, paddleboats; dockage. View of lake. Cr cds: A, DS, MC, V.

Herkimer

Settled: 1725 **Pop:** 8,383 **Elev:** 407 ft (124 m) **Area code:** 315 **Zip:** 13350

Motels

★ ★HERKIMER. *100 Marginal Rd. 315/866-0490.* 60 rms, 2 story, 17 kits. S $34–$53; D $48–$72; each addl $6; kit. units, studio rms $57–$72; under 13 free; wkly rates. Crib free. TV; cable. Heated pool. Cafe 6:30 am–11 pm (winter to 10 pm); Thurs–Sat open 24 hrs. Bar 11–2 am. Ck-out 11 am. Coin lndry. Meeting rms. Sundries. Gift shop. Downhill/x-country ski 7 mi. Picnic tables. Cr cds: A, DS, MC, V.

✔ ★ ★PROSPECT INN. *200 North Prospect. 315/866-4400.* 47 rms, 2–4 story, 8 kits. S $35–$40; D $42–$50; each addl $5; suites $42–$55; under 12 free. Crib $7. TV; cable. Indoor pool; sauna. Free continental bkfst. Cafe 11:30 am–2 pm, 5–9 pm; Fri to 9:30 pm. Bar 11 am–2 pm, 4 pm–closing; entertainment Wed. Ck-out 11 am. Meeting rms. Beauty shop. Downhill/x-country ski 20 mi. Cr cds: A, C, D, MC, V.

Hudson

Settled: 1783 **Pop:** 7,986 **Elev:** 80 ft (24 m) **Area code:** 518 **Zip:** 12534

Hotel

✔ ★ ★ST CHARLES. *14 Park Pl. 518/828-4165.* 38 rms, 3 story. S $40–$88; D $46–$100; each addl $6; under 12 free; wkly, ski rates. Crib free. TV; cable. Cafe adj. No rm serv. Bar to 1 am. Ck-out 11 am. Meeting rms. Downhill ski 15 mi. Historic hotel (1850); rms individually decorated. Cr cds: A, C, D, DS, MC, V.

Hyde Park

Settled: 1740 **Pop:** 2,550 **Elev:** 188 ft (57 m) **Area code:** 914 **Zip:** 12538

Motels

✔★**DUTCH PATROON.** *1 mi S on US 9. 914/229-7141.* 33 units, 10 kits. May–Oct: S $29–$34; D $35–$45; kit. units $39–$44; under 5 free; wkly rates; lower rates rest of yr. Crib $5. TV; cable. Pool. Continental bkfst. Ck-out 11 am. Lawn games. Picnic tables, grills. Cr cds: A, MC, V.

★**ROOSEVELT INN.** *38 Albany Post Rd, ¼ mi S on US 9. 914/229-2443.* 26 rms, 2 story. May–Oct: S $40–$48; D $45–$58; each addl $4; lower rates Mar–Apr, Nov–Dec. Closed rest of yr. TV; cable. Cafe 7–11 am. Ck-out 11 am. X-country ski 5 mi. Balconies. Cr cds: A, MC, V. Ⓓ

✔★**SUPER 8.** *½ mi S on US 9. 914/229-0088.* 61 rms, 2 story. Apr–Oct: S $40; D $44; each addl $4; higher rates special events; lower rates rest of yr. Crib $5. TV; cable. Cafe adj open 24 hrs. Ck-out 11 am. Cr cds: A, C, D, DS, MC, V.

Ithaca

Settled: 1789 **Pop:** 28,732 **Elev:** 405 ft (123 m) **Area code:** 607 **Zip:** 14850

Motels

(Rates may be higher special college events)

★★★**BEST WESTERN UNIVERSITY INN.** *1020 Ellis Hollow Rd, East Hill Plaza. 607/272-6100.* 70 rms. S, D $60–$70; each addl $10; under 12 free; wkly rates. Crib $10. TV; cable, in-rm movies. Pool; lifeguard. Cafe 6 am–8 pm; Sat from 7 am; Sun 7 am–2 pm. Rm serv 6–11 am, 5–10 pm. Ck-out noon. Meeting rms. Airport transportation. Golf, health club privileges. Refrigerators. Cr cds: A, C, D, DS, ER, MC, V.

✔★★**COLLEGETOWN MOTOR LODGE.** *312 College Ave, 1½ blks S of Cornell University. 607/273-3542; res: 800/666-7666.* 41 rms, 1–3 story. S $55–$64; D $64–$85. Crib $3. TV; cable. Meeting rm. In-rm coffee. Ck-out noon. Sundries. X-country ski 10 mi. Refrigerators; some bathrm phones. Cr cds: A, D, DS, MC, V. Ⓙ

★★★**HOLIDAY INN.** *2310 N Triphammer Rd. 607/257-3100.* 120 rms, 2 story. S, D $57–$95; each addl $8–$12; under 12 free; higher rates wkends, special events. Crib free. TV; cable. Pool; wading pool, poolside serv, lifeguard. Cafe 7 am–2 pm, 5:30–10 pm. Rm serv. Bar 4 pm–1 am. Ck-out noon. Meeting rms. Valet serv. Free airport, Cornell Univ transportation. Health club privileges. Cr cds: A, C, D, DS, MC, V.

✔★★**HOWARD JOHNSON.** *3½ mi N on NY 13 at N Triphammer Rd. 607/257-1212.* 72 rms, 2 story. S $54–$76; D $64–$86; each addl $8; suites $125; under 18 free; ski plan; lower rates Dec–Feb; higher rates special events. Crib free. TV; cable. Pool; lifeguard. Cafe 6 am–midnight. Ck-out noon. Meeting rms. Valet serv. Sundries. Many private patios. Cr cds: A, C, D, DS, MC, V.

Motor Hotel

✔★★**RAMADA INN.** *222 S Cayuga St. 607/272-1000.* 178 rms, 10 story. S $50–$75; D $60–$95; each addl $10; suites $235; under 18 free. Crib free. TV; cable, in-rm movies. Indoor pool; sauna, lifeguard. Cafe 7 am–10 pm. Rm serv. Bar noon–1 am; entertainment. Ck-out noon.

Meeting rms. Bellhops. Concierge. Sundries. Gift shop. Free airport, bus depot transportation. Some bathrm phones. Cr cds: A, C, D, MC, V. Ⓓ Ⓕ

Jamestown

Settled: 1811 **Pop:** 35,775 **Elev:** 1,370 ft (418 m) **Area code:** 716 **Zip:** 14701

Motels

✔ ★★**COLONY.** *620 Fairmount Ave. 716/488-1904.* 45 rms, 1–2 story, 3 kits. D $32–$37; each addl $4; kit. units $42. Crib free. TV; cable. Heated pool. Playground. Cafe 7–10:30 am; Fri, Sat 5:15–8:15 pm. Bar 5–9 pm. Ck-out 11 am. Cr cds: A, C, D, MC, V.

★★**COMFORT INN.** *2800 N Main St. 716/664-5920.* 101 rms, 2 story. June–mid-Sep: S from $44.95; D from $49.95; each addl $5; under 16 free; wkly rates; lower rates rest of yr. Crib free. TV; cable, in-rm movies. Playground. Free continental bkfst. Ck-out noon. Meeting rms. Downhill ski 20 mi. Some in-rm whirlpools. Cr cds: A, C, D, MC, V.

✔ ★★**HERITAGE HOUSE MOTOR INN.** *(2 E Main St, Falconer 14733) NY 17 exit 13. 716/665-4410.* 35 rms, 2 story. S $27; D $33–$35; each addl $5; wkly rates. Crib free. TV; cable. Cafe 7 am–10 pm; Sun to 4 pm. Bar noon–midnight. Ck-out noon. Coin lndry. Meeting rms. Drugstore. Cr cds: A, MC, V.

★**RED COACH INN.** *(284 E Fairmount Ave, Lakewood 14750) 716/763-8548.* 51 rms, 2 story. S $34.50; D $40; each addl $5; under 8 free; wkend ski plan. Crib $2.50. TV; cable. Cafe 6–10 am, 5–10 pm. Rm serv. Bar 4 pm–2 am; entertainment, dancing exc Sun. Ck-out noon. Meeting rms. Balconies. Lake ½ mi; private beach privileges. Cr cds: MC, V.

Lake George Village

Pop: 1,047 **Elev:** 353 ft (108 m) **Area code:** 518 **Zip:** 12845

Motels

✔ ★**BRIAR DELL.** *(Box 2372, RD 2) Lake Shore Dr, 1 mi N on NY 9N; I-87 exit 22, on lake. 518/668-4819.* 6 motel rms, 16 cabins. Late June–Labor Day: S, D $39–$53; each addl $4; cabins for 4, $60; lower rates Memorial Day–late June, after Labor Day–mid-Oct. Closed rest of yr. Crib $1. TV; cable. Playground. Cafe adj 8 am–9 pm. Ck-out 11 am. Private beach; boats, dockage. Lawn games. Game rm. Picnic tables, grill.

★★**COLONIAL MANOR.** *(Box 528) ¼ mi S on US 9, NY 9N, 2 blks N of I-87 exit 21. 518/668-4884.* 35 motel rms, 1–2 story, 9 cottages, 11 (2-bedrm) kit. cottages. Late June–Labor Day: S, D $54–$125; each addl $6–$10; under 12 free (motel only); kit. units to 4, $500–$550/wk; each addl $50–$90; lower rates rest of yr. Crib free. TV; cable. Pool. Playground. Cafe opp open 24 hrs. Ck-out 11 am (kit. cottages 10 am). Downhill ski 10 mi; x-country ski 8 mi. Lawn games. Picnic tables, grill for kit. units. Refrigerator rentals. Shaded grounds. Porch on cottages. Cr cds: A, C, D, DS, MC, V. Ⓓ Ⓕ

★**LAKE HAVEN.** *(Box 581) Canada St, just N at jct US 9, NY 9N; I-87 exit 22. 518/668-2260.* 30 rms. July–Labor Day: S, D $50–$78; each addl $5; lower rates mid-Apr–June, after Labor Day–Oct. Closed rest of yr. Crib free. TV; cable. Heated pool. Cafe adj 7 am–10 pm. Ck-out 10 am. Free bus depot transportation. Game rm. Some refrigerators. Grill. Cr cds: A, MC, V.

★★**MOHAWK MOTEL & COTTAGES.** *477 Canada St, 1 blk from lake. 518/668-2143.* 30 rms, 8 kits., 7 kit. cottages. Late June–Labor Day: S, D $49–$79; each addl $8; kit. units, cottages from $79; lower rates rest of yr. Crib free. TV; cable. Heated pool. Playground. Cafe opp 9 am–11 pm. Ck-out 11 am, kit. units 10 am. Free bus depot transportation. Downhill/x-country ski 8 mi. Lawn games. Some fireplaces. Picnic tables, grills. Cr cds: MC, V.

Lake Luzerne

Pop: 1,988 **Elev:** 610 ft (186 m) **Area code:** 518 **Zip:** 12846

Motels

★**ISLAND VIEW.** *2220 Lake Ave, I-87 exit 21.* 518/696-3079. 10 rms, 4 kits. June–Sep: S $46–$52; D $50–$58; each addl $5; kit. units $57–$62; under 6 free; wkly rates; lower rates rest of yr. Crib free. TV; cable. Cafe nearby. Ck-out 11 am. Lawn games. Some refrigerators. Picnic tables, grills. Private beach, boats. Cr cds: MC, V.

✔ ★**PINE POINT COTTAGES.** *3205 Lake Ave, I-87 exit 21, on Lake Vanare.* 518/696-3015. 8 rms in motel, 10 kit. cottages. No A/C. S, D $37–$45; each addl $3–$5; kit. units $50; kit. cottages for 2–4, $75; wkly rates. Crib free. TV; cable. Playground. Cafe adj 7–3 am. Ck-out 10 am. Free airport, bus depot transportation. Downhill ski 15 mi; x-country ski 1 mi. Lawn games. Community kit. Private sand beach; boats, waterbikes. Many fireplaces, porches. Picnic tables, grills. Cr cds: MC, V. Ⓓ

★**WAGON WHEEL.** *½ mi N on NY 9N, on lake.* 518/696-2311. 11 motel rms, 1 2-rm log cabin, 2 kits. Mid-May–Sep: S, D $42–$48; each addl $6; kit. units $55–$58. Closed rest of yr. Crib free. TV; cable. Pool. Cafe nearby. Ck-out 11 am. Rowboats. Some refrigerators. Picnic tables, grill. Private beach. Cr cds: A, MC, V.

Lake Placid

Pop: 2,490 **Elev:** 1,882 ft (574 m) **Area code:** 518 **Zip:** 12946

Motels

✔ ★ ★**ALPINE.** *Wilmington Rd, ¾ mi E of NY 86.* 518/523-2180. 17 rms, 2 story; kit. units avail. July–Aug, ski season: S $38–$44; D $44–$62; each addl $4; kit. units $64; under 12 free; lower rates rest of yr. Crib $3. TV. Heated pool. Cafe nearby. Bar 3 pm–3 am. Ck-out 11 am. 45-hole golf privileges opp. Downhill ski 8 mi; x-country ski 1 mi. Sun deck. Balconies. Cr cds: A, D, MC, V.

★ ★**ART DEVLIN'S OLYMPIC.** *350 Main St, 1 blk S on NY 86, at jct NY 73.* 518/523-3700. 40 rms, 2 story. June–Oct: S $46–$76; D $52–$82; each addl $5; under 12 free; golf packages. Crib free. TV; cable. Pool; wading pool. Playground. Cafe 7:30–11 am. Ck-out 11 am. Airport, bus depot transportation. Downhill ski 8 mi; x-country ski 2 mi. Some balconies. Sun deck. Picnic tables, grills. Cr cds: A, MC, V. Ⓓ

★ ★ ★**HOWARD JOHNSON.** *Saranac Ave, ¾ mi W on NY 86.* 518/523-9555. 92 rms, 2 story. S $45–$105; D $48–$105; each addl $8; suites $100–$135; under 18 free; ski plan. Crib free. TV; cable. Indoor pool; whirlpool. Cafe 7 am–11 pm. Bar noon–11 pm. Ck-out noon. Coin lndry. Meeting rms. Sundries. Tennis. Downhill ski 10 mi; x-country ski on site. Rec rm. Lawn games. Boats, paddleboats; dockage. Balconies. Picnic tables, grills. Cr cds: A, C, D, DS, ER, MC, V. Ⓕ

★**PLACID BAY MOTOR INN.** *70 Saranac Ave.* 518/523-2001. 20 units, 2 story, 8 kits. Late June–Labor Day: S, D $50–$70; each addl $5; kit. units $58–$78; family rates; lower rates rest of yr. Crib free. TV; cable. Heated pool. Playground. Cafe nearby. Ck-out 11 am.

Airport, bus depot transportation. Downhill ski 8 mi; x-country ski 2 mi. Canoes, rowboats. Lawn games. Picnic table, grill. Cr cds: A, DS, MC, V.

🛏️ 🏊 🛬 🚫 SC

✔️ ★PLACID MANOR, INC. *(Box 870) 2½ mi W on NY 86, ½ mi N on shore of Lake Placid.* 518/523-2573. 35 rms in lodges, cottages, 3 A/C, 1 share bath, 1–3 story. Mid-June–mid-Oct & ski season: S, D $40–$85; each addl $10; family rates; lower rates rest of yr. Crib free. TV. Playground. Cafe 8–10 am, 11:30 am–2 pm, 6–9 pm; Fri, Sat to 10 pm; Sun 11 am–2 pm. Bar 11 am–midnight. Ck-out noon. Downhill ski 14 mi; x-country ski 1 mi. Boats avail. Lawn games. Private beach. Paddle boats, canoes. Scenic view. Antique furnished. Cr cds: A, MC, V.

🛏️ 🏊 🛬 🚫 SC

★★TOWN & COUNTRY. *67 Saranac Ave.* 518/523-9268. 24 rms, 2 story. June–Oct, Dec–Mar: S, D $44–$65; each addl $5; suites $84–$96; kit. units $70–$80; family, golf rates; lower rates rest of yr. Closed Apr. Crib $5. TV; cable. Heated pool. Free coffee in lobby. Cafe nearby. Ck-out 11 am. Downhill ski 12 mi; x-country ski 2 mi. Most refrigerators. Balconies. Picnic tables, grills. Cr cds: A, MC, V. ⒟ Ⓔ

🏊 🛬 🚫

Letchworth State Park

(Entrances at Castile, Mt Morris, Perry and Portageville) **Area code:** 716

Motel

★PETER'S. *(Sonyea Rd, Mt Morris 14510) NY 36.* 716/658-4500. 23 rms. S $29; D $27–$39; each addl $7. Crib free. TV. Pool. Cafe nearby. Ck-out 11 am. X-country ski 1 mi. Cr cds: D, MC, V. ⒟

🅿️ 🏊 🛬 🚫

Inns

✔️ ★★GENESEE FALLS. *(Box 396, Portageville 14536) E of S park entrance on NY 436.* 716/493-2484. 12 rms, 10 A/C, 10 baths, 3 story. No rm phones. Apr–Nov: S, D $18–$36; each addl $3. Closed rest of yr. Crib $3. Cafe 11 am–2 pm, 5–9 pm exc Tu; Sat 8:30 am–2 pm, 5–8:30 pm; Sun 8:30–11 am, 4–7 pm. Bar. Ck-out 11 am. Spacious grounds; on river. Inn since 1870s.

🛏️ 🚫

✔️ ★★GLEN IRIS. *(Castile 14427) In park, 1 mi N of S park entrance.* 716/493-2622. 14 rms, 3 story; also 7 motel units with kit. No elvtr. No rm phones. Apr–Oct: S, D $39–$45; each addl $8; suites $59–$64; kit. units for 2, $39. Closed rest of yr. TV in motel rms. Playground. Cafe 8–9:30 am, noon–2 pm, 5:30–9 pm; Sat to 10 pm; Sun 8–10 am, 12:30–8 pm. Serv bar. Ck-out noon. Meeting rm. Sundries. Gift shop. Some refrigerators. Picnic tables, grill. Inn built early 1800s; overlooks falls. Cr cds: A, MC, V. ⒟

🚶 🚫

Long Lake

Pop: 500 (est) **Elev:** 1,683 ft (513 m) **Area code:** 518 **Zip:** 12847

Motels

★★LONG LAKE. *(Box 206) Boat Landing Rd, 2 blks N, off NY 30.* 518/624-2613. 8 motel rms, 8 cottages, 4 kits. No A/C. July–Aug: S, D $45; each addl $5; kit. cottages for 2–4, $300–$450/wk; lower rates mid-May–June, Sep–mid-Oct. Closed rest of yr. Crib $5. TV; cable. Coffee in rms. Cafe nearby. Ck-out 10:30 am; cottages 10 am. Lawn games. Private sand beach. Private screened patios overlook woods, lake. Cr cds: MC, V.

🛏️ 🛬

✔️ ★★SANDY POINT. *(Box 8) 2 mi S of jct NY 28, 30.* 518/624-3871. 10 units, 2 story, 6 kits. No A/C. Mid-June–Labor Day, fall foliage season: S, D $42–$47; each addl $5; kit. units $7 addl (7-day min); higher rates special events; lower rates rest of yr. Crib $4. TV; cable. Free coffee in rms. Cafe nearby. Ck-out 10:30 am. Private sand beach; boats: canoes, motorboats, dockage. Sauna. Screened-in patios. Balconies. Cr cds: MC, V.

✓ ★**SHAMROCK.** *(Box 205) 1 mi S on NY 28, 30. 518/624-3861.* 10 motel rms, 7 kit. cottages (3-day min). No A/C. Memorial Day–Labor Day: S, D $40–$45; each addl $5; cottages for 2–6 $275–$375/wk; family rates; higher rates special events; lower rates after Labor Day–Oct. Closed rest of yr. Crib $3. TV, some B/W. Playground. Free coffee in rms. Ck-out 10:30 am. Coin lndry. Private sand beach; boats, pontoon boat, canoes, paddleboat, motor avail. Lawn games. Rec rm. Refrigerators. Marina, waterskiing adj. Picnic tables, grill. Cr cds: DS, MC, V. Ⓕ

Massena

Settled: 1792 **Pop:** 12,851 **Elev:** 210 ft (64 m) **Area code:** 315 **Zip:** 13662

Motels

★**EDGEWATER.** *(RD 1, Box 14, Waddington 13694) 16 mi W on NY 37, opp St Lawrence Seaway. 315/388-5912.* 12 rms, 5 kit. cottages. Apr–mid-Dec: S $30–$45; D $40–$45; each addl $5; kit. cottages $45–$75; under 12 free. Closed rest of yr. Crib free. TV. Pool. Playground. Cafe nearby. Ck-out 10 am. Sundries. Lawn games. Boat dock, rentals. Refrigerators. Picnic table. Cr cds: A, MC, V. Ⓕ

✓ ★★**FLANDERS INN.** *W Orvis & Main Sts. 315/769-2441; res: 800/654-6212 (exc NY), 800/622-0162 (NY).* 126 rms, 4 story. S $32–$36; D $36–$40; each addl $8; suites $102; under 12 free. Crib free. TV; cable. Cafe 7 am–2 pm, 5:30–9 pm; Sun buffet 8 am–noon. Bar 11–2 am exc Sun. Ck-out noon. Meeting rms. Barber, beauty shop. Cr cds: A, D, MC, V. Ⓓ Ⓔ

✓ ★**MEADOW VIEW.** *(RD 1) 2½ mi W on NY 37. 315/764-0246.* 25 rms. S $28; D $34–$42; suites $60–$76; family rates. Crib $2. TV; cable. Pool. Cafe 7–10:30 am, 5–9 pm; Sun 7 am–9 pm. Ck-out 11 am. Cr cds: A, C, D, MC, V. Ⓓ

★**VILLAGE.** *Maple St Rd, 1 mi W on NY 37B. 315/769-3561.* 29 rms, 3 kit units. Mid-June–Labor Day: S, D $30–$38; each addl $3; kit. units $36–$42; lower rates rest of yr. Crib $3. TV; cable, in-rm movies. Pool. Cafe adj. Ck-out 11 am. Some refrigerators. Picnic tables. Beach nearby. Cr cds: A, C, D, MC, V.

Newburgh

Settled: 1709 **Pop:** 23,438 **Elev:** 139 ft (42 m) **Area code:** 914 **Zip:** 12550

Motels

✓ ★★**DIPLOMAT.** *845 Union Ave. 914/564-7550.* 88 rms, 2 story, 5 kits. S $46–$50; D $50–$58; each addl $4; kit. units $58–$64; higher rates special events. Crib $4. TV; cable. Indoor pool; whirlpool, sauna. Free coffee. Cafe 11 am–10 pm. Ck-out 11 am. Coin lndry. Meeting rms. Downhill/x-country ski 15 mi. Overlooks lake. Cr cds: A, C, D, DS, MC, V. Ⓓ

✓ ★**SUPER 8.** *1058B Union Ave. 914/564-5700.* 108 rms, 2 story. S $41; D $47–$55; each addl $5.31; under 12 free. TV; cable. Free coffee. Cafe opp open 24 hours. Ck-out 11 am. Downhill/x-country ski 5 mi. Cr cds: A, C, D, DS, MC, V.

New Paltz

Founded: 1678 **Pop:** 4,938 **Elev:** 196 ft (60 m) **Area code:** 914 **Zip:** 12561

Motels

✔ ★**ANZOR.** *601 Main St, 1¼ mi E on NY 299, 1 mi E of I-87 exit 18. 914/883-7373.* 21 rms. S $32–$48; D $36–$58; each addl $5; under 7 free; higher rates special events. Crib $5. TV; cable. Pool. Free coffee. Free continental bkfst (winter). Cafe nearby. Ck-out 11 am. X-country ski 5 mi. Bicycles. Picnic area. Cr cds: A, D, DS, MC, V.

✔ ★★**THUNDERBIRD.** *1 mi E on NY 299, ½ mi E of I-87 exit 18. 914/255-6200.* 36 units, 2 story. May–Nov: S $40–$46; D $46–$58; each addl $3–$6; wkly rates; higher rates Memorial Day, July 4, Labor Day; under 3 free; lower rates rest of yr. Crib $6. TV; cable. Pool. Free continental bkfst. Cafe nearby. Bar. Ck-out 11 am. Meeting rms. X-country ski 5 mi. Cr cds: A, D, MC, V.

Niagara Falls

Settled: 1806 **Pop:** 71,384 **Elev:** 610 ft (186 m) **Area code:** 716

Motels

★**BEACON.** *9900 Niagara Falls Blvd (14304), I-190 Niagara Falls Blvd exit. 716/297-3647.* 10 rms. No rm phones. Mid-May–mid-Oct: D $38–$50; each addl $6; higher rates hol wkends; lower rates rest of yr. Crib free. TV; cable. Pool. Cafe adj 7 am–10 pm. Ck-out 11 am. Free airport transportation. Picnic tables, grills. Cr cds: MC, V. ①

★**BUDGET HOST.** *219 4th St (14303), at Rainbow Blvd. 716/282-1743.* 57 rms, 2 story. Apr–Oct: S $40–$50; D $45–$55; each addl $4–$7; lower rates rest of yr. Crib $4. TV. Cafe adj open 24 hrs. Ck-out 11 am. Coin lndry. Valet serv. Airport transportation. Cr cds: A, C, D, DS, MC, V.

★**DRIFTWOOD.** *2754 Niagara Falls Blvd (14304), 7½ mi S of Falls. 716/692-6650.* 20 rms. No rm phones. Mid-June–mid-Sep: S $38; D $38–$49; each addl $5; higher rates hol wkends; lower rates rest of yr. Crib $5. TV. Heated pool. Ck-out 10:30 am. Cr cds: A, MC, V. ①

★**HOLIDAY.** *6650 Niagara Falls Blvd (14304), 3 mi E of Falls. 716/283-8974.* 17 rms. No rm phones. Mid-May–early Sep: D $30–$48; each addl $5; higher rates hol wkends; lower rates rest of yr. Crib free. TV; cable. Heated pool. Cafe opp 7 am–midnight. Ck-out 11 am. Picnic tables. Cr cds: A, MC, V.

✔ ★★**HOWARD JOHNSON-EAST.** *6505 Niagara Falls Blvd (14304), at I-190. 716/283-8791.* 84 rms, 2 story. S $39–$66; D $44–$76; each addl $6–$8; under 18 free; wkend plans. Crib free. TV; cable. Pool; lifeguard. Cafe 7 am–midnight. Bar 4 pm–1 am. Ck-out noon. Coin lndry. Meeting rms. Valet serv. Game rm. Private patios, balconies. Cr cds: A, C, D, DS, ER, MC, V.

★**PORTAGE HOUSE.** *(280 Portage Rd, Lewiston 14092) 7 mi N of Falls, at entrance to Artpark. 716/754-8295.* 20 rms, 2 story. No rm phones. Late May–Labor Day: S $45; D $48; each addl $5; under 12 free; lower rates rest of yr. Crib free. TV. Free coffee. Cafe adj 6 am–8 pm. Ck-out 11 am. Cr cds: A, MC, V.

Motor Hotels

✔ ★★**BEST WESTERN RED JACKET INN.** *7001 Buffalo Ave (14304), 3 mi E of Falls, I-90 Buffalo Ave exit. 716/283-7612.* 150 rms, 8 story. Late May–Sep: S $44–$68; D $50–$74; each addl $6; under 18 free; midwk, wkend plans; lower rates rest of yr. Crib free. TV. Pool; lifeguard. Cafe 7 am–2 pm, 4:30–9:30 pm. Rm serv. Bar noon–midnight; entertainment, dancing

Wed, Fri, Sat. Ck-out noon. Meeting rms. Airport transportation. Game rm. Boat docking. On Niagara River. Cr cds: A, C, D, DS, ER, MC, V. Ⓔ Ⓕ

✔ ★ ★ **HOWARD JOHNSON-DOWNTOWN.** *454 Main St (14301). 716/285-5261.* 75 rms, 5 story. June–Labor Day: S $45–$90; D $50–$100; each addl $6–$8; under 18 free; higher rates hols, special events; lower rates rest of yr. Crib free. TV. Indoor pool; sauna; lifeguard. Cafe 6:30 am–11 pm; summer open 24 hrs. Serv bar. Ck-out noon. Coin lndry. Sundries. Airport, bus depot transportation. Game rm. Near falls. Cr cds: A, C, D, DS, MC, V.

Ogdensburg (Thousand Islands)

Settled: 1749 **Pop:** 12,375 **Elev:** 280 ft (85 m) **Area code:** 315 **Zip:** 13669

Motels

✔ ★ **ALTA.** *(RD 4) Riverside Dr, 1½ mi W on NY 37. 315/393-6860.* 21 units, 1–2 story, 15 kits. (no equipt). June–Sep: S $29–$39; D $29–$49; each addl $5–$7; suites, kit. units $29–$69; under 12 free; wkly rates; lower rates rest of yr. Crib $5. TV; cable. Heated pool. Free coffee in rms. Ck-out 11 am. Coin lndry. Some refrigerators. Picnic tables. Cr cds: A, MC, V. Ⓕ Ⓘ

✔ ★ ★ **QUALITY INN GRAN-VIEW.** *Riverside Dr, 3 mi SW on NY 37. 315/393-4550.* 48 rms, 2 story. Mid-May–mid-Sep: S $39; D $53–$56; each addl $7; under 16 free; wkend plans; higher rates special events; lower rates rest of yr. Crib free. TV; cable. Pool. Cafe 6:30 am–11 pm; Mon from 11 am; Fri, Sat 5 pm–midnight; Sun 7–11 am, 5–9 pm. Rm serv. Bar 11–2 am; entertainment, dancing Tu-Sat. Ck-out 11 am. Meeting rms. Sundries. Lawn games. Private patios, balconies. Picnic tables, grills. Docking facilities. Overlooks river. Cr cds: A, C, D, DS, MC, V. Ⓕ Ⓘ

★ **WINDJAMMER.** *Riverside Dr, 5 mi SW on NY 37. 315/393-3730.* 20 rms. June–Sep: S $34–$38; D $54–$64; each addl $2; lower rates rest of yr. TV; cable. Pool. Playground. Ck-out 11 am. Picnic tables. Boat dockage. Overlooks St Lawrence Seaway. Cr cds: A, MC, V.

Old Forge

Pop: 1,061 **Elev:** 1,712 ft (522 m) **Area code:** 315 **Zip:** 13420

Motels

✔ ★ **BLUE SPRUCE.** *Main St, ½ mi S on NY 28. 315/369-3817.* 13 rms. No A/C. July–Labor Day, Dec–Mar: D $40–$50; each addl $5; lower rates rest of yr. Crib free. TV. Pool. Cafe adj 7 am–midnight. Ck-out 11 am. Downhill/x-country ski 3 mi. Snowmobile trails nearby. Cr cds: A, DS, MC, V.

★ **COUNTRY CLUB.** *(Box 419) 1 mi S on NY 28. 315/369-6340.* 17 rms. No rm phones. Late June–Labor Day: S, D $50–$60; each addl $5; wkly rates; under 12 free; lower rates rest of yr. Crib free. TV; cable. Pool. Free coffee in rms. Cafe nearby. Ck-out 11 am. Tennis privileges. 18-hole golf privileges, greens fee $14. Downhill ski 2 mi; x-country ski 4 mi. Lawn games. Cr cds: A, DS, MC, V.

✔ ★ **19TH GREEN.** *NY 28. 315/369-3575.* 13 rms. No rm phones. Late June–Sep, Dec–Mar: S $35–$37; D $45–$50; each addl $5; family rates; lower rates rest of yr. Crib $5. TV.

Pool. Cafe opp 7 am–10 pm. Ck-out 11 am. Golf adj. Downhill ski 3 mi; x-country ski 4 mi. Game rm. Lawn games. Refrigerators. Snowmobile trails adj. Cr cds: A, MC, V.

✔ ★★SUNSET. *1 mi S on NY 28. 315/369-6836.* 52 rms, 37 A/C, 1–2 story. Late June–Labor Day, late Dec–early Apr: S $40–$58; D $47–$65; each addl $6; lower rates rest of yr. Crib $6. TV; cable. Indoor pool; whirlpool, sauna. Playground. Free coffee in rms. Cafe nearby. Ck-out 11 am. Lndry. Meeting rm. Tennis. Putting green. Downhill ski 3 mi; x-country ski 4 mi. Game rm. Some balconies. Picnic tables. Cr cds: A, DS, MC, V.

Oneida

Settled: 1834 **Pop:** 10,810 **Elev:** 443 ft (135 m) **Area code:** 315 **Zip:** 13421

Motel

✔ ★COACHWAY. *(NY 5 & NY 31, Vernon 13476) 6 mi E on NY 5 just past NY 31, 4 mi S of I-90 exit 33. 315/829-2380.* 10 rms. S $34–$48; D $40–$52; each addl $5; higher rates special events. Crib $3. TV; cable. Pool. Playground. Ck-out 11 am. Lawn games. Picnic tables, grills. Cr cds: A, DS, MC, V.

Oneonta

Settled: 1780 **Pop:** 14,933 **Elev:** 1,085 ft (331 m) **Area code:** 607 **Zip:** 13820

Motels

✔ ★KNOTT'S. *5 mi N on NY 28, 1 mi N of I-88 exit 17, on lake. 607/432-5948.* 25 units, 21 A/C, 10 kits. Some rm phones. S $34–$42; D $42–$48; each addl $3; kit. units $50–$54; wkly rates. Crib free. TV; cable. Free coffee. Cafe nearby. Ck-out 11 am. Free airport, bus depot transportation. Tennis. Rec rm. Lawn games. Waterskiing; sailboats avail. Picnic tables, grill. Private beach. Cr cds: MC, V.

★TOWN HOUSE MOTOR INN. *318 Main St. 607/432-1313.* 40 rms, 2 story. S $38; D $50; each addl $6; under 10 free. Crib free. TV; cable, in-rm movies. Free continental bkfst. Cafe nearby. Ck-out noon. Meeting rms. Downhill/x-country ski 20 mi. Picnic tables. Cr cds: A, DS, MC, V.

Penn Yan

Founded: 1787 **Pop:** 5,242 **Elev:** 737 ft (225 m) **Area code:** 315 **Zip:** 14527

Motels

★TOWNE. *206 Elm St, at jct NY 54A and 14A. 315/536-4474.* 24 rms, 2 story. S $28; D $34–$40; each addl $4. Crib free. TV; cable. Ck-out 11 am. In-rm steam baths. 2 blks from beach. Cr cds: A, MC, V.

✔ ★★VIKING. *680 East Lake Rd, 6 mi S on NY 54. 315/536-7061.* 39 units, 32 kit. units, 2 story. May–Oct: S, D $35–$95; each addl $10; wkly, family rates. Closed rest of yr. Crib free. TV; cable. Pool; whirlpool, sauna. Cafe nearby. Ck-out 11 am. Lawn games. Private beach; waterskiing. Rowboats, sailboats, dockage. Nightly motorboat cruises. Refrigerators. Private patios, balconies. Picnic tables, grills. On Lake Keuka.

Plattsburgh

Pop: 21,057 **Elev:** 135 ft (41 m) **Area code:** 518 **Zip:** 12901

Motels

✔ ★**ECONO LODGE.** *I-87 exit 37, at NY 3. 518/561-1500.* 100 rms, 2 story. May–Labor Day: S $40.95; D $50.95; each addl $4; lower rates rest of yr. Crib free. TV; cable. Pool. Free coffee in lobby. Cafe nearby. Ck-out 11 am. Refrigerators. Cr cds: A, C, D, DS, MC, V.

★**PIONEER.** *US 9 N, I-87 exits 39(N), 40(S). 518/563-3050.* 23 rms. No A/C. June–Labor Day: S $34–$38; D $45; each addl $5; lower rates rest of yr. Crib $5. TV; cable. Playground. Ck-out 11 am. Sundries. Lakeshore privileges. Cr cds: A, MC, V.

★**STONEHELM.** *4½ mi N on I-87, exit 40. 518/563-4800.* 40 rms. July–Aug: S $37–$42; D $42–$57; each addl $5; higher rates college graduation; lower rates rest of yr. Crib free. TV; cable. Pool. Ck-out 11 am. Downhill skí 10 mi. Refrigerators. Picnic tables. Cr cds: A, MC, V.

Potsdam

Founded: 1807 **Pop:** 10,635 **Elev:** 433 ft (32 m) **Area code:** 315 **Zip:** 13676

Motels

★**POTSDAM.** *(Box 102) 2 mi SW on US 11. 315/265-7200.* 15 rms. S $32–$36; D $36–$50; each addl $3–$4; higher rates some college wkends. Crib $3. TV; cable. Pool. Ck-out 11 am. Cr cds: C, D, MC, V.

✔ ★**SMALLING.** *NY 56N, 2 mi N on NY 56. 315/265-4640.* 15 rms. S $32–$39; D $40–$44; each addl $2; under 5 free. Crib $4. TV; cable. Pool. Free coffee. Ck-out 11 am. Picnic tables, grills. Cr cds: A, MC, V.

Poughkeepsie

Settled: 1687 **Pop:** 29,757 **Elev:** 176 ft (54 m) **Area code:** 914

Motels

★★**BINDER'S.** *62 Haight Ave & E Arterial Hwy (12603), 1¼ mi E on US 44, NY 55. 914/454-1010.* 41 rms, 2 story. S $49; D $55; each addl $4; under 12 free. Crib $5. TV; cable. Pool; lifeguard. Free coffee. Cafe nearby. Ck-out 11 am. Meeting rm. Valet serv. Sundries. Balconies. Vassar nearby. Cr cds: A, C, D, DS, MC, V.

★★**PO'KEEPSIE.** *418 South Rd (12601). 914/452-5453.* 115 rms, 1–2 story. S, D $50.95–$56.95; each addl $6; kit. units $54.95–$60.95; under 18 free; monthly rates. Crib free. TV; cable. Pool. Free continental bkfst. Cafe opp open 24 hrs. Ck-out noon. Coin lndry. Meeting rms. Valet serv. Some refrigerators. Balconies. Cr cds: A, C, D, MC, V.

★★**RAMADA INN.** *679 South Rd (US 9) (12601). 914/462-4600.* 154 rms, 3 story. No elvtr. S, D $54–$150; each addl $6; suites $150–$250; under 18 free; wkend rates; higher rates Vassar graduation. TV; cable. Pool; lifeguard. Cafe 6:30 am–2 pm, 5–10 pm; wkends 8 am–noon, 5–10 pm. Rm serv. Bar 4 pm–midnight; Sat, Sun from 5 pm. Ck-out noon. Coin lndry. Meeting rms. Sundries. Health club privileges. Cr cds: A, C, D, DS, MC, V. ⒺⒻ

Rhinebeck

Settled: 1686 **Pop:** 2,542 **Elev:** 200 ft (61 m) **Area code:** 914 **Zip:** 12572

Motel

★★**VILLAGE INN.** *(Box 491) ½ mi S on US 9; NY 308 exit for Rhinebeck from Taconic St Pkwy.* 914/876-7000. 16 units. S, D $46–$56; each addl $5; under 16 free; wkly rates; higher rates Dutchess County fair, hols. Crib free. TV; cable. Free continental bkfst, wine. Ck-out 11 am. X-country ski 5 mi. Cr cds: A, C, D, DS, MC, V.

Inn

★★★**BEEKMAN ARMS.** *Beekman Sq, on US 9, 308.* 914/876-7077. 49 rms, 48 A/C, 3 story. No elvtr. S, D $55–$85; each addl $8; suites $85–$110; under 12 free. Crib free. Some TV; cable. Cafe 8–10 am, 11:30 am–3 pm, 5–10 pm; Sun 3:30–9 pm. Bar 11–3 am. Ck-out 11 am. Meeting rms. Historic inn, opened 1766. Antiques. Cr cds: A, C, D, MC, V.

Rochester

Founded: 1803 **Pop:** 241,741 **Elev:** 515 ft (157 m) **Area code:** 716

Motels

✔★**COMFORT INN.** *395 Buell Rd (14624), opp Rochester Monroe County Airport.* 716/436-4400. 73 rms, 2 story. S $36.95–$42.95; D $41.95–$50.95; each addl $5; under 18 free. Crib free. TV; cable, in-rm movies. Free coffee. Cafe adj open 24 hrs. Ck-out noon. Valet serv. Free airport transportation. Whirlpool. Cr cds: A, D, MC, V.

★**ECONO LODGE.** *940 Jefferson Rd (14623).* 716/427-2700. 101 rms, 3 story. S $34.95–$37.95; D $38.95–$41.95; each addl $5; suites $65; under 12 free. Crib free. TV; cable, in-rm movies. Continental bkfst. Cafe opp open 24 hrs. Ck-out 11 am. Coin lndry. Meeting rms. Valet serv. Some in-rm whirlpools. Cr cds: A, C, D, DS, MC, V. Ⓕ

✔★★**HAMPTON INN.** *717 E Henrietta Rd (14623).* 716/272-7800. 113 rms, 5 story. S $40–$44; D $46–$50; under 18 free. Crib free. TV; in-rm movies. Free continental bkfst. Cafe adj 7 am–midnight. Ck-out noon. Meeting rms. Valet serv. Cr cds: A, C, D, DS, MC, V.

✔★★**HOWARD JOHNSON LODGE.** *3350 W Henrietta Rd (14623), I-90 exit 46.* 716/475-1661. 96 rms, 2 story. S, D $50–$65; each addl $8; under 18 free; some wkend rates. Crib free. TV; cable. Pool; lifeguard. Cafe nearby. Ck-out noon. Meeting rms. Valet serv. Downhill ski 20 mi. Private patios, balconies. Cr cds: A, C, D, DS, ER, MC, V. Ⓔ

✔★★**KING JAMES.** *2835 Monroe Ave (14618), I-90 exit 46.* 716/442-9220. 70 rms, 2 story, 4 kit. suites. S $38–$42; D $41–$47; each addl $3; kit. suites from $60; under 12 free. Crib $3. TV; cable. Cafe 11 am–midnight. Bar 11–2 am. Ck-out noon. Meeting rm. Valet serv. Some refrigerators. Near Canal Park. Cr cds: A, D, MC, V. Ⓕ

★★**LUXURY BUDGET INN-NORTH.** *1635 W Ridge Rd (14615).* 716/621-2060. 99 rms, 4 story. S $31.99; D $39.99; each addl $4; suites $39.99–$52.99; under 12 free. Crib $2. TV; cable, in-rm movies. Cafe adj 7 am–11 pm. Ck-out 11 am. Cr cds: A, D, DS, MC, V. Ⓔ

✔★★**QUALITY INN.** *800 Jefferson Rd (14623), I-390 exit 15.* 716/475-9190. 145 rms, 3 story. S $51; D $51–$53; each addl $5; studio rms $46–$50; under 16 free. Crib free. TV; cable, in-room movies. Pool; poolside serv, lifeguard. Cafe 6:30 am–11 pm; Sat to midnight. Rm serv.

Bar. Ck-out noon. Meeting rms. Free airport transportation. Game rm. Cr cds: A, C, D, DS, MC, V.

★RED ROOF INN. *4820 W Henrietta Rd (14467), I-90 exit 46.* 716/359-1100. 109 rms, 2 story. S $32.95–$38.95; D $34.95–$42.95; each addl $6; under 18 free. Crib free. TV; in-rm movies. Cafe nearby. Ck-out noon. Cr cds: A, D, DS, MC, V.

✔ ★ ★RODEWAY INN. *(4600 W Henrietta Rd, Henrietta 14467) I-90 exit 46.* 716/334-1230. 69 rms, 1–2 story. S $30–$45; D $34–$55; each addl $6; under 12 free; higher rates graduation. Crib $10. TV; in-rm movies. Pool; wading pool. Cafe 6:30 am–11 pm. Bar 7–2 am. Ck-out 11 am. Meeting rms. Some balconies. Cr cds: A, C, D, DS, MC, V.

Saranac Lake

Settled: 1819 **Pop:** 5,578 **Elev:** 1,534 ft (468 m) **Area code:** 518 **Zip:** 12983

Motels

★BURKE'S LAKE FLOWER. *15 Lake Flower Ave.* 518/891-2310. 14 rms. No A/C. July–Oct, Feb wknds: D $46–$50; each addl $5; under 10 free (1 child only); higher rates winter carnival; lower rates rest of yr. TV; cable. Pool. Cafe nearby. Ck-out 11 am. Downhill ski 20 mi; x-country ski 2 mi. Picnic tables. On Lake Flower. Cr cds: A, C, D, MC, V.

★LAKE SIDE. *27 Lake Flower Ave.* 518/891-4333. 22 rms, 4 A/C. July–mid-Oct: S $38–$48; D $42–$52; each addl $4; kit. units $50–$60; higher rates some hol wknds, special events; lower rates rest of yr. Closed Nov & Apr. Crib free. TV; cable. Heated pool. Cafe nearby. Ck-out 11 am. Downhill ski 20 mi; x-country ski 2 mi. Private sand beach; canoe. Picnic tables, grills. Patio overlooks lake. Cr cds: A, MC, V. Ⓓ

Hotel

✔ ★ ★HOTEL SARANAC OF PAUL SMITH'S COLLEGE. *101 Main St.* 518/891-2200. 92 rms. No A/C. S $40–$60; D $48–$68; each addl $5; under 6 free; golf, fishing, canoeing plans; higher rates wknds. TV; cable. Cafe 7 am–2 pm, 5–10 pm; Sun 10 am–2 pm. Bar 11–1 am. Ck-out 11 am. Meeting rms. Gift shop. X-country ski 2 mi. Game rm. Hotel opened 1927; the lobby is a replica of the foyer in the Danvanzati Palace in Florence, Italy. Cr cds: A, C, D, DS, MC, V.

Saratoga Springs

Settled: 1773 **Pop:** 23,906 **Elev:** 316 ft (96 m) **Area code:** 518 **Zip:** 12866

Motels

✔ ★ ★BEST WESTERN PLAYMORE FARMS. *S Broadway, 1½ mi S on US 9; ¾ mi N of I-87 exit 13N.* 518/584-2350. 36 rms. S, D $42–$75; each addl $10; suites $75–$95; family, wkly rates (exc Aug); higher rates Aug. Crib $5. TV; cable, in-rm movies. Heated pool. Free coffee. Cafe nearby. Ck-out 11 am. X-country ski 2 mi. Refrigerators. State park nearby. Cr cds: A, C, D, DS, MC, V.

★DESIGN. *S Broadway, 2 mi S on US 9.* 518/584-1630. 14 rms. July–Aug: S, D $50–$100; each addl $7; lower rates rest of yr. Crib free. TV; cable. Pool. Cafe adj 11 am–midnight. Ck-out 11 am. Sundries. X-country ski 3 mi. Lawn games. Refrigerators. Cr cds: A, C, D, MC, V.

✔ ★**DOWNTOWNER SARATOGA.** *413 Broadway. 518/584-6160.* 42 units, 2 story. Sep–June: S, D $36–$45; each addl $7; under 17 free; ski, wkend plans off-season; higher rates July–Aug, college wkends. Crib free. TV; cable. Indoor pool. Free continental bkfst. Ck-out 11 am. Gift shop. X-country ski 3 mi. Some balconies. Cr cds: A, C, D, DS, MC, V.

✔ ★ ★**GRAND UNION.** *92 S Broadway. 518/584-9000.* 64 units. S $36–$56; D $46–$60; each addl $5–$10; higher rates Aug, racing season, special events. Crib free. TV; cable. Pool; wading pool. Free coffee in lobby. Cafe adj 6 am–midnight. Ck-out 11 am. Bellhops. Sundries. Downhill ski 20 mi; x-country ski 1 mi. Lawn games. Some refrigerators. Grills. Victorian-style lobby. Mineral bath spa.

★**SPRINGS.** *165 Broadway. 518/584-6336.* 28 rms, 2 story. Late June–Aug: S $44–$110; D $48–$110; each addl $3–$5; under 12 free; higher rates special events; varied lower rates rest of yr. Crib free. TV. Pool. Free coffee in rms. Cafe nearby. Ck-out 11 am. Downhill ski 15 mi; x-country ski 2 mi. Cr cds: A, D, MC, V.

✔ ★**TOP HILL.** *S Broadway, 2½ mi S on US 9; ¾ mi N of I-87 exit 13N. 518/584-5232.* 14 rms. Sep–May: S $25–$53; D $30–$53; each addl $10; higher rates: June–Aug, college events, racing season; lower rates rest of yr. Crib $5. TV. Pool. Cafe nearby. Ck-out 11 am. X-country ski 2 mi. Refrigerators. State park adj. Cr cds: A, C, D, MC, V.

Schroon Lake

Pop: 1,000 (est) **Elev:** 867 ft (264 m) **Area code:** 518 **Zip:** 12870

Motels

★**BEN-GEE'S.** *2 mi N on US 9, just N of I-87 exit 28. 518/532-7541.* 7 rms. July–Labor Day: S $32; D $36; each addl $2; wkly rates; lower rates early May–June, after Labor Day–Oct. Closed rest of yr. Crib $4. TV, some B/W; cable. Playground. Free coffee in rms. Cafe nearby. Ck-out 11 am. Picnic tables, grills. Cr cds: MC, V.

✔ ★**DAVIS.** *½ mi S of US 9. 518/532-7583.* 20 rms in motel, 14 A/C, 4 kits. Late June–Labor Day: S, D $39–$45; each addl $5; kit. units $50; cottages $425–$475/wk; family, wkly rates; lower rates rest of yr. Crib $5. TV; cable. Heated pool. Playground. Cafe nearby. Ck-out 11 am. Downhill ski 18 mi; x-country ski 2 mi. Motor boats. Lawn games. Picnic tables, grills. Cr cds: A, MC, V.

★**DUN ROAMIN CABINS.** *US 9, 1½ mi N on US 9. 518/532-7277.* 9 cabins, 6 kits. No A/C. S, D $34; kit. units $40–$60. Crib free. TV; cable. Cafe nearby. Ck-out 10 am. Downhill ski 20 mi; x-country ski 4 mi. Rec rm. Lawn games. Waterskiing, instruction. Fireplace in some cabins; free firewood. Picnic tables, grills. Cr cds: MC, V.

Skaneateles

Settled: 1794 **Pop:** 2,789 **Elev:** 919 ft (280 m) **Area code:** 315 **Zip:** 13152

Motels

★**BIRD'S NEST.** *E Genesee Rd, 1½ mi E on US 20. 315/685-5641.* 28 rms, 3 kits. Mid-May–Sep: S $30–$49; D $35–$52; each addl $5; kit. units $50–$65; under 3 free; wkly rates; some wkend rates; lower rates rest of yr. Crib $5. TV; cable. Pool. Playground. Cafe nearby. Ck-out 11 am. Lawn games. Some refrigerators, whirlpools. Picnic tables, grill. Duck pond. Cr cds: A, C, D, DS, MC, V. Ⓔ Ⓕ

✔ ★**COLONIAL.** *W Genesee Rd, 1½ mi W on US 20.* 315/685-5751. 15 rms. May–Oct: S, D $42–$46; each addl $5–$7. Closed rest of yr. Crib avail. TV. Pool. Free coffee. Cafe nearby. Ck-out 11 am. Picnic tables, grill. Landscaped grounds. Cr cds: A, MC, V.

★**HI-WAY HOST.** *W Genesee Rd, ½ mi W on US 20.* 315/685-7633. 12 rms. May–Nov: S $38; D $45; each addl $5; lower rates rest of yr. Crib avail. TV; cable. Cafe opp 6 am–9 pm. Ck-out 11 am. Cr cds: MC, V.

✔ ★**STEAMBOAT LANDING MOTOR LODGE.** *(Box 372) W Genesee St, ¾ mi W on US 20.* 315/685-8925. 12 rms. May–Dec: S $42; D $44–$46; each addl $6; lower rates rest of year. Crib avail. TV; cable. Free continental bkfst. Cafe adj 6 am–9 pm. Ck-out 11 am. Sundries. Walking distance from lake. Cr cds: A, MC, V.

Southampton, L. I.

Settled: 1640 **Pop:** 4,000 **Elev:** 25 ft (8 m) **Area code:** 516 **Zip:** 11968

Motel

★**SHINNECOCK.** *(NY 27A) 240 Montauk Hwy.* 516/283-2406. 30 rms. Late May–mid-Sep: S, D $80–$95; each addl $10; under 5 free; lower rates rest of yr. TV; cable. Pool; lifeguard. Cafe 7–11:30 am. Ck-out noon. Tennis, pro. Bay, ocean swimming nearby. Cr cds: A, C, D, MC, V.

Stamford

Pop: 1,240 **Elev:** 1,827 ft (557 m) **Area code:** 607 **Zip:** 12167

Motels

✔ ★**COLONIAL.** *(Box 350, Grand Gorge 12434) 8 mi E via NY 23, on Main St.* 607/588-6122. 14 units, 3 A/C, 11 air-cooled, 1–2 story, 3 kits. S $34–$40; D $42–$54; kits. $54–$62. Crib $5. TV; cable. Pool. Free coffee. Cafe adj 5 am–7 pm. Ck-out 11 am. Downhill/x-country ski 8 mi. Lawn games. Picnic tables, grills. Family-owned 30 yrs. Cr cds: MC, V.

✔ ★★**RED CARPET MOTOR INN.** *At jct NY 10, 23.* 607/652-7394. 36 rms, 2 story. S $42–$55; D $52–$74; each addl $6. Crib $2. TV; cable. Pool. Cafe noon–2:30 pm, 5:30–9:30 pm; bkfst wkends. Rm serv. Bar from noon; entertainment, dancing Fri-Sat. Ck-out noon. Meeting rms. Downhill/x-country ski 3 mi. Private patios, balconies. Golf nearby. Cr cds: A, C, D, DS, MC, V.

Syracuse

Settled: 1789 **Pop:** 170,105 **Elev:** 406 ft (124 m) **Area code:** 315

Motels

★**DAYS INN-EAST.** *6609 Thompson Rd (13206), I-90 exit 35.* 315/437-5998. 100 rms, 4 story. June–Aug: S $35.99–$39.99; D $40.99–$44.99; each addl $4; under 12 free; lower rates rest of yr. Crib $2. TV; cable, in-rm movies. Free continental bkfst. Cafe opp open 24 hrs. Ck-out 11 am. Valet serv. Cr cds: A, C, D, DS, MC, V.

✔ ★★**HAMPTON INN.** *(6605 Old Collamer Rd, East Syracuse 13057) I-90 exit 35, NY Thrwy at Carrier Circle to NY 298 E, then L on College Pl.* 315/463-6443. 117 rms, 4 story. S $40–$45; D $46–$47; suites $50–$55; under 18 free. Crib free. TV; cable, in-rm movies. Free continental bkfst. Ck-out 1 pm. Meeting rm. Valet serv. Game rm. Refrigerator in some suites. Cr cds: A, C, D, DS, ER, MC, V.

✔ ★HOWARD JOHNSON. *Thompson Rd at Carrier Circle (13206), 5 mi E on NY 298 at I-90 exit 35.* 315/437-2711. 90 rms, 2 story. S $45–$60; D $50–$70; each addl $6; under 18 free. Crib free. TV; cable. Pool. Cafe 6 am–midnight. Bar. Ck-out noon. Meeting rm. Valet serv. Balconies. Cr cds: A, C, D, DS, ER, MC, V.

✔ ★JOURNEY'S END. *(6577 Court St Rd, East Syracuse 13057) ½ mi E on I-90, exit 35, through Carrier Circle to NY 298 E, then L on College Pl to Court St Rd.* 315/433-1300; res: 800/668-4200. 90 rms, 2 story. S $34.88–$36.88; D $41.88–$43.88; each addl $4; under 12 free. Crib free. TV; cable. Free continental bkfst. Ck-out 11 am. Valet serv. Cr cds: A, C, D, MC, V.

✔ ★ ★LE MOYNE MANOR. *(629 Old Liverpool Rd, Liverpool 13088) 4 mi NW off NY 57, ½ mi SE of I-90 exit 37.* 315/457-1240. 64 rms, 2–3 story. No elvtr. June–Sep: S, D $29.95–$39.95; each addl $5; suites $50–$60; under 12 free; lower rates rest of yr. Crib free. TV; cable. Cafe 9 am–11 pm; Sun noon–10 pm. Bar noon–midnight; entertainment, dancing Fri–Sat. Ck-out 11 am. Meeting rms. Lake 1 blk. Cr cds: A, C, D, MC, V. ①

★LUXURY BUDGET INN. *401-407 7th North St (13088), at jct I-81 exit 25 & I-90 exit 36.* 315/451-6000. 84 rms, 4 story. May–Aug: S $35.99; D $41.99; each addl $4; suites $47.99; under 12 free; higher rates special events; lower rates rest of yr. Crib $2. TV; cable. Free continental bkfst. Cafe adj 6 am–midnight. Ck-out 11 am. Cr cds: A, C, D, DS, MC, V.

Inn

★ ★GREEN GATE. *(2 Main St, Camillus 13031) Approx 5 mi W via NY 5.* 315/672-9276. 6 rms. S, D $55–$90. No children. Some B/W TVs. Free continental bkfst. Cafe 11:30 am–3 pm, 5–10 pm; Fri to 11 pm; Sat 5–11 pm; Sun noon–8 pm. Rm serv. Ck-out 11 am, ck-in 3 pm. 2 whirlpools. Built 1861; first town wedding held here. Totally nonsmoking. Cr cds: A, MC, V.

Troy

Settled: 1786 **Pop:** 56,638 **Elev:** 37 ft (11 m) **Area code:** 518

Motel

✔ ★SUSSE CHALET. *(RD 2, Box 103, East Greenbush 12061) Approx 8 mi S on US 4, at I-90 exit 9.* 518/477-7984. 105 rms, 4 story. S $36.70; D $40.70; each addl $3. Crib $2. TV; cable, in-rm movies. Pool; lifeguard. Continental bkfst. Cafe adj open 24 hrs. Ck-out 11 am. Coin lndry. Sundries. Cr cds: A, C, D, MC, V.

Inn

★ ★ ★GREGORY HOUSE. *(Box 401, Averill Park 12018) 8 mi SE via NY 66 to Averill Park, on NY 43.* 518/674-3774. 12 rms, 2 story. S $45–$65; D $50–$70; wkly rates. TV; cable in common rm. Pool. Free continental bkfst. Cafe 5–9 pm exc Mon; Sun 4–8 pm. Bar. Fireplace in common rm; Oriental rugs, antiques. Cr cds: A, C, D, MC, V.

Tupper Lake

Settled: 1890 **Pop:** 4,478 **Elev:** 1,600 ft (488 m) **Area code:** 518 **Zip:** 12986

Motels

✔ ★**PINE TERRACE MOTEL & TENNIS CLUB.** *Moody Rd, 2½ mi S on NY 30. 518/ 359-9258.* 18 cottage units, 8 kits. No A/C. May–Oct: D $34–$52; each addl $5; kit. units $240–$325/wk; family, tennis rates. Closed rest of yr. Crib avail. TV; cable. Pool; wading pool. Cafe 7–10 am. Ck-out 11 am. Lighted tennis. Lawn games. Boats, dock. Refrigerators avail. Picnic tables, grills. Beach opp. View of lake, mountains. Cr cds: ER, MC, V.

✔ ★**SHAHEEN'S.** *310 Park St, ½ mi E on NY 3, 30. 518/359-3384.* 32 rms, 15 A/C, 2 story. S, D $42–$57; each addl $5; family units for up to 6, $60. Crib $3. TV; cable. Pool. Playground. Free coffee in rms. Cafe opp 7 am–11 pm. Ck-out 11 am. Downhill ski 5 mi. Balconies. Picnic tables, grills. Cr cds: A, C, D, MC, V.

★**SUNSET PARK.** *De Mars Blvd, ½ mi W on NY 3. 518/359-3995.* 11 rms, 4 kits. No A/C. Mid-June–Oct: S, D $32–$42; each addl $4; kit. units $38–$42; lower rates rest of yr. Crib free. TV; cable. Free coffee in rms. Cafe nearby. Ck-out 11 am. Downhill ski 3 mi. Lawn games. Picnic tables, grills. On Tupper Lake; private sand beach; boats, motors, canoes, dock for small boats. Cr cds: A, MC, V.

★**TUPPER LAKE.** *259 Park St. 518/359-3381.* 18 rms. No A/C. Late June–mid-Oct: S $38–$40; D $43–$45; each addl $4; wkly rates; lower rates rest of yr. Crib $3. TV; cable. Pool. Free coffee in rms. Cafe nearby. Ck-out 11 am. Downhill ski 5 mi; x-country ski 10 mi. Refrigerators avail. Cr cds: A, MC, V.

Utica

Pop: 75,632 **Elev:** 423 ft (129 m) **Area code:** 315

Motels

✔ ★**BEACHLEY'S.** *(NY 12, Barneveld 13304) 12 mi N on NY 12, 10 mi N of I-90 exit 31. 315/896-2613.* 21 rms, 8 kits. June–Labor Day: S $25; D $28–$32; each addl $4; studio rms $30; kit. units $32–$38; under 12 free; wkly rates; lower rates rest of yr. Crib $4. TV; cable. Pool. Free coffee in rms. Cafe nearby. Ck-out 11 am. Downhill/x-country ski 15 mi. Lawn games. Some refrigerators. Picnic tables, grills. Cr cds: A, MC, V. Ⓓ

★★**HOLIDAY INN.** *(Campion Rd, New Hartford 13413) 5 mi S of I-90 exit 31 on NY 5, 8, 12 at New York Mills exit. 315/735-3392.* 113 rms, 2 story. S $50–$60; D $54–$65; each addl $7; under 18 free. Crib free. TV; cable. Pool. Cafe 6:30 am–2 pm, 5–10 pm. Rm serv. Bar 11:30–2 am; Sat from 5 pm; Sun 5 pm–midnight. Ck-out noon. Coin lndry. Meeting rms. Valet serv. Tennis, health club adj. Downhill ski 5 mi; x-country ski 2 mi. Game rm. Cr cds: A, C, D, DS, MC, V.

★**JOURNEY'S END.** *150 N Genesee St (13502). 315/797-8743.* 61 rms, 2 story. S $34.88–$36.88; D $41.88–$43.88; each addl $4; under 12 free. Crib free. TV; cable. Ck-out 11 am. Valet serv. Downhill ski 15 mi; x-country ski 2 mi. Cr cds: A, C, D, MC, V.

★**TRAVELODGE.** *1700 Genesee St (13502). 315/724-2101.* 47 rms, 2 story. S $35–$50; D $43–$62; each addl $6; under 18 free; wkend rates. Crib free. TV; cable. Pool. Cafe nearby 7 am–midnight. Ck-out noon. Valet serv. Sundries. Downhill ski 20 mi; x-country ski 1 mi. Some balconies. Cr cds: A, C, D, DS, ER, MC, V.

✔ ★★**TRINKAUS MANOR.** *(Box U, Oriskany 13424) 311 Utica St, 5 mi W on NY 69; 5 mi NE of I-90 exit 32. 315/736-3355.* 40 rms, 2 story. S $38; D $45–$48; each addl $5; under 12 free; wkend rates; winter packages. Crib free. TV; cable. Pool. Cafe 7–10 am; Sun 8–11 am; dining rm 5–9 pm; Fri, Sat to 10 pm; Sun, hols 1–8 pm. Rm serv. Ck-out 11 am. Meeting rms. Bellhops.

Sundries. Airport transportation. Downhill ski 8 mi; x-country ski 3 mi. Lawn games. Cr cds: A, C, D, DS, MC, V.

Watertown

Settled: 1799 **Pop:** 27,861 **Elev:** 478 ft (145 m) **Area code:** 315 **Zip:** 13601

Motels

★**ARSENAL STREET.** *1165 Arsenal St, at I-81 exit 45.* 315/788-3760. 15 rms. Some rm phones. June–mid-Oct: D $40–$46; each addl $5; under 12 free; lower rates rest of yr. Crib free. TV; cable, in-rm movies. Cafe opp open 24 hrs. Ck-out 11 am. Cr cds: MC, V.

✔ ★★**DAVIDSON'S.** *Black River Rd.* 315/782-3861. 20 rms, 1 kit. June–Sep: S $26–$30; D $34–$38; each addl $3; lower rates rest of yr. Crib free. TV; cable. Heated pool. Ck-out 10 am. Sundries. Picnic table, grills. Shaded grounds; nature walk. Near Ft Drum. Cr cds: A, MC, V.

✔ ★★**NEW PARROT.** *Outer Washington St, 2 mi S on NY 11, 4 mi N of I-81 exit 44.* 315/788-5080. 26 rms, 21 A/C. July–mid-Sep: S $30–$35; D $40–$48; each addl $4; family rates off-season; lower rates rest of yr. Crib $4. TV; cable, in-rm movies. Indoor pool. Cafe adj 6 am–9 pm. Ck-out 11 am. Meeting rm. Picnic tables, grills. Cr cds: A, C, D, DS, MC, V. Ⓔ Ⓕ

★**REDWOOD MOTOR LODGE.** *Utica Rd & Gifford St, 2 mi SE on NY 12.* 315/788-2850. 27 rms, 2 story. Some rm phones. June–Sep: S $28; D $38; each addl $3; under 12 free; wkly rates off-season; lower rates rest of yr. Crib $1. TV; cable. Pool. Free coffee. Ck-out 11 am. Cr cds: A, MC, V.

Watkins Glen

Pop: 2,440 **Elev:** 550 ft (168 m) **Area code:** 607 **Zip:** 14891

Motels

(Rates may be higher race wkends)

★**BELLEVUE.** *(Box 52) 3 mi N on NY 14 at jct NY 14A.* 607/535-4232. 7 rms, 1 efficiency, 4 cottages. No rm phones. May–mid-Nov: S $28–$40; D $38–$45; each addl $3; efficiency $45–$60; cottages $175/wk. Closed rest of yr. TV, some B/W. Cafe nearby. Ck-out 11 am. Some refrigerators. Picnic tables, grills. Hiking. Opp lake. Cr cds: MC, V. Ⓓ

✔ ★**CHALET LEON AT HECTOR FALLS.** *(Box 388) 3 mi N on NY 414.* 607/546-7171. 11 rms, 1–3 story, 8 cottages. No A/C. No elvtr. S $35–$39; D $45–$59; each addl $5; cottages $35–$50; under 10 free; wkly rates; higher rates special events. Crib $5. TV in motel rms; cable. Continental bkfst 8–10 am. Ck-out 11 am. Fishing dock. Lawn games. Picnic tables; grills. Waterfall. Nature trails. On lake. Cr cds: MC, V.

★**CHIEFTAIN.** *(RD 1) 3 mi N on NY 14 at jct NY 14A.* 607/535-4759. 14 rms. May–Oct: S, D $28–$40; each addl $3. Closed rest of yr. Crib free. TV. Pool. Cafe nearby. Ck-out 11 am. On hillside. Cr cds: MC, V.

✔ ★**FINGER LAKES MOTOR INN.** *435 S Franklin St, on NY 14; ¼ mi S of main entrance Watkins Glen State Park.* 607/535-4800. 21 rms. Mid-June–mid-Oct: S $30–$45; D $40–$55; each addl $5; under 12 free; lower rates rest of yr. Crib free. TV; cable. Pool. Free coffee. Bkfst cafe. Ck-out 11 am. Picnic tables. Cr cds: A, C, D, DS, MC, V.

★★**LONGHOUSE LODGE.** *(Box 111) NY 14 at Abrams Rd. 607/535-2565.* 13 rms. No rm phones. Mid-Apr–Dec: S $40–$50; D $45–$55; each addl $5; under 18 free. Closed rest of yr. Crib $5. TV; cable. Pool. Playground. Continental bkfst (summer). Ck-out 11 am. 9-hole golf privileges. Lawn games. Some refrigerators. Private patios. Picnic tables, grills. Cr cds: A, DS, MC, V.

★**QUEEN CATHERINE.** *436 S Franklin St, just S of jct NY 14, 414. 607/535-2517.* 15 rms. May–Oct: S $30–$50; D $40–$50; higher rates special events; lower rates rest of yr. Crib free. TV; cable, in-rm movies. Free coffee in rms. Cafe nearby. Ck-out 11 am. Some refrigerators. Cr cds: MC, V.

Waverly

Pop: 4,738 **Elev:** 850 ft (259 m) **Area code:** 607 **Zip:** 14892

Motel

✔ ★★**O'BRIEN'S INN.** *(Box 108) Atop Waverly Hill, 1 mi W on NY 17C. 607/565-2817.* 24 rms, 3 story. No elvtr. July–Nov: S $32–$42; D $37–$52; each addl $7.50; under 5 free; wkend rates (Nov–Apr); lower rates rest of yr. Crib free. TV. Cafe 7 am–9:30 pm; Sat to 10 pm. Bar 11–1 am; entertainment, dancing Fri–Sat. Ck-out 11 am. Meeting rms. Golf ½ mi. Balconies. Cr cds: A, C, D, MC, V. ⑦

Wilmington

Pop: 500 (est) **Elev:** 1,020 ft (311 m) **Area code:** 518 **Zip:** 12997

Motels

★**HIGH VALLEY.** *1 mi SW on NY 86. 518/946-2355.* 20 rms, 1-2 story. Mid-June–Labor Day, ski season: S, D $36–$46; each addl $4; lower rates rest of yr. Crib $4. TV. Heated pool. Playground. Cafe nearby. Ck-out 11 am. Cr cds: A, MC, V.

✔ ★★**HOLIDAY LODGE.** *(North Pole 12946) At jct NY 86, 431. 518/946-2251.* 31 rms, 2 story. Mid-June–mid-Oct, late Dec–mid-Mar: S $29–$45; D $39–$55; each addl $5; suites $69–$89; wkly, ski rates; lower rates rest of yr. Crib free. TV; cable. Heated pool; wading pool, whirlpool. Playground. Cafe 7:30–10:30 am, 5–8:30 pm. Bar noon–11 pm. Ck-out 11 am. Downhill ski 3 mi; x-country ski 10 mi. Game rm. Some balconies. Picnic tables, grills. Cr cds: A, C, D, DS, MC, V.

✔ ★**WINKELMAN.** *Just E of jct NY 86, 431. 518/946-7761.* 16 rms, 5 A/C. Mid-June–mid-Oct: S, D $38–$48. Closed rest of yr. Crib $4. TV; cable. Heated pool. Playground. Cafe adj 7 am–9 pm. Ck-out 11 am. Refrigerators. Picnic tables, grills. Cr cds: A, C, D, DS, MC, V.

Inn

★★**WHITEFACE CHALET.** *(Box 68) Springfield Rd, 1½ mi S, ½ mi E of NY 86. 518/946-2207.* 18 rms, 15 with A/C & bath. No rm phones. June–Oct, mid-Nov–Mar: S, D $45–$53; each addl $5; suites $57–$70; under 12 free; wkly, ski rates; MAP avail; lower rates rest of yr. Crib free. TV, some B/W; cable. Pool. Playground. Cafe 8–10 am, 6–8 pm. Bar noon–1 am. Ck-out 11 am. Meeting rm. Airport, RR station, bus depot transportation. Tennis. Downhill ski 2 mi; x-country ski 12 mi. Hiking. Lawn games. Rec rm. Fireplace in lounge & living room. Balconies. Cr cds: A, DS, MC, V.

Woodstock

Pop: 2,280 **Elev:** 512 ft (156 m) **Area code:** 914 **Zip:** 12498

Inns

★★**MT TREMPER.** *(Box 51, Mt Tremper 12457) 10 mi W on NY 212, ⅓ mi N of NY 28. 914/688-5329.* 12 rms, 2 with bath, 2 story. No rm phones. S, D $55–$70; suite $85; under 16 free. Free full bkfst. Cafe adj. Ck-out 11 am, ck-in 2 pm. Lawn games. Built as a guest house 1850. Antique furnishings. View of river. Totally nonsmoking. Cr cds: MC, V.

★**TWIN GABLES.** *73 Tinker St. 914/679-9479.* 9 rms, 3 with bath, 2 story. No rm phones. S $27–$48; D $38–$48; wkly rates; some lower rates winter. Closed Mar. Cafe adj. Ck-out noon, ck-in 1 pm. Antique furnishings. 75-year-old guest house.

New York City

Settled: 1615

Population: 7,071,639

Elevation: 0–410 ft (0–125 m)

Getting Around

There are many different ways to see New York. For those desiring a general overview of the city, several sightseeing tours are available.

City traffic is very heavy; it is wise to avoid driving in the city unless you must. Traffic is heaviest during the rush hours and from Thanksgiving through Christmas week—which is an almost continuous rush hour. Most avenues and streets in Manhattan are one way. To assist tourists in finding the cross streets nearest an avenue address in Manhattan, telephone books and several tourist guides contain an address locator table. Since parking is scarce and/or expensive, taxis are a common means of transportation in New York.

The Metropolitan Transit Authority operates the buses and subways (fare $1). The subway system carries more than 4,000,000 people on weekdays and is quite crowded during rush hours. It covers every borough except Staten Island, which has its own transportation system. Maps are posted in every car and station. For further information contact the Metropolitan Transportation Authority, 347 Madison Ave, 10017; phone 330-1234; or the Convention & Visitors Bureau, phone 397-8222.

Weather

The average mean temperature for New York is 51°F (10°C) in spring, 74°F (23°C) in summer, 58°F (14°C) in fall, and 40°F (4°C) in winter. In summer the temperature is rarely above 90°F (32°C) (maximum recorded: 106°F or 41°C), but the humidity can be high. In winter the temperature is rarely lower than 10°F (-12°C), but has gone as low as -14°F (-25°C).

Visitor Information

Contact the New York Convention and Visitors Bureau, 2 Columbus Circle, 10019; 397-8222. The bureau has free maps, "twofers" to Broadway shows, bulletins and brochures on attractions, events, shopping, restaurants and hotels. For a listing of free events throughout the city, phone 360-1333 or contact the visitors bureau. For events of the week, visitors should get copies of *The New Yorker* and *New York* magazines, and *The New York Times.* For those who intend to stay for some time and want to delve more deeply into the city, we suggest browsing in libraries and bookstores for the numerous guidebooks which detail what to see and do.

Room Rate Information

New York City is a major city and has higher room rates for two (double) than indicated on the cover of this Guide. However, the lodgings listed in this city offer a good value when compared to others of their type in the area. The lodgings listed for New York City have double room rates of $105 or less.

Manhattan

Area code: 212

Hotels

★★**COMFORT INN MURRAY HILL.** *42 W 35th St (10001). 212/947-0200.* 120 rms, 12 story. S $90–$115; D $100–$130; each addl $12; under 16 free; lower rates July–Aug. Crib free. TV. Free continental bkfst. Ck-out 1 pm. Cr cds: A, C, D, DS, MC, V. ⒺⒻ

🚫 🐾 SC

★**EDISON.** *228 W 47th St (10036). 212/840-5000; res: 800/637-7070 (exc NY).* 1,000 rms, 22 story. S $82–$86; D $92–$96; each addl $10; suites $112–$120; family rms

$100–$105. Crib free. Garage $15. TV. Cafe 7–11 am; dining rm noon–1 am. Bar noon–2 am. Ck-out 1 pm. Meeting rm. Gift shop. Beauty shop. Airport transportation. Theater on premises. Cr cds: A, C, D, DS, MC, V. ⑤ ⑥ ⑦ ①

★★**EMPIRE.** *63rd & Broadway (10023), at Lincoln Center. 212/265-7400; res: 800/545-7400.* 500 rms, 11 story. S $85–$145; D $100–$155; each addl $15; suites $185–$300; under 14 free. Crib free. Garage $15.50. TV. Cafe 7 am–11 pm; dining rm 11:30–12:30 am. Bar noon–1 am. Ck-out noon. Airport transportation. Cr cds: A, C, D, MC, V. ⑤ ⑥ ⑦ ①

★**GORHAM.** *136 W 55th (10019). 212/245-1800.* 163 kit. units, 17 story. S $75–$115; D $85–$130; each addl $10–$20; suites $110–$150. Crib $10. Garage adj $20. TV. Dining rm noon–10:30 pm. Rm serv 7–2 am. Bar. Ck-out 1 pm. Concierge. Cr cds: A, C, D, MC, V. ⑤ ⑥ ⑦

★★**SALISBURY.** *123 W 57th St (10019). 212/246-1300; res: 800/223-0680.* 320 rms, 17 story. S $89–$99; D $99–$109; each addl $15; suites $169–$195; under 12 free. Crib free. TV. Cafe 7 am–9 pm. Ck-out noon. Meeting rms. Most rms with serv pantry, refrigerator. Cr cds: A, C, D, MC, V. ⑤ ⑥ ⑦

Ohio

Population: 10,797,624
Land area: 41,004 sq mi (106,200 sq km)
Elevation: 433–1,550 ft (132–472 m)
Highest point: Campbell Hill (Logan Co)
Entered Union: March 1, 1803 (17th state)
Capital: Columbus
Motto: With God, all things are possible
Nickname: Buckeye State
State flower: Scarlet carnation
State bird: Cardinal
State tree: Ohio buckeye
State fair: August 3–20, 1989 in Columbus
Time zone: Eastern

Interstate Highway System

The following alphabetical listing of Ohio towns in *Mobil Travel Guide* shows that these cities are within 10 miles (16 kilometers) of the indicated Interstate highways. A highway map should, however, be checked for the nearest exit.

INTERSTATE 70: Cambridge, Columbus, Dayton, Martins Ferry, Newark, St Clairsville, Springfield, Vandalia, Zanesville.

INTERSTATE 71: Akron, Cincinnati, Cleveland, Columbus, Delaware, Lebanon, Mansfield, Mason, Medina, Mount Gilead, Strongsville, Wilmington.

INTERSTATE 75: Bluffton, Bowling Green, Cincinnati, Dayton, Findlay, Lebanon, Lima, Mason, Middletown, Piqua, Sidney, Toledo, Troy, Vandalia, Wapakoneta.

INTERSTATE 76: Akron, Kent, Youngstown.

INTERSTATE 77: Akron, Cambridge, Canton, Cleveland, Gnadenhutten, Marietta, Massillon, New Philadelphia.

INTERSTATE 80: Akron, Aurora, Bellevue, Cleveland, Elyria, Fremont, Kent, Lorain, Medina, Milan, Montpelier, Norwalk, Port Clinton, Sandusky, Strongsville, Toledo, Warren, Wauseon, Youngstown.

INTERSTATE 90: Ashtabula, Chardon, Cleveland, Geneva-on-the-Lake, Mentor, Painesville.

Weather Statistics*

	WINTER	SPRING	SUMMER	FALL
Statewide	32°F (0°C)	53°F (12°C)	74°F (23°C)	56°F (13°C)

*Average mean temperatures are listed for the entire state. Averages for specific regions are given if significant differences exist.

Visitor Information

For free travel information contact Ohio Division of Travel and Tourism, 30 E Broad St, PO Box 1001, Columbus 43266-0101; 800/BUCKEYE (Mon–Fri, 8 am–9 pm; Sat, Sun 9 am–6 pm). The

Ohio Historical Society is a good source for historical information; contact Director, 1985 Velma Ave, Columbus 43211; 614/297-2300.

The Ohio Guide (Oxford University Press, New York, 1940), one of the American Guide Series, is excellent for history and background. Also *Life in the Slow Lane* (Backroad Chronicles, P.O. Box 292066, Columbus, OH, 1986).

Travel information centers are located on Interstate Highways at nine key roadside rest areas. These centers offer free brochures containing information on Ohio's attractions and events; staff are also on hand to answer any questions.

Akron

Founded: 1825 **Pop:** 237,177 **Elev:** 1,027 ft (313 m) **Area code:** 216

Motels

✔ ★ ★ **BEST WESTERN EXECUTIVE INN.** *2677 Gilchrist Rd (44305). 216/794-1050.* 121 rms, 3 story. S $40–$47; D $46–$53; each addl $6; under 17 free. Crib free. TV; cable. Heated pool. Cafe 6 am–10 pm; Sat from 7 am; Sun 7 am–8 pm. Rm serv 8 am–9 pm; Sun to 8 pm. Bar 11–2 am exc Sun. Ck-out noon. Meeting rms. Valet serv. Cr cds: A, C, D, DS, MC, V.

★ **COLONIAL.** *(827 Cleveland Rd, Mogadore 44260) I-76 exit 29. 216/628-4861.* 14 rms. May–Sep: S $34.50; D $44.50; each addl $4; lower rates rest of yr. TV. Playground. Cafe nearby. Ck-out 11 am. Some refrigerators. Cr cds: A, MC, V.

✔ ★ **KNIGHTS INN.** *3237 S Arlington St (44312). 216/644-1204.* 124 units, 11 kit. units. S $30.50–$36.50; D $31.50–$37.50; each addl $3; kit. units $40.50–$46.50; under 18 free. Crib $3. TV; satellite. Pool. Cafe opp 6 am–11 pm. Ck-out noon. Meeting rm. Airport transportation. Cr cds: A, C, D, MC, V.

✔ ★ **RED ROOF INN.** *99 Rothrock Rd (44321), OH 18 & I-77. 216/666-0566.* 109 rms, 2 story. S $30.95–$36.95; D $32.95–$38.95; each addl $6; under 18 free. Crib free. TV; satellite, in-rm movies. Free coffee. Cafe adj 6:30 am–10:30 pm. Ck-out noon. Cr cds: A, D, DS, MC, V.

Ashtabula

Settled: 1796 **Pop:** 23,449 **Elev:** 695 ft (212 m) **Area code:** 216 **Zip:** 44004

Motels

★ **CEDARS.** *2015 W Prospect Rd. 216/992-5406.* 16 rms. S $27–$31; D $28–$35; each addl $3; under 12 free. Crib free. TV; cable. Cafes nearby. Ck-out 11 am. Picnic table. Cr cds: A, C, D, MC, V. Ⓓ

✔ ★ ★ **TRAVELODGE.** *(Austinburg 44010) 8 mi SW at jct OH 45, I-90 Ashtabula exit 223. 216/275-2011.* 48 rms, 2 story. S $30–$44; D $41–$60; each addl $5; bridal suites $63; under 18 free. Crib free. TV; cable. Heated pool. Free coffee in rms, continental bkfst in lobby. Cafe opp open 24 hrs. Ck-out noon. Meeting rm. Valet serv. Sundries. Putting green. Cr cds: A, C, D, ER, MC, V.

Bellefontaine

Settled: 1806 **Pop:** 11,888 **Elev:** 1,251 ft (381 m) **Area code:** 513 **Zip:** 43311

Motels

★ ★HOLIDAY INN. *1134 N Main St. 513/593-8515.* 103 rms, 2 story. S $46–$59; D $51–$59; each addl $5; under 18 free. Crib free. TV; cable. Indoor pool; sauna, poolside serv, hot tub. Cafe 6 am–2:30 pm, 5–10 pm. Rm serv. Bar 11:30–2:30 am; entertainment, dancing exc Sun. Ck-out noon. Coin lndry. Meeting rms. Bellhops. Valet serv. Sundries. Free local airport transportation. Downhill ski 5 mi. Cr cds: A, C, D, DS, MC, V.

✓ ★L-K. *308 N Main St. 513/593-1015.* 50 rms, 2 story. S $33–$36; D $45–$48; each addl $6; under 18 free. Crib free. TV; cable. Pool. Cafe open 24 hrs. Bar 5 pm–2 am exc Sun. Ck-out noon. Downhill ski 6 mi. Cr cds: A, C, D, DS, MC, V.

Bowling Green

Founded: 1834 **Pop:** 25,728 **Elev:** 705 ft (215 m) **Area code:** 419 **Zip:** 43402

Motels

(Rates may be higher special university wkends)

★ ★BEST WESTERN FALCON PLAZA. *1450 E Wooster St; I-75 exit 181, opp Bowling Green Univ. 419/352-4671.* 50 rms, 2 story. S $38–$46; D $44–$54; each addl $4; studio rms $44–$68; under 12 free; wkly, monthly rates. Crib free. TV; cable. Cafe 6 am–10 pm. Ck-out noon. Meeting rms. Valet serv. Free local airport, bus depot transportation. Cr cds: A, C, D, DS, MC, V.

✓ ★BUCKEYE BUDGET MOTOR INN. *1740 E Wooster St; I-75 exit 181. 419/352-1520.* 94 rms, 2 story. S $29–$33; D, kit. units $33–$36; each addl $4; under 13 free; wkly rates; higher rates special events. Crib free. TV; cable, in-rm movies. Heated pool. Playground adj. Cafe 6 am–10 pm. Bar. Ck-out noon. Coin lndry. Cr cds: A, D, DS, MC, V.

✓ ★ ★HOLLEY LODGE. *1630 E Wooster St. 419/352-2521; res: 800/322-7829.* 100 rms, 2 story. S $34.95; D, studio rms $39.95; each addl $5; suites $49.95; under 16 free; higher rates special wkend events. Crib free. TV; cable. Indoor pool; whirlpool. Cafe 6 am–10 pm. Rm serv. Bar to 2 am. Ck-out 11 am. Meeting rms. Bellhops. Lawn games. Private patios, balconies. Cr cds: A, D, DS, MC, V.

Cambridge

Founded: 1806 **Pop:** 13,573 **Elev:** 886 ft (270 m) **Area code:** 614 **Zip:** 43725

Motels

(Rates may be higher during Jamboree in the Hills Festival)

✓ ★BEST WESTERN. *1945 Southgate Pkwy, I-70 exit 178. 614/439-3581.* 96 rms, 2 story. S $29–$45; D $37–$50; each addl $5; under 18 free; higher rates Salt Fork Arts Festival. Crib free. TV; cable. Pool. Cafe adj open 24 hrs. Bar 11–2 am exc Sun. Ck-out 11 am. Sundries. Cr cds: A, C, D, DS, MC, V.

✓ ★DAYS INN. *2328 Southgate Pkwy, I-70 exit 178. 614/432-5691.* 103 rms, 4 story. S $39; D $45; each addl $4; under 18 free; higher rates special events. Crib free. TV; cable. Pool; sauna. Cafe adj 6 am–midnight. Ck-out noon. Some in-rm steam baths. Cr cds: A, C, D, DS, MC, V.

★ ★ ★HOLIDAY INN. *Southgate Pkwy, 1 mi SW on OH 209, ¼ mi N of jct I-70 exit 178. 614/432-7313.* 107 rms, 2 story. S $44–$49; D $49–$53; each addl $5; under 18 free. Crib free.

TV; cable, in-rm movies. Pool. Cafe 6 am–10 pm. Rm serv. Bar 4 pm–midnight, Sun 5–10 pm; dancing exc Sun. Ck-out noon. Meeting rms. Health club privileges. Cr cds: A, C, D, DS, MC, V.

✔ ★TRAVELODGE. At jct OH 209, I-70 exit 178. 614/432-7375. 48 rms, 2 story. S $38; D $43–$48; each addl $4; under 18 free. Crib free. TV; cable, in-rm movies. Heated pool. Cafe adj 6 am–10 pm. Ck-out noon. Valet serv. Sundries. Exercise equipt; weights, bicycles, whirlpool, sauna. Some balconies. Cr cds: A, C, D, DS, ER, MC, V.

Canton

Settled: 1805 Pop: 93,077 Elev: 1,060 ft (323 m) Area code: 216

Motels

✔ ★ ★HAMPTON INN. 5335 Broadmoor Circle (44709). 216/492-0151. 108 rms, 4 story. S $40–$43; D $46–$49; under 18 free; wkend rates; higher rates pro football wkend. Crib free. TV; satellite. Free continental bkfst. Cafe adj 7 am–9 pm. Ck-out 1 pm. Meeting rms. Valet serv. Airport transportation. Exercise equipt; weight machines, bicycles. Cr cds: A, C, D, DS, MC, V.

✔ ★KNIGHTS INN. 3950 Convenience Circle (44718), I-77 exit 109. 216/492-5030. 102 units, 11 kit. units. June–Oct: S $30.50–$31.50; D $36.50–$37.50; each addl $3; kit. units $30.50–$40.50; under 18 free; wkly rates; lower rates rest of yr. Crib $3. TV; satellite. Pool. Free coffee. Cafe nearby. Ck-out noon. Meeting rms. Cr cds: A, C, D, MC, V.

✔ ★RED ROOF INN. 5353 Inn Circle Ct NW (44720), I-77 exit 109. 216/499-1970. 109 rms, 2 story. S $28.95–$34.95; D $30.95–$36.95; each addl $2; under 18 free. Crib free. TV. Cafe adj 6 am–10 pm. Ck-out noon. Sundries. Cr cds: A, D, DS, MC, V.

Chillicothe

Settled: 1796 Pop: 23,420 Elev: 620 ft (189 m) Area code: 614 Zip: 45601

Motels

★ ★HOLIDAY INN. 1250 N Bridge St. 614/775-7000. 155 rms, 2 story. S $40–$51; D $42–$54; each addl $6; under 19 free. Crib free. TV; cable. Heated pool; poolside serv. Cafe 6 am–10 pm; Sat from 7 am; Sun 7 am–8 pm. Rm serv. Bar 11–2 am; entertainment. Ck-out noon. Coin lndry. Meeting rms. Valet serv. Cr cds: A, C, D, DS, MC, V.

✔ ★ ★RODEWAY INN. 20 North Plaza Blvd. 614/775-3500. 100 rms, 2 story. S $43–$48; D $49–$54; each addl $5; under 17 free. Crib free. TV; cable, in-rm movies. Heated pool. Free continental bkfst. Cafe adj. Bar 11–2:30 am, Sat to 2 am, Sun 1 pm–midnight; entertainment, dancing Fri, Sat. Ck-out noon. Meeting rms. Valet serv. Sundries. Some in-rm whirlpools. Cr cds: A, C, D, DS, MC, V.

Cincinnati

Settled: 1788 Pop: 385,457 Elev: 683 ft (208 m) Area code: 513

Motels

(Rates may be higher during Kool Jazz Festival)

✔ ★ ★BEST WESTERN MARIEMONT INN. 6880 Wooster Pike (45227). 513/271-2100. 60 rms, 3 story. S $41–$46; D $48–$54; each addl $5; suites $60–$70; under 12 free. Crib free.

TV; cable. Cafe 6:30 am–2 pm, 5:30–10 pm; Sat, Sun from 7:30 am; Fri, Sat to 10:30 pm; Sun 5–9 pm. Bar 11 am–midnight. Ck-out noon. Coin lndry. Valet serv. Cr cds: A, C, D, DS, MC, V.

✔ ★★HAMPSHIRE HOUSE. *(30 Tri-County Pkwy, Springdale 45246) I-275 exit 42.* 513/772-5440; res: 800/543-4211 (exc OH), 800/582-5503 (OH). 152 units, 2 story. S, D $38–$49; suites $59; under 18 free; wkly rates; higher rates special events. Crib free. TV; in-rm movies. Indoor pool; whirlpool, sauna, poolside serv. Free coffee. Cafe 6:30 am–10 pm; wkends from 7 am. Rm serv. Bar 11–2 am, Sun 3 pm–midnight; dancing. Ck-out 1 pm. Meeting rms. Bathrm phone in suites. Cr cds: A, C, D, DS, MC, V. Ⓔ

✔ ★★HAMPTON INN. *10900 Crowne Point Dr (45241), off I-75 exit 15.* 513/771-6888. 130 rms, 4 story. June–Aug: S $44–$47; D $49–$52; under 18 free; higher rates special events; lower rates rest of yr. Crib free. TV; cable, in-rm movies. Pool. Free continental bkfst. Cafe nearby. Ck-out noon. Meeting rms. Cr cds: A, C, D, DS, MC, V.

✔ ★★LA QUINTA. *11335 Chester Rd (45246), I-75 Sharon Rd exit 15.* 513/772-3140. 144 rms, 2 story. S $39–$44; D $44–$49; each addl $5; under 19 free. Crib free. TV; satellite. Pool. Free continental bkfst. Cafe adj 11 am–11 pm. Bar 11:30–2 am. Ck-out noon. Valet serv. Sundries. Airport transportation. Tennis, racquetball privileges. Cr cds: A, C, D, DS, MC, V.

★RED ROOF INN. *11345 Chester Rd (45246), I-75 Sharon Rd exit 15.* 513/771-5141. 109 rms, 2 story. S $29.95–$31.95; D $35.95–$37.95; each addl $2; under 18 free. Crib free. TV. Cafe adj 6 pm–midnight. Ck-out noon. Cr cds: A, C, D, DS, MC, V.

✔ ★★★RODEWAY INN. *400 Glensprings Dr (45246), I-275 exit 41.* 513/825-3129. 120 rms, 2 story. S $38–$48; D $43–$65; each addl $6; under 17 free. Crib free. TV; cable. Pool. Free coffee. Cafe open 24 hrs. Ck-out noon. Meeting rms. Valet serv. Cr cds: A, C, D, DS, MC, V.

✔ ★SIGNATURE INN. *8870 Governor's Hill Dr (45249), off I-71 exit 19.* 513/683-3086. 100 rms, 2 story. Memorial Day–Labor Day: S $41–$70; D $47–$70; each addl $6; under 17 free; lower rates rest of yr. Crib free. TV; in-rm movies. Pool. Playground. Free continental bkfst. Ck-out noon. Meeting rms. Game rm. Cr cds: A, C, D, MC, V.

Motor Hotel

✔ ★★IMPERIAL HOUSE-WEST. *5510 Rybolt Rd (45248), I-74 exit 11.* 513/574-6000; res: 800/543-3018 (exc OH), 800/582-4050 (OH). 200 rms, 5 story, 27 kits. S $38–$45; D $46–$56; each addl $5; suites $75–$85; kit. units for 2 persons $700–$750/month; under 12 free; higher rates special events. Crib free. TV; cable. Pool. Playground. Cafe 6:30 am–10 pm. Rm serv. Bar 11–2:30 am, Sun 1–11 pm; entertainment, dancing exc Sun. Ck-out noon. Coin lndry. Meeting rms. Valet serv. Sundries. Exercise equipt; weights, bicycles, whirlpool, steam rm. Some refrigerators. Cr cds: A, C, D, MC, V.

Cleveland

Founded: 1796 **Pop:** 573,822 **Elev:** 680 ft (207 m) **Area code:** 216

Motels

★BUDGETEL INN. *(1421 Golden Gate Blvd, Mayfield Heights 44124), at I-271 & Mayfield Rd W.* 216/442-8400. 103 rms, 3 story, 2 kit. units. S $32.95–$37.95; D $38.95–$40.95; each addl $5; suites, kit. units $59.95; under 18 free. Crib free. TV; satellite. Cafe adj 6:30 am–11 pm. Ck-out noon. Coin lndry. Valet serv. Downhill ski 5 mi; x-country ski 2 mi. Cr cds: A, C, D, DS, MC, V. Ⓔ

✔ ★KNIGHTS INN. *(4501 E Royalton Rd, Broadview Heights 44147) I-77 exit 149.* 216/526-0640. 110 units, 2 story, 10 kit. units. S $30.50–$32.50; D $36.50–$38.50; each addl $4; kit. units $40.50–$54.50; under 18 free. Crib $3. TV; satellite. Pool. Cafe adj open 24 hrs. Ck-out noon. Meeting rms. Cr cds: A, C, D, MC, V.

🅿 ➡ 🚫 ⊗ SC

✔ ★L-K. *(275 Highland Rd, Macedonia 44056) On OH 8 at I-271, 3 mi N of OH Tpke exit 12.* 216/467-1516. 70 rms, 2 story. S $36; D $42; each addl $6; under 18 free. Crib free. TV; cable. Pool. Cafe adj 6 am–midnight. Ck-out 11 am. Downhill/x-country ski 3 mi. Picnic tables. Cr cds: A, C, D, DS, MC, V.

🏊 ➡ 🚫 ⊗ SC

★RED ROOF INN. *(6020 Quarry Lane, Independence 44131) I-77 Rockside exit.* 216/447-0030. 109 rms, 2 story. S $31.95–$37.95; D $33.95–$42.95; each addl $6; under 18 free. Crib free. TV; cable, in-rm movies. Free coffee. Cafe adj 6 am–11 pm. Ck-out noon. Sundries. Cr cds: A, D, DS, MC, V.

🅿 🚫 ⊗ SC

✔ ★TRAVELODGE-BEACHWOOD. *(3795 Orange Pl, Beachwood 44122) at I-271 Chagrin Blvd, OH 422 exit.* 216/831-7200. 128 rms, 2 story. S $39–$40; D $45–$46; each addl $4; under 18 free; summer packages. Crib free. TV; satellite. Free continental bkfst. Ck-out noon. Meeting rms. Sundries. Airport transportation. Cr cds: A, C, D, DS, ER, MC, V.

♿ 🚫 ⊗ SC

✔ ★TRAVELODGE-WILLOUGHBY. *(34600 Maplegrove Rd, Willoughby 44094) Off I-90, exit 189.* 216/585-1900. 111 rms, 2 story. S $35–$36; D $41–$42; each addl $4; under 18 free. Crib free. TV; satellite. Free continental bkfst. Cafe adj 6 am–10 pm; Fri, Sat open 24 hrs. Ck-out noon. Meeting rms. Airport transportation. X-country ski 4 mi. Cr cds: A, C, D, DS, ER, MC, V.

♿ 🏊 🚫 ⊗ SC

Columbus

Founded: 1812 **Pop:** 565,032 **Elev:** 780 ft (238 m) **Area code:** 614

Motels

✔ ★★CROSS COUNTRY INN-NORTH. *4875 Sinclair Rd (43229).* 614/431-3670. 136 rms, 2 story. S $28.95–$30.95; D $30.95–$36.95; each addl $6; under 18 free. Crib free. TV; cable. Heated pool. Cafe adj 6 am–11 pm. Ck-out noon. Health club privileges. Cr cds: A, C, D, MC, V.

♿ ➡ 🚫 ⊗ SC

✔ ★★CROSS COUNTRY INN-NORTHWEST. *6364 Frantz Rd (43017).* 614/764-4545. 112 rms, 2 story. S $28.95–$34.95; D $30.95–$36.95; each addl $2; under 19 free. Crib free. TV; cable. Pool. Cafe adj 6 am–11 pm. Ck-out noon. Health club privileges. Cr cds: A, MC, V.

♿ ➡ 🚫 ⊗ SC

★HOMESTEAD. *4182 E Main St (43213), I-70 Hamilton exit.* 614/235-2348. 22 rms. S $28–$30; D $35–$40; each addl $2.50; under 10 free. Crib $2. TV; cable. Pool; wading pool. Playground. Cafe adj 6 am–3 pm. Ck-out 11 am. Picnic tables. Cr cds: A, C, D, ER, MC, V.

➡ ⊗

✔ ★KNIGHTS INN-EAST. *5950 Scarborough Blvd (43232), I-70 Brice Rd exit.* 614/864-4670. 164 rms, 9 kit. units. S $28.50–$40.50; D $34.50–$46.50; each addl $3; kit. units $38.50–$46.50; under 18 free. Crib $2. TV; satellite. Pool. Cafe nearby. Ck-out noon. Meeting rm. Cr cds: A, C, D, MC, V.

🅿 ➡ 🚫 ⊗ SC

★L-K. *(50 E Wilson Bridge Rd, Worthington 43085) N on I-71.* 614/846-8830. 50 rms, 2 story. S $37–$40; D $47–$50; each addl $6; suites $52–$62; kit units $41–$45; studio rms $47–$53; under 18 free. Crib free. TV. Ck-out noon. Cafe nearby. Valet serv. Cr cds: A, C, D, DS, MC, V.

🚫 ⊗ SC

✔ ★★**RAMADA INN-EAST.** *(2100 Brice Rd, Reynoldsburg 43068) I-70 Brice Rd exit.* *614/864-1280.* 142 rms, 2 story. May–Dec: S $46–$56; D $54–$64; each addl $10; suites $100–$125; under 17 free; higher rates special events; lower rates rest of yr. Crib free. TV; cable, in-rm movies. Pool; poolside serv. Free coffee. Cafe 6 am–10 pm. Rm serv. Bar 4 pm–midnight; entertainment Fri, Sat. Ck-out noon. Meeting rms. Bellhops. Sundries. Free airport transportation. Lawn games. Cr cds: A, C, D, DS, MC, V.

⊠ 🐾 sc

★**RED ROOF INN-MORSE ROAD.** *750 Morse Rd (43229), I-71 Morse-Sinclair exit.* *614/846-8520.* 107 rms, 2 story. S $28.95–$30.95; D $34.95–$36.95; each addl $2; under 19 free. Crib free. Free coffee. TV; in-rm movies. Cafe nearby. Ck-out noon. Sundries. Cr cds: A, C, D, DS, MC, V.

🐕 ⊘ 🐾 sc

★**TRAVELODGE.** *(7480 N High St, Worthington 43085)* 614/431-2525. 108 rms, 3 story. S $38; D $44; each addl $4; under 18 free. Crib free. TV; cable. Free continental bkfst. Cafe 6:30 am–11 pm. Ck-out noon. Meeting rms. Cr cds: A, C, D, DS, MC, V.

♿ ⊘ 🐾 sc

Motor Hotels

✔ ★**ENVOY INN.** *35 W Spring St (43215).* *614/228-3200; res: 800/227-7378.* 164 rms, 6 story. S $39–$44; D $44–$49; each addl $5; under 17 free. Garage $3 in/out. TV; in-rm movies. Cafe 6:30–2 am. Bar 11–1:30 am. Ck-out noon. Meeting rms. Sundries. Gift shop. Cr cds: A, C, D, DS, MC, V.

♿ 🐕 ⊘ 🐾 sc

✔ ★★★**LENOX INN.** *At I-70E exit 112B (OH 256) (43068).* *614/861-7800; res: 800/821-0007.* 152 rms, 2 story, 36 suites. S $36–$51; D $42–$56; each addl $4; suites $50; under 18 free; wknd package. Crib free. TV; satellite, in-rm movies. Pool; wading pool, poolside serv. Playground. Cafe 6:30 am–10 pm. Rm serv. Bar. Ck-out 1 pm. Meeting rms. Valet serv. Sundries. Free airport transportation. 36-hole golf privileges. Cr cds: A, C, D, DS, MC, V.

♿ 🐕 🚲 ⊠ 🐾 sc

Dayton

Founded: 1796 **Pop:** 193,444 **Elev:** 757 ft (231 m) **Area code:** 513

Motels

✔ ★**DAYS INN.** *7470 Miller Ln (45414), just off I-75 exit 60.* *513/898-4946.* 188 rms, 2 story. S $25; D $30; each addl $5; under 18, $1. Crib free. TV; satellite. Pool. Cafe 6 am–9 pm. Ck-out 11 am. Cr cds: A, C, D, DS, MC, V.

⊠ ⊘ 🐾 sc S

★★**HAMPTON INN.** *(20 Rockridge Rd, Englewood 45322)* I-70 exit 29. 513/832-2222. 130 rms, 4 story. S $41–$45; D $46–$50; under 18 free. TV; satellite, in-rm movies. Free continental bkfst. Cafe adj. Ck-out noon. Meeting rm. Valet serv. Sundries. Free airport transportation. Exercise equipt; weight machines, bicycles. Cr cds: A, C, D, DS, MC, V.

♿ 🏃 ⊘ 🐾 sc

★**KNIGHTS INN-NORTH.** *3663 Maxton Rd (45414), at I-75 Little York exit 60.* 513/898-1212. 107 rms, 2 story. S $29.50–$35; D $30.50–$36; each addl $3; kit. units $39–$45; under 18 free. Crib $5. TV; satellite. Pool. Cafe opp 5 am–midnight. Ck-out noon. Some refrigerators. Cr cds: A, C, D, MC, V.

🐕 ⊠ ⊘ 🐾 sc

✔ ★**LA QUINTA MOTOR INN.** *2140 Edwin C Moses Blvd (45408), at I-75 exit 51.* 513/223-0166. 118 rms, 2 story. S $33–$37; D $38–$42; each addl $5; under 18 free. Crib free. TV; satellite. Pool. Cafe adj open 24 hrs. Bar 2 pm–2:30 am; Sat from 5 pm. Ck-out noon. Coin lndry. Meeting rms. Valet serv. Airport transportation. Some in-rm steam baths. Cr cds: A, C, D, DS, MC, V.

⊠ ⊘ 🐾 sc S

★**PATTERSON INN-FAIRBORN.** *(800 N Broad St, Fairborn 45324) I-70 exit 44A.* *513/879-3920; res: 800/553-1212.* 151 rms, 2 story. S $47–$60; D $52–$65; each addl $5; under 18 free. Crib free. TV. Pool; wading pool. Cafe 6 am–2 pm, 5–10 pm. Rm serv from 7 am. Bar 11–1 am; entertainment, dancing Fri, Sat. Ck-out noon. Meeting rms. Gift shop. Barber, beauty shop. Exercise equipt; weights, bicycles. Game rm. Cr cds: A, C, D, DS, MC, V.

★**RED ROOF INN.** *(222 Byers Rd, Miamisburg 45342) I-75 exit 44. 513/866-0705.* 107 rms, 2 story. S $28.95–$30.95; D $34.95–$36.95; each addl $2; under 18 free. Crib free. TV. Cafe adj 6 am–midnight. Ck-out noon. Cr cds: A, C, D, DS, MC, V.

✔★★**RODEWAY INN.** *7575 Poe Rd (45414).* *513/454-0550.* 120 units, 2 story. S $35–$45; D $40–$50; suites $50–$60; under 17 free. Crib free. TV; cable. Pool. Free continental bkfst. Bar 5 pm–midnight. Ck-out noon. Meeting rms. Valet serv. Free airport transportation. Health club privileges. Cr cds: A, C, D, DS, MC, V.

✔★**TRAVELODGE.** *3636 N Dixie Dr (45414), I-75 exit 57B. 513/276-6151.* 119 rms, 2–3 story. S $39–$44; D $44–$54; each addl $5; suites $50–$75; under 18 free; slightly higher rates special events. Crib free. TV; satellite. Pool. Cafe adj open 24 hrs. Rm serv 7 am–11 pm. Ck-out noon. Coin lndry. Meeting rms. Valet serv. Airport transportation. Some in-rm steam baths. Cr cds: A, C, D, DS, ER, MC, V.

Delaware

Founded: 1808 **Pop:** 18,780 **Elev:** 880 ft (268 m) **Area code:** 614 **Zip:** 43015

Motels

✔★**GATHERING INN.** *259 S Sandusky St, at US 42. 614/363-1143.* 48 rms. S $28.95; D $35.50; each addl $3; suite $35; under 12 free. Crib $3. TV; in-rm movies. Pool. Cafe 7 am–2 pm, 5–8 pm; Sun 8 am–1 pm. Ck-out noon. Meeting rms. Valet serv. Sundries. Cr cds: A, D, MC, V.

✔★**L-K.** *(Box 747) 1001 US 23. 614/369-4421.* 32 rms, 1–2 story. S $33–$35; D $39–$41; each addl $6; under 18 free; higher rates Little Brown Jug harness race. Crib free. TV; cable. Cafe 6 am–midnight. Ck-out noon. Meeting rms. Cr cds: A, C, D, DS, MC, V.

Findlay

Founded: 1821 **Pop:** 35,594 **Elev:** 780 ft (238 m) **Area code:** 419 **Zip:** 45840

Motels

✔★**FINDLAY.** *820 Tiffin Ave, at I-75 exit 157 & 159. 419/422-5516.* 38 rms. S $16–$37; D $20–$48; each addl $5; kit. units $160/wk–$264/wk. Crib $3. TV; cable. Heated pool. Cafe 6 am–9 pm. Rm serv. Ck-out noon. Coin lndry. Airport transportation. Some refrigerators. Picnic tables. Cr cds: A, C, D, DS, MC, V.

★★**HOLIDAY INN.** *820 Trenton Ave, I-75 exit 159. 419/423-8212.* 140 rms, 2 story. S $48; D $54; each addl $6; suite $57; under 19 free. Crib free. TV; in-rm movies. Pool. Cafe 7 am–2 pm, 5–10 pm. Rm serv. Bar 11–2 am. Ck-out noon. Coin lndry. Meeting rms. Golf nearby. Racquetball, health club privileges. Cr cds: A, C, D, DS, MC, V.

★**HOLIDAY MOTEL.** *428 Lima Ave, I-75 exit 156. 419/423-0575.* 12 rms, 10 A/C. S $17; D $18–$21; each addl $1. Closed mid-Dec–mid-Jan. Crib $2. TV; cable. Ck-out 11 am.

★ ★ ★IMPERIAL HOUSE. *1305 W Main Cross St, I-75 exit 157. 419/423-7171.* 116 rms, 2 story. S $45–$56; D $50–$62; wkend rates. Crib free. TV; cable, in-rm movies. Pool; poolside serv, lifeguard in season. Free coffee in rms. Cafe 6:30 am–10 pm; Sat from 7 am; Sun 8 am–8 pm. Rm serv. Bar 11–2 am; entertainment, dancing exc Sun. Ck-out noon. Meeting rms. Bellhops. Valet serv. Local airport, bus depot transportation. Golf privileges nearby. Game rm. Lawn games. Cr cds: A, D, MC, V.

Fremont

Founded: 1820 **Pop:** 17,834 **Elev:** 601 ft (183 m) **Area code:** 419 **Zip:** 43420

Motels

★FREMONT TURNPIKE. *520 E County Rd 89. 419/332-6489.* 20 rms. Late May–mid-Sep: S $38; D $42–$49; lower rates rest of yr. Crib $4. TV. Free coffee in rms. Cafe nearby. Ck-out 11 am. Cr cds: MC, V.

★GREAT LAKES. *1737 E State St, OH Tpke exit 6. 419/334-9797.* 18 rms. Memorial Day–Labor Day: S $30–$36; D $38–$46; each addl $4; lower rates rest of yr. TV; in-rm movies. Ck-out 11 am. Fish cleaning facilities. Cr cds: MC, V.

✔★L-K. *1750 Cedar St, just S at Stone St. 419/334-9517.* 51 rms, 2 story. May–Sep: S $42; D $48–$54; each addl $6; kit. units $54–$58; under 18 free; lower rates rest of yr. Crib free. TV; cable. Pool. Cafe 6 am–11 pm. Ck-out 11 am. Cr cds: A, C, D, DS, MC, V. ⒺⒹ

Hamilton

Founded: 1791 **Pop:** 63,189 **Elev:** 580 ft (178 m) **Area code:** 513

Hotel

✔★★★HAMILTONIAN. *1 Riverfront Plaza (45011). 513/896-6200; res: 800/522-5570.* 120 rms, 6 story. S $45–$58; D $43–$52; each addl $5; suites $92–$97; under 18 free; wkend packages. Crib $5. TV; cable. Pool. Cafe 6:30 am–10 pm. Bar 11–1 am, Fri, Sat to 2 am; entertainment exc Sun. Ck-out noon. Meeting rms. Concierge. Airport transportation. Indoor tennis privileges. On river. *LUXURY LEVEL:* 16 rms, 4 suites. S $50–$56; D $61; suites $90–$95. Private lounge. Complimentary coffee, newspaper. In-rm movies. Minibars. Some in-rm whirlpools. Deluxe toiletry amenities.
Cr cds: A, C, D, MC, V. ⒺⒻⒹ

Kent

Pop: 26,164 **Elev:** 1,097 ft (334 m) **Area code:** 216 **Zip:** 44240

Motels

(Rates may be higher for special university wkends)

★INN OF KENT. *303 E Main St, OH Tpke exit 13. 216/673-3411.* 57 rms, 2 story, some kits. June–Labor Day: S, D $38–$60; each addl $3; lower rates rest of yr. Crib free. TV. Cafe. Rm serv. Bar exc Sun. Ck-out noon. Cr cds: A, C, D, MC, V.

✔★★KNIGHTS INN. *4423 OH 43, 3 mi S on OH 43 at jct I-76. 216/678-5250.* 100 rms, 30 kit. units. May–Sep: S, D $35.50; each addl $3–$6; kit. units $44.50; under 18 free; some lower rates rest of yr. Crib $3. TV; satellite. Pool. Cafe adj 10 am–10 pm. Ck-out noon. Meeting rm. Sundries. Some refrigerators. Cr cds: A, MC, V.

★UNIVERSITY INN. *540 S Water St. 216/678-0123.* 107 rms, 7 story. June–Sep: S $35; D $38–$48; each addl $2; lower rates rest of yr. Crib free. TV. Heated pool. Cafe 6 am–10 pm. Bar 11–1 am. Ck-out noon. Coin lndry. Meeting rms. Many refrigerators. Private patios, balconies. Cr cds: A, D, DS, MC, V.

Lancaster

Founded: 1800 **Pop:** 34,953 **Elev:** 860 ft (262 m) **Area code:** 614 **Zip:** 43130

Motel

★★HOLIDAY INN. *1858 N Memorial Dr. 614/653-3040.* 167 rms, 2 story. S $45–$53; D $47–$55; under 19 free; wkend rates. Crib free. TV; cable, in-rm movies. Pool. Cafe 6 am–10 pm. Rm serv from 7 am. Bar 11–1 am; entertainment, dancing Tu–Sat. Ck-out noon. Coin lndry. Meeting rms. Bellhops. Valet serv. Free airport transportation. Putting green. Lawn games. Cr cds: A, C, D, DS, MC, V.

Hotel

✔★★R.J. PITCHER'S. *123 N Broad St, OH 33, Broad St exit. 614/653-5522.* 26 rms, 6 story. S $23–$36; D $31–$40; each addl $4; suites $44.50; under 12 free. Crib free. TV. Cafe 7 am–2 pm, 5–10 pm; Sat from 5 pm. Bar 11–2 am. Ck-out 1 pm. Meeting rms. Cr cds: A, D, MC, V.

Lima

Founded: 1831 **Pop:** 47,381 **Elev:** 880 ft (268 m) **Area code:** 419

Motels

★DAVIS PLAZA. *1650 Harding Hwy (45804), I-75 exit 125B. 419/222-1080.* 32 rms. S $24; D $28. Crib free. TV; cable. Heated pool. Free coffee. Cafe nearby. Ck-out noon. Meeting rm. Sundries. Putting green. Cr cds: A, ER, MC, V.

★★HOWARD JOHNSON. *1430 Bellefontaine Ave (45804). 419/227-2221.* 76 rms, 2 story. S $36–$51; D $42–$58; each addl $8; under 18 free. Crib free. TV; cable, in-rm movies. Heated pool. Ck-out noon. Private patios, balconies. Cr cds: A, C, D, DS, MC, V.

✔★★QUALITY INN LIMA. *1201 Neubrecht Rd (45801), I-75 exit 127B. 419/222-0596.* 145 units, 2 story. S $37–$40; D $42–$45; each addl $5; kit. units $45–$50; under 16 free; higher rates special events. Crib free. TV; cable. Heated pool. Playground. Cafe 6:30 am–10 pm. Rm serv. Bar 11–1 am; dancing wkends. Ck-out noon. Coin lndry. Meeting rms. Valet serv. Sundries. Exercise equipt; weights, bicycles. Picnic tables. Cr cds: A, C, D, DS, MC, V.

✔★★RAMADA INN. *1210 Neubrecht Rd (45801), I-75 exit 127B. 419/228-4251.* 123 rms, 2 story. S $42–$47; D $50–$55; each addl $8; suites $70; under 18 free. Crib free. TV; cable. Heated pool. Playground. Cafe 6 am–2 pm, 5–10 pm. Rm serv. Bar 11–1 am; dancing exc Sun. Ck-out noon. Meeting rms. Valet serv. Sundries. Cr cds: A, C, D, DS, MC, V.

Mansfield

Founded: 1808 **Pop:** 53,927 **Elev:** 1,230 ft (375 m) **Area code:** 419

Motels

✔ ★ ★**BEST WESTERN INN.** *880 Laver Rd (44905). 419/589-2200.* 105 rms, 2 story. S $35-$45; D $41-$51; each addl $6; under 12 free; higher rates special events, summer wkends. Crib free. TV; cable, in-rm movies. Heated pool; poolside serv. Playground. Cafe 6:30 am-2 pm, 5-10 pm; Sun 7 am-8 pm. Rm serv. Bar 11:30-2 am; entertainment, dancing exc Sun. Ck-out noon. Meeting rms. Lawn games. Cr cds: A, C, D, DS, MC, V.

⊠ ⊗ sc

★**L-K.** *(178 Mansfield Ave, Shelby 44875) 419/347-2141.* 32 rms, 1-2 story. S $31-$34; D, kit. units $43-$46; each addl $6; under 18 free. Crib free. TV; cable. Cafe 6 am-10 pm; Fri, Sat to midnight. Ck-out noon. Meeting rm. Cr cds: A, C, D, DS, MC, V.

⊕ ⊗ sc

✔ ★ ★**L-K NORTH.** *(Box 195, Rte 11, 44903) Koogle Rd, 8 mi NE at jct US 30, I-71. 419/589-3938.* 52 rms, 2 story. S $34-$37; D $43-$46; each addl $6; kit. units $50-$65; under 18 free; wkly, monthly rates. Crib free. TV; cable. Pool. Cafe 6 am-11 pm. Ck-out noon. Downhill/x-country ski 10 mi. Cr cds: A, C, D, DS, MC, V.

⊕ ⊁ ⊠ ⊗ sc

✔ ★ ★**L-K SOUTH.** *(Rte 10, 44904) 90 Hanley Rd. 419/756-7600.* 93 rms, 2 story. S $34-$37; D $46-$49; each addl $6; kit. units $50-$65; under 18 free; wkend rates. Crib free. TV; cable. Pool. Cafe 6 am-10 pm. Ck-out noon. Meeting rms. Downhill/x-country ski 2 mi. Cr cds: A, C, D, DS, MC, V.

⊁ ⊠ ⊗ sc

★ ★**TRAVELODGE.** *137 Park Ave W (44902). 419/522-5142.* 50 rms, 2 story. S $40-$48; D $53; each addl $5; family rates. Crib free. TV; cable. Free continental bkfst. Cafe nearby. Ck-out noon. Valet serv. Sundries. Downhill ski 5 mi; x-country ski 6 mi. Balconies. Cr cds: A, C, D, DS, ER, MC, V.

⊕ ⊕ ⊁ ⊗ sc ⑤

Marietta

Founded: 1788 **Pop:** 16,467 **Elev:** 616 ft (188 m) **Area code:** 614 **Zip:** 45750

Motels

★**BEST WESTERN.** *279 Muskingum Dr, I-77 exit 6. 614/374-7211.* 47 rms, 1-2 story. S $28-$32; D $38-$42; each addl $5; under 12 free. Crib free. TV. Free coffee, continental bkfst. Cafe nearby. Ck-out noon. Sundries. Health club privileges. Refrigerators. Picnic tables, grill. On Muskingum River; dockage. Cr cds: A, C, D, DS, MC, V.

⊕ ⊖ ⊗ ⊠ sc

★**ECONO LODGE.** *702 Pike St, I-77 exit 1. 614/374-8481.* 48 rms, 2 story. S $27.95-$35.95; D $35.95-$45.95; each addl $3-$5; family rates. Crib $3. TV; cable. Heated pool. Free coffee. Cafe nearby. Ck-out noon. Cr cds: A, C, D, DS, MC, V.

⊕ ⊖ ⊗ ⊠ sc ⑤

✔ ★ ★**HOLIDAY INN.** *701 Pike St, I-77 exit 1. 614/374-9660.* 109 rms, 2 story. S, D $39-$49; under 18 free. Crib free. TV. Heated pool; wading pool. Cafe 6 am-2 pm, 5-10 pm; wkends from 7 am. Rm serv. Bar 4 pm-2 am; entertainment, dancing exc Sun. Ck-out noon. Meeting rms. Valet serv. Sundries. Cr cds: A, C, D, DS, MC, V.

⊕ ⊖ ⊗ ⊠ sc ⑤

✔ ★**KNIGHTS INN.** *506 Pike St, I-77 exit 1. 614/373-7373.* 110 units, 14 kit. units. S $29.50-$30.50; D $35.50-$36.50; first addl $3; kit. units $39.50-$45.50; under 18 free; wkly rates kit. units. Crib $3. TV; cable. Pool. Free coffee. Cafe adj 6 am–11 pm; wkends open 24 hrs. Meeting rms. Cr cds: A, C, D, MC, V.

Motor Hotel

✔ ★★**RAMADA INN.** *601 Pike St.* 614/374-8190. 119 rms, 4 story. S $42–$43; D $46–$47; each addl $6; suites $75; under 18 free. Crib free. TV; cable. Heated pool. Free coffee. Cafe 6 am–10 pm; Sun to 8 pm. Rm serv. Bar noon–midnight; entertainment, dancing exc Sun. Ck-out 1 pm. Meeting rms. Cr cds: A, C, D, MC, V.

Marion

Settled: 1820 Pop: 37,040 Elev: 956 ft (291 m) Area code: 614 Zip: 43302

Motels

★**HARDING MOTOR LODGE.** *1065 Delaware Ave.* 614/383-6771; res: 800/258-1980. 157 rms, 2 story. S $34.95; D $38.95; each addl $4; suites $40.95; under 13 free. Crib free. TV; cable. Pool. Playground. Cafe 6 am–10 pm; Sun 8 am–4 pm. Rm serv. Bar 11–2 am. Ck-out 11 am. Coin lndry. Meeting rms. Valet serv. Sundries. Cr cds: A, C, D, DS, MC, V.

✔ ★**L-K.** *1952 Marion-Mt Gilead Rd.* 614/389-4671. 98 rms, 2 story. S $35–$37; D $39–$41; each addl $6; suites $48–$68; under 18 free. Crib free. TV; satellite. 2 pools. Free continental bkfst. Cafe adj 6 am–midnight. Ck-out noon. Meeting rms. Valet serv. 18-hole golf, racquetball, health club privileges adj. Picnic tables. Cr cds: A, C, D, DS, MC, V. ⓓ

Medina

Pop: 15,268 Elev: 1,092 ft (333 m) Area code: 216 Zip: 44256

Motels

✔ ★★**BEST WESTERN.** *2875 Medina Rd, OH 18 & I-71.* 216/725-4571. 129 rms, 2 story. S $29–$39; D $34–$40; each addl $5; under 12 free. Crib $3. TV; satellite. Pool. Cafe 7 am–9 pm. Rm serv. Bar 11–2:30 am. Ck-out noon. Meeting rms. Airport transportation. Cr cds: A, C, D, DS, MC, V.

★**L-K.** *431 W Liberty St.* 216/725-6691. 48 rms, 2 story. S $30–$36; D $36–$42; each addl $6; kit. units $39.75–$41.50; under 19 free. Crib free. TV; cable. Cafe open 24 hrs; Sun, Mon to 10 pm. Meeting rm. Cr cds: A, C, D, DS, MC, V.

Middletown (Butler Co)

Pop: 43,719 Elev: 650 ft (198 m) Area code: 513 Zip: 45042

Motels

✔ ★★**DAYS INN.** *(Box 365) 3 mi E at jct OH 122, I-75 exit 32.* 513/424-1201. 120 rms, 2 story. S $49–$51; D $48–$54; each addl $5; under 19 free; wkend rates. Crib free. TV; cable, in-rm movies. Heated pool. Cafe 6 am–2 pm, 5:30–10 pm. Rm serv. Bar 3:30 pm–2:30 am; entertainment, dancing Tu–Sat. Ck-out noon. Meeting rms. Valet serv. Sundries. Cr cds: A, C, D, DS, MC, V.

✔ ★★HOWARD JOHNSON. *(I-75 & OH 122, Franklin 45005)* 513/424-3551. 96 rms, 2 story. S $32–$56; D $37–$61; each addl $6–$8; under 18 free. Crib free. TV; cable. Pool. Cafe 6 am–midnight. Bar 11–1 am, Fri to 2 am, Sat 5 pm–2 am, Sun 5 pm–midnight; entertainment Fri, Sat. Ck-out noon. Meeting rms. Sundries. Private patios, balconies. Cr cds: A, C, D, DS, ER, MC, V.

★KNIGHTS INN. *(8500 Claude-Thomas Rd, Franklin 45005)* At jct I-75, OH 73, exit 38. 513/746-2841. 70 rms. S $30.50–$40.50; D $37.50–$46.50; each addl $3; kit. units $40.50–$46.50; under 18 free. Crib $3. TV; satellite, in-rm movies. Pool. Ck-out noon. Cr cds: A, C, D, MC, V.

★SUPER 8. *(3553 Commerce Dr, Franklin 45005)* At I-75 & OH 122. 513/422-4888. 48 units, 2 story. S $34–$39; D $39; suite $55. Crib free. TV; satellite. Free continental bkfst. Ck-out 11 am. Cr cds: A, C, D, DS, MC, V.

Montpelier

Pop: 4,431 **Elev:** 760 ft (232 m) **Area code:** 419 **Zip:** 43543

Motels

✔ ★★HOLIDAY INN. *(RR 3) 3 mi NE on OH 15 at OH Tpke exit 2.* 419/485-5555. 120 rms, 2 story. S $42–$52; D $47–$54; each addl $8; under 20 free. Crib free. TV; cable. Pool; wading pool. Cafe open 24 hrs. Rm serv 7 am–10 pm. Bar 11–2 am; entertainment, dancing exc Sun. Ck-out noon. Coin lndry. Meeting rms. Bellhops. Sundries. On lake. Cr cds: A, C, D, DS, MC, V.

★M & D SUBURBAN INN. *(Bryan 43506) 3 mi S on OH 15, 6 mi S of OH Tpke exit 2.* 419/636-4205. 24 units, some kits. S $23–$27; D $30–$35; each addl $3.50. Crib $3.50. TV; cable. Free continental bkfst. Ck-out 11 am. Coin lndry. Cr cds: MC, V.

Mount Gilead

Pop: 2,911 **Elev:** 1,130 ft (344 m) **Area code:** 419 **Zip:** 43338

Motel

✔ ★DERRICK. *(RR 3) 6 mi SE on OH 95, ¼ mi W of I-71 exit 151.* 419/946-6010. 47 rms. May–Sep: S $25–$32; D $30–$40; each addl $5; suites $55–$79; higher rates state & county fairs, auto races; lower rates rest of yr. Crib free. TV; in-rm movies. Cafe 7 am–9 pm. Rm serv. Ck-out 11 am. Meeting rms. Downhill ski 15 mi. Miniature golf. State park nearby. Cr cds: A, D, DS, ER, MC, V.

Mount Vernon

Founded: 1805 **Pop:** 14,323 **Elev:** 990 ft (302 m) **Area code:** 614 **Zip:** 43050

Motel

✔ ★★CURTIS. *12 Public Sq at jct US 36, OH 3, 13, 229.* 614/397-4334; res: 800/828-7847 *(exc OH),* 800/634-6835 *(OH).* 72 rms, 2 story. S $35–$42; D $40–$53; each addl $3–$7; under 13 free. Crib free. TV; cable. Free coffee in rm. Cafe 7–10 am, 11 am–2 pm, 5–9 pm. Rm serv. Bar 11–1 am. Ck-out 2 pm, wkends noon. Coin lndry. Bellhops. Valet serv. Refrigerators. Cr cds: A, DS, MC, V.

Newark

Founded: 1802 **Pop:** 41,200 **Elev:** 829 ft (253 m) **Area code:** 614 **Zip:** 43055

Motel

✔ ★★**HOWARD JOHNSON.** *775 Hebron Rd, I-70 exit 129 B. 614/522-3191.* 72 rms, 2 story. S $44–$70; D $46–$75; each addl $8; suites $50–$99; under 18 free; higher rates special events. Crib free. TV; cable. Indoor pool. Bar 5 pm–1 am exc Sun. Ck-out noon. Meeting rms. Sundries. Health club privileges. Private patios, balconies. Cr cds: A, C, D, DS, MC, V.

New Philadelphia

Founded: 1804 **Pop:** 16,883 **Elev:** 910 ft (277 m) **Area code:** 216 **Zip:** 44663

Motels

★★**BEST WESTERN VALLEY INN.** *131 Bluebell Dr, I-77 exit 81. 216/339-7731.* 155 rms, 2 story. S $25.95–$35.95; D $31.95–$43.95; each addl $4; under 12 free; wkend rates; higher rates Hall of Fame Week, Ohio Swiss Festival. Crib free. TV; cable. Heated pool; whirlpool. Free full bkfst. Cafe 7 am–10 pm. Rm serv 7:30 am–9 pm. Bar 11:30–2:30 am. Ck-out noon. Meeting rms. Bellhops. Valet serv. Sundries. Cr cds: A, D, DS, MC, V.

✔ ★★**DELPHIAN MOTOR INN.** *(Box 430) 1281 W High Ave, I-77 exit 81. 216/339-6644.* 107 rms, 2 story. S $31–$38; D $35–$40; each addl $5; under 18 free; wkend rates. Crib free. TV; cable. Indoor pool. Free full bkfst. Cafe 6 am–9 pm; Sun to noon. Bar 11:30–2 am; entertainment, dancing Tu-Sat. Ck-out noon. Meeting rms. Sundries. Cr cds: A, C, D, DS, MC, V.

★★**L-K.** *(Box 727) 1256 W High Ave, at jct I-77 exit 81. 216/339-6671.* 62 rms, 2 story. S $26–$32; D, kit. units $31–$42; each addl $5; under 18 free. Crib free. TV; cable. Pool. Cafe open 24 hrs. Ck-out noon. Cr cds: A, C, D, DS, MC, V.

✔ ★★**L-K COUNTRY HEARTH INN.** *(111 McCauley Dr, Uhrichsville 44683) Approx 5 mi SE on US 250. 614/922-0774.* 48 rms, 2 story, 4 kit. units. S $35–$37; D $37–$43; each addl $6; suites $52–$58; kit. units $49–$55; under 18 free; MAP avail; wkly rates. Crib free. TV; in-rm movies. Continental bkfst. Cafe open 24 hrs. Ck-out noon. Some in-rm whirlpools, refrigerators. Beach 6 mi. Cr cds: A, D, DS, MC, V.

★**MOTEL 6.** *181 Bluebell Dr, I-77 exit 81. 216/339-6446.* 83 rms, 2 story. S $20.95; D $26.95; each addl $4; under 18 free. Crib free. TV; cable, in-rm movies. Heated pool. Cafe opp open 24 hrs. Ck-out noon. Cr cds: C, D, DS, MC, V.

Portsmouth

Founded: 1803 **Pop:** 25,943 **Elev:** 533 ft (162 m) **Area code:** 614 **Zip:** 45662

Motel

★**HOLIDAY INN.** *(Box 1190) 4 mi N on US 23. 614/354-2851.* 100 rms, 2 story. S $45–$50; D $52–$57; each addl $4; under 18 free; higher rates special events. Crib free. TV; cable. Pool. Cafe 6 am–2 pm, 5–10 pm. Rm serv. Bar 2 pm–2 am. Ck-out noon. Meeting rms. Valet serv. Picnic tables. Cr cds: A, C, D, DS, MC, V.

Motor Hotel

✔ ★**RAMADA INN.** *711 2d St at jct US 23, 52. 614/354-7711.* 119 rms, 5 story. S $40–$48; D $46–$60; each addl $5; under 18 free. Crib free. TV; cable. Indoor pool; wading pool, poolside serv, hot tub. Cafe 6 am–10 pm; Fri, Sat to 11 pm; Sun 7 am–8 pm. Rm serv. Bar 11–2 am, Sun 1–8 pm; entertainment, dancing exc Sun. Ck-out noon. Meeting rms. Valet serv. Sundries. Gift shop. Airport transportation. Health club privileges. Dockage. Some refrigerators. Cr cds: A, C, D, DS, MC, V.

🖼 🏃 🚫 🐾 SC

Salem

Settled: 1801 **Pop:** 12,869 **Elev:** 1,226 ft (374 m) **Area code:** 216 **Zip:** 44460

Motels

✔ ★**BARNETT'S.** *31257 US 62W. 216/337-8758.* 24 rms, 2 kit. units. S $24–$27; D $29–$34; each addl $4; kit. units $120–$135/wk. Crib $5. TV. Pool. Cafe adj 6 am–8 pm. Ck-out 11 am. Sundries. Picnic tables. Cr cds: A, C, MC, V. Ⓓ Ⓕ

🖼

★★**TIMBERLANES MOTOR INN.** *544 E Pershing St. 216/337-9901.* 58 rms, 2 story. S $39.50–$44.50; D $42.50–$47.50; suites $60–$65; each addl $5; under 12 free. Crib free. TV; cable. Cafe 7 am–10 pm; Fri to 11 pm; Sat 8 am–midnight; Sun 8 am–9 pm. Rm serv. Bar 10:30–2 am; entertainment Fri, Sat. Ck-out 1 pm. Meeting rms. Valet serv. Cr cds: A, MC, V.

Sandusky

Settled: 1816 **Pop:** 31,360 **Elev:** 600 ft (183 m) **Area code:** 419 **Zip:** 44870

Motels

✔ ★★★**BEST WESTERN RESORT INN.** *1530 Cleveland Rd. 419/625-9234.* 105 rms, 2 story. S $35–$105; D $35–$115; each addl $8; suites $125–$250; kit. units $200–$250; under 12 free. Crib $8. TV; cable. Heated pool; wading pool. Cafe 6:30 am–midnight. Rm serv to 10 pm. Ck-out 11 am. Sundries. Game rm. Picnic tables. Cr cds: A, C, D, DS, MC, V. Ⓔ

🖼 🐾 SC

★**MECCA.** *2227 Cleveland Rd. 419/626-1284.* 27 rms. Mid-May–mid-Sep: S $39–$79; D $49–$99; each addl $5–$10; suites $65–$115; lower rates Apr–mid-May, mid-Sep–Oct. Closed rest of yr. Crib $2. TV; cable. Heated pool. Cafe nearby. Ck-out 10:30 am. Miniature golf. Picnic tables. Cr cds: MC, V.

🖼 🚫 🐾

Sidney

Pop: 17,657 **Elev:** 956 ft (291 m) **Area code:** 513 **Zip:** 45365

Motels

✔ ★**DAYS INN.** *I-75 & OH 47. 513/492-1104.* 122 rms, 2 story. S $32–$41; D $37–$48; each addl $5; under 18 $1. Crib free. TV; cable. Pool. Playground. Cafe 6 am–9 pm. Ck-out 11 am. Sundries. Cr cds: A, C, D, DS, MC, V.

🖼 🚫 SC 💲

★★**HOLIDAY INN.** *1 mi W on OH 47 & I-75 exit 92. 513/492-1131.* 135 rms, 2 story. S $44–$46; D $49–$54; each addl $5; under 19 free; bridal package plans. Crib free. TV; cable. Pool; wading pool, sauna. Cafe 6:30 am–10 pm; Sat from 7 am; Sun to 9 pm. Rm serv. Bar 11 am–midnight, Fri, Sat to 1 am. Ck-out noon. Coin lndry. Meeting rms. Bellhops. Valet serv. Sundries. Game rm. Cr cds: A, C, D, DS, MC, V.

♿ 🏃 🖼 SC

Steubenville

Settled: 1797 **Pop:** 26,400 **Elev:** 715 ft (217 m) **Area code:** 614 **Zip:** 43952

Motor Hotel

✔ ★ ★**HOLIDAY INN.** *University Blvd, 1½ mi NW on US 22. 614/282-0901.* 121 rms, 2–3 story. No elvtr. S $44–$50; D $50–$56; each addl $5; under 18 free. TV; cable. Heated pool; poolside serv. Cafe 6 am–10 pm. Rm serv from 7 am. Bar 11 am–midnight. Ck-out noon. Coin lndry. Bellhops. Valet serv. Airport transportation. Private patios, balconies. Cr cds: A, C, D, DS, MC, V.

Toledo

Settled: 1817 **Pop:** 354,635 **Elev:** 587 ft (179 m) **Area code:** 419

Motels

✔ ★ ★**COMFORT INN WEST.** *(1426 Reynolds Rd, Maumee 43537) 9 mi SW via US 20. 419/893-2800.* 77 units, 2 story. S $38–$40; D $45–$47; each addl $5; suites $70; under 12 free. Crib $4. TV; cable. Indoor pool; whirlpool. Free coffee. Cafe adj 6:30 am–11 pm. Ck-out 11 am. Meeting rms. Sundries. Some refrigerators. Cr cds: A, C, D, DS, ER, MC, V.

✔ ★ ★**CROSS COUNTRY INN.** *(1704 Tollgate Dr, Maumee 43537) 1 mi S off I-80/90 exit 4. 419/891-0880.* 120 rms, 2 story. S $27.95; D $34.95; each addl $5; under 21 free. Crib free. TV; cable, in-rm movies. Heated pool. Free coffee. Cafe adj open 24 hrs. Ck-out noon. Sundries. Cr cds: A, MC, V.

★**CROWN INN.** *1727 W Alexis Rd (43613). 419/473-1485.* 40 rms, some kits. S $32.95–$36.95; D $35.95–$39.95; each addl $4; suites $66.95–$89.95; kits $39.95–$43.95; under 18 free. Crib $3. TV; cable, in-rm movies. Heated pool; whirlpool. Free continental bkfst. Cafe nearby. Ck-out noon. Meeting rms. Sundries. Some refrigerators, hot tubs. Cr cds: A, C, DS, MC, V. Ⓓ

★**DAYS INN.** *(10667 Fremont Pike, Perrysburg 43551) 8 mi S on US 20 off I-75 exit 193. 419/874-8771.* 125 rms, 2 story. S $39–$44; D $45–$50; each addl $6; suites $44–$50; under 17 $1. Crib free. TV; cable. Pool. Free continental bkfst. Cafe opp open 24 hrs. Rm serv. Ck-out noon. Sundries. X-country ski 6 mi. Cr cds: A, C, D, DS, ER, MC, V.

✔ ★ ★**HAMPTON INN-TOLEDO SOUTH.** *(1409 Reynolds Rd, Maumee 43537) ¼ mi S off I-80/90 exit 4. 419/893-1004.* 131 rms, 4 story. S $36–$40; D $40–$50; suite $60; under 18 free; wkend rates. Crib free. TV; satellite, in-rm movies. Heated pool. Free continental bkfst. Cafe adj open 24 hrs. Rm serv 10 am–8 pm. Ck-out noon. Valet serv. Sundries. Free airport transportation. Cr cds: A, C, D, DS, MC, V.

✔ ★**KNIGHTS INN.** *(1120 Buck Rd, Rossford 43460) 4 mi S off I-75 exit 197. 419/666-9911.* 150 rms, 18 kit. units. S $28.50–$36; D $34–$35; each addl $3; kit. units $38–$44; under 18 free. Crib $3. TV; satellite. Pool. Cafe adj open 24 hrs. Ck-out noon. Meeting rm. Some refrigerators. Cr cds: A, D, MC, V.

✔ ★ ★**L-K COUNTRY HEARTH INN.** *(150 Dussel Dr, Maumee 43537) 1 mi S off I-80/90 exit 4. 419/893-5866.* 120 units, 2 story, 6 suites, 4 kits. S $38–$44; D $44–$50; each addl $6; suites $56–$62; kit. units $46–$52; under 18 free; wkly rates. Crib free. TV; satellite. Pool. Free continental bkfst. Cafe adj open 24 hrs. Rm serv 11 am–10 pm. Ck-out noon. Valet serv. Airport transportation. Some refrigerators. Cr cds: A, C, D, DS, MC, V. Ⓔ

Motor Hotels

✔ ★ ★ **BEST WESTERN EXECUTIVE INN.** *(27441 Helen Dr, Perrysburg 43551) 8 mi S on US 20. 419/874-9181.* 102 rms, 2 story. S $41–$46; D $46–$51; each addl $5; under 12 free. Crib free. TV; satellite, in-rm movies. Indoor pool; whirlpool, sauna. Free coffee. Free continental bkfst Tu–Fri. Cafe adj open 24 hrs. Rm serv. Ck-out noon. Coin lndry. Meeting rms. Valet serv. Sundries. X-country ski 2–5 mi. Cr cds: A, C, D, DS, ER, MC, V.

🏨 🏋 ➰ ⊘ 🐾 SC

✔ ★ **QUALITY INN-NORTH.** *1821 E Manhattan Blvd (43608). 419/729-3901.* 160 rms, 2–4 story. S $28–$38; D $34–$44; each addl $6; under 18 free. Crib free. TV; in-rm movies. Heated pool. Cafe 6 am–2 pm, 5–10 pm; Sun 7 am–7 pm. Rm serv 7 am–2 pm, 5–9 pm. Bar 2 pm–midnight exc Sun. Ck-out 11 am. Coin lndry. Meeting rms. Bellhops. Valet serv. Sundries. Some in-rm steam baths, in-rm whirlpools. Private patios, balconies. Cr cds: A, C, D, DS, ER, MC, V.

🐾 ➰ ⊘ 🐾 SC $

✔ ★ **QUALITY INN-SOUTH.** *(2426 Oregon Rd, Northwood 43619) 3 mi S, 1 blk E of I-75 Wales Rd exit 198. 419/666-2600.* 153 rms, 2 story, 46 kit. units. S $35–$42; D $45–$55; each addl $5; under 16 free; monthly rates. Crib free. TV; cable, in-rm movies. Heated pool; whirlpool. Cafe 6:30 am–2 pm, 5–10 pm; Sat 7:30 am–2:30 pm; Sun 7:30 am–8 pm. Rm serv 7 am–9 pm. Bar 11–1 am; Sun 1–8 pm. Ck-out noon. Coin lndry. Meeting rms. Bellhops. Valet serv. Sundries. Cr cds: A, C, D, DS, ER, MC, V.

➰ ⊘ 🐾 SC

Troy

Pop: 19,086 **Elev:** 820 ft (250 m) **Area code:** 513 **Zip:** 45373

Motel

★ ★ **HOLIDAY INN.** *2 mi SW on OH 55 at I-75 exit 73. 513/335-0021.* 100 rms, 2 story. S $48–$60; D $53–$64; each addl $5; suites, studio rms $48–$90; under 18 free; wkend rates. Crib free. TV; cable. Heated pool; wading pool, poolside serv. Cafe 6 am–10 pm. Rm serv from 7 am. Bar 11–2 am. Ck-out noon. Coin lndry. Meeting rms. Bellhops. Valet serv. Cr cds: A, C, D, DS, MC, V.

🏨 🐾 ➰ SC

Vermilion

Settled: 1808 **Pop:** 11,012 **Elev:** 600 ft (183 m) **Area code:** 216 **Zip:** 44089

Motel

★ **MOTEL PLAZA.** *4645 Liberty Ave. 216/967-3191.* 14 rms. May–Labor Day: S $28–$64; D $36–$70; each addl $4; higher rates fish festival, Memorial, Labor Day wkends; lower rates rest of yr. Crib $2. TV; some B/W. Cafe opp 6 am–11 pm. Ck-out noon. Sundries. Shopping center adj. Cr cds: DS, MC, V.

⊘ 🐾

Wauseon

Pop: 6,173 **Elev:** 757 ft (231 m) **Area code:** 419 **Zip:** 43567

Motels

✔ ★ ★ **BEST WESTERN DEL-MAR.** *(Box 47, RR 3) 2 mi N on OH 108 at OH Tpke exit 3. 419/335-1565.* 40 rms. June–Sep: S $42–$47; D $44–$51; each addl $8; suites $69–$94; under

12 free; lower rates rest of yr. Crib $4. TV; cable. Heated pool. Playground. Free coffee, continental bkfst. Cafe nearby. Ck-out 11 am. Cr cds: A, C, D, DS, MC, V.

★**CHIEF WAUSEON.** *1500 N Shoop Ave, 2 mi N at jct 20A, OH 2; 2 mi SE of OH Tpke exit 3 on N Shoop Ave.* 419/335-8011. 20 rms. S $23–$31; D $25–$34; each addl $3. Crib $2. TV; cable. Free coffee in rms. Cafe nearby. Ck-out 11 am. Sundries. Picnic table. Cr cds: DS, MC, V.

Youngstown

Settled: 1797 **Pop:** 115,436 **Elev:** 861 ft (262 m) **Area code:** 216

Motels

✔ ★★**BEST WESTERN.** *4249 Belmont Ave (44505).* 216/759-3190. 82 rms, 2 story. June–Sep: S $36–$46; D $44–$54; each addl $6; under 12 free; wkly, monthly rates; lower rates rest of yr. Crib $4. TV. Pool. Free continental bkfst. Cafe 4 pm–2 am; also opp open 24 hrs. Rm serv. Bar. Ck-out 11 am. Meeting rm. Valet serv. Sundries. Private patios, balconies. Cr cds: A, C, D, DS, MC, V.

✔ ★**BUDGET LUXURY INN.** *5425 Clarkins Dr (44515), 8 mi NW on OH 46, 1 blk from I-80 Niles exit.* 216/793-9806. 122 rms, 2 story. June–Aug: S $37; D $42; each addl $5; under 18, $1; lower rates rest of yr. Crib free. TV; cable. Pool. Cafe open 24 hrs. Bar. Ck-out noon. Coin lndry. Sundries. Game rm. Rec rm. Cr cds: A, C, D, MC, V.

★**CAMELOT INN.** *4250 Belmont Ave (44505), 5 mi N on OH 193, ¼ mi N of I-80 Belmont exit.* 216/759-0040. 50 rms. Apr–Nov: S $22–$45; D $26–$50; each addl $2; under 17 free; wkly, wkend rates; lower rates rest of yr. TV; satellite, in-rm movies. Whirlpool. Free coffee in rms. Cafe 6–1 am; open 24 hrs in summer. Rm serv. Bar 11–2 am exc Sun. Ck-out 11 am. Sundries. Cr cds: A, C, D, DS, MC, V.

★**DAYS INN.** *(1610 Motor Inn Dr, Girard 44420) 5 mi N at jct OH 193 & I-80.* 216/759-3410. 138 rms, 2 story. S $28–$38; D $33–$43; each addl $5; under 18, $1. Crib free. TV; satellite, in-rm movies. Heated pool. Playground. Cafe open 24 hrs. Bar. Ck-out noon. Coin lndry. Valet serv. Free airport transportation. Cr cds: A, D, DS, MC, V.

✔ ★★**KNIGHTS INN.** *5431 Seventy-Six Dr (44515), 8 mi W on I-80 at OH 46 exit 5.* 216/793-9305. 127 rms, 10 kit. units. S $29.50–$31.50; D $30.50–$37; each addl $3; kit. units $39.50–$45; under 18 free; wkly, monthly rates for kit. units only. Crib $3. TV; cable. Pool. Cafe adj open 24 hrs. Ck-out noon. Meeting rm. Some refrigerators. Cr cds: A, D, MC, V.

★★**RAMADA INN.** *4255 Belmont Ave (44505).* 216/759-7850. 139 rms, 2 story. S $46–$56; D $51–$61; each addl $7; suites $75–$150; under 18 free. Crib free. Indoor pool; poolside serv. Cafe 6 am–11 pm; Sun to 8 pm. Rm serv 9–11:30 am, 1:30–10 pm. Bar 11–2:30 am; entertainment, dancing Tu–Sat. Ck-out noon. Meeting rms. Bellhops. Valet serv. Sundries. Barber, beauty shop. Free airport, bus depot transportation. Cr cds: A, C, D, DS, MC, V.

Motor Hotels

★★**HOLIDAY INN-METRO.** *(1620 Motor Inn Dr, Girard 44420) 5 mi N on OH 193, ¼ mi N of I-80 Belmont Ave exit.* 216/759-3850. 151 rms, 4 story. S $50–$54; D $54–$56; each addl $5; under 18 free. Crib free. TV; cable, in-rm movies. Heated pool; wading pool. Cafe 6:30 am–10 pm; Fri, Sat to 1 am. Rm serv. Bar 11–2 am, Sun to 10 pm; entertainment, dancing Fri, Sat. Ck-out noon. Coin lndry. Meeting rms. Bellhops. Valet serv. Free airport, bus depot transportation. 18-hole golf privileges. Rec rm. Cr cds: A, C, D, DS, MC, V.

★★**HOWARD JOHNSON.** *4055 Belmont Ave (44505). 216/759-3180.* 152 rms, 6 story. S $44–$55; D $54–$68; suites $70–$90; each addl $7; under 18 free. Crib free. TV; satellite, in-rm movies. Indoor pool; whirlpool. Cafe 6 am–midnight. Rm serv 8 am–9 pm. Bar 5 pm–midnight. Ck-out noon. Meeting rms. Valet serv. Sundries. Free airport transportation. Game rm. Some refrigerators. Private balconies. Cr cds: A, C, D, DS, MC, V.

♿ 🐾 🏊 🚫 SC

Zanesville

Settled: 1797 **Pop:** 28,655 **Elev:** 705 ft (215 m) **Area code:** 614 **Zip:** 43701

Motels

★★**HOLIDAY INN.** *4645 E Pike, off I-70 exit 160.* 614/453-0771. 100 rms, 2 story. S $46–$51; D $54–$59; each addl $5; under 20 free. Crib free. TV; cable. Heated pool; whirlpool, sauna, poolside serv. Playground. Free coffee in rms. Cafe 6 am–2 pm, 5–10 pm; Sat, Sun 6 am–10 pm. Rm serv. Bars noon–midnight. Ck-out noon. Coin lndry. Meeting rms. Bellhops. Sundries. Free airport transportation. Tennis, fee. Golf, greens fee, putting green. Racquetball. Game rm. Rec rm. Cr cds: A, C, D, DS, MC, V.

♿ 🐾 🎾 🏊 🚫 🐾 SC

✔★**HOWARD JOHNSON.** *4925 East Pike, 6 mi E at Airport Rd jct I-70 exit 160.* 614/453-0681. 60 rms, 2 story. S $35–$46; D $43–$54; each addl $8; under 18 free. Crib free. TV; cable. Pool. Cafe adj 6 am–10 pm. Ck-out noon. Sundries. Private patios, balconies. Cr cds: A, C, D, DS, ER, MC, V.

🐾 🏊 🚫 🐾 SC

✔★**TRAVELODGE.** *58 N 6th St, 1 blk N of US 22, 40.* 614/453-0611. 54 rms, 3 story. S $32–$36; D $39–$45; each addl $3–$5; under 17 free. Crib free. TV; cable. Free coffee in rm. Cafe nearby. Ck-out noon. Coin lndry. Meeting rm. Sundries. Exercise equipt; weights, bicycles. Some refrigerators. Balconies. Cr cds: A, C, D, DS, ER, MC, V.

🏃 🚫 🐾 SC $

Pennsylvania

Population: 11,864,751

Land area: 44,892 sq mi (116,270 sq km)

Elevation: 0–3,213 ft (0–979 m)

Highest point: Mt Davis (Somerset Co)

Entered Union: Second of original 13 states (December 12, 1787)

Capital: Harrisburg

Motto: Virtue, Liberty and Independence

Nickname: Keystone State

State flower: Mountain laurel

State bird: Ruffed grouse

State tree: Eastern hemlock

State fair: Mid-January, 1989 in Harrisburg

Time zone: Eastern

Interstate Highway System

The following alphabetical listing of Pennsylvania towns in *Mobil Travel Guide* shows that these cities are within 10 miles (16 kilometers) of the indicated Interstate highways. A highway map should, however, be checked for the nearest exit.

INTERSTATE 70: Bedford, Breezewood, Donegal, Greensburg, New Stanton, Somerset, Washington.

INTERSTATE 76: Beaver Falls, Bedford, Breezewood, Bristol, Carlisle, Chambersburg, Denver/Adamstown, Donegal, Downington, Ephrata, Gettysburg, Greensburg, Harrisburg, Hershey, Jenkintown, King of Prussia, Lancaster, Lebanon, Ligonier, New Castle, New Stanton, Norristown, Philadelphia, Pittsburgh, Pottstown, Reading, Somerset, Valley Forge National Historical Park, Willow Grove.

INTERSTATE 78: Allentown, Bethlehem, Easton, Hamburg, Kutztown, Lebanon, Shartlesville.

INTERSTATE 79: Conneaut Lake, Edinboro, Erie, Harmony, Meadville, Mercer, Pittsburgh, Washington.

INTERSTATE 80: Bellefonte, Bloomsburg, Brookville, Clarion, Clearfield, Danville, Du Bois, Hazleton, Lewisburg, Lock Haven, Mercer, Mount Pocono, Sharon, Shawnee on Delaware, Stroudsburg, Tannersville, White Haven.

INTERSTATE 81: Ashland, Carlisle, Chambersburg, Harrisburg, Hazleton, Scranton, Waynesboro, Wilkes-Barre.

INTERSTATE 83: Harrisburg, York.

INTERSTATE 84: Milford, Scranton.

INTERSTATE 90: Erie, North East.

INTERSTATE 95: Bristol, Philadelphia.

Weather Statistics*

	WINTER	SPRING	SUMMER	FALL
Erie	26°F (-3°C)	44°F (7°C)	67°F (19°C)	51°F (11°C)
Harrisburg	32°F (0°C)	52°F (11°C)	74°F (23°C)	56°F (13°C)
Philadelphia	34°F (1°C)	53°F (12°C)	75°F (24°C)	57°F (14°C)
Pittsburgh	32°F (0°C)	52°F (11°C)	73°F (23°C)	56°F (13°C)

*Average mean temperatures are usually listed for the entire state. Averages for specific regions, or cities that represent specific regions, are given if significant differences exist.

Despite its close proximity to the Atlantic Ocean, Pennsylvania has a continental climate since the prevailing winds are from the west. This makes for extreme heat and cold although not as marked as in the central states. There are only minor variations throughout the state caused by altitude and geographical features. The frost-free period is longest in southeastern Pennsylvania, the Ohio and Monongahela river valleys, and the region bordering Lake Erie. The higher lands have only three to five months free from frost. The rainfall is usually adequate for temperate zone crops.

Visitor Information

Pennsylvania Division of Travel Marketing, Department of Commerce, 453 Forum Building, Harrisburg 17120; 717/787-5453 or 800/VISIT PA, ext 274, has numerous pamphlets on vacationing, historical tours, farm vacations, skiing, campgrounds, resorts, etc. For a free vacation guide, write the bureau, Dept PR.

There are eight state-run traveler information centers in Pennsylvania; visitors who stop by will find information and brochures most helpful in planning stops at points of interest. Their locations are as follows: in Cumberland Co, off I-81 northbound at the first rest area N of Newville Interchange (Rte 233); in Delaware Co, off I-95 northbound at first rest area N of DE border (near Marcus Hook, PA); in Crawford Co, off I-79 southbound near Edinboro, PA; in Fulton Co, off I-70 northbound at first rest area N of MD border; in Mercer Co, off I-80 eastbound at first rest area E of OH border; also in Fulton County, off PA Tpke east and westbound (between exits 12 & 13) at the Howard Johnson service area; in Susquehanna Co, off I-81 southbound at first rest area S of NY border; and in York Co, off I-83 northbound at first rest area N of MD border. (June–Sep, 8 am–6 pm; Oct–May, 8 am–5 pm)

Room Rate Information

The following major city has higher room rates for two (double) than indicated on the cover of this Guide. However, the lodgings listed in this city offer a good value when compared to others of their type in the area.

Philadelphia $90

Allentown

Founded: 1762 **Pop:** 103,758 **Elev:** 364 ft (111 m) **Area code:** 215

Motels

✔ ★**ALLENWOOD.** *(RD Box 4, 18104) 3 mi W; from jct US 22, PA 309 exit 33, & 1/2 mi E on US 22, then ¾ mi S on PA 309, W on Tilghman St to light, then ¾ mi N on Hausman Rd, turn left at dead end.* 215/395-3707. 22 rms. S, D, studio rms $36; each addl $3. Crib free. TV; cable. Cafe nearby. Ck-out noon. Cr cds: MC, V.

🐾

✔ ★**DAYS INN.** *15th St & PA 22 (18103).* 215/435-7880. 84 rms, 4 story. S $33.99–$35.99; D $39.99–$45.99; each addl $4; under 18, $1. Crib $3. TV; cable. Free continental bkfst. Cafe nearby. Ck-out 11 am. Downhill ski 19 mi. Cr cds: A, D, DS, MC, V.

🚫 🐾 🚫 🚫 SC

Altoona

Founded: 1849 **Pop:** 57,078 **Elev:** 1,170 ft (357 m) **Area code:** 814

Motor Hotel

★★★**SHERATON.** *1 Sheraton Dr (16601), 5 mi S on US 220. 814/946-1631.* 219 rms, 2–3 story. Jan–May: S $50–$53; D $50–$72; each addl $8; suites $138–$146; studio rms $69–$76; under 18 free; some wkend rates; higher rates: football games, ski season; lower rates rest of yr. Crib $3. TV; cable, in-rm movies. Indoor pool; wading pool, lifeguard. Cafe 6:30 am–2:30 pm, 5:30–10 pm; Sat to 11 pm. Rm serv. Bar 11–2 am; entertainment, dancing exc Sun. Ck-out noon. Meeting rms. Bellhops. Valet serv. Sundries. Airport transportation. 18-hole golf privileges. Downhill ski 20 mi. Exercise rm: instructor, weights, bicycles, whirlpool, sauna. Racquetball. Rec rm. In-rm steam baths. Cr cds: A, C, D, ER, MC, V. Ⓓ Ⓕ

🛄 🐾 🏂 🛅 🏊 🏃 SC

Beaver Falls

Founded: 1806 **Pop:** 12,525 **Elev:** 800 ft (244 m) **Area code:** 412 **Zip:** 15010

Motels

★**BEAVER VALLEY.** *Big Beaver Blvd, on SR 18, ½ mi N of Tpke exit 2. 412/843-0630.* 27 units. S $30.75–$38.16; D $43.46–$49.82; each addl $3; kit. units $39.22–$51.95; wkly rates. Crib free. TV; cable. Ck-out noon. Cr cds: A, C, D, DS, MC, V.

🛄 🐾 🕥 SC

✔ ★★**BEST WESTERN CONLEY'S MOTOR INN.** *Big Beaver Blvd, on SR 18, ¼ mi S of Tpke exit 2. 412/843-9300.* 54 rms, 4 kits. S $45; D $55; each addl $8; under 12 free; wkly, monthly rates. TV; cable. Pool; lifeguard. Free full bkfst. Cafe 6:30 am–10 pm. Bar 6 pm–2 am. Ck-out noon. Meeting rms. Sundries. Cr cds: A, C, D, MC, V.

🏊 Ⓧ SC

Bedford

Settled: 1751 **Pop:** 3,326 **Elev:** 1,106 ft (337 m) **Area code:** 814 **Zip:** 15522

Motels

✔ ★★**BEST WESTERN.** *(RD 2, Box 33B) 2 mi N via US 220 Business, PA Tpke exit 11. 814/623-9006.* 108 rms, 2 story. S $30–$45; D $36–$50; each addl $6; under 12 free. Crib free. TV; cable. Pool; sauna, poolside serv, lifeguard. Cafe 6:30 am–9 pm. Rm serv. Bar 4 pm–midnight. Ck-out noon. Meeting rms. Game rm. Cr cds: A, C, D, DS, MC, V.

🛄 🐾 🏊 Ⓧ SC

★**BUDGET MOTOR LODGE.** *(RD 2) 2¼ mi N on US 220 Business, ¼ mi S of PA Tpke exit 11. 814/623-5111.* 35 rms. S $30–$36; D $38–$51; each addl $4.50; family rates; golf, wkend plans. Crib $3. TV; cable. Pool; wading pool, lifeguard. Playground. Cafe adj 7 am–9 pm. Ck-out 11 am. Meeting rm. Sundries. Airport, bus depot transportation. Downhill ski 18 mi; x-country ski 15 mi. Lawn games. Basketball court. Picnic tables, grill. Cr cds: A, C, D, MC, V.

🐾 🏂 🏊 SC Ⓢ

✔ ★★**QUALITY INN.** *(RD 2, Box 171) 2 mi N on US 220 Business, 1 blk N of PA Tpke exit 11. 814/623-5188.* 49 rms. S $34–$42; D $40–$46; each addl $6; under 16 free. Crib $4. TV; cable. Pool. Cafe 7 am–10 pm. Bar 11 am–11 pm. Ck-out 11 am. Meeting rms. Valet serv. Downhill ski 20 mi. Cr cds: A, C, D, MC, V.

🐾 🏂 🏊 Ⓧ SC

Bethlehem

Founded: 1741 **Pop:** 70,419 **Elev:** 340 ft (104 m) **Area code:** 215

Motels

✔ ★★**COMFORT INN.** *3191 Highfield Dr (18017), US 22 exit 191.* *215/865-6300.* 116 rms, 2½ story. S $33.95–$52.95; D $41.95–$62.95; each addl $6; under 16 free; ski plan. Crib free. TV; cable. Free continental bkfst. Cafe adj. Bar noon–2 am; entertainment. Ck-out noon. Meeting rms. Valet serv. Cr cds: A, C, D, DS, ER, MC, V.

 SC

✔ ★★**ECONO LODGE.** *US 22 (18018) at Airport Rd S exit.* *215/867-8681.* 119 rms. S $29.95–$34.95; D $38.95–$39.95; each addl $5; under 12 free. Crib free. TV; cable, free in-rm movies. Pool; lifeguard. Playground. Free continental bkfst. Cafe 7–2 am. Serv bar. Ck-out noon. Meeting rm. Valet serv. Free airport transportation 9 am–5 pm. Tennis. Cr cds: A, C, D, MC, V.

SC

Hotel

★★★**BETHLEHEM.** *437 Main St (18018).* *215/867-3711.* 126 rms, 9 story, 6 kits. S $45–$67; D $50–$77; each addl $10; suites $85–$137; kit. units $65; studio rms $45; under 13 free. Crib free. TV; cable, in-rm movies. Cafe 6:30 am–10:30 pm. Bar 11:30–2 am. Ck-out 11 am. Meeting rms. Shopping arcade. Free garage parking. Free airport, RR station, bus depot transportation. Refrigerators. Cr cds: A, C, D, MC, V. Ⓔ

Bloomsburg

Settled: 1802 **Pop:** 11,717 **Elev:** 530 ft (162 m) **Area code:** 717 **Zip:** 17815

Motel

✔ ★★**QUALITY INN-BUCKHORN PLAZA.** *US 80 at Buckhorn exit 34.* *717/784-5300.* 120 rms, 2 story. S $44.90–$57.90; D $42.90–$55.90; each addl $5; under 16 free. Crib $5. TV; cable. Cafe adj open 24 hrs. Bar 11–2 am. Ck-out noon. Sundries. Balconies. Cr cds: A, C, D, ER, MC, V.

SC $

Hotel

✔ ★**MAGEE.** *(Box 149) 20 W Main St.* *717/784-3200.* 52 rms, 3 story. S $25–$55; D $30–$65; each addl $5; under 18 free. TV. Cafe 7 am–9 pm; Fri, Sat to 10 pm; Sun to 8 pm. Bar 11–2 am; Sun to 11 pm. Ck-out noon. Meeting rms. Same owner over 60 yrs. Cr cds: A, C, D, MC, V. Ⓓ Ⓔ

Breezewood

Pop: 180 (est) **Elev:** 1,356 ft (413 m) **Area code:** 814 **Zip:** 15533

Motels

★★**BEST WESTERN PLAZA MOTOR LODGE.** *On US 30 at jct I-70, 1 blk W of PA Tpke exit 12.* *814/735-4352.* 89 rms, 2 story. S $28; D $35; each addl $6. Crib $6. TV; cable. Pool; lifeguard. Cafe 7 am–11 pm. Ck-out 11 am. Meeting rm. Sundries. Cr cds: A, C, D, DS, MC, V.

✔ ★★**PENN AIRE.** *½ mi W of PA Tpke exit 12.* *814/735-4351.* 31 rms. Mid-Apr–Oct: S $32–$37; D $33–$38; each addl $3; suites $48–$69; family rates; lower rates rest of yr. Crib $3. TV; cable. Pool. Cafe adj 6 am–11 pm. Ck-out 11 am. Meeting rm. Back from hwy. Cr cds: A, C, D, MC, V. Ⓕ

✔ ★★**QUALITY INN BREEZE MANOR.** *(Box 36, Rte 1) E on US 30, 1 blk E of I-70 & PA Tpke exit 12.* *814/735-4311.* 50 rms, 1–2 story. Mar–Nov: S $37–$41; D $41–$51; each addl $3;

family rates; lower rates rest of yr. Crib $3. TV; cable. Heated pool; wading pool, lifeguard. Playground. Cafe opp open 24 hrs. Ck-out noon. Sundries. Cr cds: A, C, D, DS, ER, MC, V.

★**WILTSHIRE.** *(Box 1, Star Rte 2) On US 30, 1 blk W of I-70, ⅛ mi W of PA Tpke exit 12. 814/735-4361.* 12 rms. May–Oct: S $26–$30; D $32–$34; each addl $4; family rates; slightly lower rates rest of yr. Crib free. TV; cable. Free coffee in rm. Cafe opp 7 am–11 pm. Ck-out 11 am. Sundries. Cr cds: A, MC, V.

Brookville

Settled: 1801 **Pop:** 4,568 **Elev:** 1,269 ft (387 m) **Area code:** 814 **Zip:** 15825

Motels

✔ ★★**DAYS INN OF BROOKVILLE.** *1 mi W via US 322, PA 36, S of I-80 exit 13. 814/849-8001.* 134 rms, 3 story. S, D $35–$40; each addl $5; under 18 $1; higher rates hunting season. Crib free. TV; cable. Heated pool; wading pool, poolside serv, lifeguard. Cafe 6 am–2 pm, 4–10 pm; winter from 7 am. Rm serv. Bar 4 pm–2 am, Sun to 7 pm. Ck-out noon. Coin lndry. X-country ski 17 mi. Game rm. Cr cds: A, D, DS, MC, V.

★**ECONO LODGE.** *(Box 151, RD 5) ¼ mi W via US 322, PA 36, off I-80 exit 13. 814/849-8381.* 68 rms, 3 story. S $29.99–$39.99; D $37.99–$47.99; each addl $5; under 12 free; higher rates hunting season. Crib free. TV; cable. Pool; lifeguard. Free coffee in lobby. Cafe adj 7 am–10 pm. Ck-out noon. Coin lndry. Meeting rm. Sundries. X-country ski 16 mi. Private patios, balconies. Cr cds: A, C, D, DS, MC, V.

Carlisle

Settled: 1720 **Pop:** 18,314 **Elev:** 478 ft (146 m) **Area code:** 717 **Zip:** 17013

Motels

✔ ★★**HOWARD JOHNSON.** *1255 Harrisburg Pike (US 11), jct I-81 N exit 17W. 717/243-6000.* 96 rms, 2 story. May–Oct: S $39–$45; D $44–$58; each addl $6; under 18 free; lower rates rest of yr. Crib free. TV. Pool; lifeguard. Cafe open 24 hrs. Ck-out noon. Coin lndry. Valet serv. Sundries. Private patios, balconies. Cr cds: A, C, D, DS, MC, V.

✔ ★**KENMAR.** *(RD 1, Newburg 17240) At PA Tpke exit 15. 717/423-5915.* 15 rms. S $35–$38; D $42–$48; each addl $6. Crib $2. TV; satellite. Pool. Free continental bkfst. Ck-out 11 am. Lawn games. Cr cds: A, D, MC, V.

Chambersburg

Settled: 1730 **Pop:** 16,174 **Elev:** 621 ft (189 m) **Area code:** 717 **Zip:** 17201

Motels

★**ELBY'S CHAMBERSBURG MOTOR INN.** *30 Falling Spring Rd, I-81 exit 6. 717/263-1288; res: call collect.* 107 rms, 3 story. S $34; D $41; each addl $5; suites $50; under 17 free. Crib free. TV; cable. Cafe 6 am–11 pm. Ck-out 11 am. Meeting rms. YMCA & golf privileges. Downhill ski 20 mi. Game rm. Cr cds: A, C, D, DS, MC, V.

✔ ★★★**HOLIDAY INN.** *Wayne Ave (PA 316) at I-81 exit 5. 717/263-3400.* 137 rms, 2 story. S $42–$50; D $53–$60; each addl $7; under 18 free. Crib free. TV; cable, in-rm movies. Pool; wading pool, poolside serv, lifeguard. Playground. Cafe 6 am–2 pm, 5–10 pm. Rm serv. Bar 4 pm–midnight. Ck-out noon. Meeting rms. Valet serv. Downhill ski 20 mi. Cr cds: A, C, D, DS, MC, V.

♿ 🐾 🍴 🏊 🚭 Ⓝ SC

★ ★ ★HOWARD JOHNSON LODGE. *1123 Lincoln Way E (US 30), just off I-81 exit 6.* *717/263-9191.* 132 rms, 3 story. S $46–$53; D $52–$60; each addl $7; under 18 free. Crib free. TV; cable. Indoor pool; sauna. Free coffee in rms. Cafe 6 am–11 pm; Fri & Sat open 24 hrs. Bar 11–2 am; Sun 2 pm–midnight. Ck-out noon. Meeting rms. Valet serv. Sundries. Downhill ski 20 mi. Refrigerators. Private patios, balconies. Cr cds: A, C, D, DS, MC, V.

🏊 🍴 🚭 Ⓝ SC

✔ ★ ★TRAVELODGE. *565 Lincoln Way E. 717/264-4187.* 50 rms, 3 story. S $39–$45; D $44–$59; each addl $6; under 18 free. Crib free. TV. Cafe 6:30 am–2 pm, 4:30–9:30 pm. Rm serv. Bar 11 am–2 pm, 4:30–11 pm; Sun 1–2 pm, 5–9:30 pm. Ck-out noon. Meeting rm. Sundries. Free local airport transportation. Some balconies. Cr cds: A, C, D, DS, ER, MC, V.

♿ 🐾 🍴 🚭 Ⓝ SC $

Clarion

Founded: 1839 **Pop:** 6,198 **Elev:** 1,491 ft (454 m) **Area code:** 814 **Zip:** 16214

Motels

✔ ★ ★DAYS INN. *1½ mi S at jct PA 68, I-80 exit 9. 814/226-8682.* 160 rms, 2 story. S $40–$50; D $45–$55; each addl $5; under 18 free; golf, ski plans; higher rates Autumn Leaf Festival, hunting season. Crib free. TV. Heated pool; poolside serv, lifeguard. Cafe 7 am–2 pm, 5–10 pm. Rm serv. Bar 4 pm–2 am; entertainment, dancing. Ck-out noon. Coin lndry. Meeting rms. Sundries. Cr cds: A, C, D, MC, V.

♿ 🐾 🍴 🏊 🚭 Ⓝ SC $

✔ ★KNIGHTS INN. *(RD 3) I-80 exit 9. 814/226-4550.* 99 rms, 9 kits. S $33–$38; D $34–$44; each addl $5; kit. units $40–$44; wkly, monthly rates; under 18 free. Crib $3. TV; cable. Pool; lifeguard. Cafe adj 6 am–10 pm. Ck-out noon. Meeting rm. Cr cds: A, C, D, MC, V.

🐾 🍴 🚭 Ⓝ SC

Danville

Pop: 5,239 **Elev:** 490 ft (149 m) **Area code:** 717 **Zip:** 17821

Motel

✔ ★ ★BEST WESTERN. *Keystone Shortway, I-80 exit 33. 717/275-4640.* 121 rms, 2 story. June–Sep: S $31.50–$37.50; D $39.50–$47.50; each addl $4; under 18 free; lower rates rest of yr. Crib free. TV; cable. Pool; lifeguard. Cafe 7 am–2 pm, 4–10 pm. Bar 4 pm–2 am; entertainment, dancing in season exc Sun. Ck-out noon. Meeting rms. Cr cds: A, C, D, MC, V.

♿ 🐾 🍴 🚭 SC $

Inn

✔ ★ ★PINE BARN. *645 Bloom St. 717/275-2071.* 69 rms in inn, motel, 1–2 story; 6 rms in adjoining guest house. S $34–$45; D $38–$60; guest house S $19; D $21; each addl $2; under 16 free. Crib $1. TV; cable. Cafe 7 am–10 pm; Sun 8 am–8 pm. Rm serv. Bar 11 am–midnight; Sun from 1 pm. Ck-out 1 pm. Meeting rms. Valet serv. Sundries. Geisinger Medical Center adj. Cr cds: A, C, D, DS, MC, V.

Du Bois

Settled: 1865 **Pop:** 9,290 **Elev:** 1,420 ft (433 m) **Area code:** 814 **Zip:** 15801

Motels

✔★**BEST WESTERN-PENN ROSE MOTOR INN.** *82 N Park Place, 1 mi N at jct US 219, 255.* 814/371-6200. 49 rms, 3 story. Mid-May–mid-Oct: S $35–$40; D $43–$48; each addl $5; suite $54; under 18 free; lower rates rest of yr. Crib free. TV; cable. Playground. Free continental bkfst in lobby. Cafe nearby. Ck-out noon. Meeting rms. Sundries. Game rm. Tennis privileges adj. Golf privileges. Picnic tables. Cr cds: A, C, D, DS, MC, V.

★★**HOLIDAY INN.** *½ mi N on US 219 at I-80 exit 16.* 814/371-5100. 164 rms, 2 story. S $49–$62; D $54–$67; each addl $5; studio rms $49; under 18 free. TV; cable, in-rm movies. Pool; wading pool, poolside serv, lifeguard. Cafe 7 am–2 pm, 5–10 pm. Rm serv. Bar 4 pm–2 am exc Sun; entertainment, dancing. Ck-out noon. Coin lndry. Meeting rms. Bellhops. Free airport transportation. Cr cds: A, C, D, DS, MC, V.

Erie

Settled: 1753 **Pop:** 119,123 **Elev:** 744 ft (227 m) **Area code:** 814

Motels

★★**BEST WESTERN PRESQUE ISLE COUNTRY INN.** *(6467 Sterrettania Rd, Fairview 16415) 8½ mi W via I-90, exit 5.* 814/838-7647. 130 rms, 2 story. June–early Sep: S $46–$68; D $54–$78; each addl $6; under 12 free; lower rates rest of yr. Crib $6. TV; satellite. Heated pool; lifeguard. Cafe 6 am–2 pm, 5–10 pm. Rm serv. Bar 5 pm–2 am; entertainment, dancing. Ck-out noon. Meeting rms. Valet serv. Free airport, RR station, bus depot transportation by appt. Downhill/x-country ski 15 mi. Some refrigerators. Near public golf course. Cr cds: A, C, D, DS, MC, V.

✔★★**DAYS INN.** *7400 Schultz Rd (16509), I-90 & Rte 97.* 814/868-8521. 110 units, 4 story. Apr–Sep: S $46–$50; D $52–$65; each addl $5; suites $85–$125; studio rm $46–$50; under 18 free; ski plans; lower rates rest of yr. TV; cable. Heated pool. Free continental bkfst. Cafe adj open 24 hrs. Ck-out noon. Meeting rms. Downhill/x-country ski 15 mi. Some refrigerators. Cr cds: A, D, MC, V. Ⓔ Ⓕ

★**GLASS HOUSE INN.** *3202 W 26th St (16506).* 814/833-7751. 30 rms. Late May–Labor Day: S, D $42–$66; each addl $5; family rates; lower rates rest of yr. Crib $3. TV; cable. Heated pool; sauna, lifeguard. Cafe nearby. Ck-out 11 am. Sundries. Downhill/x-country ski 20 mi. Cr cds: A, C, D, MC, V.

✔★**KNIGHTS INN.** *7455 Schultz Rd (16509), on PA 97 at I-90 exit 7.* 814/868-0879. 105 rms. S $32.50; D $38.50; each addl $6; under 18 free. Crib $3. Pool privileges. TV; cable. Free coffee. Cafe adj 6:30 am–11:30 pm. Ck-out noon. Meeting rm. Refrigerators. Cr cds: A, C, D, MC, V.

✔★★★**RAMADA INN.** *6101 Wattsburg Rd (16509), exit 8 off I-90 to PA 8.* 814/825-3100. 122 rms, 2 story. July–Sep: S $46–$52; D $54–$61; each addl $8; suites $65–$90; under 18 free; ski, wkend plans; lower rates rest of yr. Crib free. TV; cable. Heated pool; wading pool, lifeguard. Cafe 6:30 am–10 pm. Rm serv. Bar 2 pm–midnight, Sun from noon; entertainment, dancing Wed, Fri, Sat. Ck-out noon. Meeting rms. Sundries. Downhill ski 15 mi. Game rm. Cr cds: A, C, D, ER, MC, V.

★**SCOTT'S.** *2930 W 6th St (PA 832) (16505).* 814/838-1961. 58 rms, 1–2 story, 14 kits. (no equipt). June–Labor Day: S, D $48–$79; each addl $5; kit. units $75–$90; lower rates rest of yr. Crib $5. TV; cable. Playground. Heated pool; wading pool, lifeguard. Ck-out 11 am. Downhill/x-country ski 20 mi. Lawn games. Cr cds: A, C, D, MC, V.

Gettysburg

Founded: 1798 Pop: 7,194 Elev: 560 ft (171 m) Area code: 717 Zip: 17325

Motels

✔ ★**ECONO LODGE.** *(RD 1) 945 Baltimore Pike. 717/334-6715.* 40 rms, 2 story. S $38–$48; D $40–$60; each addl $3. Crib $4. TV. Pool; lifeguard. Cafe 11 am–10 pm. Bar to 2 am. Ck-out 11 am. Downhill ski 8 mi. Cr cds: A, C, D, DS, MC, V.

★**HOMESTEAD MOTOR LODGE.** *1650 York Rd (US 30). 717/334-3866.* 10 rms. June–Oct: S $40–$50; D $45–$60; each addl $4; higher rates: Memorial Day, July 4, parents wkend at college; lower rates rest of yr. Closed Dec–Feb. TV; cable. Cafe nearby. Ck-out 10 am. Cr cds: DS, MC, V.

✔ ★**PERFECT REST.** *2450 Emmitsburg Rd, at edge of National Military Park. 717/334-1345.* 25 rms. June–Aug: S, D $48–$58; suites $75–$84; higher rates: spring & fall wkends, college & area events; lower rates early Apr–May & Sep–Oct. Closed rest of yr. Crib $3. TV. Pool. Cafe nearby. Ck-out 11 am. Same owner over 26 yrs. Cr cds: MC, V.

✔ ★ ★**QUALITY INN LARSON'S.** *401 Buford Ave. 717/334-3141.* 41 rms. Mid-June–early Sep: S $44–$60; D $50–$60; each addl $3; under 17 free; lower rates rest of yr. Crib $1. TV. Pool. Cafe 7 am–9 pm. Bar noon–9 pm. Ck-out noon. Bellhops. Bus depot transportation. Putting green. Downhill ski 6 mi. General Lee's Headquarters museum adj. Cr cds: A, C, D, DS, ER, MC, V. ①

Harrisburg

Settled: 1718 Pop: 53,264 Elev: 360 ft (110 m) Area code: 717

Motels

✔ ★ ★**BEST WESTERN.** *(17112) 7 mi NE on I-81, exit 26 (Linglestown). 717/652-7180.* 48 rms, 2 story. S $38–$77; D $46–$80; each addl $3; under 13 free. Crib $4. TV; cable. Cafe 6:30 am–9 pm. Bar 11 am–11 pm. Ck-out 11 am. Meeting rms. Sundries. Airport, RR station, bus depot transportation. Cr cds: A, C, D, DS, MC, V.

✔ ★ ★**EXCELLENT INN.** *4125 N Front St (17110). 717/233-5891.* 58 rms, 2 story. S $34–$42; D $44–$52; each addl $5; under 12 free. Crib free. TV; cable, in-rm movies. Pool; lifeguard. Cafe 7 am–10 pm exc Sun. Bar 11–2 am. Ck-out noon. Meeting rms. Sundries. Airport, RR station, bus depot transportation. Cr cds: A, C, D, MC, V.

★**RED ROOF INN.** *950 Eisenhower Blvd (17111). 717/939-1331.* 111 rms, 2 story. S $32.95–$34.95; D $38.95–$40.95; each addl $2. Crib free. TV. Cafe adj open 24 hrs. Ck-out noon. Airport, RR station, bus depot transportation. Cr cds: A, C, D, DS, MC, V.

Hershey

Founded: 1903 Pop: 13,249 Elev: 420 ft (128 m) Area code: 717 Zip: 17033

Motels

✔ ★**BRUWIN.** *150 E Governor Rd (US 322E). 717/533-2591.* 12 rms. Memorial Day–Labor Day: S $37–$41; D $50–$53; each addl $4; lower rates rest of yr. TV; cable. Cafe nearby. Ck-out 11 am. Sundries. Gift shop. Airport, RR station, bus depot transportation. 18-hole golf privileges, greens fee $11–$12. Picnic tables. Cr cds: MC, V.

✔ ★★**PALMYRA.** *(1071 East Main St, Palmyra 17078) 4 mi E on US 422. 717/838-1324.* 30 rms. Mid-June–Labor Day: S $48–$76; D $52–$76; each addl $5; kit. units $64–$80; higher rates antique auto show; lower rates rest of yr. Crib $5. TV; cable. Heated pool; lifeguard. Playground. Cafe nearby. Ck-out 11 am. Cr cds: A, MC, V.

Indiana

Founded: 1805 **Pop:** 16,051 **Elev:** 1,310 ft (399 m) **Area code:** 412 **Zip:** 15701

Motel

✔ ★★**BEST WESTERN UNIVERSITY INN.** *1545 Wayne Ave. 412/349-9620.* 107 rms, 2 story. S $41; D $46.50; studio rms $38–$46; each addl $5; suites $69; under 12 free; higher rates special university events. Crib free. TV; cable. Heated pool. Cafe 6:30 am–1:30 pm, 5–9 pm. Bar 4 pm–midnight. Ck-out noon. Meeting rms. Cr cds: A, C, D, DS, MC, V.

Jim Thorpe

Settled: 1815 **Pop:** 5,263 **Elev:** 600 ft (183 m) **Area code:** 717 **Zip:** 18229

Motel

✔ ★**COUNTRY.** *4 mi NE, just off PA 903. 717/325-2214.* 14 units. S $36–$40; D $38–$54; kit. unit $61; each addl $7; higher rates wkends. TV. Pool. Cafe 5–10 pm. Bar. Ck-out noon. Located in mountains, on 9 wooded acres (4 hectares). Antique furnishings. Fishing, horseback riding, whitewater rafting nearby. Cr cds: A, MC, V.

King of Prussia

Settled: early 1700s **Pop:** 18,200 (est) **Elev:** 200 ft (61 m) **Area code:** 215 **Zip:** 19406

Motel

✔ ★**McINTOSH.** *260 N Gulph Rd. 215/768-9500.* 212 rms, 7 story. S $35.95; D $42.95; each addl $3; higher rates wkends. Crib $3. TV. Cafe adj open 24 hrs. Ck-out 11 am. Valet serv Mon–Fri. Cr cds: A, MC, V. Ⓔ

Lancaster

Settled: 1721 **Pop:** 54,725 **Elev:** 380 ft (116 m) **Area code:** 717

Motels

✔ ★**QUIET HAVEN.** *(2556 Siegrist Rd, Ronks 17572) 5½ mi E, just off PA 896 between US 30 & PA 340. 717/397-6231.* 15 rms. June–Oct: D $44–$48; each addl $3; varied lower rates rest of yr. Crib $2. TV. Cafe nearby. Ck-out 11 am. Sundries. Airport, RR station, bus depot transportation.

✔ ★**RED CABOOSE.** *(Box 102, Strasburg 17579) On railroad siding, 6 mi E at jct PA 896, 741. 717/687-6646.* 45 units, 7 kits. April–Oct: S $48–$50; D $52–$62; each addl $3; lower rates rest of yr. Crib $3. TV. Playground. Cafe 8 am–8 pm in season. Ck-out 10:30 am. Shopping arcade. Converted railroad cabooses; ice cream parlor car; Amish buggy rides. Cr cds: A, DS, MC, V.

✔ ★**1722 MOTOR LODGE.** *1722 Old Philadelphia Pike (17602).* 717/397-4791. 21 rms. Late June–Labor Day: S, D $49; each addl $5; varied lower rates rest of yr. Crib $4. TV. Playground. Free continental bkfst. Cafe nearby. Ck-out 11 am. Coin lndry. Sundries. Lawn games. Picnic tables. Cr cds: A, MC, V.

✔ ★**WEATHERVANE.** *(15 Eastbrook Rd, Ronks 17572)* Jct US 30 & PA 896. 717/397-3398. 34 rms. May–Oct: S $40–$60; D $45–$65; each addl $5; lower rates rest of yr. TV; cable. Playground. Cafe adj 10:30 am–11 pm. Rm serv. Ck-out 11 am. Picnic tables. Cr cds: MC, V.

Lewisburg

Settled: 1785 **Pop:** 5,407 **Elev:** 460 ft (140 m) **Area code:** 717 **Zip:** 17837

Motels

★**COLONIAL CREST.** *(Box 527)* 1¼ mi S on US 15. 717/523-1106. 33 rms, 2 story. S $30–$34; D $34–$42; each addl $3; under 5 free. Crib free. TV. Cafe 7 am–9 pm. Bar 11–2:30 am; dancing. Ck-out 11 am. Meeting rms. Sundries. Par 3, 9-hole golf. Cr cds: A, D, DS, MC, V.

✔ ★ ★**UNIVERSITY MOTOR INN.** *US 15, 1 blk S of jct PA 192.* 717/523-1171. 108 rms, 2 story. S $35–$45; D $38–$51; each addl $4–$5; under 16 free. Crib free. TV; cable. Pool; lifeguard. Cafe 7 am–9 pm. Bar 3 pm–2 am. Ck-out noon. Cr cds: A, C, D, DS, MC, V.

Ligonier

Founded: 1816 **Pop:** 1,917 **Elev:** 1,200 ft (366 m) **Area code:** 412 **Zip:** 15658

Motels

★ ★**FORT LIGONIER MOTOR LODGE.** *(US 30 E)* 2 blks S on US 30, jct PA 711. 412/238-6677. 35 rms, 2 story. May–Oct: S $45; D $50; under 12 free; higher rates special events; lower rates rest of yr. Crib $4. TV; cable. Pool. Free coffee. Cafe nearby. Ck-out 11 am. Sundries. Downhill/x-country ski 7 mi. Picnic tables. Trout stream. Cr cds: A, MC, V. Ⓔ

✔ ★ ★**LORD LIGONIER INN.** *Loyalhanna St.* 412/238-9545. 55 rms, 3 story. S $38–$52; D $44–$58; each addl $6; under 19 free; ski plans; wkly rates. Crib free. TV; cable. Pool; lifeguard. Cafe 7 am–8 pm; Fri, Sat to 10 pm. Rm serv 8 am–7 pm. Bar noon–2 am; entertainment, dancing Fri, Sat. Ck-out noon. Meeting rms. Sundries. Game rm. Refrigerators. Cr cds: A, C, D, MC, V.

Inn

✔ ★ ★**GRANT HOUSE.** *244 W Church St.* 412/238-5135. 3 rms, some shared baths. S $42–$47; D $45–$50; each addl $10. TV in front rm. Complimentary bkfst. Ck-out 11 am, ck-in 2 pm. Airport transportation. Tennis. 18 and 9-hole golf privileges, pro, putting green. Private patios. Picnic tables, grills. Antique furnished. Victorian mansion built 1888. Large and spacious.

Mansfield

Pop: 3,322 **Elev:** 1,120 ft (341 m) **Area code:** 717 **Zip:** 16933

Motels

★★**MANSFIELD.** *26 S Main St (US 15). 717/662-2136.* 26 rms, 2 story. May–Oct: S $47–$54; D $55–$65; each addl $5; under 18 free; lower rates rest of yr. Closed Dec 24–25 & Dec 31–Jan 1. Crib $5. TV; cable. Cafe adj 7 am–10 pm. Rm serv. Ck-out 11 am. Sundries. Cr cds: A, DS, MC, V.

[icons]

✔★**WEST'S DELUXE.** *(Box 97, RD 1) 3 mi S on US 15. 717/659-5141.* 20 rms. S $25–$28; D $32–$40; each addl $4. Crib $4. TV; cable. Pool. Cafe 3–9:30 pm. Bar 3 pm–2 am. Ck-out 11 am. Sundries. Picnic tables, grills. Cr cds: A, DS, MC, V.

[icons]

Meadville

Settled: 1788 **Pop:** 15,544 **Elev:** 1,100 ft (335 m) **Area code:** 814 **Zip:** 16335

Motels

✔★★**DAVID MEAD INN.** *(Box 395) 455 Chestnut St (US 19). 814/336-1692.* 67 rms, 2 story. S $44–$49; D $49–$59; each addl $5; suites $48–$123; under 18 free; wkly, wkend rates. Crib free. TV; cable. Heated pool; wading pool, poolside serv, lifeguard. Playground. Cafe 7 am–2 pm, 5:30–10 pm; Sun 8 am–2 pm. Bar 11:30–1 am, Fri, Sat to 2 am. Ck-out 1 pm. Meeting rms. Cr cds: A, C, D, DS, MC, V.

[icons]

★★**DAYS INN.** *240 Conneaut Lake Rd, I-79 exit 39A, E 2 mi. 814/337-4264.* 162 rms, 3 story. May–Sep: S $50–$60; D $55–$65; each addl $5; under 18, $1; higher rates special events; lower rates rest of yr. Crib free. TV; cable. Indoor pool; whirlpool, lifeguard. Cafe 7 am–10 pm; Sun to 9 pm. Bar noon–2 am. Ck-out 11 am. Coin lndry. Meeting rms. Sundries. Game rm. Cr cds: A, DS, MC, V. ①

[icons]

Mercer

Settled: 1795 **Pop:** 2,532 **Elev:** 1,270 ft (387 m) **Area code:** 412 **Zip:** 16137

Motel

★★★**HOWARD JOHNSON.** *2 mi S on US 19, just off I-80 exit 2. 412/748-3030.* 102 rms, 2 story. S $54–$57; D $55–$63; each addl $6; suites $79–$106; under 18 free; higher rates special events. Crib free. TV; cable. Heated pool; wading pool, lifeguard. Playground. Cafe open 24 hrs. Rm serv. Bar. Ck-out noon. Coin lndry. Meeting rms. Bellhops. Sundries. Bus depot transportation. Exercise equipt, weights, bicycles, sauna. Game rm. Private patios, balconies. Amish crafts shop in lobby. Cr cds: A, C, D, DS, MC, V.

[icons]

Mount Pocono

Pop: 1,237 **Elev:** 1,840 ft (561 m) **Area code:** 717 **Zip:** 18344

Motels

★**MT POCONO.** *(PO Box 38) 25 Knob Rd. 717/839-9407.* 28 units, 2 kits. S $36–$53; D $38–$56; each addl $5; suites $58–$85; kit. units $45–$57. Crib $5. TV. Pool; lifeguard. Cafe nearby. Ck-out 11 am. Sundries. Airport, bus depot transportation. Game rm. Cr cds: A, C, D, DS, MC, V. ⒺDS

✔★**POCONO FOUNTAIN.** *1½ mi S on PA 611. 717/839-7728.* 37 rms, 4 kits. Mid-Apr–Oct: S $42–$54; D $44–$57; each addl $5; kit. unit $55–$60; higher rates wkends, hols;

lower rates rest of yr. Crib $5. TV. Pool; lifeguard. Playground. Cafe 6 am–9 pm. Ck-out 11 am. Sundries. Gift shop. Airport, RR station, bus depot transportation. Game rm. Private patios, picnic tables. Cr cds: A, C, D, DS, MC, V.

New Hope (Bucks Co)

Founded: 1681 **Pop:** 1,473 **Elev:** 76 ft (23 m) **Area code:** 215 **Zip:** 18938

Inn

✔ ★★**PINEAPPLE HILL.** *1324 River Rd. 215/862-9608.* 5 units, 3 baths, 3 story. No elvtr. No rm phones. D $50–$70; each addl $15; suites $70–$90. Children over 12 yrs only. Pool. Complimentary bkfst, refreshments. Ck-out 11 am, ck-in 2 pm. Downhill ski 5 mi; x-country ski 1 mi. Picnic tables. Built 1780; antiques. Totally nonsmoking. Cr cd: A.

New Stanton

Pop: 2,600 **Elev:** 980 ft (299 m) **Area code:** 412 **Zip:** 15672

Motels

★**CARDINAL.** *(Box B) 1 blk N off US 119, ¼ mi SW of PA Tpke exit 8. 412/925-2162.* 20 rms. S $30–$32; D $34–$40; each addl $3. Crib $4. TV; cable. Cafe opp 7 am–midnight. Bar to 2 am; Sun 1–10 pm. Ck-out 11 am. Cr cds: A, C, D, DS, MC, V. ⓕ ①

✔ ★★**INN AMERICA.** *(Box J) ¼ mi SW at jct I-70, US 119, PA Tpke exit 8. 412/925-3591.* 150 rms, 3 story. S $30–$38; D $38–$50; each addl $5; under 16 free. Crib free. TV. Pool; lifeguard. Cafe 6:30 am–10 pm; Sun 6:30 am–8 pm. Rm serv. Bar 11–2 am; Sun 1–8 pm (summer); entertainment, dancing Tu–Sat. Ck-out noon. Meeting rms. Valet serv. Sundries. Cr cds: A, C, D, MC, V.

★**PAGANO'S MOTOR LODGE.** *(Box B) 1 blk N off US 19, ¼ mi SW of PA Tpke exit 8. 412/925-7223.* 15 rms, 2 story. S $28–$30; D $32–$38; each addl $4; under 14 free. Crib $4. TV; cable. Cafe 7 am–midnight. Bar 7–2 am; Sun 1–10 pm. Ck-out noon. Cr cds: A, C, D, MC, V. ①

Motor Hotel

✔ ★★**HOWARD JOHNSON.** *(Box 214) 1 blk S off US 119, ¼ mi SW of PA Tpke exit 8. 412/925-3511.* 87 rms, 2 story. Mid-May–Sep: S $37–$60; D $45–$63; each addl $5; suite $53; under 18 free; lower rates rest of yr. Crib free. TV; cable. Heated pool; lifeguard. Cafe open 24 hrs. Rm serv 7:30 am–9 pm. Bar 11–2 am; Sun 1–10 pm. Ck-out noon. Valet serv. Private patios, balconies. Cr cds: A, C, D, DS, MC, V.

North East

Settled: 1801 **Pop:** 4,568 **Elev:** 801 ft (244 m) **Area code:** 814 **Zip:** 16428

Motel

✔ ★**MUMS MOTOR LODGE.** *(Box 566) US 20, jct I-90 exit 12. 814/725-4554.* 34 rms, 1–2 story. Mid-June–Labor Day: S $34; D $38–$49; each addl $5; under 18 free; ski package plan; lower rates rest of yr. Crib $5. TV; in-rm movies. Pool; whirlpool, wading pool, sauna, lifeguard. Playground. Free continental bkfst in lobby. Bar from 6 pm. Ck-out noon. Sundries. Downhill/x-country ski 18 mi. 13 acres of chrysanthemums. Near Lake Erie. Cr cds: A, DS, ER, MC, V.

Philadelphia

Founded: 1682 **Pop:** 1,688,210 **Elev:** 45 ft (14 m) **Area code:** 215

Motels

✔ ★ ★**COMFORT INN.** *(3660 Street Rd, Bensalem 19020) N on US 1 to Street Rd exit, S 1 mi. 215/245-0100.* 141 units, 3 story. S $39.95–$89.95; D $49.95–$89.95; each addl $6; suites $89.95; family rates. Crib free. TV; cable. Free continental bkfst. Cafe nearby. Bar 11–1 am; entertainment, dancing Mon–Fri. Ck-out noon. Meeting rms. Sundries. Airport, RR station, bus depot transportation. Exercise equipt; weights, bicycles. Game rm. Cr cds: A, C, D, DS, ER, MC, V.

★ ★**HOLIDAY INN-NORTHEAST.** *(3499 Street Rd, Bensalem 19020) 25 mi NE via US 1. 215/638-1500.* 117 rms, 2 story. S $79; D $87; each addl $8; under 18 free; wkend rates. Crib free. TV; cable, in-rm movies (fee). Pool; poolside bar, lifeguard. Cafe 7 am–2 pm, 5–10 pm. Rm serv. Bar 11–2 am; entertainment, dancing. Ck-out noon. Coin lndry. Meeting rms. Cr cds: A, C, D, DS, MC, V.

✔ ★**RED ROOF INN.** *(3100 Cabot Blvd W, Langhorne 19047) NE via I-95 at Oxford Valley Rd. 215/750-6200.* 91 rms, 3 story. S $34.95; D $36.95–$44.95; under 18 free. Crib free. TV; in-rm movies. Ck-out noon. Cr cds: A, D, DS, MC, V.

Motor Hotels

★ ★**HOLIDAY INN-PHILADELPHIA INTL AIRPORT.** *(45 Industrial Hwy, Essington 19029) 8 mi SW on PA 291 at jct PA 420, I-95. 215/521-2400.* 306 rms, 6 story. S $84–$94; D $87–$97; each addl $10; suites $195; under 12 free; wkend rates. Crib free. TV; cable, in-rm movies. Pool; poolside serv, lifeguard. Cafe 7 am–10 pm; Fri, Sat to 11 pm. Rm serv. Bar 11–2 am; entertainment, dancing Fri, Sat. Ck-out 1 pm. Meeting rms. Bellhops. Free airport transportation. Cr cds: A, C, D, DS, MC, V. Ⓔ Ⓘ

★ ★**SHERATON INN-NORTHEAST.** *9461 Roosevelt Blvd (19114). 215/671-9600.* 188 rms, 6 story. S $78–$98; D $88–$110; each addl $8; suites $98–$118; under 18 free; wkend rates. Crib $5. TV; in-rm movies. Indoor pool; lifeguard. Cafe 6:30 am–9:30 pm. Rm serv. Bar 11–2 am. Ck-out noon. Meeting rms. Bellhops. Cr cds: A, C, D, MC, V. Ⓔ Ⓕ

Pittsburgh

Settled: 1758 **Pop:** 422,959 **Elev:** 760 ft (232 m) **Area code:** 412

Motels

✔ ★**COMFORT INN.** *1170 Thorn Run Rd (15108), jct PA 60 & Thorn Run Rd. 412/269-0990.* 100 rms, 2 story. S $37–$41; D $42–$46; each addl $5; under 16 free. Crib free. TV; cable, in-rm movies. Free coffee. Continental bkfst. Cafe adj 7 am–11 pm. Ck-out noon. Meeting rms. Valet serv. Free airport transportation. Cr cds: A, C, D, DS, ER, MC, V.

✔ ★ ★**DAYS INN-REDWOOD.** *2898 Banksville Rd (US 19) (15216), 3 mi S. 412/343-3000.* 95 rms, 4 story. S $48–$58; D $52–$62; each addl $5; under 12 free; some wkend rates. Crib free. TV; cable. Pool; lifeguard. Cafe 6:30 am–2 pm, 6–9 pm; Sat 8 am–noon, 5:30–9 pm; Sun 8 am–1 pm. Rm serv. Bar 11–2 am; entertainment Tu–Sat, dancing Fri, Sat. Ck-out noon. Meeting rms. Bellhops. Valet serv. Airport transportation. Cr cds: A, C, D, DS, MC, V. Ⓘ

✔ ★ ★**HAMPTON INN.** *(210 Executive Dr, Mars 16046) I-79 N to exit 25, E 3 mi. 412/776-1000.* 118 rms, 4 story. S $45; D $50; under 18 free. Crib free. TV; cable, in-rm movies. Indoor pool; whirlpool, lifeguard. Free continental bkfst. Cafe adj open 24 hrs. Ck-out noon. Meeting rms. Valet serv. Game rm. Some refrigerators. Picnic tables. Cr cds: A, C, D, DS, MC, V.

✔ ★KNIGHTS INN. *4800 Steubenville Pike (PA 60, off I-79) (15205).* 412/922-6900. 109 units, 13 kits. S $29.50–$35.50; D $35.50–$41.50; each addl $3; kit. units $39.50–$49.60; under 18 free; wkly, monthly rates. Crib $3. TV. Pool; lifeguard. Cafe adj open 24 hrs. Ck-out noon. Meeting rms. Some refrigerators. Cr cds: A, C, D, MC, V.

★RED ROOF INN. *6404 Steubenville Pike (PA 60) (15205).* 412/787-7870. 122 rms, 2 story. S $29.95–$31.95; D $35.95–$40.95; under 18 free. Crib free. TV. Free morning coffee. Cafe adj open 24 hrs. Ck-out noon. Cr cds: A, D, DS, MC, V.

Motor Hotels

✔ ★★HAMPTON INN-NORTHWEST. *(1420 Beers School Rd, Coraopolis 15108) N of airport on PA 60.* 412/264-0020. 128 rms, 5 story. S $49–$53; D $54–$57; under 18 free; wkend rates. Crib free. TV; in-rm movies. Free continental bkfst. Cafe adj 6 am–10 pm. Ck-out noon. Meeting rms. Valet serv. Airport transportation. Picnic tables, grills. Cr cds: A, C, D, DS, MC, V.
Ⓕ

✔ ★★HOWARD JOHNSON-MONROEVILLE. *(Monroeville 15146) 17 mi E on PA 48; exit 6 off PA Tpke.* 412/372-5500. 261 rms, 9 story. S $34–$52; D $42.95–$60.95; each addl $8; kit. suites $85–$125; under 18 free; wkend rates. Crib free. TV. Indoor pool; poolside serv, lifeguard. Cafe 6:30 am–midnight. Rm serv. Bar 11:30–2 am, Sun from 1 pm; entertainment, dancing. Ck-out noon. Coin lndry. Meeting rms. Bellhops. Sundries. Gift shop. Barber shop. Airport transportation. Balconies. Grills. Cr cds: A, C, D, DS, MC, V.

Reading

Founded: 1748 **Pop:** 78,686 **Elev:** 260 ft (79 m) **Area code:** 215

Motels

✔ ★★DUTCH COLONY MOTOR INN. *4635 Perkiomen Ave (19606).* 215/779-2345. 77 rms, 2 story. S $43; D $48; each addl $4. Crib free. TV. Heated pool; lifeguard. Cafe 7 am–10 pm. Rm serv. Bar 11–2 am. Ck-out noon. Meeting rms. Valet serv. Sundries. Lawn games. Balconies. Cr cds: A, C, D, ER, MC, V.

✔ ★LUXURY BUDGET INN. *(Rte 422 at Papermill Rd, Wyomissing 19610) 2 mi W on 422, Park Rd exit; on Spring St, access from Park & Papermill Rds.* 215/378-5105; res: 800/441-4479 (exc PA), 800/242-6778 (PA). 84 rms, 4 story. June–Sep: S $34.99–$37.99; D $41.99–$46.99; each addl $4; under 12 free; lower rates rest of yr. Crib $2. TV; cable. Free continenta! bkfst. Cafe nearby. Ck-out 11 am. Cr cds: A, D, DS, ER, MC, V.

Scranton

Settled: 1771 **Pop:** 88,117 **Elev:** 754 ft (230 m) **Area code:** 717

Motels

✔ ★★DAYS INN. *(1100 O'Neill Hwy, Dunmore 18512) NE via I-81, exit 55A.* 717/348-6101. 90 rms, 4 story. June–Sep: S $36–$40; D $44–$48; each addl $4; under 18, $1; lower rates rest of yr. TV; cable. Free continental bkfst. Cafe adj. Ck-out 11 am. Cr cds: A, C, D, DS, MC, V.

✔ ★DAYS INN. *(US 6 & 11, Clarks Summit 18411) NE via I-81, exit 58. 717/586-9100.* 67 rms, 4 story. June–Sep: S $33.99–$36.99; D $43.99–$46.99; each addl $4; family rates; lower rates rest of yr. Crib $2. TV; cable. Free continental bkfst. Cafe adj. Ck-out 11 am. Cr cds: A, C, D, DS, MC, V.

🏊 🚫 Ⓦ sc S

✔ ★★HOWARD JOHNSON. *(Pittston 18640) 8 mi SE on I-81, exit 48. 717/654-3301.* 120 rms, 2 story. S $40–$50; D $50–$62; each addl $7; under 18 free; higher rates: Pocono races, car shows, hol wkends. Crib free. TV; cable. Pool; poolside serv, lifeguard. Cafe open 24 hrs. Bar 4 pm–2 am; entertainment Wed, Fri–Sun. Ck-out 11 am. Meeting rm. Sundries. Downhill ski 6 mi; x-country ski 20 mi. Private patios. Cr cds: A, C, D, DS, ER, MC, V.

🏊 ⚡ ➳ 🚫 sc

Shamokin Dam

Settled: 1790 **Pop:** 1,562 **Elev:** 500 ft (152 m) **Area code:** 717 **Zip:** 17876

Motels

✔ ★★HOLIDAY INN. *On US 15. 717/743-1111.* 151 rms, 2 story. S $40–$49; D $50–$59; each addl $5; under 12 free. Crib free $5. TV; cable. Pool; poolside serv, lifeguard. Cafe 7 am–10 pm. Rm serv. Bar 10 pm–2 am; entertainment Sun. Ck-out noon. Meeting rms. Valet serv. Sundries. Cr cds: A, C, D, MC, V.

🏊 ➳ sc

★PHILLIPS. *US 15 & 11th Ave. 717/743-1431.* 38 rms. S $28–$30; D $34–$36; each addl $4; higher rates special college wkends. Crib $4. TV; cable. Cafe adj open 24 hrs. Ck-out 11 am. Cr cds: A, C, D, DS, MC, V.

State College

Settled: 1859 **Pop:** 36,130 **Elev:** 1,154 ft (352 m) **Area code:** 814

Motels

(Rates higher football, art festival & special wkends; may be 2-day min)

✔ ★★★AUTOPORT. *1405 S Atherton St (US Business 322) (16801). 814/237-7666.* 86 rms, 3 story, 12 kit. units. S $39–$53; D, studio rms $53–$63; each addl $5; suites, kit. units $58; under 16 free; wkly, wkend rates. Crib free. TV; cable. Heated pool; lifeguard. Cafe 6 am–11 pm; dining rm 11:30 am–2 pm, 4:30–10 pm. Bar 11–2 am; Sun to midnight; entertainment exc Sun. Ck-out noon. Coin lndry. Meeting rms. Sundries. Downhill ski 4 mi. Rms vary. Cr cds: A, C, D, MC, V.

♿ ⚡ ➳ 🚫 sc

✔ ★★HAMPTON INN. *1101 E College Ave (16801). 814/231-1590.* 121 rms, 3 story. S $40–$48; D $44–$52; suites $48–$52; under 18 free; ski, golf plans; higher rates college events. Crib free. TV; cable. Heated pool; lifeguard. Free continental bkfst. Meeting rm. Valet serv. Sundries. Downhill/x-country ski 10 mi. Picnic tables. Cr cds: A, C, D, DS, MC, V. Ⓓ Ⓔ Ⓘ

♿ 🏊 ⚡ ➳ 🎿 🚫 sc

✔ ★★HOLIDAY INN-PENN STATE. *1450 S Atherton St (16801). 814/238-3001.* 289 rms, 2 story. S $44–$49; D $51–$56; each addl $7; suites $75; under 19 free; some wkend rates. Crib free. TV; cable. 2 pools; wading pool, lifeguard. Cafe 7 am–2 pm, 5–10 pm. Rm serv. Bar 11–1am; entertainment 5 nights. Ck-out noon. Coin lndry. Meeting rms. Bellhops. Lighted tennis, pro. Game rm. Cr cds: A, C, D, DS, MC, V. Ⓘ

♿ Ⓦ ➳ 🚫 sc

★IMPERIAL INN. *118 S Atherton St (US Business 322) (16801). 814/237-7686.* 35 rms, 2 story. S $38–$75; D $46–$75; each addl $5; under 16 free. Crib free. TV; cable. Heated pool; lifeguard. Free morning coffee. Cafe nearby. Ck-out noon. Airport transportation. Downhill ski 4 mi. Cr cds: A, C, D, DS, MC, V.

⚡ ➳ sc S

★STEVENS. *1275 N Atherton St (US Business 322) (16803). 814/238-2438.* 18 rms, 2 story. S $26–$32; D $32–$38; each addl $4. Crib $4. TV; cable. Free coffee. Cafe opp. Ck-out 11 am. Sundries. Cr cds: A, D, DS, MC, V.

Stroudsburg

Settled: 1769 **Pop:** 5,148 **Elev:** 430 ft (131 m) **Area code:** 717 **Zip:** 18360

Motels

✔ ★BUDGET. *(Box 216, E Stroudsburg 18301) 1 mi E on I-80, exit 51. 717/424-5451; res: 800/233-8144 (exc PA), 800/532-8220 (PA).* 110 rms, 2–3 story. No elvtr. S $27–$36; D $36–$45; each addl $3; higher rates: special events, hols, some wkends. Crib free. TV; cable. Cafe 6–11 am; 5–10 pm. Bar 4 pm–midnight. Ck-out 10 am. Health club privileges. Game rm. Cr cds: A, C, D, DS, MC, V. ⊙

★WALTER'S. *2011 W Main St. 717/424-1862.* 27 rms, 9 A/C; 13 kit. cottages. S $34; D $39; cottages $250–$285/wk. Crib $5. TV. Pool. Playground. Cafe nearby. Ck-out 11 am. Downhill/x-country ski 8 mi. Lawn games. Picnic tables, grill. Cr cds: MC, V.

Uniontown

Settled: 1768 **Pop:** 14,510 **Elev:** 999 ft (304 m) **Area code:** 412 **Zip:** 15401

Resort

✔ ★★★MOUNT SUMMIT INN. *(Box T) 6 mi E on US 40. 412/438-8594.* 106 rms, 3 story. No elvtr. July–Labor Day, EP: S $35–$64; D $49–$79; suites $80–$145; family rates; golf package plan, MAP avail (2 night min); some wkend rates; lower rates mid-Apr–June, after Labor Day–early Nov. Closed rest of yr. Crib $8. TV. Indoor/outdoor pool; wading pool, whirlpool, lifeguard. Playground. Cafe (public by res) 8–11 am, noon–2 pm, 6–8:30 pm. Rm serv. Box lunches, snacks, cookouts. Bar 11–1 am. Ck-out 1 pm, ck-in 4 pm. Grocery, package store 3 mi. Free bus depot transportation. Tennis. 9-hole golf, greens fee $6, pro, putting green. Scenic boat cruises. Rec rm. Soc dir; entertainment, dancing. Picnic tables, grills. Beautiful view; atop Mt Summit. Well-maintained older inn. Cr cds: A, C, MC, V.

Warren

Founded: 1795 **Pop:** 12,146 **Elev:** 1,200 ft (366 m) **Area code:** 814 **Zip:** 16365

Motel

✔ ★PENN LAUREL INN. *706 Penn Ave W, ¼ mi W on US 6 & 62. 814/723-8300.* 60 units. S $33–$38; D $37–$43; each addl $5; under 18 free. Crib free. TV; cable. Cafe 7 am–9 pm; Sun 8 am–2 pm. Bar 11–2 am exc Sun; entertainment Wed. Ck-out noon. Meeting rms. On Allegheny River. Cr cds: A, C, D, DS, MC, V.

Motor Hotel

★★★HOLIDAY INN. *210 Ludlow, ½ mi W on US 56, Ludlow exit. 814/726-3000.* 110 rms, 4 story, 1 kit. S $48–$56; D $54–$65; each addl $5; under 18 free. Crib free. TV; cable, in-rm movies. Indoor pool; sauna, lifeguard. Cafe 6:30 am–10 pm; Sat from 7:30 am; Sun 8 am–8 pm. Rm serv. Bar 11–2 am; Sun to 8 pm; entertainment, dancing exc Sun. Ck-out noon. Meeting rms. Valet serv. X-country ski 10 mi. Game rm. Balconies. Cr cds: A, C, D, DS, MC, V.

Washington

Founded: 1781 **Pop:** 18,363 **Elev:** 1,120 ft (311 m) **Area code:** 412 **Zip:** 15301

Motels

✔ ★★**BEST WESTERN.** *1385 W Chestnut St.* 412/222-6500. 62 rms, 1–2 story. S $34–$50; D $45–$60; each addl $6; studio rms $46–$56; under 18 free. Crib free. TV; cable. Pool; lifeguard. Cafe adj open 24 hrs. Ck-out 11 am. Bellhops. Airport, bus depot transportation. Cr cds: A, C, D, DS, MC, V.

⊞ ⊞ ⊘ SC

✔ ★★**HOWARD JOHNSON.** *1370 W Chestnut St.* 412/225-8500. 105 rms, 2 story. S $30–$46; D $38–$56; each addl $6; studio rms $55–$70; under 18 free. Crib free. TV; cable. Pool; lifeguard. Cafe adj. Ck-out noon. Meeting rm. Bellhops. Sundries. Balconies. Cr cds: A, C, D, DS, MC, V. Ⓔ

⊞ ⊞ SC

★**RED ROOF INN.** *1399 W Chestnut St.* 412/228-5750. 111 rms, 2 story. May–Oct: S $30.95–$32.95; D $36.95–$38.95; each addl $2; under 18 free; lower rates rest of yr. Crib free. TV; in-rm movies. Free morning coffee. Cafe adj open 24 hrs. Ck-out noon. Cr cds: A, C, D, DS, MC, V.

⊞ ⊘

Hotel

✔ ★**CENTURY PLAZA.** *1880 W Chestnut St.* 412/225-9290. 65 rms, 2 story. S $37–$43; D $48; each addl $5. TV. Pool; wading pool, lifeguard. Cafe 7 am–2 pm, 5–9 pm. Bar 4–11 pm; Fri, Sat to 2 am; dancing Fri, Sat. Ck-out noon. Meeting rms. Cr cds: A, C, D, ER, MC, V. Ⓔ

⊞ ⊞ ⑤

Wellsboro

Settled: 1799 **Pop:** 3,805 **Elev:** 1,311 ft (400 m) **Area code:** 717 **Zip:** 16901

Motels

★**CANYON.** *18 East Ave.* 717/724-1681. 27 rms. S $30–$35; D $30–$37; each addl $5; under 12 free; golf & ski package plans. Crib $5. TV; cable. Heated pool; lifeguard. Playground. Free continental bkfst. Cafe nearby. Ck-out 11 am. Downhill/x-country ski 20 mi. Refrigerators. Picnic tables, grills. Cr cds: A, C, D, DS, MC, V.

⊞ ⊞ ⊞ ⊞ ⊘

✔ ★★**PENN-WELLS LODGE.** *(PO Box 158) 4 Main St.* 717/724-3463. 55 rms, 2 story. S $35–$48; D $44–$54; each addl $5; under 12 free. Closed Dec 25. Crib $5. TV; cable. 2 pools, 1 indoor; lifeguard. Playground. Cafe nearby. Ck-out noon. Valet serv. Downhill/x-country ski 17 mi. Exercise rm; instructor, weights, bicycles, whirlpool, sauna. Community-owned. Cr cds: A, C, D, DS, MC, V.

⊞ ⊞ ⊞ ⊞ ⊞ ⊞ ⊞ ⊘

★**SHERWOOD.** *2 Main St.* 717/724-3424. 32 rms, 2 story. S $28–$32; D $32–$37; each addl $5; golf & ski package plans. Crib $5. TV; cable. Heated pool; lifeguard. Playground. Free coffee. Cafe nearby. Ck-out 11 am. Downhill/x-country ski 17 mi. Refrigerators. Cr cds: A, C, D, DS, MC, V.

⊞ ⊞ ⊞ ⊞ ⊘

Hotel

✔ ★★**PENN-WELLS.** *(PO Box 158) 62 Main St.* 717/724-2111. 75 rms. S $22–$30; D $26–$39; each addl $4; under 12 free; golf rates. Closed Dec 25. Crib $5. TV; cable. 2 pools, 1 indoor. Playground. Cafe 7 am–1:30 pm, 5–10 pm. Bar 11:30–1 am; entertainment Fri, Sat. Ck-out noon. Meeting rms. Downhill/x-country ski 17 mi. Exercise rm; instructor, weights, bicycles, whirlpool, sauna. Built 1869. Community-owned. Cr cds: A, C, D, DS, MC, V.

West Chester

Founded: 1788 **Pop:** 17,435 **Elev:** 459 ft (140 m) **Area code:** 215 **Zip:** 19380

Motel

✔ ★**ABBEY GREEN MOTOR LODGE.** *1036 Wilmington Pike, 1 mi S on US 202.* 215/ *692-3310.* 18 rms. S $37–$39; D $45–$48; each addl $4; cottages with kit. $39–$42; under 6 free; wkend rates. Crib free. TV. Playground. Cafe nearby. Ck-out 11 am. Gift shop. Package store nearby. RR station, bus depot transportation. Picnic tables. Cr cds: A, D, MC, V.

West Middlesex

Pop: 1,064 **Elev:** 840 ft (256 m) **Area code:** 412 **Zip:** 15379

Motel

✔ ★ ★**HOLIDAY INN.** *3200 S Hermitage Rd, jct I-80 & AL 60.* 412/981-1530. 180 rms, 3 story. S $43–$55; D $45–$60; each addl $6; under 18 free; golf packages avail. Crib free. TV; satellite, in-rm movies. Heated pool; poolside serv, lifeguard. Playground. Cafe 6:30 am–10 pm; Dec–Mar 6:30 am–2 pm, 5–10 pm. Bar 11–2 am; entertainment, dancing. Ck-out 11 am. Coin lndry. Meeting rms. Valet serv. Sundries. Game rm. Cr cds: A, D, DS, ER, MC, V.

White Haven

Pop: 1,921 **Elev:** 1,221 ft (372 m) **Area code:** 717 **Zip:** 18661

Motel

★ ★**POCONO MOUNTAIN LODGE.** *(Box 141) PA 940 and I-80.* 717/443-8461. 123 rms, 6 story. S $43–$53; D $51–$66; each addl $8; under 18 free; ski plans. Crib free. TV. Pool; lifeguard. Cafe adj open 24 hrs. Bar 11–2 am. Ck-out noon. Meeting rms. Downhill/x-country ski 4 mi. Hiking trails. Game rm. Cr cds: A, C, D, DS, MC, V.

Wilkes-Barre

Founded: 1769 **Pop:** 51,551 **Elev:** 550 ft (168 m) **Area code:** 717

Motel

★ ★**THE STATION COMPLEX.** *33 Wilkes-Barre Blvd (18701).* 717/829-0000; res: 800/444-1354 (exc PA), 800/242-1077 (PA). 90 rms. S $49; D $54; each addl $5; under 16 free. Crib free. TV; cable. Cafe 6:30 am–11 pm; Sun to 10 pm. Entertainment, dancing. Ck-out noon. Meeting rms. Downhill ski 12 mi. Originally railroad depot (1868); all rail cars converted into staterooms. Victorian decor. Cr cds: A, C, D, DS, MC, V.

Motor Hotels

✔ ★ ★**BEST WESTERN GENETTI MOTOR INN.** *77 Market St (18701).* 717/823-6152. 68 rms, 7 story. S $45–$50; D $55–$60; each addl $6; studio rms $75–$85; under 18 free. TV; cable.

Pool; lifeguard. Cafe 7 am–9 pm. Rm serv. Bar 11–2 am; DJ. Ck-out noon. Meeting rms. Valet serv. Airport transportation. Game rm. Cr cds: A, C, D, DS, MC, V. Ⓔ

  [icons]

✔ ★ ★ ★ **WOODLANDS INN & RESORT.** *1073 PA 315 (18702).* 717/824-9831; res: 800/ *556-2222 (exc PA), 800/762-2222 (PA).* 208 rms, 9 story, 25 apts. S $45–$80; D $50–$95; each addl $5; package plans; wkend rates. Crib $5. TV; cable. 2 pools, 1 indoor; poolside serv, lifeguard. Cafe 7 am–11 pm. Rm serv. Bar 11–2 am; entertainment, dancing. Ck-out 1 pm. Meeting rms. Bellhops. Sundries. Barber, beauty shop. Lighted tennis. Exercise rm; instructor, weights, bicycles, whirlpool, steam rm, sauna. Game rm. Rec rm. Lawn games. Private patios, balconies. Cr cds: A, D, MC, V.

  [icons]

Williamsport

Settled: 1795 **Pop:** 33,401 **Elev:** 528 ft (161 m) **Area code:** 717 **Zip:** 17701

Motels

★ ★ **CITY VIEW.** *(Box 550, RD 4) 2 mi S on US 15.* 717/326-2601. 44 rms, 2 story. S, D $38–$42; each addl $1. Crib free. TV; cable. Playground. Cafe. Ck-out 11 am. Sundries. Balconies. Picnic table. Picture windows overlook city, Little League World Series Ball Park.

  [icons]

✔ ★ ★ **HOLIDAY INN.** *1840 E 3d St (US 220).* 717/326-1981. 198 rms, 2 story. S $38–$52; D $44–$68; each addl $5; under 18 free; higher rates Little League World Series. Crib free. TV. Pool; poolside serv, lifeguard. Playground. Cafe 6 am–2 pm, 5:30–10 pm. Rm serv. Bar 4 pm–2 am; entertainment, dancing. Ck-out noon. Coin lndry. Meeting rms. Cr cds: A, D, MC, V.

  [icons]

★ **KING'S.** *590 Montgomery Pike. 1¾ mi S on US 15.* 717/322-4707. 48 rms, 2 story. S $29–$32; D $33–$40; each addl $5; suites $40–$60; under 12 free. Crib $5. TV; cable. Continental bkfst. Cafe adj 4:30–10 pm. Bar 4 pm–2 am; band wkends; organist, dancing Tu–Sat. Ck-out 11 am. Cr cds: A, C, D, DS, MC, V.

  [icons]

✔ ★ ★ ★ **QUALITY INN.** *234 Montgomery Pike (US 15).* 717/323-9801. 115 rms, 3 story. No elvtr. S $39–$54; D, kit. units, studio rms $45–$54; each addl $6; suites $44–$75; under 16 free. Crib $3. TV; cable. Pool; poolside serv, lifeguard. Cafe 6:30 am–2 pm, 5–10 pm. Rm serv. Bar noon–2 am; entertainment. Ck-out noon. Valet serv. Sundries. Airport, bus depot transportation. Downhill/x-country ski 10 mi. Game rm. Cr cds: A, C, D, DS, ER, MC, V. Ⓕ

  [icons]

Inn

★ ★ **EAGLES MERE.** *(PO Box 356, Eagles Mere 17731) 38 mi NE, just off PA 42; I-80 exit 34, take PA 42 N.* 717/525-3273. 15 air-cooled rms, 2–3 story. No elvtr. Some rm phones. May–Oct, MAP: S $75–$85; D $55–$62/person; each addl $40; suites $69/person; varied lower rates rest of yr. TV in lounge. Pool privileges. Cafe 8–9:30 am, 6–8 pm; Nov–Apr wkends only. No rm serv. Bar 5–10 pm. Ck-out 11 am, ck-in 3 pm. Airport transportation $20. Tennis privileges. X-country ski adj. Originally Lewis Hotel (1878); many antique furnishings. Cr cds: A, MC, V.

  [icons]

York

Founded: 1741 **Pop:** 44,619 **Elev:** 400 ft (122 m) **Area code:** 717

Motels

✔ ★ ★ **HOWARD JOHNSON.** *Arsenal Rd (US 30) (17402), at I-83 exit 9E.* 717/843-9971. 124 rms, 2 story. S $38–$68; D $44–$74; each addl $6. Crib free. TV; cable. Heated pool;

lifeguard. Cafe 6 am–midnight; Fri, Sat to 2 am. Bar 4 pm–midnight. Ck-out noon. Meeting rms. Sundries. Cr cds: A, C, D, DS, MC, V.

★**LUXURY BUDGET INN.** *125 Arsenal Rd (17404). 717/846-6260.* 100 rms, 4 story. S $34.99–$37.99; D $41.99–$44.99; each addl $4; suites $46.99; under 12 free; ski plans; higher rates: York Festival, tournaments. Crib $2. TV; cable. Cafe nearby. Ck-out 11 am. Downhill ski 20 mi. Cr cds: A, D, DS, MC, V.

★**SPIRIT OF 76.** *(RD 3, 17402) 1162 Haines Rd. 717/755-1068.* 20 rms, 1–2 story. S $30–$32; D $35–$40; each addl $4; under 12 free. Crib $2. TV; cable. Cafe adj open 24 hrs. Ck-out 11 am. Some refrigerators. Cr cds: A, MC, V.

Hotel

✔ ★ ★ ★**YORKTOWNE.** *(Box 1106) E Market & Duke Sts (17405). 717/848-1111.* 175 rms, 8 story. S $42–$65; D $49–$73; each addl $7; suites $90–$125. Crib free. TV; cable. Cafe 6:30–2 am; dining rm 5:30–9:30 pm. Bar 11–2 am; entertainment Fri, Sat. Ck-out noon. Meeting rms. Shopping arcade. Airport transportation. Cr cds: A, C, D, DS, MC, V.

Rhode Island

Population: 947,154	
Land area: 1,054 sq mi (2,730 sq km)	
Elevation: 0–812 ft (0–247 m)	
Highest point: Jerimoth Hill (Providence Co)	
Entered Union: Thirteenth of original 13 states (May 29, 1790)	
Capital: Providence	
Motto: Hope	
Nickname: Ocean State	
State flower: Violet	
State bird: Rhode Island Red	
State tree: Red Maple	
Time zone: Eastern	

Interstate Highway System

The following alphabetical listing of Rhode Island towns in *Mobil Travel Guide* shows that these cities are within 10 miles (16 kilometers) of the indicated Interstate highway. A highway map should, however, be checked for the nearest exit.

INTERSTATE 95: East Greenwich, Pawtucket, Providence, Warwick, Westerly.

Weather Statistics*

	WINTER	SPRING	SUMMER	FALL
Statewide	30°F (-1°C)	48°F (9°C)	69°F (21°C)	53°F (12°C)

*Average mean temperatures are listed for the entire state. Averages for specific regions are given if significant differences exist.

Visitor Information

Contact the Rhode Island Dept of Economic Development, Tourism/Promotion Div, 7 Jackson Walkway, Providence 02903; 401/277-2601 or 800/556-2484 (from Maine to Virginia, West Virginia, & Northern Ohio; RI not included). There are several information centers in Rhode Island. Three of the centers are located: off I-95 in Richmond; off I-295 in Lincoln; and 7 miles S of Providence in Warwick at Theodore Francis Green Airport.

Room Rate Information

The following major city and resort areas have higher room rates for two (double) than indicated on the cover of this Guide. However, the lodgings listed in these cities offer a good value when compared to others of their type in the area.

Newport	$80	Westerly	$60
Providence	75		

Kingston

Pop: 5,479 **Elev:** 242 ft (74 m) **Area code:** 401 **Zip:** 02881

Inn

✔ ★★**LARCHWOOD INN.** *(176 Main St, Wakefield 02879). 401/783-5454.* 18 rms, 9 with bath, 3 story. No A/C. No elvtr. Some phones. S, D $30–$65; each addl $7.50. Crib $7.50. TV in lobby. Cafe 7:30 am–2:30 pm, 5:30–9 pm; wkends to 10 pm. Bar 11–1 am; entertainment, dancing Fri, Sat. Ck-out noon. Meeting rms. Private patio. Cr cds: A, C, D, DS, MC, V.

Newport

Founded: 1639 **Pop:** 29,259 **Elev:** 96 ft (29 m) **Area code:** 401 **Zip:** 02840

Motels

★★**HOWARD JOHNSON LODGE.** *(351 W Main Rd, Middletown 02840)* On RI 138 at jct RI 114. *401/849-2000.* 155 rms, 2 story. Late May–mid-Oct: S $77–$92; D $77–$98; each addl $7–$8; suites $164–$206; studio rms $101–$130; family rates; some wkend rates; lower rates rest of yr. Crib free. TV. Heated pool; sauna, lifeguard. Cafe open 24 hrs. Bar 5 pm–1 am. Ck-out 11 am. Meeting rms. Bellhops. Valet serv. Sundries. Tennis. Private patios, balconies. Cr cds: A, C, D, DS, MC, V.

★★★**INN AT CASTLE HILL.** *Ocean Drive, 4 mi S. 401/849-3800.* 10 rms in inn, 3 story, 1 suite, 18 kit. cottages. No A/C. No elvtr. No phones. June–Oct: S, D $80–$220; each addl $20; suite $220; kit. cottages $600–$650/wk; lower rates rest of yr. Children over 12 yrs only. Continental bkfst. Cafe noon–2:30 pm, 6–9 pm. Bar; entertainment Tu–Sun. Ck-out 11 am. Victorian home (1874); antique furnishings. Cr cds: A, MC, V.

Motor Hotel

★★★**MILL STREET INN.** *75 Mill St. 401/849-9500.* 23 air-cooled rms, 3 story. No elvtr. May–Oct: S, D, suites $79–$175; each addl $15; under 18 free; lower rates rest of yr. Crib free. Free continental bkfst. Ck-out 11 am. Meeting rms. Free garage parking. Many private patios. Cr cds: A, C, D, MC, V. Ⓔ Ⓕ Ⓘ

Providence

Settled: 1636 **Pop:** 156,804 **Elev:** 24 ft (7 m) **Area code:** 401

Motels

★**HI-WAY MOTOR INN.** *(1880 Hartford Ave, Johnston 02919)* Jct US 6, I-295. *401/351-7810.* 35 rms. S $34–$42; D $43–$50; each addl $4; suites $54. TV; cable. Cafe nearby. Ck-out 11 am. Cr cds: A, DS, MC, V.

✔ ★★★**JOHNSON & WALES INN.** *(MA 114A & US 44, Seekonk, MA 02771)* I-95E, exit 1 in MA, left onto MA 114A to jct US 44, turn right on US 44. *617/336-8700.* 62 units, 39 suites, 2–3 story. S, D $55–$65; suites $69–$95. TV; cable. Cafe 6:30–10 am, 11:30 am–2:30 pm, 5–10 pm; Sat 6–11 pm. Rm serv 6:30 am–midnight. Bar; entertainment, dancing Sat, Sun. Ck-out 11 am. Meeting rms. Bellhops. Valet serv. Sundries. Tennis, golf, racquetball, health club privileges. Many refrigerators. Cr cds: A, C, D, MC, V. Ⓓ Ⓔ Ⓕ

★★**RAMADA INN.** *(940 Fall River Ave, Seekonk MA 02771)* 4 mi E at exit 1, jct I-195 & MA 114A. *617/336-7300.* 128 rms, 2 story. S $68–$77; D $73–$85; each addl $5; suites $107–$134; under 18 free; wkend specials late fall, winter. Crib free. TV; satellite. Indoor pool; whirlpool, sauna. Playground. Cafe 7 am–10:30 pm. Rm serv. Bar noon–1:30 am; entertainment, dancing. Ck-out noon. Meeting rms. Tennis. Putting green. Lawn games. Cr cds: A, C, D, DS, MC, V. Ⓔ

Westerly

Founded: 1669 **Pop:** 14,093 **Elev:** 50 ft (15 m) **Area code:** 401 **Zip:** 02891

Motel

★★**PINE LODGE.** *(Box 562, RFD 3) 3½ mi N of Westerly on US 1. 401/322-0333.* 11 rms, 19 cottages, 30 kits. Mid-June–mid-Sep: S, D $59–$74; each addl $8; kit. cottages $53–$74, $320–$375/wk; under 16 free; wkly rates; lower rates rest of yr. Crib free. TV, most B/W. Playground. Cafe nearby. Ck-out 11 am. Airport, RR station transportation. Lawn games. Refrigerators. Picnic tables, grills. Off hwy in wooded area. Cr cds: A, C, D, DS, MC, V.

Vermont

Population: 511,456

Land area: 9,273 sq mi (24,017 sq km)

Elevation: 95–4,393 ft (29–1,339 m)

Highest point: Mt Mansfield (Lamoille Co)

Entered Union: Mar 4, 1791 (14th state)

Capital: Montpelier

Motto: Freedom and Unity

Nickname: Green Mountain State

State flower: Red clover

State bird: Hermit thrush

State tree: Sugar maple

State fair: September 2–10, 1989 in Rutland

Time zone: Eastern

Interstate Highway System

The following alphabetical listing of Vermont towns in *Mobil Travel Guide* shows that these cities are within 10 miles (16 kilometers) of the indicated Interstate highways. A highway map should, however, be checked for the nearest exit.

INTERSTATE 89: Barre, Burlington, Highgate Springs, Montpelier, Northfield, Norwich, St Albans, Waterbury, White River Junction.

INTERSTATE 91: Bellows Falls, Brattleboro, Fairlee, Grafton, Lyndonville, Newfane, Newport, Norwich, St Johnsbury, Springfield, White River Junction, Windsor, Woodstock.

Weather Statistics*

	WINTER	SPRING	SUMMER	FALL
Statewide	22°F (-6°C)	54°F (12°C)	70°F (21°C)	43°F (6°C)

*Average mean temperatures are listed for the entire state. Averages for specific regions are given if significant differences exist.

Visitor Information

Few states are as well documented as Vermont. The Vermont Official Transportation Map as well as numerous descriptive folders are distributed free by the Vermont Travel Division, 134 State St, Montpelier 05602; phone 802/828-3236. Visitor centers are located: off I-89 in Guilford (daily); off I-89 in Highgate Springs (daily); off US 4 in Fair Haven (daily); and off I-93 in Waterford (daily).

The Vermont Chamber of Commerce, Box 37, Montpelier 05602, distributes *Vermont Traveler's Guidebook* of accommodations, restaurants and attractions. *Vermont Life,* one of the nation's best known and respected regional quarterlies, presents photo essays on various aspects of life in the state, available by writing *Vermont Life,* 61 Elm St, Montpelier 05602. Another excellent source of information on the state is *Vermont: An Explorer's Guide* (The Countryman Press, Woodstock, VT, 1983) by Christina Tree and Peter Jennison, a comprehensive book covering attractions, events, recreational facilities, accommodations, restaurants and places to shop. Obtain it in bookstores and by writing *Vermont Life. Vermont—A Guide to the Green Mountain State* (Houghton Mifflin Co, Boston, revised 1968), one of the American Guide series, gives a comprehensive description of the state, its history and points of interest.

Various books on Vermont are also available from the Vermont Historical Society, Vermont Museum, Pavilion Bldg, Montpelier 05602.

For road condition information contact the Vermont Agency of Transportation, Montpelier 05602; phone 802/828-2648. For weather information contact the National Weather Service, Burlington International Airport, Burlington 05401; 802/862-2475.

For information regarding Vermont's Long Trail, along with other hiking trails in the state, contact the Green Mountain Club, PO Box 889, 43 State St, Montpelier 05602. The Department of Agriculture, Dept SS, Montpelier 05602, has information on farms offering vacations and maple sugarhouses open to visitors.

Several Vermont-based companies offer inn-to-inn bicycle tours from roughly May through October. Tours range in length from two days to several weeks; most are designed to accommodate all levels of bikers. Bicycling enthusiasts can obtain a brochure entitled *Bicycle Touring in Vermont* from the Vermont Travel Division, 134 State St, Montpelier 05602; 802/828-3236. *25 Bicycle Tours in Vermont* by John Freidin, can be obtained from New Hampshire Publishing Co, Box 70, Somersworth, NH 03878.

Barre

Settled: 1788 **Pop:** 9,824 **Elev:** 609 ft (186 m) **Area code:** 802 **Zip:** 05641

Motels

★**ARNHOLM'S.** *891 N Main St, 2 mi W on US 302. 802/476-5921.* 6 suites. May–Oct: S $23; D $25; each addl $3. Closed rest of yr. Crib $3. TV. Cafe ½ mi. Ck-out 11 am.

✔ ★★**SIR ANTHONY.** *173 S Main St. 802/476-6678.* 45 rms, 1–2 story. Mid-May–mid-Oct: S $38–$46; D $42–$58; each addl $5; suite avail; MAP avail; higher rates special events; lower rates rest of yr. Crib $5. TV; cable, in-rm movies. Indoor pool; whirlpool. Cafe 7–10 am, dining rm 5–9:30 pm. Bar 4:30 pm–midnight. Ck-out 11 am. Meeting rms. X-country ski 8 mi. Refrigerators. Cr cds: A, C, D, DS, MC, V.

Bennington

Settled: 1761 **Pop:** 15,815 **Elev:** 681 ft (208 m) **Area code:** 802 **Zip:** 05201

Motels

(Rates may be higher fall foliage season)

★**BAYBERRY.** *(RR 1A, Box 137, Shaftsbury 05262) 8 mi N on VT Historic Rte 7A. 802/447-7180.* 9 rms. No rm phones. S, D $34–$38; each addl $8. Free continental bkfst 7:30–10 am. Rm serv. Ck-out 11 am. Gift shop. Downhill ski 19 mi; x-country ski 10 mi. Lawn games. Picnic tables. Cr cds: MC, V.

★**BENNINGTON MOTOR INN.** *143 W Main St (VT 9). 802/442-5479.* 16 rms, 1–2 story. May–Sep: S $38–$44; D $38–$48; each addl $4; suites $52–$66; family rates; lower rates rest of yr. Crib $4. TV; cable. Cafe adj 11 am–10 pm. Ck-out 11 am. Sundries. Downhill/x-country ski 10 mi. Some refrigerators. Balconies. Cr cds: A, C, D, MC, V.

✔ ★★**BEST WESTERN NEW ENGLANDER.** *220 Northside Dr (VT Historic Rte 7A). 802/442-6311.* 51 rms, 1–2 story. Mid-June–late Oct: S $38–$46; D $52–$69; each addl $5; suites $63–$80; under 12 free; lower rates rest of yr. Crib free. TV; cable, in-rm movies. Heated pool. Playground. Free coffee in rms. Cafe 7 am–10 pm. Bar from noon. Ck-out 11 am. Meeting rm. Free airport transportation. Downhill/x-country ski 9 mi. Lawn games. Some in-rm steam baths & whirlpools ($4–$6), refrigerators. Picnic tables. Near Bennington College. Cr cds: A, C, D, DS, MC, V. ⓓ

★**CATAMOUNT.** *500 South St. 802/442-5977.* 17 rms, 1 kit. Mid-May–Oct: S, D $36–$46; each addl $5; kit. unit $42–$46; wkly, monthly rates; lower rates rest of yr. Crib free.

TV; cable. Pool. Free coffee in rms. Cafe nearby. Ck-out 11 am. Downhill/x-country ski 9 mi. Lawn games. Picnic tables. Cr cds: DS, MC, V.

✔ ★★**HARWOOD HILL.** *2 mi N on VT Historic Rte 7A. 802/442-6278.* 16 rms, 3 cottages. May–Oct: S, D $34–$44; each addl $6; cottages $38–$40; wkly rates; higher rates hols; lower rates rest of yr. Crib free. TV. Free coffee in rms. Cafe adj 5–9 pm; Fri, Sat to 10 pm. Ck-out 11 am. Downhill/x-country ski 9 mi. Lawn games. Porches. Picnic tables. Cr cds: A, C, D, DS, MC, V.

★**HILLBROOK.** *(RFD 1, Shaftsbury 05262) 6 mi N on VT Historic Rte 7A. 802/442-4095.* 17 rms, 4 kits. (no ovens). No rm phones. May–Oct: S, D $40–$46; each addl $4; kit. units $44–$50; wkly rates; ski plan; higher rates special events, some hols; lower rates rest of yr. Crib free. TV. Heated pool. Free coffee in rms. Ck-out 11 am. Downhill/x-country ski 12 mi. Lawn games. Some refrigerators. Picnic tables, grills. Beautiful view; back from hwy. Cr cds: A, MC, V.

✔ ★★**IRON KETTLE.** *(Box 195, Shaftsbury 05262) 6 mi N on VT Historic Rte 7A. 802/442-4316.* 20 rms. No rm phones. S $38–$40; D $40–$50; each addl $5; family, wkly rates. Closed Jan–Mar. Crib free. TV. Pool. Free coffee in rms. Cafe opp 7 am–9 pm. Ck-out 11 am. Coin lndry. Meeting rms. Downhill ski 19 mi; x-country ski 8 mi. Putting green. Rec rm. Picnic tables, grills. Cr cds: A, MC, V.

✔ ★★**WHISPERING PINES.** *(Woodford 05201) 8 mi E on VT 9. 802/447-7149.* 17 rms, 1 kit., 2 story. No rm phones. Mid-Dec–mid-Mar: S, D $36–$58; each addl $7–$10; suite $120–$140; wkly rates; higher rates hols; lower rates rest of yr. Crib $5. TV. Pool. Cafe 7:30–10 am. Bus depot transportation. Downhill/x-country ski adj. Lawn games. Some refrigerators. Picnic tables, grills. Cr cds: A, MC, V.

Brattleboro

Settled: 1724 **Pop:** 8,596 **Elev:** 240 ft (73 m) **Area code:** 802 **Zip:** 05301

Motels

✔ ★**HOLLY.** *243 Canal St. 802/254-2360.* 42 rms, 1–2 story. S $28–$41; D $41–$48; each addl $4; under 10 free. Crib free. TV; cable. Cafe nearby. Ck-out 11 am. Balconies. Picnic tables. Cr cds: DS, ER, MC, V.

★**MOLLY STARK MOTEL.** *(RD 4, Box 53, W Brattleboro) 4 mi W on VT 9; 3 mi W of I-91, exit 2. 802/254-2440.* 14 rms. S, D $32–$45; each addl $5; under 5 free; higher rates hol wkends. Crib $5. TV; cable. Ck-out 10 am. Downhill ski 20 mi; x-country ski 15 mi. Picnic tables. Cr cds: ER, MC, V. Ⓓ

★★**QUALITY INN.** *Putney Rd, exit 3, 3 mi N on US 5. 802/254-8701.* 100 rms, 2 story. Mid-Sep–Oct: S, D $52–$86; each addl $10; family rates; lower rates rest of yr. TV; cable. 2 pools, 1 indoor. Cafe 6:30–10 am, 5:30–9:30 pm. Rm serv. Bar from 4 pm. Ck-out 11 am. Meeting rms. X-country ski 10 mi. Exercise equipt; weight machines, bicycles, whirlpool, sauna. Game rm. Picnic tables. Cr cds: A, C, D, DS, ER, MC, V.

Burlington

Settled: 1773 **Pop:** 37,712 **Elev:** 113 ft (34 m) **Area code:** 802 **Zip:** 05401

Motels

★**BEL-AIRE.** *111 Shelburne St (US 7). 802/863-3116.* 13 rms, 1–2 story. July–Oct: S $55; D $55–$65; each addl $4; suites $75; lower rates rest of yr. Crib $3. TV; cable. Free coffee in lobby. Cafe nearby. Ck-out 11 am. Near recreational facilities. Cr cds: A, MC, V.

✔ ★**HANDY'S TOWN HOUSE.** *(1330 Shelburne Rd, S Burlington) 3 mi S on US 7, 1 mi S of I-89 exit 13. 802/862-9608.* 24 rms. Mid-Sep–mid-Oct: S, D $40–$58; each addl $4; lower rates rest of yr. TV; cable. Pool. Playground. Free coffee in rms. Cafe adj 7 am–11 pm. Ck-out 11 am. Basketball. Some refrigerators. Cr cds: A, C, D, DS, ER, MC, V.

≈

✔ ★**HO-HUM.** *(1660 Williston Rd, S Burlington) 3 mi E on US 2, 1 mi E of I-89 exit 14E. 802/863-4551.* 26 rms. Early June–late Oct: S $34–$51; D $45–$61; lower rates rest of yr. Crib free. TV; cable. Pool. Cafe opp 7 am–11 pm. Ck-out 11 am. Cr cds: A, MC, V.

≈

✔ ★**LAKE VIEW.** *(1860 Shelburne Rd, S Burlington) S on US 7. 802/862-0230.* 22 rms, 2 story, 6 kits. July–Oct: S $36–$48; D $42–$56; each addl $4; kits. $5 addl; under 12 free; lower rates rest of yr. Crib free. TV; cable. Pool. Free coffee. Cafe nearby. Ck-out 11 am. Some refrigerators. Cr cds: A, C, D, DS, MC, V.

🚹 ≈ 🚫 sc

Fairlee

Pop: 770 **Elev:** 436 ft (133 m) **Area code:** 802 **Zip:** 05045

Resort

★★**RUTLEDGE INN & COTTAGES.** *Lake Morey Dr W, ½ mi W off US 5. 802/333-9722.* 5 rms in inn, 2 story, 2 kits; 32 cottages. No A/C. AP, mid-June–Labor Day: D $53–$61/person; family rates; under 3, $8. Closed rest of yr. Crib free. Playground, supervised play. Cafe 8–9 am, 12:30–2 pm, 6–7:30 pm. Box lunches, picnics. Setups. Ck-out 11 am. Meeting rms. Grocery, coin lndry 1 mi. Airport, RR station, bus depot transportation. Sports dir. Private beach; waterskiing; boats, rowboats, canoes, sailboats. Tennis. Soc dir; entertainment. Lawn games. Game rm. Rec rm. Library. Some refrigerators, fireplaces. Picnic tables. Ⓔ Ⓕ

🛏 🐾 ≈ 🏃

Grafton

Pop: 604 **Elev:** 841 ft (256 m) **Area code:** 802 **Zip:** 05146

Inn

✔ ★★★**OLD TAVERN.** *Main St. 802/843-2231.* 34 air-cooled rms, 3 story, 6 houses. No rm phones. Mid-Sep–late Oct, late Dec–early Jan: S, D $50–$110; each addl $20; kit. cottages $110–$300; children under 8 permitted only in 3 cottages; lower rates rest of yr. Closed Dec 25; also Apr. TV in lounge; cable. Cafe (guests only) 8–9:30 am, noon–2 pm, 6:30–9 pm; afternoon tea Fri, Sat; jacket required. Bar from 5:30 pm; Fri, Sat from 4 pm. Ck-out 11 am, ck-in 4 pm. Coin lndry. Tennis, paddle tennis. Downhill ski 12 mi; x-country ski on site. Hiking trails. Bicycles. Game rm. Chippendale & Windsor furniture. Porches, balconies. Restored 1801 inn. Many famous authors have stayed here. Natural swimming pond. Cr cds: A, MC, V. Ⓓ Ⓔ Ⓕ

🛏 🐾 🐾 🚲 ≈ 🏃 🎿

Island Pond

Pop: 1,216 **Elev:** 1,191 ft (363 m) **Area code:** 802 **Zip:** 05846

Motel

✔ ★★**LAKEFRONT MOTEL.** *(Box 161) VT 105, 114 to Cross St. 802/723-6507 or -4316.* 21 rms, 2 story, 4 kits. S $34; D $45; each addl $5; kit. units $55; lower rates off-season. Crib $5.

TV; cable. Cafe adj 7 am–10 pm. Bar from 5 pm. Meeting rms. Sundries. Downhill/x-country ski 16 mi. Boat rentals. Scenic location on lake with fine view. Cr cds: MC, V. Ⓕ

Jeffersonville

Pop: 491 **Elev:** 459 ft (140 m) **Area code:** 802 **Zip:** 05464

Motels

✔ ★★**BEST WESTERN DEERRUN.** *¼ mi E on VT 15.* 802/644-8866. 26 rms, 2 story. July–mid-Oct, mid-Dec–mid-Apr: S $40–$46; D $46–$56; each addl $4; MAP high season; lower rates rest of yr. Crib free. TV. Pool; sauna. Cafe 7:30–9:30 am, 5:30–8:30 pm, high season. Ck-out 11 am. Downhill/x-country ski 7 mi. Some balconies. Picnic tables. Cr cds: A, C, D, DS, MC, V.

★**HIGHLANDER.** *(Rte 108) 1½ mi S on VT 108.* 802/644-2725. 15 rms. No A/C. Dec–Easter: S, D $46–$64; each addl $4; dorm rates; lower rates rest of yr. Crib free. TV. 2 pools, 1 natural with waterfall; sauna. Playground. Cafe 7:30–10 am. Ck-out 11 am. Downhill/x-country ski 3 mi. Lawn games. Rec rm. Picnic tables, grill. View of mountains. Cr cds: A, C, D, MC, V. Ⓓ

Killington

Pop: 50 (est) **Elev:** 1,229 ft (375 m) **Area code:** 802 **Zip:** 05751

Motels

(Rates may be higher during fall foliage season)

✔ ★★**EDELWEISS.** *7 mi E of Rutland on US 4.* 802/775-5577. 38 rms, 14 A/C, 1–2 story, 7 chalets. Mid-Nov–Apr, Sep–Oct: S, D $46–$90; each addl $5–$12; suites, kit. units, studio rms $86–$175; family, wkly rates; ski plan; higher rates some hols; lower rates rest of yr. Crib free. TV; satellite. Heated pool. Playground. Free continental bkfst (winter). Free coffee in rms. Ck-out 11 am. Downhill ski 1 mi; x-country ski 2 mi. Exercise equipt; weights, rowing machines, whirlpool, sauna. Game rm. Rec rm. Some refrigerators. Picnic tables, grill. Fireplace in lobby. Adj to Pico ski area. Cr cds: A, C, D, MC, V.

✔ ★★**TYROL.** *On US 4, 5 mi W of jct VT 100; 5½ mi E of Rutland.* 802/773-7485; res: 800/631-1019. 18 rms, 13 A/C, 2 story, 2 kit. units. No rm phones. Mid-Dec–mid-Apr: D $49–$86; each addl $12–$14; kit. units $92–$195; under 12 free in summer; wkly rates; ski, golf, tennis plans; higher rates some hols; lower rates rest of yr. Crib free. TV; satellite. Heated pool; whirlpool. Playground. Free full bkfst fall & winter exc kit. units, 8–10 am, wkends 7–9:30 am. Ck-out 11 am. Downhill ski 1 mi; x-country ski 5 mi. Lawn games. Some refrigerators; hot tub avail. Picnic tables. Cr cds: MC, V.

★★**VAL ROC.** *On US 4, ½ mi W of jct VT 100 S.* 802/422-3881; res: 800/238-8762. 24 rms, 11 A/C, 1–2 story, 2 kits. Mid-Dec–mid-Apr: D $44–$84; each addl $12; kit. units $84; family, wkly rates; higher rates wk of Dec 25; lower rates rest of yr. Crib $6. TV; satellite, in-rm movies. Heated pool. Free coffee in rms. Free continental bkfst (winter). Ck-out 11 am. Tennis. Downhill ski 4 mi; x-country ski 3 mi. Game rm. Lawn games. Balconies. Picnic tables. Also condominiums. Cr cds: A, C, D, MC, V.

Londonderry

Founded: 1770 **Pop:** 1,510 **Elev:** 1,151 ft (351 m) **Area code:** 802 **Zip:** 05148

Motels

★★★**DOSTAL'S.** *(Box 31, RD 1) 3 mi SE, off VT 11 at Magic Mt.* 802/824-6700; res: 800/255-5373. 50 rms, 2 story. No A/C. Mid-Dec–Mar, MAP: S $59–$93; D $41–$69/person; each addl $25–$35; under 12 free in summer & fall; EP off-season; ski plan; some wkend rates; lower rates mid-June–Oct. Closed rest of yr. Serv charge 15%. Crib $12. TV; cable. 2 pools, 1 indoor; 2 whirlpools. Cafe 8–10 am, 6:30–8:30 pm. Bar from 4 pm. Ck-out 11 am. Tennis. Downhill ski ¼ mi; x-country ski 1 mi. Game rm. Balconies. Cr cds: DS, ER, MC, V. ⓓ

✔ ★★**SNOWDON.** *(Box 137) 1½ mi E on VT 11.* 802/824-6047. 12 air-cooled rms, 1–2 story. Mid-Dec–mid-Apr: S $27–$36; D $39–$53; each addl $10; family, wkly rates; ski plan; higher rates fall foliage season; lower rates rest of yr. Crib $5. TV; cable. Playground. Cafe 8–9:30 am. Ck-out 11 am. Downhill ski ½ mi; x-country ski 1 mi. Lawn games. Balconies. Picnic tables, grills. ⓓ Ⓔ Ⓕ

Inn

✔ ★★**LONDONDERRY.** *(Box 301X, S Londonderry 05155) 3 mi S on VT 100; 4 mi N of jct VT 30.* 802/824-5226. 25 air-cooled rms, 20 baths, some share bath, 3 story. No rm phones. Mid-Dec–Mar: S $30–$69; D $40–$69; each addl $9–$18; higher rates winter wkends, hols, Volvo tennis tournament, fall foliage, Dec 25–Dec 31; lower rates rest of yr. Crib $5. TV in lounge; cable. Pool. Free bkfst 7:30–9:30 am. Cafe 6:30–9:30 pm (exc Tu, Easter–mid-June, late Oct–mid-Dec). No rm serv. Bar from 4 pm. Ck-out 11 am, ck-in 1 pm. Downhill ski 6 mi; x-country ski 4 mi. Lawn games. Converted farmhouse built in 1826.

Ludlow

Chartered: 1761 **Pop:** 2,414 **Elev:** 1,067 ft (325 m) **Area code:** 802 **Zip:** 05149

Motel

★★**TIMBER INN.** *S Main St (VT 103).* 802/228-8666. 16 rms, 2 story. Late Nov–Mar: S, D $52–$65; each addl $12; wkly rates; ski plan; lower rates rest of yr. Crib free. TV; cable. Pool; whirlpool, sauna. Playground. Free continental bkfst. Cafe nearby. Ck-out 11 am. Free bus depot transportation. Lawn games. Picnic tables. Cr cds: A, C, D, MC, V.

Inns

★★**COMBES FAMILY INN.** *(RFD 1, Box 275) 5 mi N via VT 103, VT 100, follow signs.* 802/228-8799. 12 air-cooled units, 8 baths, 2 story. No rm phones. Mid-Sep–mid-Apr, MAP: S $74; D, suites $52/person; each addl $28; family, wkly rates; ski, golf, theater package plans; lower rates rest of yr. Closed mid-Apr–mid-May. Cafe (public by res) 8–9:30 am; dinner (1 sitting) 7 pm. Rm serv 8–9:30 am. Ck-out 11 am, ck-in 2 pm. Bus depot transportation. Downhill ski 4 mi; x-country ski 3 mi. Game rm. Rec rm. Lawn games. Picnic tables, grills. Restored 1850 farmhouse; 50 acres of grounds. Near Lake Rescue. Cr cds: A, ER, MC, V. Ⓕ

✔ ★★★**ECHO LAKE.** *(Box 154) 5 mi N on VT 100.* 802/228-8602. 26 air-cooled rms, 14 baths, some share bath, 2 suites, 6 condos, 3 story. No elvtr. S, D $32–$72; each addl $20–$30; suites $58–$67; kit. units from $195; no children under 5 yrs; MAP avail; family, wkly rates; ski plan; wkends, fall foliage season 2-day min. Closed Apr. TV in lounge & suite; cable. Pool; wading pool, steam rm, poolside serv. Cafe 7–9:30 am, 6–9 pm. Rm serv bkfst only. Bar from 4 pm. Ck-out 11 am, ck-in 2 pm. Bellhops. Bus depot transportation. Lighted tennis. Boating. Downhill ski 10 mi; x-country ski 5 mi. Lawn games. Bicycle rentals. Picnic tables. Cr cds: MC, V.

Manchester & Manchester Center

Settled: 1764 **Pop:** 1,719 **Elev:** 899 & 753 ft (274 & 230 m) **Area code:** 802 **Zip:** Manchester 05254; Manchester Center 05255

Motels

(Rates may be higher during fall foliage season)

★★**ASPEN.** *(Box 548, Manchester Center)* 1 mi N on US 7. 802/362-2450. 24 rms. No rm phones. Mid-May–Oct, mid-Dec–Mar: S, D $45–$70; each addl $8; wkly rates; ski plan; lower rates rest of yr. Closed 1st 2 wks Dec. Crib $4. TV; cable. Pool. Free coffee in rms. Ck-out 11 am. Free bus depot transportation. Tennis privileges. Golf privileges, greens fee $25, pro. Downhill ski 8 mi; x-country ski 3 mi. Lawn games. Refrigerators avail. Picnic tables, grills. Cr cds: A, DS, MC, V.

★★**BARNSTEAD INNSTEAD.** *(Box 988, Manchester Center)* On VT 30, 2 blks N of jct US 7, VT 30. 802/362-1619. 12 rms, 1–3 story. S, D $49–$65; each addl $8; suites $90–$120; ski plan; higher rates special events. TV; cable. Heated pool. Free coffee in rms. Cafe nearby. Ck-out 11 am. Tennis privileges. Golf privileges, greens fee $25, pro. Downhill ski 10 mi; x-country ski 7 mi. Health club privileges. Rec rm. Antiques. Converted barn. Fairgrounds opp. Cr cds: A, MC, V.

★★**EYRIE.** *(Box 501, RD 1, E Dorset 05253)* 7 mi N, just E of US 7. 802/362-1208. 12 air-cooled rms. No rm phones. July–Oct, late Dec–mid-Mar: S, D $48–$55; each addl $10; golf plan; higher rates special events, winter hols; lower rates rest of yr. Crib $5. TV. Pool. Free continental bkfst. Ck-out 11 am. Tennis privileges. Golf privileges, greens fee $25, pro. Downhill ski 10 mi; x-country ski on site. Hiking. Lawn games. Refrigerators. Picnic tables. Early Amer decor; lounge with fireplace. On 22 acres; sweeping view. Cr cds: A, C, D, MC, V.

✔★**MARBLEDGE MOTOR INN.** *(PO, E Dorset 05253)* 5 mi N on US 7. 802/362-1418. 113 rms, 2 story. Mid-June–Mar: S $36–$40; D $38–$48; each addl $8; kit. cottages $48; family, wkly rates; ski plan; lower rates rest of yr. Crib free. TV; cable. Cafe 7–11 am, 5–8:30 pm. Bar. Ck-out 11 am. Tennis privileges. Golf privileges, greens fee $25, pro. Downhill ski 12 mi; x-country ski 10 mi. Private patios, balconies. On mountainside. Cr cds: A, MC, V. Ⓓ

★★**PALMER HOUSE.** *(PO, Manchester Center)* ½ mi N on US 7. 802/362-3600. 36 rms. D $50–$140; each addl $10; suites $120–$150; ski plans; higher rates Volvo tennis tournament; over 16 yrs only. TV; cable. Heated pool. Free coffee in rms. Continental bkfst. Cafe adj. Ck-out 11 am. Meeting rms. 2 tennis courts. 18-hole golf privileges, greens fee $25, pro, putting green, 9 hole chip & putt area. Downhill ski 7 mi; x-country ski 3 mi. Exercise equipt; rowing machine, bicycles, whirlpool, sauna. Lawn games. Stocked trout pond. Row boats. Refrigerators, ceiling fans. Private patios, balconies. Picnic tables, grills. Summer entertainment Wed. Cr cds: A, DS, MC, V. Ⓓ Ⓕ Ⓘ

✔★**STAMFORD.** *(PO, Manchester Center)* 1½ mi N on US 7. 802/362-2342. 14 rms, 1–2 story. July–mid-Oct: S $36–$44; D $38–$48; each addl $6; family, wkly rates; ski plan; lower rates rest of yr. Crib $3. TV; cable. Heated pool. Coffee in rms. Ck-out 11 am. Tennis privileges. Golf privileges, greens fee $25, pro. Downhill ski 6 mi; x-country ski 2½ mi. Lawn games. Balconies. Picnic tables. Cr cds: A, C, D, DS, MC, V.

✔★**SUNDERLAND.** *(Box 375, Manchester)* 5 mi S on VT Historic Rte 7A. 802/362-1176. 15 rms, 10 A/C. No rm phones. S $30–$40; D $40–$50; each addl $6; wkly rates; higher rates in Oct; lower rates rest of yr. TV. Pool. Continental bkfst 7:30–9 am. Downhill ski 10 mi; x-country ski 5 mi. Hiking trails. Lawn games. In-rm steam baths. Picnic tables. Cr cds: A, MC, V.

Middlebury

Settled: 1761 **Pop:** 5,591 **Elev:** 366 ft (112 m) **Area code:** 802 **Zip:** 05753

Motels

✔ ★**BLUE SPRUCE.** *(RD 3) 3 mi S on US 7. 802/388-4091.* 16 rms, 6 cottages, 4 kits. S $36–$48; D $38–$52; each addl $10; kit. units $5 addl. Crib $5. TV; cable. Coffee in rms. Ck-out 10 am. Downhill ski 8 mi; x-country ski 6 mi. Picnic tables. Cr cds: A, MC, V.

★**GREY STONE.** *(RD 4, Box 1284) 2 mi S on US 7. 802/388-4935.* 10 rms. Mid-May–Oct: D $42–$52; each addl $10; lower rates rest of yr. Crib $6. TV; cable. Cafe nearby. Ck-out 10 am. Downhill ski 11 mi; x-country ski 9 mi. Cr cds: MC, V.

Newfane

Settled: 1774 **Pop:** 119 **Elev:** 536 ft (163 m) **Area code:** 802 **Zip:** 05345

Motel

✔ ★**RIVER BEND.** *2½ mi N on VT 30. 802/365-7952.* 20 rms, 2 story. No A/C. No rm phones. S $29–$42; D $36–$50; each addl $10; wkly rates; higher rates: Volvo tennis tournament, fall foliage, hols. Crib $5. Cafe adj. Ck-out 11 am. Downhill, x-country ski 20 mi. Beach, on river. Cr cds: DS, MC, V.

Newport

Settled: 1793 **Pop:** 4,756 **Elev:** 723 ft (220 m) **Area code:** 802 **Zip:** 05855

Motels

✔ ★★**BORDER.** *(PO, Derby 05829) 3½ mi E on US 5 at jct VT 105, 1 mi NE of I-91 exit 28. 802/766-2213; res: 800/255-1559 (VT).* 46 rms, 2 story. S $34–$38; D $42–$48; each addl $6; under 12 free. Crib $6. TV; cable. Cafe 6–10 am, 5–9 pm; wkend hrs vary. Bar 5 pm–midnight; entertainment Fri, Sat. Ck-out 11 am. Meeting rms. Downhill/x-country ski 17 mi. Cr cds: MC, V. ℗

★**NEWPORT CITY.** *974 E Main St (US 5). 802/334-6558.* 65 rms, 2 story. S, D $40–$46; each addl $6. Crib $4. TV; cable. Cafe opp 5 am–9 pm. Ck-out 11 am. Meeting rm. Sundries. Downhill/x-country ski 15 mi. Balconies. Cr cds: A, C, D, DS, MC, V. ℗

North Hero

Pop: 442 **Elev:** 111 ft (34 m) **Area code:** 802 **Zip:** 05474

Inn

✔ ★★**NORTH HERO HOUSE.** *In center of village on US 2. 802/372-8237.* 23 units, 2 story. No A/C. Mid-June–late Oct: S, D $42–$95; each addl $15. Serv charge 14%. Closed rest of yr. TV in lobby. Cafe 8–10 am, noon–1 pm, 6–8 pm. Bar 5:30–11 pm. Ck-out 10:30 am. Craft shop. Airport, RR station, bus depot transportation. Clay tennis court. Waterskiing, snorkeling, windsurfing; boats, sailboats, canoes, dockage. Fishing tackle rentals. Bicycles. Shuffleboard. Game rm. Sauna. Some private patios, balconies. Rms vary. Fireplace in lobby. Built in 1800. On beach & lake.

Rutland

Settled: 1761 Pop: 18,436 Elev: 648 ft (198 m) Area code: 802 Zip: 05701

Motels

(Rates may be higher during fall foliage season)

✔ ★**COUNTRY SQUIRE.** *(PO, N Clarendon 05759) 4 mi S, just E of US 7, VT 7B at jct VT 103. 802/773-3805.* 12 air-cooled rms. S $30; D $40; each addl $5; family, wkly rates. Crib $5. TV. Playground. Free continental bkfst. Ck-out 11 am. Airport transportation. Downhill ski 12 mi; x-country ski 15 mi. Picnic tables, grill. Cr cds: A, MC, V.

⊕ ▶ SC

✔ ★**GREEN-MONT.** *138 N Main St (US 7). 802/775-2575.* 29 rms, 1–2 story. No rm phones. Mid-Sep, Oct, mid-Dec–mid-Mar: S $25–$65; D $30–$75; each addl $3–$4; family, wkly rates; higher rates State Fair, hol wks; lower rates rest of yr. Crib free. TV; cable, in-rm movies. Pool. Free coffee in rms. Cafe nearby. Ck-out 11 am. Downhill/x-country ski 16 mi. Picnic tables. Vermont General Store adj. Cr cds: A, C, D, DS, MC, V.

🏊 ⊕ ▶ ➤ 🐾 SC

✔ ★★**HOWARD JOHNSON.** *S Main St (US 7). 802/775-4303.* 96 rms, 2 story. July–Apr: S $34–$60; D $44–$62; each addl $6; under 12 free; higher rates: ski wkends (Jan–Mar), Washington's Birthday wk; varied lower rates rest of yr. Crib free. TV; cable. Indoor pool; sauna. Cafe 6–1 am. Bar from noon. Ck-out noon. Meeting rms. Downhill/x-country ski 16 mi. Game rm. Rec rm. Private patios, balconies. Cr cds: A, C, D, DS, MC, V.

⊕ ▶ ➤ SC

★★**TRAVELODGE.** *253 S Main St (US 7). 802/773-3361.* 75 rms, 2 story, 3 kits. S $47–$71; D $53–$89; each addl $6; kit. units $89–$159; family rates. Crib free. TV; cable, in-rm movies. Indoor pool; sauna. Free coffee in rms. Cafe 6:30–11 am. Rm serv. Bar Tu–Fri 6–11 pm. Ck-out 11 am. Meeting rm. Downhill/x-country ski 16 mi. Balconies. Cr cds: A, C, D, DS, ER, MC, V.

♿ ⊕ ▶ ➤ 🐾 SC $

Shelburne

Settled: 1763 Pop: 5,000 Elev: 148 ft (45 m) Area code: 802 Zip: 05482

Motels

★★**SHELBURNE INN.** *(Box 2) Center of village on US 7. 802/985-3305.* 40 rms, 2 story. Mid-May–mid-Sep: S, D $53–$78; each addl $5; under 14 free; ski, museum plans; lower rates rest of yr. Crib $5. TV. Cafe 7:30–10:30 am, noon–2:30 pm, 5:30–9 pm. Bar 11:30 am–midnight. Ck-out 11 am. Meeting rms. Cr cds: A, C, D, MC, V.

★★**T-BIRD.** *Shelburne Rd, ¾ mi N on US 7. 802/985-3663.* 24 rms. May–Oct: D $34–$65; each addl $5; higher rates: fall foliage season, hol wkends, graduations. Closed Dec–Mar. Crib $5. TV; cable. Pool; whirlpool. Cafe nearby. Ck-out 11 am. Downhill ski 20 mi; x-country ski 4 mi. Lawn games. Picnic tables. Cr cds: A, C, D, DS, MC, V.

▶ ➤

✔ ★★**YANKEE DOODLE.** *2027 Shelburne Rd, 1 mi N of Shelburne Museum on US 7. 802/985-8004.* 15 rms. May–Oct: S $28–$54; D $38–$68; each addl $4; under 12 free; lower rates rest of yr. Crib free. TV; cable. Pool. Free coffee in rms; free continental bkfst. Cafe adj. Ck-out 11 am. X-country ski 15 mi. Picnic area. Colonial decor; antiques. Shopping mall adj. Cr cds: A, MC, V.

▶ ➤

Springfield

Settled: 1774 Pop: 5,603 Elev: 410 ft (125 m) Area code: 802 Zip: 05156

Motel

✔ ★ **ABBY LYN.** *(PO, N Springfield 05150) 4 mi N at jct VT 10, 106.* 802/886-2223. 24 rms, 2 A/C, 22 air-cooled. S $28–$34; D $38–$45; each addl $6; family, wkly rates; ski plan; higher rates fall foliage season, winter wkends. Crib free. TV; cable. Heated pool. Playground. Ck-out 11 am. Sundries, gift shop. Free airport, bus depot transportation. Health club privileges. Miniature golf. Downhill ski 13 mi; x-country ski 14 mi. Lawn games. Some refrigerators. Picnic tables, grill. Cr cds: A, MC, V.

Inn

✔ ★ **STONE HEARTH.** *(VT 11, Chester 05143) I-91 exit 6, then W on VT 11.* 802/875-2525. 10 air-cooled rms, 8 baths, 3 story. No elvtr. No rm phones. S $36–$60; D $48–$80; each addl $12–$40; wkly, ski rates; higher rates fall foliage. Closed 3 wks Nov. Crib $6. TV in lounge. Cafe 7:30–9 am, 11:30 am–1:30 pm, 6–8 pm. Bar from 11 am. Ck-out 11 am, ck-in 3 pm. Whirlpool. Downhill ski 7 mi; x-country ski 6 mi. Game rm. Lawn games. Picnic tables, grills. Restored farm house; built 1810; antiques. Cr cds: A, DS, MC, V. Ⓓ Ⓕ

Stowe

Settled: 1794 **Pop:** 531 **Elev:** 723 ft (220 m) **Area code:** 802 **Zip:** 05672

Motels

(Rates may be higher during fall foliage season)

✔ ★ **INNSBRUCK INN.** *Mt Mansfield Rd, 4 mi W on VT 108.* 802/253-8582. 28 rms, 14 A/C, 2 story, 4 kits. Mid-Dec–mid-Apr: S $47–$64; D $50–$75; each addl $6; under 10 free off-season; ski plan; lower rates rest of yr. Crib $5. TV. Heated pool; whirlpool, sauna. Cafe fall, winter only 7:30–10 am; also adj 7:30–10 am. Bar (fall & winter only) 4 pm–1 am. Ck-out 11 am. Indoor tennis privileges. Downhill ski 2 mi; x-country ski adj. Game rm. Refrigerators. Balconies. Picnic tables. Cr cds: A, C, D, DS, MC, V.

✔ ★ ★ **MOUNTAIN ROAD.** *(Box 8) 1 mi NW on VT 108.* 802/253-4566; res: 800/367-6873. 16 rms. June–Oct, late Nov–mid-Apr: S $45–$65; D $50–$70; each addl $6–$12; 3-bedrm chalet for up to 8, $175–$325; 5–11 yrs, $5–$7; under 5 free; wkly rates; golf, ski plans; higher rates hols, special events; lower rates rest of yr. Closed Nov 1–Thanksgiving, mid-Apr–mid-May. Crib $5. TV; cable, in-rm movies. Heated pool; whirlpool, sauna. Playground. In-rm coffee. Continental bkfst. Afternoon refreshments. Cafe opp 7 am–9 pm. Ck-out 11 am. Sundries. Airport, RR station, bus depot transportation. Downhill ski 4 mi; x-country ski 2½ mi. Lawn games. Refrigerators. Picnic tables, grills. Bicycles. Cr cds: A, C, D, DS, MC, V. Ⓕ

✔ ★ ★ **SNOWDRIFT.** *(RD 1) Mountain Rd, 2 mi NW on VT 108.* 802/253-7305; res: 800/346-2702. 40 rms, 25 units, 1–2 story, 15 kit. units (no ovens). S $46–$58, D $48–$64; each addl $6; kit. units $54–$70; rms with fireplaces $70–$85; apts $75–$150; under 6 free; higher rates: Washington's Birthday wk, Christmas wk; varied lower rates rest of yr. Crib $5. TV. Heated pool; whirlpool. Playground. Free coffee in rms; free continental bkfst (winter). Cafe nearby. Free afternoon wine & cheese in winter. Setups. Ck-out 11 am. Downhill ski 4 mi; x-country ski ¼ mi. Trout stream. Bicycle trail. Lawn games. Rec rm. Refrigerators; fireplaces. Picnic tables, grills. Cr cds: A, DS, MC, V.

✔ ★ ★ **STOWE.** *(Box 3020) Mountain Rd, 2½ mi NW on VT 108.* 802/253-7629. 17 units, 14 kits., 2 chalets. No A/C. Ski season: D, kit. units $45–$65; each addl $4–$6; chalets to 10, $1,100/wk; under 6 free; higher rates some hols; lower rates rest of yr. Crib free. TV. Heated pool. Cafe nearby. Ck-out 11 am. Downhill ski 4½ mi; x-country ski 2½ mi. Tennis. Lawn games. Refrigerators; some fireplaces. Picnic tables, grill. View of mountains; on 4½ acres. Cr cds: A, C, D, DS, MC, V.

✔ ★ ★ **SUNSET.** *(Box 2480, RR 1, Morrisville 05661) 10 mi NE at jct VT 15, 100. 802/888-4956.* 36 rms. S $32–$54; D $38–$58; each addl $5–$10; kit. suites $60–$145; under 12 free; higher rates hols. Crib $5. TV; cable. Pool. Playground. Cafe adj 6 am–10 pm. Bar. Ck-out 11 am. Free airport transportation. Downhill ski 9 mi; x-country ski 4 mi. Picnic tables, grills. Cr cds: A, C, D, DS, MC, V. Ⓕ

Inn

★ **SCANDINAVIA INN AND CHALETS.** *Mountain Rd, 3¾ mi NW on VT 108. 802/253-8555.* 18 rms, 3 chalets, 2 story. Ski season, MAP: D $48–$62/person; each addl $34; under 3 free; EP avail; wkly rates; ski plans; lower rates rest of yr. Closed mid-Oct–late Nov. Heated pool; hot tub, sauna. Cafe 7:30–9:30 am; summer 8–9:30 am. Setups. Ck-out 11 am, ck-in noon. Downhill ski 2½ mi; x-country ski ⅛ mi. Game rm. Lawn games. Picnic tables, grills. Family-style dinner offered at 7 pm for one sitting. Cr cds: A, DS, MC, V.

Stratton Mountain

Area code: 802 Zip: 05155

Motel

✔ ★ ★ ★ **BIRKENHAUS.** *Stratton Mountain Rd, 1½ mi N of jct VT 100 N, 30 N. 802/297-2000.* 18 rms, 2 story. No A/C. S $37.50–$58.50; D $47.50–$78.50; each addl $25; under 6 free; wkly rates; ski, golf, tennis plans; MAP avail. Serv charge 15%. Closed late Oct–late Nov. Crib free. TV; cable. Heated pool. Free coffee in rms. Cafe 7:30–9 am; 6:30–9 pm. Rm serv. Bar 4 pm–midnight. Ck-out noon. Meeting rms. Barber, beauty shop. Lighted indoor tennis privileges. 27-hole golf privileges, greens fee $35, pro. Downhill/x-country ski on site. Exercise rm; instructor, weights, bicycles, whirlpool, steam rm, sauna. Many refrigerators. Private patios, balconies. Cr cds: A, ER, MC, V. Ⓓ Ⓔ

Resort

✔ ★ ★ ★ **INN AT BEAR CREEK.** *(Rt 30, Rawsonville 05155) At jct VT 100N, 30. 802/297-1700.* 18 rms, 25 condo units, 2 story. No A/C. Dec–Apr: S $35–$65; D $20–$50/person; each addl $10; suites $100–$150; condo units $150–$250; under 6 free; bkfst plan in winter; MAP avail winter; ski, golf plans; higher rates Volvo tennis tournament; some wkend rates; lower rates rest of yr. Crib free. Maid serv $25. TV; cable. 2 pools; whirlpool, sauna. Cafe 7:45–9 am, 5–11 pm. Box lunches, snack bar, picnics. Rm serv. Bar from 4 pm. Ck-out 11 am, ck-in 2 pm. Meeting rms. Valet serv. Package store 3 mi. Airport, RR station, bus depot, ski area transportation. Sports dir. Tennis. Downhill/x-country ski 1½ mi. Sleigh rides. Lawn games. Bicycles. Soc dir; entertainment, dancing. Game rm. Refrigerators, fireplaces. Private patios, grills. Cr cds: A, MC, V. Ⓓ

Waterbury

Pop: 1,892 Elev: 428 ft (130 m) Area code: 802 Zip: 05676

Inn

✔ ★ **SCHNEIDER HAUS.** *(Box 283A) 5 mi S on VT 100. 802/244-7726.* 10 rms, 5 baths, 2 story. No A/C. Early Dec–late Apr: S $35; D $25/person; each addl $10; MAP avail; lower rates rest of yr. Crib avail. TV in lounge. Free bkfst. Cafe 7:30–9 am, dinner in winter. Ck-out 11 am. Downhill ski 8 mi; x-country ski 12 mi. Sauna in winter, hot tub. Rec rm. Balconies. Cr cds: A, MC, V.

West Dover

Pop: 250 (est) **Elev:** 1,674 ft (510 m) **Area code:** 802 **Zip:** 05356

Motels

✔ ★**FOUR SEASONS INN.** *(Box 6) ½ mi N on VT 100.* *802/464-8303.* 24 rms, 2 story. No A/C. Mid-Dec–mid-Apr, wkends July–foliage season: S $46–$68; D $51–$83; each addl $10; wkly rates; ski plan; higher rates: winter hol wks, early Dec. Closed rest of yr. TV; cable. Heated pool; sauna. Cafe 6–10 pm. Bar 4:30 pm–1 am. Ck-out 11 am. Downhill ski 1½ mi; x-country ski 3 mi. Game rm. Rec rm. Lawn games. Picnic tables. Cr cds: A, MC, V.

★★**IRONSTONE LODGE.** *3 mi N on VT 100.* *802/464-3796.* 33 rms, 3 story. No A/C. No elvtr. No rm phones. Dec–Mar, MAP: S $63–$100; D $45–$70/person; each addl $25–$42; wkly rates; lower rates rest of yr. Crib $4–$8. TV, some B/W, color in lounge; cable. Heated pool; sauna. Cafe 7:30–9 am, 6–8 pm. Bar from 4:30 pm. Ck-out noon. Meeting rms. Downhill ski adj; x-country ski 1 mi. Rec rm. Lawn games. Balconies. Picnic tables. Adj to Mt Snow ski area; view of Mt Snow. Cr cds: A, C, D, DS, MC, V.

✔ ★★**MATTERHORN LODGE.** *(Box 208) 2 mi N on VT 100.* *802/464-8011.* 24 rms, 3 story. No A/C. No elvtr. No rm phones. Mid-Dec–Apr, MAP: S $44–$55; D $39–$55/person; each addl $37–$52; wkly rates; ski plan. Closed Nov. Serv charge 15%. Crib free. TV; cable. Heated pool. Cafe 7:30–9:30 am, 6–8 pm; wkends to 9 pm. Bar 4:30 pm–2 am. Ck-out 11 am. Lighted tennis. Game rm. Lawn games. Picnic tables. Cr cds: A, C, D, MC, V.

White River Junction

Settled: 1764 **Pop:** 2,582 **Elev:** 368 ft (112 m) **Area code:** 802 **Zip:** 05001

Motels

✔ ★**COACH AN' FOUR.** *1 mi S on US 5 at jct I-89, I-91 exit 11.* *802/295-2210.* 12 rms. Memorial Day–mid Nov: S $31.80–$43.50; D $38.20–$47.70; each addl $5–$10; under 12 free; higher rates fall foliage season, special events; lower rates rest of yr. Crib $5. TV; cable. Cafe adj open 24 hrs. Ck-out 10:30 am. Downhill ski 15 mi; x-country ski 5 mi. Cr cds: A, MC, V.

✔ ★★**SUSSE CHALET.** *On US 5, at I-89, I-91.* *802/295-3051.* 84 rms, 2 story. June–Oct: S $32–$35; D $42–$48; each addl $3; under 7 free; higher rates fall foliage season; lower rates rest of yr. Crib free. TV; cable. Pool. Coffee in lobby. Cafe nearby. Ck-out 11 am. Coin lndry. X-country ski 6 mi. Cr cds: A, D, MC, V. Ⓕ

Hotel

✔ ★★**HOTEL COOLIDGE.** *(Box 515) 17 S Main St.* *802/295-3118.* 75 rms, 53 baths. S $24–$48; D $30–$95; each addl $5–$10; under 5 free; higher rates fall foliage season. Crib $5. TV; cable, in-rm movies. Cafe 11:30 am–10 pm. Bar to 1 am; entertainment Thurs–Sat. No rm serv. Ck-out 11 am. Meeting rms. Gift shop. X-country ski 10 mi. Game rm. Cr cds: A, DS, MC, V. Ⓕ

Woodstock

Settled: 1768 **Pop:** 1,178 **Elev:** 705 ft (215 m) **Area code:** 802 **Zip:** 05091

Motels

✔ ★OTTAUQUECHEE. *(Box 418) 4½ mi W on US 4. 802/672-3404.* 12 rms. No A/C. No rm phones. S, D $35–$90; each addl $5–$15. TV; satellite, in-rm movies. Coffee in rms. Cafe adj 7 am–9 pm. Ck-out 10 am. Downhill ski 15 mi; x-country ski 5 mi. Some refrigerators. Cr cds: A, MC, V. Ⓕ

⊁ 🖾

✔ ★SHIRE. *46 Pleasant St. 802/457-2211.* 19 rms. No rm phones. S $38–$75; D $45–$85; under 12 free; higher rates hol wkends. Crib free. TV; cable. Cafe nearby. Ck-out 11 am. Lighted tennis privileges, pro. 18-hole golf privileges, greens fee $22, pro. Downhill ski 4 mi; x-country ski 1 mi. Refrigerators. Cr cds: A, ER, MC, V. Ⓔ Ⓕ

🖘 🛏 ⊁ 🏌 🦡 🖾

Wisconsin

Population: 4,705,642

Land area: 54,424 sq mi (140,958 sq km)

Elevation: 581–1,951 ft (177–595 m)

Highest point: Timms Hill (Price Co)

Entered Union: May 29, 1848 (30th state)

Capital: Madison

Motto: Forward

Nickname: Badger State

State flower: Wood violet

State bird: Robin

State tree: Sugar maple

State fair: Late June–early August, 1989 in Milwaukee

Time zone: Central

Interstate Highway System

The following alphabetical listing of Wisconsin towns in the *Mobil Travel Guide* shows that these cities are within 10 miles (16 kilometers) of the indicated Interstate highways. A highway map should, however, be checked for the nearest exit.

> **INTERSTATE 43:** Cedarburg, Green Bay, Manitowoc, Milwaukee, Port Washington, Sheboygan.

> **INTERSTATE 90:** Baraboo, Beloit, Edgerton, Janesville, La Crosse, Madison, Mauston, Portage, Sparta, Tomah, Wisconsin Dells.

> **INTERSTATE 94:** Baldwin, Baraboo, Black River Falls, Eau Claire, Hudson, Kenosha, Madison, Mauston, Menomonie, Milwaukee, Oconomowoc, Osseo, Portage, Racine, Tomah, Watertown, Waukesha, Wisconsin Dells.

Weather Statistics*

	WINTER	SPRING	SUMMER	FALL
Statewide	19°F (-7°C)	43°F (6°C)	68°F (20°C)	46°F (8°C)

*Average mean temperatures are listed for the entire state. Averages for specific regions are given if significant differences exist.

Visitor Information

The Wisconsin Division of Tourism, Box 7606, Madison 53707; 608/266-2161 or 800/ESCAPES (northern IL, IA, MI, MN, WI only), produces a variety of publications covering sports, attractions, events, recreation, and driving tours. When requesting information, ask for the *Spring/Summer Escape Guide, Fall/Winter Escape Guide, Auto Tour Escape, Calendar of Events,* or highway map.

There are several tourist information centers in Wisconsin. Visitors who stop will find helpful information and brochures. Their locations are: I-90 rest area in Beloit; US 12 rest area in Genoa City (seasonal); I-94 rest area in Hudson; I-94 rest area in Kenosha; I-90 rest area in La Crosse; 123 W Washington Ave in Madison 53702, 608/266-2161; 211 Main St in Prairie du Chien (seasonal); and 305 E 2d St in Superior (seasonal). There is also an information center in Chicago, IL at 342 N Michigan Ave, 60601, 312/332-7274.

A bimonthly publication, *Wisconsin Trails,* may be obtained by writing Box 5650, Madison 53705. Bicycling enthusiasts can choose from 23 different tours offered by Bike Wisconsin Ltd. The price of the outings vary; destinations include such places as Door County, Black River State Forest, Devil's Lake State Park, New Glarus and Spring Green. For brochures and reservation forms write Bike Wisconsin Ltd, PO Box 9309, Madison 53715. A state of Wisconsin *Bicycle Escape Guide* may be ordered from Wisconsin Division of Tourism, PO Box 7606, Madison 53707.

Room Rate Information

The following resort areas have higher room rates for two (double) than indicated on the cover of this Guide. However, the lodgings listed in these cities offer a good value when compared to others of their type in the area.

Ellison Bay (Door County)	$60	Lake Geneva	$60
Ephraim (Door County)	70	Sister Bay (Door County)	60

Appleton

Settled: 1848 **Pop:** 58,913 **Elev:** 780 ft (238 m) **Area code:** 414

Motels

✔ ★ ★ **AMORA VILLA.** *200 N Perkins St (54914). 414/735-2733.* 96 units, 2 story. S $38.90–$43.90; D $46.90–$51.90; each addl $4; suites $65–$69; under 18 free; wkly rates. Crib free. TV. Indoor pool; whirlpool. Cafe adj 6:30 am–midnight. Bar 11–1 am. Ck-out noon. Coin lndry. Meeting rms. Valet serv. Sundries. Free airport, RR station, bus depot transportation. Game rm. Some refrigerators. Cr cds: A, C, D, MC, V.

🐾 🏊 SC

★ **EXEL INN.** *210 N Westhill Blvd. (54914), off College Ave. 414/733-5551.* 106 rms, 2 story. S $26; D $32–$40; each addl $4; under 18 free. Crib free. TV; cable, in-rm movies. Free coffee in lobby. Cafe adj open 24 hrs. Ck-out noon. Cr cds: A, C, D, DS, MC, V.

◎ SC

★ **ROAD STAR INN.** *3623 W College Ave (WI 125) (54914). 414/731-5271; res: 800/ 446-4667 (exc WI), 800/445-4667 (WI).* 102 rms, 2 story. S $28–$36; D $34–$42; each addl $6; suites $32–$40; under 12 free; wkly, monthly rates. TV; cable, in-rm movies. Free continental bkfst. Cafe adj open 24 hrs. Ck-out noon. Valet serv. Sundries. Cr cds: A, C, D, MC, V.

🚿 🏃 ⊘ SC

✔ ★ ★ **WOODFIELD SUITES.** *3730 W College Ave (WI 125) (54914), at jct US 41. 414/ 734-9231; res: 800/338-0008.* 94 rms, 2 story. Jan–June: S $29.95–$49.95; D $34.95–$54.95; each addl $5; under 19 free; lower rates rest of yr. Crib free. TV; cable, in-rm movies. 2 pools, 1 indoor; whirlpool, sauna. Cafe adj 6–1 am. Bar from 11:30 am; entertainment, dancing. Ck-out noon. Meeting rm. Valet serv. Sundries. Tennis. Volleyball. Rec rm. Cr cds: A, C, D, DS, MC, V.

🏊 🐾 🏃 ⊘

Ashland

Founded: 1854 **Pop:** 9,115 **Elev:** 671 ft (205 m) **Area code:** 715 **Zip:** 54806

Motels

★ **ASHLAND.** *2300 W Lakeshore Dr (US 2, 63, WI 13). 715/682-5503.* 34 rms, 2 story. May–mid-Oct: S $28; D $32–$44; each addl $3; family rates; lower rates rest of yr. Crib $2. TV; cable, in-rm movies. Cafe 6 am–8 pm. Ck-out 10 am. Downhill ski 15 mi; x-country ski 10 mi. Picnic tables. Overlooks Chequamegon Bay. Cr cds: A, DS, MC, V.

🚿 🍽 🐾 SC

✔ ★ ★ **BEST WESTERN HOLIDAY HOUSE.** *(Box 24) Lakeshore Dr (US 2, 63, WI 13). 715/682-5235.* 67 rms, 2 story. Mid-May–early Sep: S $30–$45; D $46–$63; each addl $5; lower rates rest of yr. Crib free. TV; in-rm movies. Indoor pool; whirlpool, sauna. Cafe. Bar. Ck-out 11 am. Downhill ski 15 mi; x-country ski opp. Many balconies. Overlooks Chequamegon Bay. Cr cds: A, C, D, DS, MC, V.

✔ ★**RED CARPET INN.** *(Box 626, Washburn 54891) On Harbor View Dr; W on US 2, then N on WI 13.* 715/373-5671. 35 rms, 2 story. Mid-May–early Oct: S $40; D $42–$50; each addl $5; under 17 free; lower rates rest of yr. Crib free. TV; cable, in-rm movies. Continental bkfst. Cafe nearby. Ck-out 11 am. Downhill ski 8 mi; x-country ski 6 mi. Whirlpool, sauna. Game rm. On lake. Cr cds: A, C, D, DS, MC, V.

Baileys Harbor (Door Co)

Settled: 1851 **Pop:** 799 **Elev:** 595 ft (181 m) **Area code:** 414 **Zip:** 54202

Motel

★**PARENT.** *8404 WI 57.* 414/839-2218. 11 units, 4 kit. cottages. July–Oct: D $38–$59; each addl $5; kit. cottages $375–$425/wk; lower rates May, June. Closed rest of yr. TV. Playground. Free coffee. Cafe adj 7 am–7 pm. Ck-out 10 am. Lawn games. Grills. Beach 1 mi.

Baraboo

Founded: 1830 **Pop:** 8,081 **Elev:** 894 ft (272 m) **Area code:** 608 **Zip:** 53913

Motel

★**SPINNING WHEEL.** *809 8th St, 2 mi E of US 12 on WI 33.* 608/356-3933. 25 rms. S $30–$48; D $32–$52; each addl $5. Crib $5. TV; cable. Cafe nearby. Downhill ski 10 mi; x-country ski 5 mi. Cr cds: C, D, DS, MC, V.

Beaver Dam

Settled: 1841 **Pop:** 14,149 **Elev:** 879 ft (268 m) **Area code:** 414 **Zip:** 53916

Motels

✔ ★★**BEST WESTERN CAMPUS INN.** *815 Park Ave, jct WI 33, US 151.* 414/887-7171. 94 rms, 4 story. S, D $40–$50; each addl $4; suites $60–$80; under 12 free. Crib $2. TV; satellite. Indoor pool. Cafe 6 am–11 pm. Rm serv. Bar 4 pm–1 am. Ck-out 11 am. Coin lndry. Meeting rms. Valet serv. Sundries. Beauty shop. Cr cds: A, C, D, DS, MC, V.

★**GRAND VIEW.** *1510 N Center.* 414/885-9208. 22 rms. S $27–$30; D $27–$39; each addl $4. Crib $3. TV; cable. Ck-out 11 am. Sundries. Cr cds: A, MC, V.

Beloit

Settled: 1836 **Pop:** 35,207 **Elev:** 750 ft (229 m) **Area code:** 608 **Zip:** 53511

Motel

✔ ★**ROAD STAR INN.** *2790 Milwaukee Rd.* 608/365-6000; res: 800/446-INNS (exc WI), 800/445-INNS (WI). 73 rms, 2 story. S $30–$40; D $35–$45; each addl $5; suites $70–$80;

under 12 free. Crib free. TV; cable, in-rm movies. Free continental bkfst. Ck-out noon. Meeting rms. Valet serv. Cr cds: A, C, D, DS, MC, V.

Black River Falls

Pop: 3,434 **Elev:** 796 ft (243 m) **Area code:** 715 **Zip:** 54615

Motel

✔ ★ ★ ★**BEST WESTERN ARROWHEAD LODGE.** *1 mi E on WI 54 at I-94.* 715/284-9471. 80 rms, 2 story. S $39–$47; D $49–$57; each addl $5; under 12 free. Crib $3. TV; satellite. Indoor pool; whirlpool, sauna. Playground. Cafe 6:30 am–2 pm, 5–10 pm. Bar; entertainment, dancing Fri & Sat. Ck-out noon. Meeting rm. Sundries. X-country ski 12 mi. Snowmobile trails. Nature/ fitness trail. Cr cds: A, C, D, DS, MC, V.

Chippewa Falls

Settled: 1836 **Pop:** 12,270 **Elev:** 902 ft (275 m) **Area code:** 715 **Zip:** 54729

Motels

✔ ★ ★**FLAME.** *1009 W Park Ave (County J), 1 blk N of WI 124.* 715/723-2281. 65 rms. S $32; D $44; each addl $5. Crib avail. TV; cable. Cafe 7–11 am; Sat, Sun 8 am–noon. Rm serv. Bar. Ck-out noon. Meeting rms. Valet serv. Sundries. Airport transportation. Some wet bars. Cr cds: A, C, D, DS, MC, V.

★**GLEN LOCH.** *1225 Jefferson Ave.* 715/723-9121. 19 rms. S $25; D $28–$38; each addl $4. TV; cable. Free coffee in lobby. Ck-out 11 am. Picnic tables. Cr cds: MC, V.

✔ ★**INDIANHEAD.** *501 Summit Ave (WI 29, 124).* 715/723-9171. 27 rms. S $27–$29; D $30–$36; each addl $5. Crib avail. TV; cable, in-rm movies. Free coffee in lobby. Cafe adj. Ck-out 11 am. Valet serv. On bluff overlooking city. Cr cds: A, C, D, DS, MC, V.

Dodgeville

Settled: 1827 **Pop:** 3,458 **Elev:** 1,222 ft (372 m) **Area code:** 608 **Zip:** 53533

Motel

✔ ★ ★ ★**DON Q. INN.** *(Box 199) 1½ mi N on WI 23, 1 mi N of jct US 18.* 608/935-2321; *res:* 800/362-2950 (exc WI), 800/242-2321 (WI). 48 rms, 1–2 story. May–Oct: S $41–$99; D $48–$99; each addl $7; specialty rms $79–$175; under 18 free; lower rates rest of yr. Crib free. TV. Indoor/ outdoor pool. Cafe 7 am–10 pm; Sun to 9 pm. Ck-out noon. Meeting rms. X-country ski 1½ mi. Game rm. Imaginatively furnished; rustic decor. 2,850-ft lighted airstrip adj. Cr cds: A, D, DS, MC, V.

Eagle River

Pop: 1,326 **Elev:** 1,647 ft (502 m) **Area code:** 715 **Zip:** 54521

Motel

✔ ★**WHITE EAGLE.** *4948 WI 70 W & WI 17.* 715/479-4426. 22 rms. No A/C. S, D $37–$40. Crib free. TV; cable. Heated pool; whirlpool, sauna. Playground. Free coffee. Cafe nearby. Ck-out 10 am. Driving range, miniature golf opp. X-country ski 3 mi. Snowmobile trails. Paddleboat. Picnic tables. On Eagle River. Cr cds: MC, V.

Resorts

✔ ★ ★ ★ **CHANTICLEER INN.** *(Dept MTG 8) 1458 E Dollar Lake Rd.* 715/479-4486. 17 rms in 1–2 story A-frame motel, 7 kit. cottages/villas, 50 1–3 bedrm units in 20 townhouses, 20 with kit., most A/C. S $37–$95; D $49.50–$95; each addl $10; under 10 free; ski, golf, dinner plans off-season; package plans; higher rates: winter hols, snowmobile derby. Crib $10. TV. Playground. Free coffee in motel rms. Cafe 8–9:30 am, 5:30–9:30 pm. Box lunches, snacks. Bar from 8 am. Ck-out 10:30 am, ck-in 3 pm. Gift shop. Grocery, package store 2½ mi. Coin lndry. Meeting rms. Free local airport transportation. 2 tennis courts, 1 lighted. 9-hole golf adj, daily greens fee. 2 sand beaches; waterskiing, boats, motors, canoes, sailboats, pontoon boats. X-country ski on site. Snowmobiles. Rec rm. Fishing guides, clean & store area. Refrigerator in motel rms. Fireplace in cottages/villas. Private patios or balconies in townhouses. On chain of 28 lakes. Cr cds: A, D, MC, V.

★ ★ **EAGLE WATERS.** *(Box 1509) 4 mi E on WI 70.* 715/479-4411. 100 rms, 28 A/C, 2 story, 16 kit. units. MAP, late May–Labor Day: D $50–$85/person; kit. units, family suites avail; lower rates rest of yr. Crib free. TV avail. Heated pool; poolside serv, lifeguard. Playground. Supervised, planned child's program. Cafe 7:30–10 am, 12:30–2 pm, 6:30–9 pm. Box lunches, outdoor barbecues. Bar 10:30–2 am. Ck-out 11 am, ck-in 2 pm. Airport, bus depot transportation. Tennis. 9-hole golf privileges adj. Private beach; fishing, boats, motors, canoes, sailboats. X-country ski on site. Health club privileges. Bicycles. Soc dir; entertainment, dancing, movies. Rec rm. Lawn games. Fishing guides, clean & store area. Some refrigerators, fireplaces. Some private patios, balconies. Cr cds: MC, V.

Eau Claire

Settled: 1844 **Pop:** 51,509 **Elev:** 796 ft (243 m) **Area code:** 715 **Zip:** 54701

Motels

★ ★ **ANTLERS.** *2245 S Hastings Way, jct US 53, US 12.* 715/834-5313. 33 rms, 1–2 story. S $32–$38; D $38–$42; each addl $4. Crib free. TV; cable, in-rm movies. Playground. Cafe adj open 24 hrs. Ck-out 11 am. Free airport transportation. Lawn games. Cr cds: A, C, D, MC, V.

✔ ★ ★ ★ **BEST WESTERN MIDWAY MOTOR LODGE.** *2851 Hendrickson Dr, WI 37 at Craig Rd.* 715/835-2242. 110 rms, 2 story. S $39–$45; D $49–$55; each addl $5; under 18 free. Crib free. TV; cable, in-rm movies. Indoor pool; whirlpool, sauna. Cafe adj 6:30 am–2:30 pm, 5–10 pm; Sun 10:30 am–2:30 pm, 5–9 pm. Rm serv. Bar 4 pm–1 am, Sun noon–9 pm; entertainment, dancing Thurs–Sat. Ck-out 1 pm. Meeting rms. Valet serv. Sundries. Barber, beauty shop. Airport, bus depot transportation. Domed recreation area. Game rm. Cr cds: A, C, D, DS, MC, V.

★ **EXEL INN.** *2305 Craig Rd.* 715/834-3193. 102 rms, 2 story. S $26.95; D $34.95; each addl $4. Crib free. TV; cable. Cafe adj open 24 hrs. Ck-out noon. Cr cds: A, C, D, DS, MC, V.

✔ ★ ★ **HOWARD JOHNSON MOTOR LODGE.** *(Box 8037) 809 W Clairemont Ave (US 12).* 715/834-6611. 120 rms, 2 story. S $38–$55; D $47–$55; each addl $6; suites $56–$65; under 18 free; wkend rates. Crib free. TV; cable. 2 pools, 1 indoor; whirlpool, sauna. Rm serv 7 am–9 pm. Bar 11–2 am; entertainment Wed–Sat. Ck-out noon. Meeting rms. Valet serv. Sundries. Rec rm. Private patios, balconies. Cr cds: A, C, D, DS, ER, MC, V.

★ **MAPLE MANOR.** *2507 S Hastings Way (US 53).* 715/834-2618; res: 800/624-3763 (exc WI). 36 rms. S $26.95; D $26.95–$36.95; each addl $3. Crib $2. TV; cable, in-rm movies. Free continental bkfst. Cafe 6:30 am–8:30 pm. Ck-out 11:30 am. Sundries. Many refrigerators. Picnic tables. Cr cds: A, C, D, DS, ER, MC, V.

🔲 sc 🔲

✔ ★★RAMADA INN. *2704 Craig Rd.* 715/835-2211. 130 rms, 2 story. S $43–$47; D $50–$54; each addl $7; under 18 free. Crib free. TV; cable. Indoor pool; sauna. Cafe 6 am–10 pm. Bar from 11 am; entertainment, dancing. Ck-out noon. Meeting rms. Valet serv. Game rm. Cr cds: A, C, D, DS, MC, V.

🔲 🔲 sc

Motor Hotels

★★CIVIC CENTER INN. *205 S Barstow St, downtown.* 715/835-6121. 124 rms, 8 story. S $46–$52; D $52–$58; each addl $6; under 18 free; wkend rates. Crib free. TV; cable. Indoor pool; sauna. Free full bkfst. Cafe 6:30 am–10 pm; dining rm 11:30 am–2 pm, 5:30–10 pm. Rm serv. Bar; entertainment exc Sun. Ck-out noon. Meeting rms. Valet serv. Free airport, bus depot transportation. Cr cds: A, C, D, DS, MC, V.

🔲 🔲 sc

★ ★★HOLIDAY INN. *(Box 266) 1202 W Clairemont Ave.* 715/834-3181. 245 rms, 2–5 story. S $46–$59; D $51–$63; each addl $3; family rates. Crib free. TV; cable. 2 pools, 1 indoor; sauna, poolside serv. Playground. Cafe 6 am–10 pm. Rm serv. Bar 10–1 am; Sun from noon. Ck-out noon. Meeting rms. Bellhops. Valet serv. Sundries. X-country ski 1 mi. Rec rm. Cr cds: A, C, D, DS, MC, V.

🔲 🔲 🔲 🔲 🔲 🔲 sc

Egg Harbor (Door Co)

Pop: 238 **Elev:** 600 ft (183 m) **Area code:** 414 **Zip:** 54209

Motel

✔ ★LULL-ABI. *7928 Egg Harbor Rd, ½ mi N on WI 42.* 414/868-3135. 20 rms, 2 story. July–Oct: D $48–$55; each addl $7; lower rates Apr–June. Closed rest of yr. Crib free. TV. Free coffee. Cafe nearby. Ck-out 11 am. Whirlpool. View of Green Bay. Cr cds: A, DS, MC, V.

🔲 🔲

Resort

✔ ★ ★ALPINE. *Alpine Rd, ¾ mi SW of WI 42, just off County G.* 414/868-3000. 60 rms in 3-story lodge (no elvtr), clubhouse; 30 1–3 bedrm cottages. No A/C. MAP, June–Aug: S $45.50–$54.75; D $53.50–$73.50; each addl $8; wkly rates avail; cottages $54–$120; kit. units $96.50–$118; lower rates late May, Sep–early Oct. Closed rest of yr. Crib $5. Heated pool. Playground. Dining rm 7:30–10 am, 6–8 pm. Box lunches. Beer, setups 7 am–midnight. Ck-out 10 am. Bellhops. Grocery ¾ mi. Free bus depot transportation. Tennis. 27-hole golf, greens fee $10.50–$14.75, putting greens. Sand beach; boats. Lawn games. Hayrides. Free train rides for children of guests. Entertainment nightly, dancing July–Aug. Rec rm. Family resort on Green Bay. Cr cds: A, MC, V.

🔲 🔲 🔲 🔲 🔲 🔲

Elkhart Lake

Pop: 1,054 **Elev:** 945 ft (288 m) **Area code:** 414 **Zip:** 53020

Resort

✔ ★★BAREFOOT BAY RESORT. *990 Lake St.* 414/876-3323; res: 800/242-7815 (exc WI). 150 units, 49 in main building. AP, May–Oct: D $50–$107/person; children $20–$30, wkly rates; under 3 free. EP avail; lower rates rest of yr. Crib free. TV avail. 2 pools, 1 indoor; sauna. Dining rm 6 am–10 pm. Box lunches, snack bar, picnics, midnight snack. Rm serv. Bar 8–1 am. Ck-out noon, ck-in 3 pm. Convention facilities. Bellhops. Valet serv. Gift shop. Valet parking. Free airport, RR station, bus depot transportation. Sports director. Tennis, pro. Miniature golf.

Private beach; swimming, waterskiing; boats, motors, rowboats, canoes, sailboats, paddleboats, pontoons. X-country ski on site. Snowmobile trails. Baseball, volleyball. Hiking trails. Lawn games. Soc dir; entertainment, dancing, free movies. Game rm. Rec rm. Masseur. Fishing guides. Private patios, balconies. Picnic tables, grills. Cr cds: A, MC, V. ⒟ⒺⒻⒾ

♿ 🛏 🐾 🔍 🏊 🧍 SC

Ellison Bay (Door Co)

Pop: 250 (est) **Elev:** 610 ft (186 m) **Area code:** 414 **Zip:** 54210

Motel

✔ ★★**GRANDVIEW.** *(Box 30) 1 mi S on WI 42.* 414/854-5150. 30 units, 2 story. Mar-Oct: S, D $38-$62; each addl $6; suites $60; under 14, $3. Closed rest of yr. TV. Free continental bkfst. Ck-out 11 am. Bellhops. Sundries. Bicycle rentals. Rec rm. Lawn games. Some refrigerators. Private patios, balconies. Cr cds: A, MC, V.

♿ 🧍 🔍 SC

Resort

★★**WAGON TRAIL.** *1041 County ZZ.* 414/854-2385; res: 800/99-WAGON. 45 units in 2-story lodge, 2 kits; 25 kit. cottages. June-Oct: S, D $59-$79; each addl $5; suites $95-$120; kit. cottages $610-$1,000/wk; under 12 free in lodge; ski packages; lower rates rest of yr. Crib free. TV. Indoor pools; whirlpool, sauna. Playground. Supervised play. Cafe 7 am-2 pm, 5-8 pm. Box lunches. Ck-out 11 am, ck-in 3 pm. Coin lndry. Package store 4 mi. Meeting rms. Barber, beauty shop. Gift shop. Bus depot transportation. Tennis. Private beach. Boats; motors, rowboats, canoes. X-country ski on site. Bicycle rentals. Movies. Game rm. Lawn games. Some refrigerators. Cottages have patio, fireplace. Picnic tables, grills. On the shores of Rowleys Bay; extensive wooded grounds. Cr cds: A, DS, MC, V.

♿ 🛏 🐾 🔍 🏊 🧍 🚫 🎣

Ephraim (Door Co)

Founded: 1853 **Pop:** 319 **Elev:** 600 ft (183 m) **Area code:** 414 **Zip:** 54211

Motels

✔ ★★**EDGEWATER.** *(Box 143) 1 blk N on WI 42.* 414/854-2734. 45 units, 2 story. July-Aug, Sep & Oct (wkends): S, D $52-$82; each addl $7; suites $104-$135; lower rates May & June. Closed Nov-Apr. Crib $3. TV. Pool. Cafe 7:30-11 am, 5:30-8 pm. Ck-out 11 am. On Green Bay. Cr cds: A, DS, MC, V.

🏊 🚫

★★**PINE GROVE.** *(Box 94M) On WI 42 in town.* 414/854-2321. 44 rms, 2 story. May-Oct: S, D $66-$84; each addl $8; suites $140; wkly rates. Closed rest of yr. Crib free. TV. Indoor pool. Free coffee. Ck-out 11 am. Coin lndry. Sundries. Free airport transportation. Exercise equipt; weights, bicycles, whirlpool, sauna. Game rm. Refrigerators. Balconies. Opp swimming beach. Cr cds: DS, MC, V.

♿ 🛏 🏊 🧍 🚫

Inns

★★**EAGLE HARBOR INN & COTTAGES.** *9914 Water St.* 414/854-2121. 9 rms, 1-2 story. 12 kit. cottages. No rm phones. Inn: S, D $58-$80. July-Aug: cottages with kit. $297-$495/wk; cottages without kit. $257-$285/wk; lower rates Sep-early Oct, late May-June. Cottages closed mid-Oct-mid-May. B/W TV in cottages. Free continental bkfst for inn guests. Cafe adj 7 am-9 pm. Ck-out 10 am, ck-in 3 pm. Airport, bus depot transportation. X-country ski 1 mi. Refrigerator in cottages. Opp beach. Decorated with turn-of-the-century antiques. Cr cds: MC, V.

🛏 🐾 🏊 🚫

★★EPHRAIM. *(Box 247) WI 42, downtown. 414/854-4515.* 17 rms, 2 story. S, D $69–$98. Closed Nov, Dec, Apr. TV. Complimentary full bkfst. Ck-out 11 am, ck-in 3 pm. Free airport, bus depot transportation. Opp beach. Overlooks Green Bay. Each rm has different theme. Cr cds: MC, V.

⬛⬛⬛⬛

Fish Creek (Door Co)

Pop: 250 (est) **Elev:** 583 ft (178 m) **Area code:** 414 **Zip:** 54212

Motels

✔★HOMESTEAD. *(Box 314) 4006 Main St (WI 42). 414/868-3748.* 20 units, 2 story. July–Aug: S, D $47.50–$64; each addl $5–$6; under 5 free; suites $60–$80; country ski package plans; lower rates Jan–Mar, May–June, Sep–Oct; open wkends only Jan–Mar. Closed Apr, Nov–late Dec. Crib free. TV. Continental bkfst in winter. Cafe nearby. Ck-out 10:30 am. Sundries. X-country ski ¼ mi. Refrigerators; fireplace in suites. Balconies. Picnic tables. Bay 4 blks. Adj to Peninsula State Park. Cr cds: DS, MC, V.

⬛⬛⬛⬛⬛ SC

✔★PENINSULA. *(Box 246) ¼ mi N on WI 42. 414/868-3281.* 16 units, 1–2 story, 1 kit. June–late Oct: S, D $52; each addl $12; kit. units for 4–6 $450/wk; lower rates rest of yr. Crib free. TV. Free continental bkfst. Cafe nearby. Ck-out 10 am. X-country ski opp. Opp Peninsula State Park. Cr cds: MC, V.

⬛⬛⬛

Inn

✔★★WHITE GULL. *(Box 159) 3 blks W of WI 42. 414/868-3517.* 14 rms in inn, 1–2 story, 4 cottages. S, D $45–$100; cottages $115–$195; winter midwk packages. Crib free. TV in cottages. Cafe 7:30 am–2:30 pm, 5:30–8 pm. Ck-out 11 am, ck-in 3 pm. X-country ski 1 mi. Balconies. Built 1896; fireplace in some rms, antiques. Cr cds: A, MC, V.

⬛⬛

Fond du Lac

Settled: 1835 **Pop:** 35,863 **Elev:** 760 ft (232 m) **Area code:** 414 **Zip:** 54935

Motels

✔★DAYS INN. *107 N Pioneer Rd, on US 41 at jct WI 23. 414/923-6790.* 58 rms, 2 story. S $29–$34; D $32–$37; each addl $3; under 12 free. Crib $3. TV; cable. Free continental bkfst 6:30–9:30 am. Ck-out noon. Valet serv. X-country ski 5 mi. Cr cds: A, C, D, DS, MC, V.

⬛⬛⬛⬛⬛ SC ⬛

★EXECUTIVE. *649 W Johnson St (WI 23), 3 blks E of US 41. 414/923-2020.* 47 rms, 2 story. S $33; D $35–$44; each addl $4; higher rates special events. Crib $2. TV; cable. Free coffee. Cafe nearby. Ck-out 11 am. X-country ski 2 mi. Cr cds: A, MC, V.

⬛

✔★MOTEL 6. *738 W Johnson St (WI 23), just E of jct US 41. 414/923-0678.* 79 rms, 2 story. S $19.95; D $25.95; each addl $6; under 18 free. Crib free. TV; in-rm movies. Pool. Cafe adj 6 am–midnight. Ck-out noon. Cr cds: C, D, DS, MC, V.

⬛⬛⬛

Green Bay

Pop: 87,899 **Elev:** 594 ft (191 m) **Area code:** 414

Motels

(Rates may be higher for special football wkends)

★**EXEL INN.** *2870 Ramada Way (54304), US 41 Oneida St exit.* 414/499-3599. 106 rms, 2 story. S $30.95; D $35–$44; each addl $2; under 12 free. Crib free. TV; cable, in-rm movies. Free coffee in lobby. Cafe adj open 24 hrs. Ck-out noon. Cr cds: A, C, D, DS, MC, V.

✓ ★**MARINER.** *2222 Riverside Dr (WI 57) (54301).* 414/437-7107. 23 rms, 2 story. S $30.50–$36.75; D $37.50–$45.50; each addl $5; under 12 free. Crib $5. TV; cable. Free continental bkfst. Cafe 11:30 am–2 pm, 5–9 pm; Fri, Sat to 10 pm. Rm serv. Ck-out 11 am. Meeting rms. Valet serv. Sundries. Beauty shop. Patios. On the Fox River; dock. Cr cds: A, MC, V. Ⓔ

✓ ★**ROAD STAR INN.** *1941 True Lane (54304), ¼ mi E of US 41 Lombardi exit.* 414/497-2666. 63 rms, 2 story. July–Oct: S $31.50; D $37.50; each addl $6; suites $33–$35; under 12 free; higher rates special events; lower rates rest of yr. TV; cable. Free continental bkfst. Cafe nearby. Ck-out noon. Some refrigerators. Cr cds: A, C, D, MC, V.

★**SKY-LIT MOTEL.** *2120 S Ashland Ave (US 41 Business, WI 32) (54304).* 414/494-5641. 21 rms. S $24–$40; D $34–$50; each addl $3; under 12 free. Crib $5. TV; cable. Cafe nearby. Ck-out 11 am. Sundries. Picnic tables. Playground. Cr cds: A, DS, MC, V.

★**VALLEY.** *116 N Military Ave (54303), US 41 Business at jct WI 29, 32.* 414/494-3455. 61 rms. S $30–$37; D $31–$39. Crib free. TV; satellite. Ck-out 11 am. Sundries. Fireplace in lobby. Cr cds: A, DS, MC, V.

Motor Hotels

✓ ★ ★**BEST WESTERN DOWNTOWNER.** *321 S Washington St (54301).* 414/437-8771. 139 rms, 2 story. S $32–$50; D $41–$58; each addl $4; under 12 free; studio rms $32–$58; wkend rates. Crib $1. TV; satellite. Indoor pool; wading pool, whirlpool, sauna. Cafe 6:30 am–2 pm, 5–10:30 pm. Rm serv. Bar 10:30–1 am. Ck-out noon. Meeting rms. Valet serv. Sundries. Solardome. Cr cds: A, C, D, DS, MC, V.

✓ ★**DAYS INN.** *406 N Washington St at Main St (54301).* 414/435-4484. 98 rms, 5 story. S $43–$49; D $49–$55; each addl $6; suites $51–$57; under 18, $1; wkend rates. Crib free. TV. Indoor pool. Cafe 6:30 am–2 pm, 5–9 pm. Rm serv. Bar 3 pm–midnight. Ck-out noon. Meeting rms. Valet serv. Sundries. Overlooks Fox River. Cr cds: A, D, DS, MC, V.

✓ ★ ★**HOWARD JOHNSON.** *US 41 & County G exit (54115).* 414/336-0611. 119 rms, 5 story. S $35–$47; D $45–$57; each addl $5; suites $53–$60; under 18 free. Crib free. TV; cable. Indoor pool; whirlpool, sauna. Cafe 5:30 pm–midnight. Rm serv 7:30 am–11 pm. Bar 11–1 am. Ck-out noon. Meeting rms. Bellhops. Sundries. Free airport, bus depot transportation. Lighted tennis. Balconies. Cr cds: A, C, D, DS, MC, V.

Hayward

Settled: 1881 **Pop:** 1,698 **Elev:** 1,198 ft (365 m) **Area code:** 715 **Zip:** 54843

Motels

★**EDELWEISS INN.** *(Rte 6) 1½ mi S on WI 27.* 715/634-4679. 8 rms. June–Sep: S $34; D $38–$45; each addl $4; lower rates rest of yr. Crib avail. TV; satellite. Continental bkfst avail. Ck-out 11 am. Gift shop. Downhill ski 20 mi; x-country ski 3 mi. Snowmobile trail. Private patios. Picnic tables. Cr cds: MC, V. Ⓓ

✔ ★NORTHERN PINES. *(Rte 6, Box 6489) 1¼ mi S on WI 27. 715/634-4959.* 28 rms, 3 kits. June–mid-Oct, mid-Dec–Feb: S $29–$37; D $34–$58; each addl $4; kit. units $4 addl; under 6 free; lower rates rest of yr. Crib avail. TV; satellite, in-rm movies. Pool; whirlpool, sauna. Playground. Free coffee. Ck-out 11 am. Free airport transportation. Downhill ski 20 mi; x-country ski 1 mi. Some refrigerators. Some patios, picnic tables. Cr cds: A, C, D, DS, MC, V.

★STROUF'S. *(Rte 2, Winter 54896) 1 blk W of Winter on WI 70. 715/266-6621.* 10 rms, 2 kits. S $21; D $27; each addl $6; kit. units $27–$33. TV; cable. Pool. Cafe nearby. Ck-out 10:30 am. X-country ski 15 mi. Cr cds: MC, V.

Hudson

Pop: 5,434 **Elev:** 780 ft (238 m) **Area code:** 715 **Zip:** 54016

Motel

✔ ★ ★BEST WESTERN HUDSON HOUSE INN. *(Box 146) 1 mi SE, just off I-94 exit 2. 715/386-2394.* 102 rms, 1–2 story. S $37; D $45; each addl $6; studio rms $55; under 13 free. Crib free. TV. Indoor pool. Cafe 5–9 pm; Fri, Sat to 10 pm; 9 am–12:30 pm, 4–9 pm. Rm serv from 9 am. Bar 11:30–1 am; entertainment Fri, Sat. Ck-out 11 am. Meeting rms. Valet serv. Sundries. Beauty shop. Downhill ski 8 mi. Cr cds: A, C, D, DS, MC, V.

Janesville

Founded: 1836 **Pop:** 51,071 **Elev:** 858 ft (262 m) **Area code:** 608 **Zip:** 53545

Motels

✔ ★ ★JANESVILLE MOTOR LODGE. *3900 Milton Ave, jct WI 26, I-90. 608/756-4511.* 107 rms, 2 story. S $38–$48; D $50–$60; each addl $4; suites $75–$85; under 12 free. Crib free. TV; cable. Indoor pool; whirlpool, sauna. Cafe 6 am–2 pm, 5–9 pm; wkends to 10 pm. Rm serv to 10 pm. Bar 11–1 am; entertainment, dancing wkends. Ck-out 1 pm. Meeting rms. Gift shop. Game rm. Cr cds: A, C, D, MC, V.

✔ ★ ★RAMADA INN. *3431 Milton Ave. 608/756-2341.* 192 rms, 2 story. S $42–$49; D $48–$58; each addl $6; under 18 free. Crib free. TV; cable. Indoor pool; whirlpool, sauna. Cafe 6 am–2:30 pm, 5–10 pm; Fri, Sat to 10:30 pm; Sun 6 am–2 pm, 4–9 pm. Rm serv to 10:30 pm. Bar 11:30–1 am; entertainment wkends, dancing exc Sun. Ck-out noon. Meeting rms. Valet serv. Sundries. Gift shop. Putting green. Game rm. Cr cds: A, C, D, DS, MC, V.

★ROAD STAR INN. *3520 Milton Ave, just S of I-90 Milton exit. 608/754-0251.* 62 rms, 2 story. S, D $28.95–$32; each addl $6; suites $29.95–$34; under 11 free; higher rates special events. TV; cable, in-rm movies. Cafe adj open 24 hrs. Ck-out noon. Sundries. Some refrigerators. Cr cds: A, D, MC, V.

Kenosha

Settled: 1835 **Pop:** 77,685 **Elev:** 610 ft (186 m) **Area code:** 414

Motel

✔ ★BUDGETEL INN. *7540 118th Ave (53142), at jct I-94, WI 50. 414/857-7911.* 95 rms, 2 story. S $29.95–$34.95; D $34.95–$39.95; each addl $5; under 18 free. Crib free. TV;

cable. Cafe adj open 24 hrs. Beer. Ck-out noon. Valet serv. Downhill ski 15 mi. Cr cds: A, C, D, DS, MC, V.

♿ 🐾 🏊 ⊘

La Crosse

Settled: 1842 **Pop:** 48,347 **Elev:** 669 ft (204 m) **Area code:** 608

Motels

(Rates may be higher during Oktoberfest)

✓ ★**BLUFF VIEW INN.** *3715 Mormon Coulee Rd (54601). 608/788-0600.* 60 rms, 2 story. S $27–$32; D $32–$42; each addl $5; suites $60–$70; under 13 free. Crib free. TV; in-rm movies. Indoor pool; sauna. Cafe 6–11 am. Bar. Ck-out noon. Meeting rms. Sundries. Downhill ski 3 mi. Cr cds: A, C, D, DS, MC, V.

🐾 🏊 ⊗ ⊘ 🦮 SC 💲

★**EXEL INN.** *2150 Rose St (54603). 608/781-0400.* 103 rms, 2 story. S $25.95–$30.95; D $30.95–$36.95; each addl $4; under 19 free. Crib free. TV; in-rm movies. Cafe nearby. Ck-out noon. Downhill/x-country ski 10 mi. Cr cds: A, C, D, DS, MC, V.

🏊 ⊘ 🦮 SC

★**GUEST HOUSE.** *810 S 4th St (54601), 5 blks S on US 14, 61, 53, WI 33. 608/784-8840.* 39 rms, 2 story. S $25–$30; D $30–$36; each addl $3. Crib free. TV; cable, in-rm movies. Heated pool. Cafe 7–11 am. Ck-out 11 am. Downhill/x-country ski 8 mi. Cr cds: A, C, D, DS, MC, V.

🏊 🏊 ⊗ 🦮 SC

✓ ★ ★**HAMPTON INN.** *2110 Rose St (54603). 608/781-5100.* 101 rms, 2 story. S $31–$39; D $38–$46; suites $75; under 19 free. Crib free. TV; cable, in-rm movies. Indoor pool; whirlpool. Cafe adj open 24 hrs. Ck-out noon. Meeting rms. Cr cds: A, C, D, DS, MC, V.

♿ 🏊 ⊗ 🦮

★**NIGHTSAVER INN.** *1906 Rose St (54603). 608/781-0200.* 75 rms, 2 story. S $27–$33; D $34.75–$38.75; each addl $2–$3; under 13 free. Crib free. TV; cable, in-rm movies. Free continental bkfst. Cafe opp opens 6 am. Ck-out 11 am. Meeting rms. Downhill/x-country ski 10 mi. Some refrigerators. Cr cds: A, C, D, DS, MC, V.

♿ 🏊 ⊗ 🦮

✓ ★ ★**RAMADA INN.** *2325 Bainbridge (54603). 608/785-0420.* 148 rms, 2 story. S $42.95–$47.95; D $47.95–$52.95; each addl $8; under 18 free. Crib free. TV; cable. Indoor pool; sauna. Cafe 6 am–10 pm. Rm serv. Bar 2 pm–1 am. Ck-out noon. Meeting rms. Valet serv. Game rm. Sundries. Free airport transportation. Downhill/x-country ski 10 mi. Cr cds: A, C, D, DS, MC, V.

🐾 🏊 ⊗ 🦮

★**ROAD STAR INN.** *2622 Rose St (54603), US 53 at I-90. 608/781-3070.* 110 rms, 2 story. S $27–$35; D $35–$41; each addl $3; under 12 free; higher rates special events. TV; cable. Free continental bkfst. Cafe adj open 24 hrs. Ck-out noon. Downhill/x-country ski 8 mi. Some refrigerators, wet bars. Cr cds: A, MC, V.

♿ 🏊 ⊗ 🦮 SC

✓ ★**SUPER 8.** *1625 Rose St (54603). 608/781-8880.* 80 rms, 2 story. S $34–$38; D $39–$44; each addl $4; under 18 free. Crib free. TV; in-rm movies. Free continental bkfst. Cafe nearby. Ck-out 11 am. Coin lndry. Meeting rms. Sundries. Downhill/x-country ski 10 mi. Whirlpool. Cr cds: A, C, D, DS, MC, V.

♿ 🏊 ⊗ 🦮 SC

★**WELCH.** *3643 Mormon Coulee Rd (54601). 608/788-1300.* 16 rms. S $24–$34; D $27–$39. Crib $2. TV. Free coffee in lobby. Cafe nearby. Ck-out 11 am. Downhill/x-country ski 3 mi. Picnic tables. Cr cds: C, D, DS, MC, V.

🏊 🦮

Lake Geneva

Settled: 1840 **Pop:** 5,612 **Elev:** 880 ft (268 m) **Area code:** 414 **Zip:** 53147

Motor Hotel

★★★**INTERLAKEN.** *WI 50, 3½ mi W. 414/248-9121; res: 800/225-5558 (exc WI).* 144 rms in 3-story lodge, 120 kit. villas. Lodge: S, D $59–$145; each addl $10; villas (2-night min) for 1–4, $155–$240; under 12 free; package plans avail. Crib free. TV. 3 pools, 1 indoor; wading pool, poolside serv. Playground. Cafe 7 am–10 pm. Rm serv. Bar 11–1 am; entertainment, dancing. Ck-out noon. Meeting rms. Valet serv. Concierge. Sundries. Gift shop. Barber, beauty shop. Tennis. Boats, waterskiing, windsurfing. Downhill ski 5 mi; x-country ski on site. Snowmobiles. Exercise rm; instructor, weights, bicycles, whirlpool, steam rm, sauna. Rec rm. Cr cds: A, C, D, DS, MC, V. Ⓔ

Resort

✔★★**NIPPERSINK.** *(Box 839, Twin Lakes 53181) 8 mi S on US 12 to Burlington Rd (County P), then 2 mi E to County O, then N and follow signs. 414/279-5281; res: 800/647-7465 (surrounding states), 800/541-5442 (WI).* 96 units in 3-story lodge (no elvtr), 65 cottage rms. AP, May–early Oct: S, D $54–$94; each addl $35; under 3 free; hol packages, golf plans; lower rates May–June & Sep. Closed rest of yr. TV in lobby & lounge. Heated pool; poolside serv, lifeguard. Playground; supervised play, teen club, child's program. Dining rm (public by res) 8–10 am, 1–2:30 pm, 7–8 pm. Snack bar. Bar 11–2 am. Ck-out 2 pm, ck-in 4 pm. Sundries. Gift shop. Coin lndry 3 mi. Meeting rms. Airport, RR station transportation. Sports dir. Tennis. 18-hole golf, pro, greens fee $10, putting green, driving range. Private beach; waterskiing; sailboats, paddleboats, canoes, rowboats. Downhill ski 5 mi. Sun deck. Lawn games. Softball, volleyball. Soc dirs; entertainment, dancing, movies. Rec rm. Game rm. Exercise rm; instructor, weights, bicycles, whirlpool, sauna. Cr cds: A, MC, V.

Land O' Lakes

Pop: 500 (est) **Elev:** 1,700 ft (518 m) **Area code:** 715 **Zip:** 54540

Motel

★**PINEAIRE.** *(Box 437) 1 mi N on US 45. 906/544-2313.* 10 rms in cottages. No A/C. D $25–$36; each addl $3. Crib free. B/W TV. Bkfst 7–11 am. Ck-out 11 am. X-country ski on site. Private beach. Boating, canoeing. Fishing guides. Lawn games. Picnic tables, grills. Early Amer decor. Spacious wooded grounds on Moon Lake.

Resort

✔★★**SUNRISE LODGE.** *5894 W Shore Dr, N off County E. 715/547-3684.* 20 units in 18 cottages, 9 kits. No A/C. Early May–mid-Oct, AP: S $53/person; D $52/person; EP: D $51; wkly, family rates; fall package plan. Also two yr-round 4–6 bedrm units. Closed rest of yr. Crib avail. Playground. Dining rm 8–10 am, noon–2 pm; Sun 8–11 am, noon–3:30 pm. Box lunches. Meeting rm. Airport, bus depot transportation. Tennis. Miniature golf. Private beach; boats, motors; canoes. Lawn games. X-country ski on site. Exercise trail. Nature trail. Rec rm. Bicycles. Basketball court. Fish/hunt guides; clean & store area. Refrigerators. Picnic tables, grills. Spacious grounds. On Lac Vieux Desert. Cr cds: DS, MC, V.

Madison

Settled: 1837 **Pop:** 170,616 **Elev:** 863 ft (263 m) **Area code:** 608

Motels

★★BEST WESTERN MIDWAY MOTOR LODGE. *3710 E Washington Ave (53704), jct US 51, 151. 608/244-2424.* 95 rms, 2 story. S $46–$52; D $52–$81; each addl $6; under 18 free. Crib free. TV; cable. Indoor pool; whirlpool, sauna. Cafe 6:30 am–9 pm. Rm serv from 8 am. Bar 11:30–2 am; dancing. Ck-out 1 pm. Meeting rms. Valet serv. Sundries. Barber shop. Sun deck. Airport transportation. Cr cds: A, C, D, DS, MC, V.

🏊 ⊘ 🐾 SC

✔★EXEL INN. *4202 East Towne Blvd (53704). 608/241-3861.* 103 rms, 2 story. S $26.95–$31.95; D $33.95–$41.95; under 18 free. Crib free. TV; cable. Cafe adj open 24 hrs. Ck-out noon. X-country ski 5 mi. Health club privileges. Cr cds: A, C, D, DS, MC, V.

♿ 🏃 ⊘ 🐾 SC

★★HOLIDAY INN SOUTHEAST. *I-90 exit US 12, 18E (53704); East Cambridge exit 142B. 608/222-9121.* 188 rms, 2 story. S $49–$53; D $53–$60; each addl $6; suites $75–$110; under 20 free. Crib free. TV; cable. Indoor pool; sauna, poolside serv. Free coffee. Cafe 6 am–10 pm. Rm serv from 7 am. Bar 11–12:45 am. Ck-out noon. Meeting rms. Valet serv. X-country ski ¼ mi. Rec rm. Cr cds: A, C, D, DS, MC, V.

🐾 🏃 🏊 🏈 ⊘ 🐾 SC

★★IVY INN. *2355 University Ave (53705). 608/233-9717.* 57 rms, 2 story. S $45; D $53; each addl $5; under 12 free. Crib free. TV; cable. Cafe 7 am–2 pm, 5–8 pm. Bar noon–12:45 am. Ck-out 1 pm. Valet serv. Sundries. X-country ski ½ mi. University, hospital shuttle bus. Cr cds: A, C, D, MC, V. Ⓓ Ⓔ Ⓕ Ⓘ Ⓙ

🏊 ⊘ 🐾 SC

★McGOVERN'S. *(820 W Main St, Sun Prairie 53590) 1 mi W of US 151, Business 151 exit. 608/837-7321.* 47 rms, 2 story. S $26–$35; D $29–$38; each addl $3. Crib $4. TV; cable. Free coffee. Cafe adj 8–1 am. Ck-out noon. Meeting rms. Sundries. Downhill ski 18 mi; x-country ski 3 mi. Cr cds: A, C, D, DS, MC, V.

♿ 🏃 ⊘ 🐾 SC Ⓢ

✔★QUALITY INN SOUTH. *4916 E Broadway (53716). 608/222-5501.* 156 rms, 2 story. S $43–$45; D $49–$51; each addl $5; under 17 free. Crib free. TV; cable. Indoor/outdoor pool; whirlpool. Cafe 6:30 am–10 pm. Bar 11–12:30 am; entertainment Thurs–Sat, dancing. Ck-out noon. Coin lndry. Meeting rms. Valet serv. Sundries. X-country ski 2 mi. Game rm. Cr cds: A, C, D, DS, MC, V.

🐾 🏃 🏊 ⊘ 🐾 SC

✔★★RAMADA INN. *3841 E Washington (53704). 608/244-2481.* 196 rms, 2 story. June–Oct: S $44–$65; D $49–$65; each addl $5; suites $65–$139; under 18 free; wkend packages; lower rates rest of yr. Crib $5. TV; cable, in-rm movies. Indoor pool; whirlpool, poolside serv. Cafe 6 am–2 pm. Rm serv 7 am–9:30 pm. Bar 2 pm–1 am; entertainment, dancing Tu–Sat. Ck-out noon. Meeting rms. Valet serv. Airport, bus depot transportation. Health club privileges. Lawn games. Some refrigerators. Cr cds: A, C, D, DS, MC, V. Ⓓ Ⓕ

🐾 🏊 ⊘ 🐾 SC

★RED ROOF INN. *4830 Hayes Rd (53704), at jct US 151, I-90/94, exit 135A. 608/241-1787.* 110 units, 2 story. Oct–late May: S $26.95–$28.95; D $32.95–$36.95; under 18 free; lower rates rest of yr. Crib free. TV; cable. Free coffee in lobby. Cafe adj open 24 hrs. Ck-out noon. X-country ski 4 mi. Cr cds: A, D, DS, MC, V.

♿ 🐾 🏃 ⊘ 🐾 SC

✔★REGAL 8 INN. *1754 Thierer Rd (53704). 608/241-8101.* 92 rms, 3 story. S $26.88; D $31.88–$36.88; under 18 free. Crib free. TV; cable. Indoor pool. Free coffee. Cafe adj open 24 hrs. Ck-out 1 pm. Sundries. Cr cds: A, C, D, DS, MC, V.

♿ 🐾 🏊 ⊘ 🐾 SC

✔★ROAD STAR INN. *3535 Evan Acres Rd (53704), at jct US 12, 18, I-90 Cambridge exit (142B). 608/221-3331; res: 800/446-4667 (exc WI), 800/445-4667 (WI).* 66 rms, 2 story. S $28.50–$34.50; D $35–$36.50; under 12 free. Crib free. TV; satellite. Free continental bkfst in lobby. Cafe adj 7 am–11 pm. Ck-out noon. Meeting rm. Sundries. X-country ski ½ mi. Cr cds: A, C, D, MC, V. Ⓔ

🏂 🚫 sc

✔ ★TRAVELODGE. *910 Ann St (53713). 608/256-8365.* 97 rms, 1–2 story. S $29–$35; D $34–$45; each addl $6; suites $53; under 18 free; higher rates special events. Crib free. TV; cable. Heated pool. Free continental bkfst. Cafe adj 10 am–10 pm. Ck-out noon. Meeting rm. X-country ski 2 mi. Cr cds: A, C, D, DS, MC, V. Ⓓ

♿ 🏂 🏊 🚫 🐾 sc $

Manitowish Waters

Pop: 625 Elev: 1,611 ft (491 m) Area code: 715 Zip: 54545

Resort

✔ ★ ★VOSS' BIRCHWOOD LODGE. *3 mi SE on US 51. 715/543-8441.* 5 suites in 2-story lodge, 10 kits; 18 1–3 bedrm cottages. No A/C. MAP, mid-June–late Sep: D $48–$60/person; family rates; wkly EP in kit. cottages, $450–$695. Closed rest of yr. Crib avail. TV in some cottages. Playground. Cafe (public by res) 7:30–10 am, 5:30–8 pm. Bar. Ck-out 10 am, ck-in 2 pm. Grocery, coin lndry, package store 1½ mi. Airport, bus depot transportation. Marina. Private beach; waterskiing. Bicycle rentals. Fishing guides, store area. Many fireplaces, refrigerators. Sun deck. Tea room 11 am–3 pm. Art gallery; antiques. Spacious grounds on Spider Lake.

⬛ 🏊 🚶 🐾

Manitowoc

Settled: 1836 Pop: 32,547 Elev: 606 ft (185 m) Area code: 414 Zip: 54220

Motels

✔ ★BUDGETEL INN. *908 Washington St, on US 151 downtown. 414/682-8271.* 53 rms, 2 story. S $25.95; D $33.95; each addl $5; under 18 free. Crib free. TV; in-rm movies. Free coffee. Cafe 6 am–midnight. Bar 3 pm–1 am. Ck-out noon. Meeting rms. Valet serv. Cr cds: A, C, D, DS, MC, V.

🐾 🚫

✔ ★DAYS INN. *4004 Calumet Ave (US 151), I-43 exit 76. 414/684-7841.* 80 rms. S $26–$31; D $36; each addl $3; under 12 free. Crib $3. TV; cable. Free continental bkfst. Cafe adj. Ck-out noon. Cr cds: A, C, D, DS, MC, V.

♿ 🐾 🚫 sc $

Marinette

Settled: 1795 Pop: 11,965 Elev: 598 ft (182 m) Area code: 715 Zip: 54143

Motels

★CHALET. *1301 Marinette Ave. 715/735-6687.* 21 rms. S $24–$32; D $26–$36; each addl $3. Crib free. TV; cable. Free coffee. Cafe nearby. Ck-out 10:30 am. Airport transportation. X-country ski 1 mi. Cr cds: A, DS, MC, V.

🏂 🐾

★COURTESY. *1450 Marinette Ave. 715/732-0594.* 18 rms. S $23–$28; D $28–$35; family unit $42–$48. Crib $2. TV; cable. Cafe adj 6 am–10 pm. Ck-out 10:30 am. Airport, bus depot transportation. X-country ski 1 mi. Refrigerators. Cr cds: DS, MC, V.

🏂 🐾 sc

✔ ★SUPER 8. *1508 Marinette Ave. 715/735-7887.* 54 rms, 2 story. S $29.88–$32.88; D $34.88–$37.88; each addl $2; under 12 free. Crib free. TV; cable. Free continental bkfst, coffee. Ck-out 11 am. Meeting rms. X-country ski 5 mi. Whirlpool, sauna. Cr cds: A, C, D, DS, MC, V.

♿ 🏊 🍽 🏂 🚭 🚫 🐾 sc

★**TARRAGON.** *W 1915 Flame Rd, 3 mi S on US 41. 715/735-9049.* 16 rms. S $25; D $30–$40. TV; satellite. Supper club 5–10 pm. Ck-out 10:30 am. Sundries. X-country ski 2 mi. Cr cds: MC, V.

♿ 🏂 🐾

Marshfield

Settled: 1872 **Pop:** 18,290 **Elev:** 1,262 ft (385 m) **Area code:** 715 **Zip:** 54449

Motels

✔ ★★**KNIGHT INN.** *2700 S Roddis Ave. 715/387-1761; res: 800/227-1761 (WI).* 102 rms, 2 story. S $34–$40; D $40–$48; each addl $5; under 18 free. Crib free. TV; cable. Heated pool; poolside serv. Cafe 6:30 am–2 pm, 5–10 pm. Rm serv. Bar 10–1 am; dancing. Ck-out noon. Coin lndry. Meeting rms. Valet serv. Sundries. Bus depot transportation. Downhill ski 14 mi; x-country ski 5 mi. Racquetball. Cr cds: A, C, D, DS, MC, V.

♿ 🏊 🏂 🍽 🐾 sc

★**OLD DUTCH INN.** *908 N Central Ave. 715/387-3407.* 11 units. S $24.50; D $28.50; each addl $4. Crib $4. TV; cable, in-rm movies. Cafe nearby. Ck-out 10 am. X-country ski 7 mi. Cr cds: MC, V.

🏂 🐾

★**PARK.** *(Box 371) 1806 Roddis Ave. 715/387-1741.* 20 rms. S $25–$29; D $31–$39; under 12 free. Crib $2. TV; cable. Cafe nearby. Ck-out noon. Sundries. X-country ski 7 mi. Cr cds: A, D, MC, V.

🏂 🐾

Mauston

Settled: 1840 **Pop:** 3,284 **Elev:** 883 ft (269 m) **Area code:** 608 **Zip:** 53948

Motels

★**K & K.** *(Rte 2, Camp Douglas 54618) ½ mi E on US 12/16 at I-90/94 exit 55. 608/427-3100.* 16 rms. S $25; D $31–$38; each addl $2. Crib free. TV; cable. Cafe opp 11 am–10 pm. Ck-out 10 am. Cr cds: MC, V.

♿ 🐾

✔ ★**RAFTERS MOTOR INN.** *(PO 87, New Lisbon 53950) 9 mi NW; ½ mi N of New Lisbon at jct WI 80, I-90/94. 608/562-5141.* 72 rms. S $28.50–$41; D $36–$51; each addl $5; studio rms $41–$51. Crib free. TV; cable. Cafe 6:30 am–9 pm. Bar 11:30–1 am. Ck-out 11 am. Meeting rm. Rec rm. Cr cds: A, MC, V.

♿ 🍽 🚫 🐾 sc

Menomonee Falls

Settled: 1843 **Pop:** 27,845 **Elev:** 840 ft (256 m) **Area code:** 414 **Zip:** 53051

Motor Hotel

✔ ★★**DAYS INN-NORTHWEST.** *14776 Main St, at jct US 41, 45, WI 74 Main-Brown Deer Rd exit. 414/255-1700.* 144 rms, 5 story. S $42–$50; D $48–$56; each addl $6; under 18 free. Crib free. TV; satellite, in-rm movies. Heated pool; poolside serv. Cafe open 24 hrs. Rm serv. Bar 3:30 pm–1 am. Ck-out noon. Coin lndry. Meeting rms. Bellhops. Valet serv. Sundries. Downhill ski 15 mi; x-country ski 13 mi. Private patios, balconies. Cr cds: A, C, D, DS, MC, V.

♿ 🏊 🏂 🍽 🚫 sc $

Menomonie

Settled: 1859 **Pop:** 12,769 **Elev:** 877 ft (267 m) **Area code:** 715 **Zip:** 54751

Motels

★★**BEST WESTERN HOLIDAY MANOR MOTOR LODGE.** *1815 N Broadway, at jct WI 25, I-94.* 715/235-9651. 106 rms. S $32–$46; D $36–$80; each addl $4; under 12 free; higher rates special events. Crib $4. TV; cable. Playground. Cafe opp open 24 hrs. Bar 5 pm–1 am. Ck-out noon. Meeting rms. Valet serv. Sundries. Downhill ski 13 mi; x-country ski 2 mi. Cr cds: A, C, D, DS, MC, V.

✔★★**BOLO COUNTRY INN.** *207 Pine Ave, just S of I-94 Menomonie exit 41A.* 715/235-5596. 25 rms. S $24–$28; D $30–$36. TV; cable. Cafe 11:30 am–11 pm; Fri, Sat to midnight. Rm serv 11:30 am–11 pm. Bar 11–1 am. Ck-out noon. Meeting rms. Picnic tables. Cr cds: A, MC, V.

Milwaukee

Settled: 1822 **Pop:** 636,236 **Elev:** 634 ft (193 m) **Area code:** 414

Motels

(Rates may be higher during state fair)

★**BUDGETEL INN.** *5442 N Lovers Lane Rd (53225), just E of I-45 Silver Spring Dr exit E.* 414/535-1300. 144 units, 3 story. S $28.95–$31.95; D $31.95–$36.95; each addl $5; suites $36.95–$50.95; under 18 free. TV; in-rm movies. Free coffee in lobby. Cafe nearby. Ck-out noon. Meeting rms. Valet serv. Cr cds: A, C, D, DS, MC, V.

★**CHALET.** *(10401 N Port Washington Rd, Mequon 53092) Off I-43 Mequon Rd exit, W to light then S 1 mi.* 414/241-4510. 36 rms, 2 story. S $29–$31; D $33–$37; each addl $3; under 12 free. Crib $3. TV. Cafe 6:30 am–9 pm. Bar. Ck-out 11 am. Some refrigerators. Cr cds: A, C, D, MC, V.

✔★★**DILLON INN.** *(11111 W North Ave, Wauwatosa 53226) 1 blk E of I-45.* 414/778-0333. 122 rms, 3 story. S $41–$56; D $47–$62; each addl $6; suites $52–$58; under 18 free. Crib free. TV; cable, in-rm movies. Free continental bkfst. Cafe adj open 24 hrs. Ck-out noon. Meeting rms. Valet serv. Sundries. Some refrigerators. Balconies. Cr cds: A, C, D, DS, MC, V.

★**EXEL INN-NORTHEAST.** *(5485 N Port Washington Rd, Glendale 53217) 7 mi N via I-43, Silver Spring exit.* 414/961-7272. 126 rms, 3 story. S $31–$38; D $38–$49; under 18 free. Crib free. TV; cable. Cafe adj 6 am–11 pm. Ck-out noon. Cr cds: A, C, D, DS, MC, V.

★**EXEL INN-SOUTH.** *1201 W College Ave (53221), just E of I-94 College Ave exit E.* 414/764-1776. 111 rms, 2 story. S $28–$31; D $33–$37; each addl $4; under 18 free. Crib free. TV; satellite, in-rm movies. Free coffee in lobby. Cafe opp 6 am–2 pm, 4–10 pm. Ck-out noon. Cr cds: A, C, D, DS, MC, V.

✔★★**HOWARD JOHNSON.** *(2275 N Mayfair Rd, Wauwatosa 53226) 8 mi NW on WI 100 at North Ave, US 45 exit 42A.* 414/771-4800. 80 rms, 2 story. S $39.95–$56; D $39.95–$67; each addl $6; under 18 free. Crib free. TV; in-rm movies. Heated pool. Cafe 6 am–11 pm. Rm serv 8 am–9 pm. Bar 4 pm–2 am exc Sat. Ck-out noon. Meeting rm. Bellhops. Valet serv. Sundries. X-country ski 2½ mi. Private patios, balconies. Cr cds: A, C, D, DS, ER, MC, V.

✔★★★**QUALITY INN.** *5311 S Howell Ave (53207), opp Mitchell Field.* 414/481-2400. 80 rms, 2 story. S $45–$52; D $48–$56; each addl $6; under 16 free. Crib free. TV; satellite, in-rm movies. Indoor pool; sauna. Free continental bkfst. Cafe 7 am–10 pm; Fri, Sat to 11 pm. Rm serv.

Bar 11:30 am–midnight. Ck-out noon. Coin lndry. Meeting rms. Bellhops. Free airport transportation. Cr cds: A, C, D, DS, MC, V. ⓓ

★RED ROOF INN. *(6360 S 13th St, Oak Creek 53154) At jct College Ave, I-94 exit 319 E.* 414/764-3500. 109 rms, 2 story. S $26–$31; D $28–$35; 3-4, $35; under 18 free. Crib free. TV; in-rm movies. Free coffee. Cafe opp 6 am–2 pm, 4–10 pm. Ck-out noon. Cr cds: A, C, D, DS, MC, V.

✔ ★ ★WHITE COURT. *4400 S 27th St (53221), just N of I-894 27th St exit 9N.* 414/282-8800. 86 rms, 1–2 story, 3 kits. S $36–$55; D $40–$65; each addl $5; kit. units avail. Crib free. TV; cable. Indoor pool. Cafe 6:30–10:30 am; Sat, Sun 7–11 am. Ck-out noon. Valet serv. Sundries. Many refrigerators. Cr cds: A, C, D, DS, MC, V. ⓓ

Motor Hotels

✔ ★ ★HOLIDAY INN-NORTHEAST. *5423 N Port Washington St (53217).* 414/962-9410. 106 rms, 4 story. S $45–$64; D $53–$73; under 18 free. Crib free. TV; cable. Heated pool. Cafe 6:30 am–2 pm, 5–10 pm. Rm serv. Bar 5 pm–midnight. Ck-out noon. Coin lndry. Bellhops. Valet serv. Sundries. Game rm. Cr cds: A, C, D, DS, MC, V.

✔ ★ ★RAMADA INN DOWNTOWN. *633 W Michigan St (53203).* 414/272-8410. 152 rms, 7 story, 6 suites. S $42–$59; D $48–$62; each addl $6; suites $65–$75; under 18 free; wkend rates. Crib free. TV; cable, in-rm movies. Heated pool. Cafe 6 am–10 pm. Rm serv. Bar 11–2 am. Ck-out noon. Meeting rms. Bellhops. Valet serv. Sundries. Gift shop. Airport transportation. Downhill ski 15 mi; x-country ski 10 mi. Cr cds: A, C, D, DS, MC, V. ⓔ ⓘ

Hotel

✔ ★ ★ ★RED CARPET. *4747 S Howell Ave (53207), I-94 Airport E exit.* 414/481-8000. 510 rms, 6 story. S $49–$73; D $49–$83; each addl $10; suites $155–$175; under 17 free; wkend package plan. Crib free. TV; in-rm movies. 2 pools, 1 indoor/outdoor. Cafes 6 am–10 pm. Bar 11–2:30 am; Sat to 3:30 am. Ck-out noon. Meeting rms. Gift shop. Barber, beauty shop. Free airport transportation. Tennis privileges. Racquetball, handball, health club privileges. Bowling adj. Cr cds: A, C, D, MC, V. ⓓ ⓔ

Minocqua

Pop: 900 (est) **Elev:** 1,603 ft (489 m) **Area code:** 715 **Zip:** 54548

Motels

★AQUA AIRE. *(Box 1031, US 51) 1 blk N on US 51.* 715/356-3433. 10 rms. Memorial Day–Labor Day: S $25–$41; D $40–$49; wkly rates; lower rates rest of yr. Crib free. TV; cable. Cafe opp 6 am–2 pm. Ck-out 10 am. Airport, bus depot transportation. X-country ski 6 mi. Picnic tables. Beach, city park opp. Cr cds: MC, V.

✔ ★ ★CROSS TRAILS. *8644 US 51 N.* 715/356-5202. 17 rms. Mid-June–mid-Aug: S, D $38–$56; each addl $4–$5; lower rates rest of yr. Crib $2. TV; cable. Cafe 6 am–9 pm; off-season to 7:30 pm. Ck-out 11 am. X-country ski 8 mi. Snowmobiling. Picnic area. Small wildlife refuge. Cr cds: A, C, D, MC, V.

★ ★LAKEVIEW. *(Box 575) 3 blks S on US 51.* 715/356-5208. 34 rms, 2 story, 2 kits. June–Sep, also hols: S $35; D $48–$66; each addl $6; suites $62; kit. units $65–$75; 2-story chalet units; lower rates rest of yr. TV. Cafe nearby. Ck-out 11 am. X-country ski 14 mi.

Snowmobiling. Some balconies. Picnic tables. On Lake Minocqua; dock. Cr cds: A, D, DS, MC, V.

★**LITTLE MINOCQUA.** *(Box 560) 4 blks S on US 51. 715/356-3288.* 19 rms, 2 story. S $35–$40; D $38–$50; each addl $4; under 12 free. Crib $3. TV; cable. Free coffee. Cafe nearby. Bar noon–2 am; winter from 3 pm. Ck-out 1 pm. Meeting rm. X-country ski 10 mi. Boats. Ice-skating. On Lake Minocqua. Cr cds: A, DS, MC, V.

✔ ★★**NORTHWOODS INN.** *(Box 325) 1¼ mi N at jct US 51, WI 70W. 715/356-9541.* 34 rms. Late June–early Sep: S $40; D $50; each addl $4; suite $60; lower rates rest of yr. Crib $2. TV; cable. Cafe adj open 24 hrs. Ck-out noon. Sundries. X-country ski 7 mi. Cr cds: MC, V.

★**PINES.** *8736 US 51, 1¼ mi N at jct US 51, WI 70W. 715/356-5228.* 30 rms. Memorial Day–mid-Oct: S $32–$49; D $37–$52; each addl $5; lower rates rest of yr. Crib $5. TV; cable. Cafe nearby. Ck-out 11 am. X-country ski 5 mi. Lawn games. Picnic tables, grills. Cr cds: A, DS, MC, V.

Neenah-Menasha

Settled: 1843 **Pop:** Neenah, 22,432; Menasha, 14,728 **Elev:** 750 ft (229 m) **Area code:** 414
Zip: Neenah, 54956; Menasha, 54952

Motel

★**PARKWAY.** *(1181 Gillingham Rd, Neenah) 2½ mi SW on US 41, Breezewood exit; 1 mi S of WI 114. 414/725-3244.* 19 rms, 2 story. May–Sep: S $23–$25; D $28–$30; each addl $2; weekly rates; lower rates rest of yr. Crib $4. TV. Heated pool. Playground. Free coffee. Cafe nearby. Ck-out 11 am. Sundries. Picnic tables, grills. Cr cds: A, DS, MC, V.

Motor Hotel

✔ ★★**VALLEY INN.** *(105 Walnut St, Neenah) 414/725-8441.* 109 rms, 7 story. S $39.50; D $45; each addl $5; under 16 free. Crib free. TV; cable. Cafe 6:30 am–10 pm. Rm serv. Bar 11–1 am; entertainment, dancing wkends. Ck-out 2 pm. Meeting rms. Bellhops. Valet serv. Free airport transportation. Refrigerators avail. Cr cds: A, C, D, DS, MC, V. Ⓓ Ⓔ Ⓕ

Oshkosh

Settled: 1836 **Pop:** 49,620 **Elev:** 767 ft (234 m) **Area code:** 414

Motels

✔ ★★**HOWARD JOHNSON.** *1919 Omro Rd (54901), at jct US 41, WI 21. 414/233-1200.* 100 rms, 2 story. S $36–$40; D $42–$46; each addl $5; studio rms $34–$41; under 18 free. Crib free. TV; cable. Indoor pool. Cafe adj 5 am–9 pm. Bar 4 pm–1 am. Ck-out noon. Meeting rms. Valet serv. Sundries. Rec rm. Private patios, balconies. Cr cds: A, C, D, DS, MC, V. Ⓓ

★**MOTEL 6.** *1015 S Washburn St (54904), US 41 exit 9th Ave. 414/235-0265.* 95 rms, 2 story. S, D $20.95; each addl $6; under 18 free. Crib free. TV. Pool. Cafe nearby. Ck-out noon. Sundries. Cr cds: C, D, DS, MC, V.

Park Falls

Pop: 3,192 **Elev:** 1,490 ft (454 m) **Area code:** 715 **Zip:** 54552

Motels

★**EDGE O' TOWN.** *N WI 13, ½ mi N. 715/762-4110.* 12 rms. S $23; D $29; each addl $3. Crib $3. TV; cable, in-rm movies. Free coffee in rms. Cafe nearby. Ck-out 11 am. X-country ski 10 mi. Cr cds: MC, V.

⊘ ⊘ ⊘

✔ ★**TIMBER INN.** *(606 N Lake Ave, Phillips 54555) 4 blks N of Phillips on WI 13. 715/ 339-3071.* 22 rms, 2 story, 2 kits. S $33; D $39; each addl $4. Crib $4. TV; cable. Cafe nearby. Ck-out 11 am. X-country ski 2 mi. Private patios, balconies. Cr cds: A, MC, V.

⊘ ⊘ ⊘ SC

Platteville

Pop: 9,580 **Elev:** 994 ft (303 m) **Area code:** 608 **Zip:** 53818

Motels

✔ ★ ★**BEST WESTERN GOVERNOR DODGE MOTOR INN.** *(Box 658) 5 blks S on US 151, ¼ mi W of jct WI 80, 81. 608/348-2301.* 74 rms, 2 story. S $38–$47; D $51–$59; each addl $5–$7; suites $42–$100; under 12 free. Crib $4. TV; cable, in-rm movies. Indoor pool; sauna. Cafe 6 am–10 pm; Sun to 7 pm. Ck-out noon. Meeting rm. Sundries. State univ 5 blks. Cr cds: A, C, D, MC, V.

⊘ ⊘ ⊘

★**MOUND VIEW.** *1455 US 151. 608/348-9518.* 16 rms. S $25–$34; D $35–$46; each addl $4. TV; cable. Free coffee in rms. Ck-out 11 am. Cr cds: A, DS, MC, V.

⊘

Port Washington

Settled: 1830 **Pop:** 8,612 **Elev:** 612 ft (187 m) **Area code:** 414 **Zip:** 53074

Motel

✔ ★ ★**BEST WESTERN HARBORSIDE MOTOR INN.** *135 E Grand Ave. 414/284-9461.* 60 rms, 4 story. S $42–$44; D $48–$51; each addl $5; under 12 free. Crib free. TV. Indoor pool; sauna. Bkfst 7–10 am. Bar 4 pm–1 am. Ck-out noon. Meeting rms. Valet serv. Game rm. On Lake Michigan. Cr cds: A, C, D, DS, MC, V.

♿ ⊘ SC

Prairie du Chien

Settled: 1736 **Pop:** 5,859 **Elev:** 642 ft (193 m) **Area code:** 608 **Zip:** 53821

Motels

✔ ★ ★**BRISBOIS MOTOR INN.** *533 N Marquette Rd. 608/326-8404; res: 800/356-5850 (exc WI), 800/362-5482 (WI).* 47 rms. S $33–$45; D $36–$54; each addl $3; under 16 free. Crib free. TV; cable. Heated pool. Playground. Free coffee in rms. Cafe adj 6 am–11 pm. Rm serv. Ck-out 11 am. Meeting rm. X-country ski 2 mi. Horse-drawn carriage rides in summer. Cr cds: A, D, MC, V.

♿ ⊘ ⊘ ⊘ ⊘ ⊘ SC

★**HOLIDAY.** *1010 S Marquette Rd. 608/326-2448; res: 800/962-3883.* 18 rms, 1–2 story. May–Oct: S, D $32–$38; studio rm $44–$52; each addl $3; under 12 free; lower rates rest of yr. Crib free. TV; cable. Cafe nearby. Ck-out 11 am. X-country ski 2 mi. Cr cds: A, DS, MC, V.

✔★**PRAIRIE.** *1616 S Marquette Rd. 608/326-6461; res: 800/526-3776.* 32 rms. June–Oct: S $27–$36; D $31–$45; each addl $3; suites avail; lower rates rest of yr. Crib $6. TV; cable. Heated pool. Playground. Free coffee in rms. Ck-out 10:30 am. X-country ski 2 mi. Miniature golf. Lawn games. Some refrigerators. Picnic tables, grills. Cr cds: A, DS, MC, V.

Racine

Founded: 1834 **Pop:** 85,725 **Elev:** 626 ft (191 m) **Area code:** 414

Motel

★**HOLIDAY INN.** *3700 Northwestern Ave (53405), at Green Bay Rd. 414/637-9311.* 112 rms, 2 story. S $47–$57; D $53–$63; each addl $5; under 18 free. Crib free. TV; in-rm movies. Pool. Cafe 6 am–2 pm, 5–10 pm. Rm serv. Bar 4 pm–2 am; entertainment Tu–Sat. Ck-out noon. Coin lndry. Meeting rms. Bellhops. Valet serv. Sundries. Airport transportation. X-country ski 3 mi. Volleyball court. Bicycles avail. Picnic tables. On Root River. Cr cds: A, C, D, DS, MC, V.

Rhinelander

Settled: 1880 **Pop:** 7,873 **Elev:** 1,554 ft (474 m) **Area code:** 715 **Zip:** 54501

Motels

✔★★**BEST WESTERN CLARIDGE MOTOR INN.** *70 N Stevens St. 715/362-7100.* 80 rms, 2-4 story. S $38–$44; D $46–$52; each addl $6; under 16 free. TV; cable. Indoor pool. Cafe 7–10:30 am, 11:30 am–2 pm, 5–10 pm; Sun, hols 7 am–2 pm, 5–9 pm. Bar 11:30 am–2 pm, 4 pm–1 am; entertainment Fri, Sat. Ck-out 11 am. Meeting rms. Valet serv. Sundries. Airport transportation. Downhill ski 20 mi; x-country ski 5 mi. Exercise equipt; bicycles, treadmill, whirlpool. Game rm. Cr cds: A, C, D, DS, MC, V.

✔★★**HOLIDAY INN.** *(Box 675) 1 mi W at jct US 8, WI 47. 715/369-3600.* 101 rms, 2 story. S $43–$49; D $49–$56; each addl $6. Crib free. TV; cable. Indoor pool. Cafe 6:30 am–2 pm, 5–10 pm; Sun from 7 am. Rm serv. Bar 11:30 am–midnight; entertainment, dancing. Ck-out noon. Coin lndry. Meeting rms. Sundries. Free airport transportation. Downhill ski 20 mi; x-country ski 5 mi. Exercise equipt; bicycles, treadmill, whirlpool, sauna. Game rm. Cr cds: A, C, D, DS, MC, V.

Rice Lake

Pop: 7,691 **Elev:** 1,140 ft (347 m) **Area code:** 715 **Zip:** 54868

Motels

✔★★**BEST WESTERN INN.** *2835 S Main. 715/234-7017.* 83 rms, 1-2 story. May–Sep: S, D $42–$48; each addl $4; lower rates rest of yr. Crib $4. TV; cable. Indoor pool; whirlpool. Free continental bkfst. Cafe adj 11 am–11 pm. Bar 4 pm–midnight exc Sun. Ck-out 11 am. Sun deck. Cr cds: A, C, D, DS, MC, V.

✔★★**CURRIER'S LAKEVIEW.** *(Rte 4, Box 464) 9 blks E of Main St on County C, east shore of Rice Lake. 715/234-7474.* 19 rms, 2 story, 7 kits. Mid-May–mid-Oct: S, D $45–$51; kit. units for 2-6, $5 addl; lower rates rest of yr. Crib $2. TV; cable. Continental bkfst. Ck-out 11 am.

Meeting rm. Free airport transportation. Downhill/x-country ski 4 mi. Snowmobile trails. Private beach; boats, motors, dockage; sailboards, paddle boats, sailboats, canoes, pontoon. Sauna, whirlpool. Hunting. Picnic tables, grill. Wooded grounds; on lake; park adj. Cr cds: A, DS, MC, V.

★**HAGEN.** *1130 S Main St. 715/234-2359.* 24 rms. May–Oct: S, D $34–$42; each addl $4; lower rates rest of yr. Crib free. TV; cable. Free coffee in rms. Cafe nearby. Ck-out 11 am. Downhill/x-country ski 5 mi. Picnic tables. Fishing nearby. Cr cds: A, DS, MC, V.

St Croix Falls

Settled: 1837 **Pop:** 1,497 **Elev:** 900 ft (274 m) **Area code:** 715 **Zip:** 54024

Motel

✔ ★ ★**DALLES HOUSE.** *(Box 664) ¾ mi S on WI 35, 1 blk S of jct US 8. 715/483-3206; res: 800/341-8000.* 51 rms, 2 story. S $35–$49; D $35–$70; each addl $5; wkday ski package plan; Crib $5. TV. Indoor pool; sauna. Cafe adj 11 am–11 pm. Bar adj 9–1 am; entertainment, dancing Fri–Sun. Ck-out 11 am. Coin lndry. Meeting rm. Downhill ski 3 mi; x-country ski ¼ mi. Interstate State Park adj. Cr cds: A, C, D, DS, MC, V.

St Germain

Pop: 200 (est) **Elev:** 1,627 ft (496 m) **Area code:** 715 **Zip:** 54558

Motel

✔ ★**RUSTIC MANOR.** *6343 US 70, ¾ mi E on WI 70. 715/479-9776.* 20 rms. S $32–$42; D $37–$55. Crib $5. TV. Free coffee in lobby. Ck-out 10 am. X-country ski 2 mi. Snowmobile trails. Cr cds: MC, V.

Shawano

Settled: 1843 **Pop:** 7,013 **Elev:** 821 ft (250 m) **Area code:** 715 **Zip:** 54166

Motels

✔ ★ ★**BEST WESTERN VILLAGE HAUS MOTOR LODGE.** *201 Airport Rd. 715/526-9595.* 65 rms, 2 story. June–Aug: S $33–$46; D $42–$62; each addl $6; under 12 free; lower rates rest of yr. Crib free. TV; cable. Indoor pool; whirlpool. Cafe. Bar 4 pm–1 am. Meeting rms. Sundries. Downhill ski 13 mi; x-country ski 5 mi. Game rm. Near lake, river; beach swimming. Cr cds: A, C, D, DS, MC, V.

✔ ★ ★**CECIL LEISURE MANOR.** *(WI 22 & County H, Cecil 54111) 8 mi NE on WI 22. 715/745-6444.* 21 kit. units. S $38; D $46; 3–4, $58; each addl $6; suite avail; some lower rates. Crib $3. TV; satellite. Indoor pool; whirlpool, sauna. Free morning coffee. Cafe nearby. Ck-out 11:30 am. Coin lndry. Sundries. Downhill ski 15 mi; x-country ski 5 mi. Game rm. Lawn games. Sun deck. Stagecoach rides. Cr cds: MC, V.

★**WISCONSIN HOUSE INN.** *216 E Green Bay St. 715/526-5353.* 55 rms, 2 story. S $29; D $38–$44; each addl $7; under 12 free; wkly rates. Crib free. TV; cable. Cafe 6:30 am–9 pm. Bar 11–1 am. Ck-out 11 am. Meeting rms. Downhill ski 4 mi; x-country ski 3 mi. Cr cds: A, D, DS, MC, V.

Sheboygan

Settled: 1818 Pop: 48,085 Elev: 633 ft (193 m) **Area code:** 414 Zip: 53081

Motels

✔ ★**BUDGETEL INN.** *2932 Kohler Memorial Dr, E of I-43 exit 53A.* 414/457-2321. 97 rms, 2 story. S $28.95–$29.95; D $33.95–$34.95; each addl $5; under 18 free. Crib free. TV; cable, in-rm movies. Free coffee in lobby. Cafe adj 6–1 am. Ck-out noon. Sundries. Cr cds: A, C, D, DS, MC, V.

🛇🐾🅱🛇

✔ ★ ★**GRAND EXECUTIVE INN.** *(Box 939) 8th St at Center Ave, 5 blks S of WI 23, 6 blks E of US 141 Business.* 414/458-5535. 54 rms, 4 story. S $36.95; D $41.95; each addl $5; higher rates special events. Crib $5. TV. Cafe 6:30–9 am, 5–9 pm; also 11:30 am–1:30 pm June–Sep. Rm serv. Bar 11–1 am; entertainment Fri–Sat. Ck-out noon. Meeting rms. Valet serv. Sundries. Exercise equipt; weights, bicycles, whirlpool, sauna. Many refrigerators. Cr cds: A, MC, V.

🛇 🏃

★**PARKWAY.** *3900 Motel Rd, 6 mi S on I-43, jct County OK, V, exit 48.* 414/458-8338; *res:* 800/341-8000. 32 rms. June–Sep: S $29.95–$35.95; D $35.95–$39.95; each addl $3; higher rates special events; lower rates rest of yr. Crib free. TV; cable. Cafe nearby. Ck-out 11 am. Sundries. X-country ski 2 mi. Most refrigerators. Picnic table, grill. Cr cds: A, DS, MC, V.

🛇🐾🏂🛇

Sister Bay (Door Co)

Pop: 564 Elev: 587 ft (179 m) **Area code:** 414 Zip: 54234

Motels

★**EDGE OF TOWN.** *1½ mi N on WI 42.* 414/854-2012. 9 rms. May–Nov: S, D $53; each addl $6; family rates. Closed rest of yr. Crib $3. TV. Free coffee. Cafe nearby. Ck-out 11 am. Refrigerators. Cr cds: MC, V.

🐾

★ ★**HELM'S 4 SEASONS.** *(Box 255) 414 Mill Rd, off WI 42.* 414/854-2356. 41 rms, 2 story. Mid-June–late Oct: S, D $52–$120; each addl $8; varied lower rates rest of yr. Crib free. TV; cable. Free continental bkfst, Labor Day–May. Cafe nearby. Ck-out 10 am. Sundries. Package store. X-country ski 5 mi. Snowmobiles. Sun deck. Refrigerators. Many private patios, balconies. On Sister Bay.

🛇🐾🏂🐾🐾

★ ★**HOTEL DU NORD.** *(Box 408) 1¼ mi N on WI 42.* 414/854-4221. 60 rms, 2 story. Some rm phones. S, D $58–$114; each addl $9. Closed Nov–Mar. Crib $5. Heated pool; whirlpool. Cafe 5:30–10 pm. Ck-out 11 am. Coin lndry. Sundries. Whirlpool in some suites. Boats. On Green Bay. Cr cds: A, MC, V.

🛇🐾🐾🐾

Spooner

Settled: 1883 Pop: 2,365 Elev: 1,065 ft (325 m) **Area code:** 715 Zip: 54801

Motels

★**COUNTRY HOUSE.** *(Box 367) ½ mi S on US 63.* 715/635-8721. 20 rms. S $25–$41; D $32–$55. Crib $3. TV; cable, in-rm movies. Playground. Cafe 6 am–10 pm. Ck-out 11 am. X-country ski 10 mi. Adj to park, State Fish Hatchery. Cr cds: A, C, D, DS, ER, MC, V.

🐾

✔ ★**GREEN ACRES.** *(Box 28) ¼ mi S on US 63.* 715/635-2177. 21 rms. S $25–$49; D $35–$59; each addl $3; higher rates special events. TV; cable, in-rm movies. Playground. Free coffee in lobby. Cafe opp 6 am–11 pm. Ck-out 10 am. Free airport transportation. X-country ski 4 mi. Snowmobile trails. Picnic tables, grills. Cr cds: A, DS, MC, V.

🖼️ 💲

Stevens Point

Settled: 1838 **Pop:** 22,970 **Elev:** 1,093 ft (333 m) **Area code:** 715 **Zip:** 54481

Motels

★**MAPLES MOTEL TOOI.** *3416 Church St.* 715/344-4857. 12 rms. June–Oct: S $18–$23; D $26–$35; each addl $3–$5; under 8 free; wkly rates; lower rates rest of yr. Crib free. TV; cable. Free coffee. Cafe nearby. Ck-out 11 am. X-country ski 2 mi. Near river. Cr cds: A, MC, V.

🖼️ 🖼️ 🖼️

✔ ★**MID-WISCONSIN MOTOR INN.** *(Box 4, Plover 54467) 7 mi S on US 51 at jct WI 54.* 715/341-7300; res: 800/433-6785 (exc WI). 104 rms, 2 story. S $24–$32; D $36–$42; each addl $4. TV; cable. Continental bkfst. Cafe adj 6 am–9 pm. Ck-out noon. Coin lndry. Sundries. Downhill ski 15 mi; x-country ski 1 mi. Game rm. Cr cds: A, D, DS, MC, V.

🖼️ 🖼️ 🖼️ 🖼️ SC

★**POINT MOTEL.** *209 Division St.* 715/344-8312. 44 rms, 2 story. S $30; D $32–$36; each addl $4. Crib $4. TV; cable. Ck-out 11 am. Downhill ski 20 mi; x-country ski 1 mi. Cr cds: A, C, D, DS, MC, V.

🖼️ 🖼️ 🖼️ SC

✔ ★**ROADSTAR INN.** *159 Division St.* 715/341-9090. 101 rms, 2 story. S, D $31–$34; each addl $3; under 12 free. Crib $3. TV; satellite, in-rm movies. Free continental bkfst. Cafe adj open 24 hrs. Ck-out noon. Valet serv. Downhill ski 15 mi; x-country ski 1 mi. Cr cds: A, D, MC, V.

🖼️ 🖼️ 🖼️ 🖼️ SC

★**TRAVELER.** *3350 Church.* 715/344-6455. 17 units. S $24; D $26–$29; each addl $2; under 18 free. Crib free. TV; cable. Free coffee in rms. Playground. Ck-out 11 am. Downhill ski 12 mi; x-country ski 2 mi. Cr cds: A, DS, MC, V.

🖼️ 🖼️ SC

Sturgeon Bay (Door Co)

Settled: 1870 **Pop:** 8,847 **Elev:** 588 ft (179 m) **Area code:** 414 **Zip:** 54235

Motels

★**CHAL-A-MOTEL.** *3910 WI 42-57.* 414/743-6788. 20 rms. S $19–$31; D $25–$39; each addl $2. Crib $2. TV; cable. Free coffee in lobby. Ck-out 10:30 am. Downhill ski 7 mi. Cr cds: MC, V.

🖼️ 🖼️ 🖼️ 🖼️

✔ ★★**SUPER 8.** *409 Green Bay Rd.* 414/743-9211. 62 rms, 2 story. June–Sep: S $45–$69; D $52–$76; under 13 free; lower rates rest of yr. Crib free. TV; cable. Pool; whirlpool. Free continental bkfst. Ck-out 11 am. Meeting rms. Valet serv. Sundries. Downhill/x-country ski 3 mi. Refrigerators. Cr cds: A, MC, V.

🖼️ 🖼️ 🖼️ 🖼️

Resort

★★**BAY SHORE INN.** *4205 Bay Shore Dr.* 414/743-4551. 19 motel & lodge units, 13 A/C, 1–2 story; 3 2–3-bedrm cottages, 5 2-bedrm chalets. July–late Aug, MAP: S, D $50–$75/ person; under 5 free; EP avail; lower rates mid-May–June, Sep–mid-Oct. Closed rest of yr. Crib free. TV. Playground. Cafe 8–10 am, 5:30–8 pm; Sun to 1 pm. Box lunches. Ck-out 1 pm, ck-in 2 pm. Grocery, coin lndry, package store 3 mi. Free airport, bus depot transportation. Tennis.

Sand beach; boats, sailboats. Lawn games. Bicycles. Rec rm. Spacious attractive grounds. Family resort on Sturgeon Bay. Cr cds: DS, MC, V.

Three Lakes

Pop: 1,864 **Elev:** 1,637 ft (499 m) **Area code:** 715 **Zip:** 54562

Motel

✔ ★ ★ONEIDA VILLAGE INN. *(Box C) 501 Superior St.* 715/546-3373. 47 rms, 2 story, 4 kits. S $33–$40; D $39.95–$50; each addl $5; kit. units $36–$44; under 11 free; special package plans; higher rates special events. Crib $5. TV; cable. Cafe 5–11 pm; winter to 10 pm. Bar 11:30–2 am; winter 4 pm–1 am; entertainment late June–early Sep. Ck-out 11 am. X-country ski 1 mi. Snowmobiles, trails, guides. Rec rm. Cr cds: DS, MC, V.

Tomah

Pop: 7,204 **Elev:** 960 ft (293 m) **Area code:** 608 **Zip:** 54660

Motels

★BUDGET HOST DAYBREAK. *215 E Clifton, just SE of jct US 12, 16.* 608/372-5946; res: 800/835-7427, ext 671. 32 rms, 1–2 story. Mid-May–mid-Oct: S $26–$33; D $32–$39; each addl $4; lower rates rest of yr. Crib $3. TV; cable. Cafe opp 10 am–midnight. Ck-out 11 am. Downhill ski 10 mi; x-country ski 1 mi. Snowmobile trails. Refrigerators. Municipal park, pool opp. Cr cds: A, DS, MC, V.

★ ★ ★HOLIDAY INN. *(Box 745) 3 mi N at jct WI 21, I-94.* 608/372-3211. 100 rms, 2 story. Mid-May–Labor Day: S $46; D $52; each addl $4; family rates; lower rates rest of yr. Crib free. TV; in-rm movies. Heated pool; poolside serv. Cafe 6 am–2 pm, 5–10 pm. Rm serv. Bar. Ck-out noon. Coin lndry. Meeting rms. Valet serv. Sundries. 5-hole golf, greens fee $3.50. X-country ski ½ mi. Rec rm. Grills. Cr cds: A, C, D, DS, MC, V.

★REST-WELL. *(Rte 3) 1½ mi E on US 12, 16, ½ mi W of I-90, I-94 Tomah-La Crosse exit.* 608/372-2471. 12 rms. S $18–$24; D $24–$38; each addl $4. Crib $2. TV; cable. Playground. Cafe nearby. Ck-out 10 am. Downhill ski 12 mi; x-country ski 1 mi. Picnic tables, grill. Cr cds: MC, V.

✔ ★SUPER 8. *(Box 48) WI 21, I-94.* 608/372-3901. 64 rms, 2 story. S $30.88–$36.88; D $37.88–$45.88; each addl $3; under 18 free. Crib free. TV. Free continental bkfst. Cafe adj open 24 hrs. Ck-out 11 am. Sundries. Downhill ski 8 mi; x-country ski 1 mi. Cr cds: A, C, D, DS, MC, V.

Two Rivers

Pop: 13,354 **Elev:** 595 ft (181 m) **Area code:** 414 **Zip:** 54241

Motel

✔ ★ ★LIGHTHOUSE INN. *1515 B Memorial Dr.* 414/793-4524; res: 800/228-6416 (exc WI), 800/362-5575 (WI). 68 rms, 2 story. Jan–May: S $40–$45; D $48–$53; each addl $5; under 18 free; lower rates rest of yr. Crib $3. TV; cable. Indoor pool; whirlpool, sauna. Cafe 6:30 am–10 pm; Sun from 7:30 am. Rm serv. Bar 11–1 am. Ck-out noon. Meeting rms. Valet serv. Sundries. Nautical decor. On Lake Michigan; park, tennis courts opp. Cr cds: A, MC, V.

Washington Island (Door Co)

Pop: 300 (est) **Elev:** 600 ft (183 m) **Area code:** 414 **Zip:** 54246

Motels

★**HOLIDAY INN FINDLAY'S.** *2 mi NE of ferry dock. 414/847-2526.* 21 rms, 13 with bath, 1 kit. No A/C. May–Oct: S $35–$52; D $40–$60; each addl $6; under 6 free; wkly rates. Closed rest of yr. Crib free. Some B/W TV. Cafe 7 am–1:30 pm, 5:30–7:30 pm. Ck-out 10 am. Beach. Lawn games. On Lake Michigan. Cr cds: MC, V.

✔**VIKING VILLAGE.** *2 mi NE of ferry dock. 414/847-2551.* 12 kit units. No A/C. S $39–$63; D $47–$66; each addl $6; suites $63–$78; under 6 free; wkly rates. Crib free. B/W TV. Cafe 7 am–1:30 pm, 5:30–7:30 pm. Ck-out 10 am. Beach. Lawn games. Picnic tables, grills. On Lake Michigan. Cr cds: MC, V.

Waukesha

Settled: 1834 **Pop:** 50,365 **Elev:** 821 ft (250 m) **Area code:** 414 **Zip:** 53186

Motels

★**COMFORT INN WAUKESHA.** *2111 E Moreland Blvd, on I-94 exit 297. 414/547-7770.* 98 rms, 2 story. S $42; D $49; each addl $6; under 18 free; higher rates special events. Crib free. TV; cable. Free continental bkfst. Cafe nearby. Ck-out 11 am. Valet serv. Sundries. Airport transportation. Exercise equipt; weights, bicycles, whirlpool, sauna. Some refrigerators. Cr cds: A, C, D, DS, MC, V.

✔★★**ROAD STAR INN.** *2510 Plaza Ct, at jct I-94 exit 297, County JJ. 414/786-6015.* 100 rms, 2-3 story. No elvtr. Apr–Nov: S, D $31.95–$39.95; each addl $6; suites $36.95–$45.95; under 12 free; lower rates rest of yr. TV; cable, in-rm movies. Free continental bkfst 6:30–8:30 am. Ck-out noon. Meeting rm. Valet serv. Sundries. X-country ski 20 mi. Some refrigerators. Cr cds: A, C, D, MC, V. Ⓔ

Wausau

Settled: 1839 **Pop:** 32,426 **Elev:** 1,195 ft (364 m) **Area code:** 715 **Zip:** 54401

Motels

★**BUDGETEL.** *1910 Stewart Ave. 715/842-0421.* 99 rms, 2 story. S $25.95–$28.95; D $30.95–$33.95; each addl $5; under 18 free. Crib free. TV; cable. Cafe nearby. Ck-out noon. Sundries. Downhill/x-country ski 2 mi. Cr cds: A, D, DS, MC, V.

★**EXEL INN.** *116 S 17th Ave. 715/842-0641.* 124 rms, 2 story. S $25.95–$30.95; D $27.95–$32.95; each addl $4; under 18 free. Crib free. TV; in-rm movies. Cafe nearby. Ck-out noon. Meeting rms. Downhill ski 2 mi; x-country ski 3 mi. View of Rib Mt. Cr cds: A, D, DS, MC, V.

★★**RIB MOUNTAIN INN.** *2900 N Mountain Way. 715/848-2802.* 16 rms, 2 story, kit. units avail. Mid-Dec–mid-Mar: S, D $35–$63; family, wkly rates; ski plan; lower rates rest of yr. TV; satellite, in-rm movies. Continental bkfst. Sandwich shop noon–midnight. Rm serv. Ck-out 11:30 am. Meeting rms. Driving range. Downhill ski ¼ mi; x-country ski 7 mi. Sauna. Lawn games. Fireplaces; some refrigerators. Patios, balconies. Picnic tables, grills. On Rib Mtn. Adj to state park. Cr cds: A, D, MC, V.

Motor Hotels

✔ ★ ★ ★ **HOLIDAY INN.** *(Box 1224) 201 N 17th Ave. 715/845-4341.* 245 rms, 5 story. S $40–$58; D $45–$63; each addl $3; under 19 free. Crib free. TV; satellite, in-rm movies. 2 pools, 1 indoor. Cafe 6 am–10 pm. Rm serv. Bar. Ck-out 1 pm. Meeting rms. Sundries. Downhill ski 2 mi; x-country ski 5 mi. Rec rm. Cr cds: A, C, D, DS, MC, V.

🈳 📶 🍽 🏃 🏊 🚫 🎾 SC

✔ ★ ★ **HOWARD JOHNSON.** *2001 N Mountain Rd, on US 51 at exit NN. 715/842-0711.* 120 rms, 2 story. S $43–$45; D $51–$53; each addl $7; under 18 free. Crib free. TV; cable. Indoor pool; whirlpool, sauna. Cafe 6 am–11 pm. Rm serv to 10 pm. Bar 1:30 pm–1 am. Ck-out noon. Meeting rms. Valet serv. Sundries. Airport, bus depot transportation. Putting green. Downhill/x-country ski 1 mi. Rec rm. Cr cds: A, C, D, DS, ER, MC, V.

🈳 📶 🍽 🏃 🏊 🚫 🎾 SC

Wisconsin Dells

Settled: 1858 **Pop:** 2,521 **Elev:** 912 ft (278 m) **Area code:** 608 **Zip:** 53965

Motels

(Some motels may have a 2-night min in season; season dates are approximate.)

✔ ★ ★ **BLACK HAWK.** *(Box 15) Broadway at Race St, ½ blk S of US 16, WI 13, 23. 608/254-7770.* 66 motel rms, 1–2 story, 9 cottages with kit. Late May–Labor Day: S $36–$75; D $46–$85; each addl $5; cottages for 2–6, $45–$90; lower rates Apr–late May, after Labor Day–Oct. Closed rest of yr. Crib $5. TV; cable, in-rm movies. Indoor/outdoor pool; wading pool, whirlpool, sauna. Playground. Cafe nearby. Ck-out 10:30 am; off-season, noon. Coin lndry. Game rm. Cr cds: A, C, D, DS, MC, V. Ⓓ

🈳 🏊 🎾 SC

★ **CHIPPEWA.** *1114 E Broadway. 608/253-3982.* 35 rms, 2 story. Mid-June–Labor Day: D $52–$75; family rates; lower rates Apr–mid-June, after Labor Day–Nov. Closed rest of yr. Crib $4. TV; cable. Heated pool. Cafe opp 7 am–10 pm. Ck-out 10 am. Picnic tables. Playground. Cr cds: A, DS, MC, V. Ⓓ

🏊 🎾 SC

✔ ★ ★ **COUNTRY EDITION INN.** *(Box 381) 1 mi E of I-90/94 exit 87, on US 12. 608/254-6444.* 100 rms, 2 story. S $28.95–$45.95; D $29.95–$72.95; each addl $2; kits. $60.95–$126.95; under 12 free. Crib $4. TV; cable. Indoor/outdoor pool; whirlpool, sauna. Cafe adj open 24 hrs. Ck-out 11 am. Downhill/x-country ski 7 mi. Game rm. Cr cds: A, C, D, DS, MC, V.

🈳 🏃 🏊 🎾 SC 💲

★ **DAY'S END.** *On US 12, WI 16 exit 85, 1 mi N of I-90/94 Rocky Arbor exit. 608/254-8171.* 26 rms. July–Labor Day: S $40; D $45–$55; each addl $5; lower rates rest of yr. Crib $1. TV. Heated pool. Playground. Coffee in rms. Ck-out 10 am. Miniature golf. Downhill ski 4 mi; x-country ski 7 mi. Picnic tables, grill. Cr cds: A, MC, V.

🏃 🏊 🚫 🎾

★ **GABLES.** *822 Oak St. 608/253-3831.* 30 rms, 2 story. June–Labor Day: D $48–$58; lower rates rest of yr. Crib free. TV; cable, in-rm movies. Heated pool. Cafe nearby. Ck-out 10 am. Sundries. Cr cds: A, DS, MC, V.

🏊 🎾

★ **HILLTOP.** *1100 Wisconsin Dells Pkwy, 2 mi S on US 12, WI 23, 2 mi N of I-90/94 exit 92. 608/253-3883.* 26 rms. June–Labor Day: D $40–$75; lower rates rest of yr. TV; cable, in-rm movies. Heated pool. Playground. Free coffee in lobby. Cafe adj 6 am–midnight. Ck-out 10:30 am. Downhill ski 8 mi; x-country ski 7 mi. Cr cds: A, D, DS, MC, V.

📶 🏃 🏊 🎾 SC

✔ ★ ★ **INN OF THE DELLS.** *(Box 190) 2¾ mi S on US 12, WI 23, 1½ mi N of I-90/94 Lake Delton exit. 608/253-1511.* 132 rms, 2–3 story. June–Aug: S $49–$85; D $49–$95; each addl $7; suites $90–$135; lower rates rest of yr. Crib free. TV; satellite. Indoor pool; whirlpool, sauna. Playground. Cafe 7 am–10 pm. Bar 11–1 am; entertainment, dancing (in season). Ck-out 11 am.

Meeting rms. Sundries. Gift shop. Platform tennis. Miniature golf. Nature trail. Game rm. Rec rm.
Cr cds: A, C, D, DS, MC, V. ⓓ

★★**RIVER INN.** *1015 River Rd. 608/253-1231.* 68 rms. 5 story. June–Sep: S, D
$52–$99; suites $99; lower rates rest of yr. TV; satellite. Indoor pool. Cafe 8 am–10 pm (in
season). Rm serv. Bar 4 pm–1 am. Ck-out 11 am. Gift shop. Package store. Downhill/x-country
ski 7 mi. Exercise equipt; weights, bicycles, whirlpool, sauna. Some balconies. Cr cds: A, C, D,
DS, MC, V.

Canada

Population: 24,343,181

Land area: 3,851,809 sq mi (9,976,185 sq km)

Highest point: Mt Logan, Yukon Territory, 19,850 ft (6,050 m)

Capital: Ottawa

Speed limit: 50 or 60 MPH (80 or 100 KPH), unless otherwise indicated

Visitor Information

Currency. The American dollar is accepted throughout Canada, but it is advisable to exchange your money into Canadian currency. Banks give the best rate of exchange. The Canadian monetary system is based on dollars and cents, and rates in this Guide are given in Canadian currency. Generally, the credit cards you use at home are also honored in Canada.

Driving in Canada. Your American driver's license is valid in Canada; no special permit is required. In Canada, the litre is the unit of measure for gasoline. One US gallon equals 3.78 litres. Traffic signs are clearly understood and in many cities are bilingual. All road speed limits and mileage signs have been posted in kilometers per hour (KPH).

Holidays. All Canada observes the following holidays: New Year's, Good Friday, Easter Monday, Victoria Day (usually 3d Mon May), Canada Day (July 1), Labour Day, Thanksgiving (2d Mon Oct), Remembrance Day (November 11), Christmas and Boxing Day (December 26).

Liquor. The sale of liquor, wine, beer, and cider varies from province to province. Restaurants must be licensed to serve liquor, and in some cases liquor may not be sold unless in accompanies a meal. Generally there are no sales on holidays. **NOTE:** It is illegal to take children into bars and cocktail lounges. Minimum age also varies.

Daylight Saving Time. Canada observes Daylight Saving Time beginning the first Sunday in April through the last Sunday in October.

Tourist information in available from Canadian embassies or consulates located in major US cities.

Room Rate Information

The following major cities and resort areas have higher room rates for two (double) than indicated on the cover of this Guide. However, the lodgings listed in these cities offer a good value when compared to others of their type in the area.

NEW BRUNSWICK		Thunder Bay	$60
St Andrews	$60	Toronto	60
ONTARIO		QUÉBEC	
Gananoque	60	Montréal	60
Kenora	65	Québec City	60
Niagara Falls	60		

Fredericton, New Brunswick

Founded: 1762 **Pop:** 43,723 **Elev:** 24 ft (7 m) **Area code:** 506

Motels

✔ ★ ★ **CONDOR MOTOR LODGE.** *Woodstock Rd (E3B 5B4), at jct Rte 2. 506/455-5537.* 50 rms, 3 story. S $36–$45; D $42–$52; each addl $5. Crib $5. TV; cable. Indoor pool. Playground. Cafe 7 am–2 pm, 5–9 pm. Rm serv. Serv bar. Ck-out 11 am. Meeting rms. Golf privileges, pro, driving range. Downhill ski 5 mi; x-country ski 10 mi. Balconies. Cr cds: A, MC, V.
Ⓕ

✔ ★ ★ ★FREDERICTON MOTOR INN. *1315 Regent St (E3C 1A1). 506/455-1430.* 174 rms, 1–3 story. July–Sep: S $46–$69; D $54–$70; each addl $10; suites $89; kit. units $95; lower rates rest of yr. Crib $5. TV; cable. Heated pool; whirlpool, poolside serv. Cafe 6:30 am–11 pm. Rm serv. Bar 11–12:45 am. Ck-out 11 am. Meeting rms. Bellhops. Sundries. Game rm. Rec rm. Some in-rm whirlpools. Balconies. Cr cds: A, MC, V. Ⓕ

Ⓐ ⇌ SC

✔ ★ ★KEDDY'S INN. *368 Forest Hill Rd (E3B 5G2), 1 blk N of Hwy 2 exit 295. 506/454-4461.* 120 rms, 3 story. S $45–$48; D $48–$60; each addl $8; under 18 free. Crib $8. TV; cable. Heated pool; sauna. Cafe 6:30 am–2 pm, 5–10 pm. Rm serv. Bar 11:30–2 am; entertainment, dancing wkends. Ck-out 1 pm. Meeting rms. Valet serv. Downhill ski 5 mi; x-country ski 10 mi. Balconies. Picnic tables. Cr cds: A, C, D, ER, MC, V. Ⓔ Ⓕ

Ⓐ ⚡ ⇌ Ⓢ SC

Moncton, New Brunswick

Pop: 54,743 **Elev:** 50 ft (15 m) **Area code:** 506

Motels

✔ ★ ★AUBERGES WANDLYN INN. *(RR 8, Box 2278, E1C 8K2) On Magnetic Hill, 1/8 mi W of Trans-Canada Hwy exit 488B. 506/384-3554.* 76 rms, 2 story. S $43–$48; D $48–$58; each addl $6; suites $60–$80; under 18 free; wkend rates. Crib $5. TV; cable. Heated pool. Cafe 7 am–9:30 pm. Bar 4:30 pm–midnight. Ck-out noon. Meeting rms. Valet serv. Sundries. Golf privileges. Resort-type motel. Cr cds: A, MC, V. Ⓕ

Ⓐ ⚓ ⇌ ⚡ SC Ⓢ

✔ ★ ★KEDDY'S MOTOR INN. *RR 6, Shediac Rd (E1C 8K1), At Hwy 2 Lakeville exit. 506/854-2210.* 82 rms, 1–2 story. S $46–$58; D $54–$64; each addl $6; cottages $50; under 12 free. Crib free. TV; cable. Heated pool; sauna. Playground. Cafe 7 am–10 pm. Bar noon–2 am. Ck-out 11:30 am. Meeting rms. Valet serv. Sundries. Tennis. Balconies. Cr cds: A, D, ER, MC, V. Ⓕ

Ⓐ ⚡ ⇌ SC

✔ ★MONCTON MOTOR INN. *1905 W Main St (Rte 6) (E1E 1H9). 506/382-2587.* 79 rms, 2 story. S $38–$44; D $45–$52; each addl $6; studio rms $45–$52; under 12 free. Crib $6. TV; cable. Heated pool. Cafe 7 am–9 pm. Bar 11 am–midnight. Ck-out noon. Meeting rms. Valet serv. Sundries. Cr cds: A, ER, MC, V. Ⓕ

Ⓐ ⇌ SC Ⓢ

St Andrews, New Brunswick

Pop: 1,760 **Elev:** 23 ft (7 m) **Area code:** 506

Motel

✔ ★AUBERGES WANDLYN INN. *(99 King St, St Stephen E3L 2C6) N via Hwy 765, N via Hwy 1. 506/466-1814; res: 800/561-0000 (CAN), 800/561-0006 (US).* 50 units, 2 story. July–Dec: S $42–$61; D $45–$66; each addl $6; under 15 free; lower rates rest of yr. Crib free. TV; cable. Cafe 7 am–10:30 pm; hrs vary off-season. Rm serv. Bar. Meeting rms. Downhill ski 6 mi. Whirlpool. Picnic tables. Cr cds: A, ER, MC, V. Ⓔ

⚿ ⚡ Ⓢ SC Ⓢ

Motor Hotel

★ ★BEST WESTERN SHIRETOWN INN. *(Box 145, E0G 2X0) 218 Water St. 506/529-8877.* 26 air-cooled rms, 3 story, 18 suites with kits. Mid-May–Oct: S $54–$80; D $60–$80; each addl $5–$10; suites, studio rms $75–$95; kit. units $80–$95; under 16 free; wkly rates; lower rates rest of yr. Crib $5. TV. Cafe 8:30 am–9:30 pm. Bar 11 am–11 pm. Ck-out noon. Meeting rms. 18-hole golf privileges. Downhill ski 20 mi; x-country ski 1/2 mi. Old World atmosphere; built in 1881. Cr cds: A, C, D, ER, MC, V. Ⓓ Ⓔ Ⓕ

Ⓐ ⚓ ⚡ ⚿

Saint John, New Brunswick

Founded: 1785 **Pop:** 80,521 **Elev:** 100 ft (31 m) **Area code:** 506

Motels

★**FUNDY LINE.** *Ocean West-Way (Hwy 100) (E2M 5H6). 506/672-2493.* 44 rms. No A/C. S $38–$42; D $46–$50; each addl $6; under 12 free. Crib $6. TV; cable. Coffee in lobby. Cafe nearby. Ck-out noon. Picnic tables. Cr cds: A, C, D, MC, V.

🐕 SC

✔ ★**FUNDY LINE-ROTHESAY AVE.** *532 Rothesay Ave (Hwy 100) (E2J 2C7). 506/633-7733.* 90 air-cooled rms. No A/C. Mid-May–mid-Sep: S $41–$44; D $49–$52; each addl $6; under 12 free; lower rates rest of yr. Crib $6. TV; cable. Cafe 6:30 am–7 pm. Ck-out noon. Picnic tables. Cr cds: A, C, D, ER, MC, V.

🐕 SC 💲

Antigonish, Nova Scotia

Pop: 5,205 **Elev:** 15 ft (5 m) **Area code:** 902

Motels

★**DINGLE MOTEL LTD.** *5 mi E on Rte 104 (B2G 2L4). 902/863-3730.* 35 rms. S $44–$50; D $54–$72; each addl $6. TV. Cafe adj 7 am–midnight. Ck-out 11 am. Coin lndry. Downhill ski 9 mi; x-country ski ½ mi. Picnic tables. Cr cds: A, ER, MC, V. Ⓕ

🐾 🚫

✔ ★**OASIS.** *(PO Box 1448, B2G 2L7) 2 mi E on Hwy 104. 902/863-3557.* 13 rms. No A/C. May–Oct: S $43–$45; D $47–$49; each addl $5; under 10 free. Closed rest of yr. Crib free. TV. Pool. Playground. Cafe opp 8 am–10 pm. Ck-out 11 am. Coin lndry. Valet serv. Picnic tables. Cr cd: V.

🏊 🚶 🚫 SC

Baddeck, Nova Scotia

Pop: 972 **Elev:** 100 ft (30 m) **Area code:** 902

Resort

✔ ★ ★ ★**INVERARY INN.** *(Box 190, B0E 1B0) ¼ mi W on Rte 205. 902/295-2674.* 117 rms in motel, inn & cottages, 24 A/C, 6 kits., 14 cottages. May–mid-Oct: S $50–$85; D $50–$90; each addl $8; kit. units $95; some lower rates rest of yr. Crib free. TV; cable. 2 pools, 1 indoor. Playground. 2 dining rms 7–9:30 am, noon–2 pm, 5:30–8:30 pm; entertainment, pianist. Serv bar. Ck-out 10:30 am. Grocery, coin lndry, package store 2 blks. Convention facilities. Airport transportation. Tennis. Golf privileges, greens fee, pro, putting green. Private beach. Canoes, sailboats, paddleboats. Hiking tours. Lawn games. Movies. Craft shop. Exercise rm; instructor, weights, bicycles, whirlpool, sauna. Fireplace in some rooms. Balconies. Boat tours. Cr cds: A, MC, V. Ⓕ

♿ 🐕 🛏 ⛳ 🔍 🎿 🚶 🚫 SC

Dartmouth, Nova Scotia

Founded: 1750 **Pop:** 62,277 **Elev:** 75 ft (23 m) **Area code:** 902

Motels

★**4 SEASONS MOTOR INN.** *40 Lakecrest Dr (B2X 1V1). 902/435-0060.* 43 rms, 2 story. Mid-May–mid-Oct: S $36–$38; D $39–$42; each addl $3; under 12 free; wkly rates in winter; lower rates rest of yr. TV; cable. Ck-out 11 am. X-country ski 5 mi. Cr cds: A, ER, MC, V. Ⓔ

🆑 ▧ ⊗

✔ ★JOURNEY'S END. *456 Windmill Rd (B3A 1J7).* *902/463-9900.* 81 rms, 2 story. S $39.88–$41.88; D $46.88–$48.88; each addl $4; under 12 free. Crib free. TV; cable. Free coffee 7–9 am. Ck-out 11 am. X-country ski 15 mi. On ocean. Cr cds: A, ER, MC, V. Ⓔ Ⓕ

🖐 ▧

Motor Hotel

✔ ★ ★DARTMOUTH INN. *9 Braemer Dr (B2Y 3H6), 1 mi NE on jct 7, 118, 101, 111, 118.* *902/469-0331; res: 800/561-7666.* 116 rms, 5 story, 10 kits. S $38–$48; D $31–$55; each addl $8; suites $100; studio rms $65; kit. units $45; under 12 free. Crib free. TV; cable. Cafe 7 am–2 pm; dining rm 5–10 pm. Bar 11:30–1 am. Ck-out 1 pm. Meeting rms. Bellhops. Valet serv. Shopping arcade. X-country ski 5 mi. Some refrigerators. Balconies. Picnic tables. Lake opp. Cr cds: A, C, D, ER, MC, V. Ⓔ Ⓕ

🖐 🆑 ▧ ⊗ ⓈⒸ

Digby, Nova Scotia

Pop: 2,558 **Elev:** 50 ft (15 m) **Area code:** 902

Motel

★KINGFISHER LTD. *(Box 280, B0V 1A0) Off Hwy 1 near St John Ferry & Hwy 101.* *902/245-4747.* 25 rms. S $40–$42; D $50; suites $55; under 10 free; some lower rates. Crib free. TV; cable. Free coffee. Ck-out noon. Picnic tables. Beach 2 mi. Cr cds: A, MC, V. Ⓓ Ⓕ

🆑 ▤ ⊗

Resort

✔ ★ ★MOUNTAIN GAP INN. *(Box 40, Smith's Cove B0S 1S0) 4 mi E of Digby on Rte 1.* *902/245-2277.* 101 rms, 13 cottages. No A/C. July–Aug: S $44–$50; D $54–$60; each addl $10; kit. units, kit. cottages $54–$100; under 16 free; wkly rates; lower rates mid-May–June, early Sep–mid-Oct. Closed rest of yr. Crib free. TV; cable. Heated pool. Playground. Dining rms 7:30–10 am, noon–2 pm, 5:30–8:30 pm. Bar noon–midnight exc Sun. Ck-out 11 am. Grocery, package store 4 mi. Gift shop. Tennis. 18-hole golf privileges. Private beach. Lawn games. Rec dir. Game rm. Private patios, grills. Rustic setting. On 45 acres. Cr cds: A, ER, MC, V. Ⓕ

🖐 ▤ 🏠 🆑 ⊃ 🏃 ⊗ ⓈⒸ

Fortress of Louisbourg National Historic

Park, Nova Scotia

(On Cape Breton Island, 22 mi or 35 km south of Sydney, via Highway 22)

Motel

✔ ★ ★FLEUR DE LIS. *1225 Main St (Rte 22) (B0A 1M0).* *902/733-2844.* 45 rms. No A/C. S $38–$43; D $48–$58; each addl $5. TV; satellite. Cafe 7 am–10:30 pm. Bar 11:30 am–midnight; entertainment, pianist. Ck-out 11 am. X-country ski 2 mi. Cr cds: A, D, MC, V. Ⓕ

▤ ▧ ⊗

Grand Pré, Nova Scotia

Pop: 305 **Elev:** 125 ft (38 m) **Area code:** 902

Motel

✔ ★**GRAND PRÉ'S EVANGELINE.** *Hwy 1 at Grand Pré Corner (B0P 1M0). 902/542-2703.* 32 rms. No A/C. May–Nov: S, D $20–$32; each addl $2. Closed rest of yr. TV. Indoor pool. Cafe 8 am–7 pm, Sun 9 am–7 pm. Ck-out 11 am. Downhill ski 20 mi; x-country ski ¼ mi. Picnic tables. Cr cds: MC, V.

Motor Hotel

★ ★**AUBERGES WANDLYN INN.** *(Hwy 101 at exit 14 & Hwy 1, Kentville B4N 3V7)* 10 *mi S on Hwy 101. 902/678-8311.* 74 units, 3 story. July–Sep: S $49–$61; D $53–$66; each addl $6; suites $68–$90; under 18 free; wkly, ski plans; lower rates rest of yr. Crib free. TV; cable. Heated pool; poolside serv. Cafe 7 am–9:30 pm. Bar 4:30 pm–1:30 am. Ck-out 1 pm. Meeting rms. Some refrigerators. Private patios, balconies, picnic tables, grills. Cr cds: A, C, D, MC, V. Ⓔ Ⓕ

Halifax, Nova Scotia

Founded: 1749 **Pop:** 114,594 **Elev:** 25–225 ft (8–69 m) **Area code:** 902

Motels

✔ ★**AUBERGES WANDLYN MOTOR INN.** *50 Bedford Hwy, (B3M 2J2)* 3½ *mi N on Hwy 2 outbound. 902/443-0416.* 70 rms, 2 story. June–Sep: S $49–$61; D $53–$66; each addl $6; under 18 free; lower rates rest of yr. TV; in-rm movies. Dining rm 7 am–2 pm, 5:30–9:30 pm. Bar 4 pm–1 am exc Sun. Ck-out 1 pm. Meeting rms. Sundries. X-country ski 5 mi. Ocean view from some rms. Cr cds: A, ER, MC, V. Ⓕ

✔ ★**BLUE NOSE.** *636 Bedford Hwy (B3M 2L8). 902/443-3171.* 34 units, 2 story, 16 kit. suites. June–Oct: S $46; D $50–$55; each addl $7; kit. suites $65–$70; under 12 free; some wkly rates; lower rates rest of yr. Crib free. TV; cable. Playground. Cafe 7 am–2 pm, 5–10 pm. Ck-out 11 am. Meeting rms. Gift shop. Balconies. Picnic tables, grills. Cr cds: A, D, ER, MC, V.

✔ ★**STARDUST.** *(Box 335, Bedford B4A 2X3)* 9 *mi E on Hwy 2. 902/835-3316.* 51 rms, 25 A/C, 2½ story, 31 kits. June–Oct: S $39–$42; D $44–$54; each addl $5; suites $5 addl; family rms $63–$75; 2-bedrm apts $80–$95; kit. units $5–$10 addl; under 4 free; lower rates rest of yr. Crib $5. TV; cable. Cafe 7 am–10 pm. Rm serv. Serv bar. Ck-out 11 am. Sundries. Some refrigerators. On Bedford Basin. Cr cds: A, ER, MC, V.

★**WEDGEWOOD.** *374 Bedford Hwy (CAN 2) (B3M 2L1). 902/443-1576.* 40 rms, 2 story. Mid-June–mid-Oct: S $53; D $53–$59; each addl $6; kit. units $10 addl; lower rates rest of yr. TV. Free continental bkfst in season. Cafe opp noon–2 am. Bar 11–3 am. Ck-out 11 am. Cr cds: A, MC, V.

Truro, Nova Scotia

Settled: 1858 **Pop:** 12,522 **Elev:** 15 ft (5 m) **Area code:** 902

Motels

★**JOURNEY'S END.** *12 Meadow Dr (B2N 5V3). 902/893-0330; res: 800/668-4200.* 81 rms, 2 story. S $41.88–$43.88; D $48.88–$50.88; each addl $4; under 12 free. Crib free. TV; cable. Ck-out 11 am. Cr cds: A, ER, MC, V. Ⓕ

✔ ★**PALLISER.** *(Box 821, B2N 5G6) Tidal Bore Rd, Hwy 102 exit 14.* 902/893-8951. 48 rms. No A/C. No rm phones. May–Oct: S $32–$39; D $41–$42; each addl $4; under 12 free; wkly rates. Closed rest of yr. Crib $2. TV; cable. Cafe 7:30 am–9 pm. Bar from 11 am. Ck-out 11 am. Meeting rm. Gift shop. Tennis privileges. 18-hole golf, putting green, driving range. Cr cds: A, C, D, ER, MC, V. ⓕ

♿ 🐾 🏋 🔍 🕹

✔ ★**STONEHOUSE.** *165 Willow St (B2N 4Z9).* 902/893-9413. 44 units, 3 kits. May–Oct: S $41–$43; D $52–$55; each addl $6; kits. $60–$70; under 12 free; wkly rates; lower rates rest of yr. TV; cable. Cafe 6 am–midnight. Bar 11 am–11 pm. Ck-out 11 am. Coin lndry. Meeting rm. Sundries. Cr cds: A, ER, MC, V.

♿ 🐾 🕹 SC

✔ ★**WILLOW BEND.** *277 Willow St (B2N 4Z9).* 902/895-5325. 27 units, 6 kits. Mid-June–mid-Sep: S $30–$38; D $36–$42; each addl $5; kits. $34–$44; under 12 free; wkly rates; lower rates rest of yr. TV; cable. Heated pool; poolside serv. Cafe 7–11 am, 5–10 pm. Rm serv from 5 pm. Bar from 5 pm. Ck-out 11 am. Golf privileges. Cr cds: A, ER, MC, V.

🏋 🌊 🕹

Yarmouth, Nova Scotia

Pop: 7,475 **Elev:** 140 ft (43 m) **Area code:** 902

Motels

✔ ★**CAPRI.** *8 Herbert St (B5A 1S6), at Main St.* 902/742-7168. 35 rms, 2 story, 2 kits. No A/C. S, D $40–$68; each addl $5; suites $55–$116; economy rms with shower only $35–$48. Crib $5. TV; cable. Heated pool privileges. Cafe adj 7 am–10 pm. Bar. Ck-out 11 am. Balconies. Cr cds: A, ER, MC, V. ⓔ ⓕ

🐾 🌊 🕹 SC

★**EL RANCHO.** *(RR 1, Box 745, B5A 4A5) Lakeside Dr.* 902/742-2408; *res: 800/565-7105 (US).* 16 rms, 1 kit. June–Sep: S, D $44–$52; each addl $5; kit. unit $49–$63; under 12 free; wkly rates; lower rates rest of yr. Crib $5. TV; cable. Free coffee. Ck-out 11 am. Sundries. Golf nearby. Picnic table. On lake. Cr cds: A, ER, MC, V. ⓔ ⓕ

🌊 🚶 🕹 SC

✔ ★ ★**HONEY HILL.** *(Box 921, RR 1, B5A 4A5) 1½ mi E of airport on Hwy 1, exit 340, off Starrs Rd.* 902/742-3596. 25 units. No A/C. No rm phones. July–mid-Sep: S, D $35–$48; each addl $5; wkly rates; lower rates mid-Sep–Oct, mid-May–June. Closed rest of yr. Crib $5. TV; cable. Playground. Cafe adj. Ck-out 11 am. Coin lndry. Private beach. Some refrigerators. Picnic tables, grills. Cr cds: MC, V. ⓔ

♿ 🐾 🌊 🕹

★**LA REINE.** *(RR 1, Box 950, B5A 4A5) 2 mi N of Yarmouth on NS 1.* 902/742-7154. 23 air-cooled rms. July–Aug: S $46; D $48–$52; each addl $5; under 12 free; lower rates mid-May–June, Sep–Oct. Closed rest of yr. Crib free. TV; cable. Heated pool. Cafe adj 8 am–10 pm. Ck-out 11 am. Picnic tables. On Doctors Lake. Cr cds: A, MC, V. ⓕ

🐾 🌊 🕹

✔ ★**LAKELAWN.** *641 Main St (B5A 1K2).* 902/742-3588. 31 rms, 25 with bathrm, 2 story. No rm phones. July–Sep: S $30–$37; D $40–$48; each addl $5; under 5 free; lower rates May–June, Oct. Closed rest of yr. Crib $5. TV; cable. Full bkfst 7–9 am. Ck-out 11 am. Picnic table. Cr cds: A, ER, MC, V. ⓔ ⓕ

🐾 🕹

★ ★**MERMAID.** *545 Main St (B5A 1S6).* 902/742-7821. 45 rms, 2 story, 5 kits. No A/C. June–Oct: S, D $49–$78; each addl $6; kit. units $65–$116; under 12 free; lower rates rest of yr. Crib $5. TV; cable. Heated pool. Cafe nearby. Ck-out 11 am. Coin lndry. Tennis, golf privileges. Some refrigerators. Deep-sea fishing arranged. Cr cds: A, MC, V. ⓕ

🐾 🌊 🏋 🔍 🌊 SC

★**VOYAGEUR.** *(RR 1, Box 1020, B5A 4A5) 2½ mi NE on Hwy 1.* 902/742-7157. 33 units, 5 suites, 4 kits. Mid-June–mid-Sep: S $44–$80; D $44–$125; each addl $6; suites $125;

kits. $52–$70; family rates; lower rates rest of yr. Crib $6. TV; cable, in-rm movies (fee). Cafe 7 am–10 pm. Ck-out 11 am. Whirlpool. Overlooks Doctors Lake. Cr cds: A, ER, MC, V. Ⓔ Ⓕ

Brantford, Ontario

Founded: 1784 **Pop:** 74,315 **Elev:** 815 ft (248 m) **Area code:** 519

Motels

✔ ★ECONO LODGE. *460 Fairview Dr (N3R 7A9), SW on ON 403. 519/759-2700.* 80 units, 2 story. S $38.95; D $45.95–$48.95; each addl $7; suites $55.95; under 18 free. Crib free. TV; cable. Free continental bkfst in lobby 7–9:15 am. Cafe nearby. Ck-out 11 am. Meeting rms. Airport transportation. Valet serv. Near shopping mall. Cr cds: A, MC, V.

✔ ★★JOLLY BARON INN. *666 Colborne St (N3S 3P8). 519/753-7371.* 96 rms, 2–3 story, 4 kits. S $36–$38; D $41–$47; suites $83–$88; kit. units $55; under 10 free. Crib $4. TV; cable. Wading pool, whirlpool, sauna. Cafe 7 am–9:30 pm; Sat from 8 am; Sun 7 am–11 pm. Rm serv. Bar 11:30–1 am. Ck-out noon. Free lndry facilities. Meeting rms. Valet serv. Rec rm. Some refrigerators. Picnic tables. Cr cds: A, ER, MC, V. Ⓕ

★SHERWOOD. *797 Colborne St (N3S 3S3). 519/756-5261.* 24 rms. S $38; D $44; wkly rates. Crib $6. TV; cable. Pool. Cafe 7 am–midnight. Ck-out 11 am. Meeting rms. Picnic tables. Cr cds: A, MC, V.

Brockville (Thousand Islands), Ontario

Settled: 1784 **Pop:** 19,896 **Elev:** 300 ft (91 m) **Area code:** 613

Motel

✔ ★QUEEN'S GRANT. *325 Stewart Blvd (K6V 5V2), at jct Hwys 401, 29. 613/345-1437.* 47 rms, 2 story. S $35; D $45. Crib free. TV; cable. Cafe 6:30 am–9 pm; Sat from 7 am. Rm serv. Bar noon–1 am. Ck-out 1 pm. Meeting rm. Sundries. Balconies. Cr cds: A, D, MC, V. Ⓓ Ⓕ

SC

Cornwall, Ontario

Pop: 46,144 **Elev:** 200 ft (62 m) **Area code:** 613

Motel

✔ ★COLONIAL MANOR. *1618 Vincent Massey Dr (Hwy 2) (K6H 5R6). 613/933-5100.* 19 rms, 4 kits. June–Aug: S $32–$44; D $46–$50; each addl $5; kit. units $47–$62; lower rates rest of yr. Crib $5. TV; cable. Heated pool. Playground. Cafe adj 8–2 am. Ck-out 11 am. X-country ski 2 mi. Picnic tables. Cr cds: A, C, D, ER, MC, V. Ⓕ

Fort Frances, Ontario

Pop: 8,906 **Elev:** 1,100 ft (335 m) **Area code:** 807

Motel

★**REID'S VOYAGEUR INN.** *525 Portage Ave (P9A 2A2). 807/274-9805.* 24 rms, 2 story. S $36; D $39; each addl $3; under 12 free. Crib $3. TV; cable. Free coffee. Cafe nearby. Ck-out 11 am. Sundries. Cr cds: A, MC, V.

Gananoque (Thousand Islands), Ontario

Pop: 4,863 **Elev:** 300 ft (91 m) **Area code:** 613

Motels

★★**BEST WESTERN PROVINCIAL.** *846 King St E (Hwy 2) (K7G 1H3) at Thousand Islands Pkwy. 613/382-2038.* 72 rms. July–Labour Day: S $55–$74; D $57–$81; each addl $4; lower rates Mar–June, after Labour Day–Oct. Closed rest of yr. Crib $6. TV; cable. Heated pool. Cafe 7:30 am–10 pm; off-season to 9 pm. Bar noon–10 pm. Ck-out 10 am. Sundries. Gift shop. Lighted tennis. Cr cds: A, D, MC, V.

✔ ★★**COUNTRY SQUIRE RESORT.** *715 King St E (Hwy 2) (K7G 1H4). 613/382-3511.* 71 rms, 1–2 story, 10 cottages. Late June–Labour Day: S $42–$70; D $58–$84; each addl $5; suites $95–$120; family, wkly rates; ice-fishing & golf package plans; higher rates hol wkends; lower rates rest of yr. Crib $5. TV; cable. 2 pools; 1 indoor. Playground. Cafes 7 am–10 pm. Rm serv. Bar. Ck-out 11 am. Meeting rms. Bellhops. Valet serv. Tennis. 18-hole golf privileges, greens fee $12. Exercise equipt; weights, bicycles, whirlpool, sauna. Squash. Rec rm. Lawn games. Some in-rm whirlpools, fireplaces. Some private patios, balconies. Picnic tables, grill. Patio. Cr cds: A, MC, V.

✔ ★**THUNDERBIRD.** *Stone St N (Hwy 32) (K7G 1Z7), jct ON 401. 613/382-2278.* 26 rms. Late June–Labour Day: S, D $42–$69; each addl $4; lower rates May–late June, after Labour Day–Oct. Closed rest of yr. Crib free. TV. Pool. Cafe 7 am–9 pm. Bar. Cr cds: MC, V.

Hamilton, Ontario

Pop: 306,434 **Elev:** 776 ft (237 m) **Area code:** 416

Motels

✔ ★★**ADMIRAL MOTOR INN.** *3500 Billings Court (L7N 3N6). 416/639-4780.* 67 rms, 2 story. S $37.95–$39.95; D $44.95–$46.95; suite $68.95; under 12 free. Crib free. TV; cable. Cafe 7 am–10 pm. Ck-out 11 am. Meeting rms. Valet serv. Cr cds: A, MC, V. ⒻD

★**JOURNEY'S END.** *183 Centennial Pkwy N (L8E 1H8). 416/560-4500.* 60 rms, 2 story. S $39.88–$41.88; D $46.88–$48.88; each addl $7; under 13 free. Crib free. TV; cable. Free coffee to 9 am. Cafe opp 7 am–11 pm. Ck-out 11 am. Valet serv. Sundries. Cr cds: A, MC, V. ⒻD

✔ ★**MAPLE FARMS.** *(RR1, Ancaster L9G 3K9) Jct ON 2, 53 & ON 2. 416/648-4466.* 22 rms, 1–2 story. 6 kits. with equipt. S, D $37–$58; each addl $7; kit. units $58. Crib free. TV. Heated pool. Playground. Free coffee in rms. Cafe opp 6 am–9 pm. Ck-out 11 am. Sundries. Balconies. Picnic tables. Cr cds: A, MC, V.

★**RIVIERA.** *(2048 Lakeshore Rd, Burlington L7R 1A3) 4 mi NE on ON 2. 416/637-2338.* 31 rms, 2 story. June–Aug: S $30–$40; D $42–$48; each addl $3; lower rates rest of yr. Crib $5. TV; cable. Cafe opp 7 am–10 pm. Ck-out 11 am. Some refrigerators. Balconies. Picnic tables. Cr cds: A, MC, V. Ⓓ Ⓙ

Kenora, Ontario

Founded: 1882 **Pop:** 9,817 **Elev:** 1,348 ft (411 m) **Area code:** 807

Motel

✔ ★ ★ **BEST WESTERN BECKETT'S VILLAGE INN.** *½ mi E on Hwy 17 (P9N 3X1). 807/468-3188.* 56 rms, 1–2 story. S $57–$64; D $61–$75; each addl $3. Crib free. TV; in-rm movies. Cafe 7 am–10 pm. Bar 11–1 am; Sun noon–10 pm. Ck-out 11 am. Meeting rms. Downhill/x-country ski 6 mi. Some in-rm whirlpools. Cr cds: A, C, D, ER, MC, V.

Kingston (Thousand Islands), Ontario

Founded: 1673 **Pop:** 52,616 **Elev:** 305 ft (93 m) **Area code:** 613

Motels

✔ ★ ★ **GREEN ACRES.** *2480 Princess St (Hwy 2) (K7M 3G4). 613/546-1796.* 33 rms, 3 kits. July–Aug: S $50–$55; D $55–$85; each addl $5; kit. suites $135; lower rates rest of yr. Crib $5. TV. Heated pool. Playground. Ck-out 11 am. Coin lndry. Meeting rms. Valet serv. X-country ski 10 mi. Lawn games. Refrigerators. Picnic tables, gas grill. Cr cds: MC, V.

✔ ★ **WALNUT GROVE.** *2327 Princess St (Hwy 2) (K7M 3G1). 613/546-2691.* 32 rms, 8 kits. July–Labour Day: S $26–$45; D $32–$54; each addl $4; efficiency $4 addl; lower rates rest of yr. Crib $4. TV; cable. Heated pool. Playground. Free coffee. Cafe 7–10 am; wkends, hols 8–11 am. Ck-out 11 am. Sundries. Some refrigerators. Picnic tables. Cr cds: A, MC, V. Ⓓ

Motor Hotel

✔ ★ ★ **LA SALLE.** *2360 Princess St (Hwy 2) (K7M 3G4). 613/546-4233.* 110 rms, 4 story. June–mid-Sep: S, D $54–$91; each addl $4; under 12 free; lower rates rest of yr. Crib free. TV; cable. Indoor pool. Playground. Cafe 6:30 am–10 pm. Rm serv. Bar noon–1 am; dancing exc Sun. Ck-out noon. Meeting rms. Sundries. Balconies. Picnic tables. Cr cds: A, C, D, MC, V. Ⓕ Ⓘ

Kitchener-Waterloo, Ontario

Pop: Kitchener, 139,734; Waterloo, 49,428 **Elev:** Kitchener, 1,100 ft (335 m); Waterloo, 1,075 ft (328 m) **Area code:** 519

Motels

★ **ASTORIA INN CAMBRIDGE.** *(650 Hespeler Rd, Cambridge N1R 6J8) S on ON 24, off Hwy 401. 519/622-1070.* 119 rms, 2 story. S $48; D $54; each addl $6; under 18 free. Crib free. TV. Heated pool. Playground. Cafe 6:30 am–8 pm. Ck-out noon. Meeting rms. Valet serv. Sundries. Tennis. Airport transportation. Cr cds: A, D, MC, V.

✔ ★ **GUEST INN.** *2933 King St E (ON 8) (N2A 1A8). 519/893-7011.* 20 rms, 1–2 story. June–Sep: S $36–$40; D $47–$50; each addl $5; under 10 free; lower rates rest of yr. Crib $5. TV; in-rm movies. Whirlpool. Cafe 7–10 pm exc Mon; Sat, Sun from 8 am. Ck-out 11 am. Airport transportation. Lawn games. Balconies. Picnic tables. Cr cds: A, MC, V.

✔ ★**JOURNEY'S END.** *2899 King St E (N2A 1A6). 519/894-3500.* 102 rms, 2 story. S $39.88–$41.88; D $46.88–$48.88; under 13 free. Crib free. TV; cable. Free coffee. Cafe opp 7 am–11 pm. Ck-out 11 am. Valet serv. Sundries. Cr cds: A, MC, V. Ⓕ

London, Ontario

Pop: 254,280 **Elev:** 912 ft (278 m) **Area code:** 519

Motels

✔ ★★**BEST WESTERN LAMPLIGHTER INN.** *591 Wellington Rd (N6C 4R3). 519/681-7151.* 125 rms, 2 story. S $53; D $55–$65; each addl $6; studio rm $56–$66; suites $175; under 12 free. TV; cable, in-rm movies. Pool. Cafe 6:30 am–11 pm; Sun 7 am–7 pm. Rm serv. Bar noon–1 am; entertainment Tu-Sat. Ck-out 11 am. Meeting rms. Some in-rm whirlpools. Private patios, balconies. Picnic tables. Cr cds: A, D, ER, MC, V. Ⓕ

★**NATIONAL TRAVELLER.** *636 York St (N5W 3S7). 519/433-8161; res: 800/263-5664.* 90 units, 2–3 story. S $43; D $49; under 18 free; wknd rates. Crib free. TV; cable. Cafe 7 am–9 pm; Sat from 8 am; Sun 8 am–2 pm. Bar; entertainment. Ck-out 11 am. Meeting rms. Airport transportation avail. Cr cds: A, ER, MC, V. Ⓓ Ⓕ

Morrisburg, Ontario

Pop: 2,308 **Elev:** 250 ft (76 m) **Area code:** 613

Motels

★★**LOYALIST.** *Jct Hwys 2, 31 (K0C 1X0). 613/543-2932.* 31 rms, 1–2 story. S $45–$55; D $55–$70; each addl $10; wknd rates. Crib free. TV. Heated pool. Cafe 7 am–1:30 pm, 4:30–9 pm. Rm serv. Bar noon–1 am. Ck-out 11 am. Cr cds: A, C, D, MC, V.

✔ ★**RIVERSIDE.** *(RR 1, K0C 1X0) 4 mi E on Hwy 2. 613/543-2162.* 10 rms, 2 family units. Mid-June–mid-Sep: S $37–$40; D $42–$48; each addl $5; under 10 free; wkly, monthly rates; lower rates rest of yr. Crib $5. TV. Pool. Playground. Free coffee. Golf nearby, greens fee $12. Picnic tables, grill. Provincial park, beach nearby. Cr cds: MC, V. Ⓕ

★**UPPER CANADA.** *(RR 1, K0C 1X0) 3 mi E on Hwy 2. 613/543-2374.* 20 rms, 6 housekeeping units, 2 story. Mid-June–mid-Sep: S $37; D $42; each addl $4; under 13 free; wkly rates; lower rates rest of yr. Crib $4. TV. Heated pool. Cafe nearby. Ck-out 11 am. Bellhops. Golf nearby. Refrigerators. Some balconies. Picnic tables. Overlooks river. Cr cds: A, MC, V. Ⓕ

Niagara Falls, Ontario

Pop: 70,960 **Elev:** 589 ft (180 m) **Area code:** 416

Motels

✔ ★★**CLOVER LEAF.** *7514 Lundy's Lane (ON 20) (L2H 1G8), 2¾ mi W of Falls at QEW. 416/354-1849.* 40 rms. No rm phones. Late June–mid-Sep: D $59–$79; each addl $5; lower rates rest of yr. Crib $3. TV. Heated pool. Playground. Cafe nearby. Ck-out 11 am. X-country ski 3 mi. Picnic tables. On landscaped grounds; back from hwy. Cr cds: A, D, MC, V.

★★**FLAMINGO.** *7701 Lundy's Lane (ON 20) (L2H 1H3), 1½ mi W of Falls. 416/356-4646.* 96 rms, 2 story. Mid-June–Labour Day: S, D $59–$90; each addl $5; honeymoon suite

$68–$159; lower rates rest of yr. Crib free. TV; satellite. Heated pool. Cafe opp 7 am–midnight. Ck-out 11 am. Gift shop. Picnic tables. Cr cds: A, C, D, MC, V. (D)(F)(I)

✔ ★ ★MASTER HOST PILGRIM MOTOR INN. *4955 Clifton Hill (L2G 3N5). 416/354-2783.* 40 rms, 3 story, no ground-floor rms. Mid-June–mid-Sep: S, D $52–$101; each addl $5; honeymoon rms $158; suites $132–$158; higher rates hols, wkends; packages; some lower rates rest of yr. Crib $5. TV; cable. Indoor pool; whirlpool, sauna. Cafe 6 am–midnight. Ck-out 11 am. Bellhops. Valet serv. Sun deck. Balconies. Cr cds: A, MC, V. (E)(F)(I)

[sc]

✔ ★ ★RITZ COMFORT INN. *5657 Victoria Ave (L2G 3L5), 3 blks N of Falls. 416/356-2461.* 88 rms, 2 story. Late Mar–Nov: S, D $34.50–$104.50; each addl $8; bridal suites $10 addl; under 18 free; higher rates hols, wkends. Closed rest of yr. Crib free. TV. Heated pool. Cafe 7 am–midnight. Bar 11–1 am. Ck-out 11 am. Cr cds: A, D, MC, V. (F)(I)

[sc]

✔ ★SURFSIDE INN. *3665 Macklem St (Niagara River Pkwy) L2G 6C8 in Chippewa Village. 416/295-4354.* 32 rms. Mid-June–mid-Sep: D $55–$101; each addl $8; suites $130–$175; higher rates hol wkends; lower rates late Sep–early Nov, Mar–early June. Closed rest of yr. Crib free. TV. Cafe nearby. Ck-out 11 am. Beach opp. On bicycle trail. Cr cds: A, MC, V. (E)(F)(I)

Motor Hotel

✔ ★ ★HOWARD JOHNSON BY THE FALLS. *5905 Victoria Ave. 416/357-4040.* 193 units, 6–7 story. S, D $49–$149; each addl $10; suites $129–$259; under 18 free; higher rates hol wkends. Crib free. TV; in-rm movies. 2 pools, 1 indoor; whirlpool, sauna. Cafe 7–1 am. Serv bar. Ck-out 11 am. Meeting rms. Sundries. Gift shop. X-country ski 2 mi. Game rm. Some in-rm whirlpools. Some balconies. Cr cds: A, C, D, ER, MC, V. (F)(I)

Ottawa, Ontario

Founded: 1827 **Pop:** 295,163 **Elev:** 374 ft (114 m) **Area code:** 613

Motels

✔ ★BUTLER. *112 Montreal Rd (Hwy 17B) (K1L 6E6). 613/746-4641.* 94 units, 2 story. May–Sep: S $40–$55; D $45–$60; each addl $5; wkly rates; lower rates rest of yr. Crib free. TV; cable. Heated pool. Cafe 6 am–9:30 pm. Bar 11–1 am. Ck-out noon. Meeting rms. Downhill/x-country ski 12 mi. Balconies. Cr cds: A, C, D, ER, MC, V. (F)

✔ ★WEBB'S. *1705 Carling Ave (Hwy 17B) (K2A 1C8). 613/728-1881.* 80 rms, 1–2 story, 7 kits. S $50; D $54; kit. units $62–$72. Crib $4. TV; cable. Cafe & bar adj. Ck-out 11:30 am. Coin lndry. Downhill ski 1 mi; x-country ski 7 mi. Some balconies. Picnic tables, grills. Cr cds: A, ER, MC, V. (F)

Motor Hotel

✔ ★BAYSHORE. *2980 Carling Ave (Hwy 17B) (K2B 7K2). 613/829-9411.* 62 rms, 3 story. S, D $40–$48; each addl $5; under 12 free; wkly, wkend package plans in winter; wkend rates. Crib free. TV; cable. Cafe 7 am–10 pm; Sun, hols 8 am–2 pm. Rm serv. Bar 11–1 am; entertainment, dancing exc Mon. Ck-out noon. Meeting rm. Bellhops. Downhill ski 1 mi; x-country ski 5 mi. Cr cds: A, MC, V. (F)

Stratford, Ontario

Pop: 26,262 **Elev:** 119 ft (36 m) **Area code:** 519

Motor Hotel

★★VICTORIAN INN. *10 Romeo St N (N5A 5M7). 519/271-4650.* 115 rms, 4 story. Mid-May–mid-Nov: S $48–$65; D $52–$93; each addl $7; suites $75–$115; under 12 free; ski plan; lower rates rest of yr. Crib $7. TV; cable. Heated pool; sauna, poolside serv. Cafes 7:30 am–11 pm; dining rm 5–11 pm. Bars 11:30–1 am; entertainment, dancing exc Sun. Ck-out 11 am. Meeting rms. Valet serv. Sundries. Some refrigerators. Balconies. On Lake Victoria. Cr cds: A, C, D, MC, V. ①

🏊 🏃

Thunder Bay, Ontario

Pop: 112,486 **Elev:** 616 ft (188 m) **Area code:** 807

Motor Hotel

✔ ★BEST WESTERN CROSSROADS. *655 W Arthur St (P7E 5R6), at jct ON 11, 17 & ON 61. 807/577-4241.* 60 rms, 2 story. May–Oct: S $49; D $57; each addl $3; under 12 free; lower rates rest of yr. Crib free. TV; cable. Free continental bkfst, coffee. Cafe opp 7 am–midnight. Ck-out noon. Valet serv. Free airport transportation. Some refrigerators. Cr cds: A, C, D, MC, V.

🐾 SC

Toronto, Ontario

Pop: 599,217 **Elev:** 569 ft (173 m) **Area code:** 416

Motels

(Rates will be higher during Canadian National Exhibition)

✔ ★★ASCOT. *(534 Rexdale Blvd, Rexdale M9W 1S2) ½ mi W on ON 27, 4½ mi NE of Lester B. Pearson Intl Airport. 416/675-3101; res: 800/263-7142.* 94 rms, 2 story. S $49–$64; D $55–$70; each addl $6; suites $110–$116; under 14 free. Crib free. TV; cable. Cafe 7 am–10 pm. Rm serv. Heated pool. Bar 11–1 am. Ck-out noon. Meeting rms. Bellhops. Airport transportation. Tennis. Private patios or balconies. Cr cds: A, C, D, ER, MC, V. ① Ⓔ Ⓕ

🔍 🐾 🏃 🐾 SC

★JOURNEY'S END. *(1500 Matheson Blvd, Mississauga L4W 3Z4) ON 401 exit 346 (Dixie Rd S); ON 403 exit Eglinton Ave to Dixie Rd, left 2 blks. 416/624-6900; res: 800/268-0405.* 121 rms, 2 story. S $47.88–$49.88; D $54.88–$56.88; each addl $4; under 13 free. Crib free. TV; cable. Free coffee 7–9 am. Cafe adj. Bar. Ck-out 11 am. Cr cds: A, ER, MC, V.

🚽 🐾

✔ ★★QUALITY INN-AIRPORT WEST. *(50 Britannia Rd E, Mississauga L4Z 2G2) 416/890-1200.* 108 rms, 2 story. June–Sep: S $53; D $58; each addl $7; suites $59–$100; under 18 free; lower rates rest of yr. Crib free. TV; cable, in-rm movies. Cafe 7 am–11 pm. Rm serv. Serv bar 11–1 am. Ck-out noon. Meeting rms. Sauna. Whirlpool, refrigerator in suites. Cr cds: A, C, D, MC, V. ① Ⓕ ①

🚽 ⊘ 🐾 SC $

✔ ★★RELAX INN-TORONTO AIRPORT. *(5599 Ambler Dr, Mississauga L4W 3Z1) SW of jct ON 401, Dixie Rd. 416/624-9500; res: 800/661-9563.* 234 rms, 6 story. S $44.95–$48.95; D $50.95–$54.95; under 13 free. Crib free. TV; cable, in-rm movies. Indoor pool; wading pool, whirlpool. Cafe 7 am–11 pm. Bar from noon. Ck-out 11 am. Meeting rms. Sundries. Cr cds: A, C, D, ER, MC, V. Ⓕ ①

🐾 ⊘ 🐾 SC

★**SIGNATURE INN.** *5585 Ambler Dr (L4W 3Z1). 416/238-3500.* 131 rms, 2 story. S $44.50; D $49.50; each addl $5; under 13 free. TV; cable. Playground. Free coffee. Ck-out 11 am. Meeting rms. Valet serv. Cr cds: A, ER, MC, V. ⓓ Ⓕ

✔ ★ ★**WESTPOINT.** *2285 Lakeshore Blvd W (ON 2) (M8V 1A6). 416/259-1138.* 58 rms, 2 story. S $45; D $56–$70; each addl $5; family rates. Crib $3. TV; cable. Pool. Playground. Cafe 7–2 am. Bar 11–1 am; entertainment, dancing. Ck-out 11 am. Most balconies. Park adj. On Lake Ontario. Cr cds: A, D, MC, V.

Motor Hotel

✔ ★**HERITAGE INN.** *(385 Rexdale Blvd, Rexdale M9W 1R9) 11 mi W on ON 27 N, ¼ mi E of Rexdale Blvd exit. 416/742-5510.* 70 rms, 3 story. S $45–$52; D $55–$62.95; each addl $6; under 12 free. Crib free. TV. Pool. Cafe noon–2:30 pm, 5 pm–midnight. Rm serv. Bars 11:30–1 am; entertainment, dancing exc Sun. Ck-out noon. Meeting rms. Valet serv. Sundries. Airport transportation. Game rm. Rec rm. Near Woodbine Racetrack. Cr cds: A, C, D, ER, MC, V.

Windsor, Ontario

Pop: 192,083 **Elev:** 622 ft (190 m) **Area code:** 519

Motels

✔ ★**JOURNEY'S END.** *2955 Dougall Ave (N9B 1S1). 519/966-7800; res: 800/268-0405.* 80 rms, 2 story. S $41.88–$44.88; D $49.88–$51.88; each addl $4; under 13 free. Crib free. TV; cable. Cafe nearby. Ck-out 11 am. Valet serv. Cr cds: A, ER, MC, V. Ⓕ Ⓘ

✔ ★**MADRID.** *2530 Ouellette Ave (N8X 1L7). 519/966-1860; res: 800/265-5021.* 99 rms, 2 story. S $40–$45; D $45–$51; each addl $7; suites $60–$67. Crib $3. TV. Cafe 7–9 am. Rm serv from 8 am. Bar noon–1 am. Ck-out noon. Meeting rms. X-country ski 3 mi. Cr cds: A, C, D, MC, V.

★**NATIONAL TRAVELLER.** *675 Goyeau St & Tuscarora (N9A 1H3). 519/258-8411.* 104 rms, 3 story. S $48.95; D $52.95; one addl $5; under 12 free. Crib free. TV; cable. Cafe 7 am–10 pm. Bar 11:30–1 am; entertainment, dancing exc Sun. Ck-out 1 pm. Meeting rms. Bellhops. Valet serv. Sundries. Bathrm phones. Picnic tables. Cr cds: A, C, D, MC, V. Ⓕ

sc

Charlottetown, Prince Edward Island

Pop: 15,282 **Elev:** 25 ft (8 m) **Area code:** 902

Motels

★**ISLANDER.** *146–148 Pownal St (C1A 3W6). 902/892-1217.* 49 rms, 2 story, 3 kits. Mid-May–mid-Oct: S $55–$58; D $47–$65; each addl $7; suites $75–$85; kit. units $75–$85; under 10 free; lower rates rest of yr. Crib $7. TV; cable. Cafe 7 am–8 pm. Rm serv. Bar 11–1 am. Ck-out 11 am. Meeting rms. Sundries. Cr cds: A, MC, V. Ⓔ Ⓕ

✔ ★ ★**SUNNY KING.** *(Box 159, Cornwall C0A 1H0) On Trans-Canada 1. 902/566-2209.* 39 rms, 1–2 story, 30 kits. No A/C. Late June–early Sep: S $40–$52; D $46–$58; each addl $8; suites $56–$78; kit. units $58–$70; under 14 free; lower rates rest of yr. Crib $6. TV; cable. Heated pool. Playground. Cafe adj 8 am–11 pm. Ck-out 11 am. Valet serv. Coin lndry. Picnic tables, grills. Cr cds: A, ER, MC, V.

Drummondville, Québec

Pop: 27,347 **Elev:** 350 ft (107 m) **Area code:** 819

Motels

★★**HOTELLERIE LE DAUPHIN.** *600 St-Joseph Blvd (J2C 2C1). 819/478-4141; res: 800/361-6162 (Québec).* 115 rms, 2 story, 4 kits. S, D $52–$57; under 18 free. Crib free. TV; cable. Pool; poolside serv. Cafe 7 am–2 pm, 5–10 pm. Rm serv. Bar 11–3 am; piano bar, dancing Wed–Sat. Ck-out noon. Meeting rms. Bellhops. Valet serv. Beauty shop. X-country ski 2 mi. Some balconies. Cr cds: A, D, ER, MC, V. Ⓟ

✔★**LE 4 SAISONS.** *(Trans-Canada 20, Notre Dame du bon conseil J0C 1A0) 8 mi E on Trans-Canada 20 exit 191. 819/336-2606.* 52 rms, 1–2 story. S $34–$40; D $40–$49; each addl $7; family rates. Crib free. TV. Cafe open 24 hrs. Rm serv. Bar 11–3 am. Ck-out 1:30 pm. Coin lndry. Meeting rms. Cr cds: A, MC, V. Ⓟ

SC

Granby, Québec

Pop: 38,069 **Elev:** 270 ft (82 m) **Area code:** 514

Motor Hotel

★**LE GRANBYEN.** *700 rue Principale (Hwy 112) (J2G 2Y4). 514/378-8406.* 65 rms, 2 story. S, D $50–$60; golf, ski plans. TV. Heated pool. Cafe 7–10:30 am, noon–1:30 pm, 5:30–9 pm. Rm serv. Bar 11–2 am. Ck-out noon. Meeting rms. Balconies. Cr cds: A, MC, V. Ⓟ

 SC

Montréal, Québec

Settled: 1642 **Pop:** 1,005,000 **Elev:** 117 ft (36 m) **Area code:** 514

Motels

★**CANADA.** *(870 Taschereau Blvd, Greenfield Park J4V 3K3) SE on Hwy 134, 1¾ mi S of Champlain Bridge. 514/676-0285.* 53 rms, 2 story. June–Sep: S, D $58–$64; each addl $10; suites $150; some lower rates rest of yr. Crib $5. TV; cable. Heated pool; wading pool; whirlpool. Free coffee. Cafe opp. Ck-out noon. Refrigerators; some in-rm whirlpools. Cr cds: A, C, D, MC, V. Ⓟ

★**FLORENCE.** *(5791 Taschereau Blvd, Brossard J4Z 1A5) 5 mi SE on Hwy 134, 1½ mi SE of Champlain Bridge. 514/676-7938.* 32 rms. May–Oct: S $45–$47; D $55–$67; each addl $6; studio rms $65–$70; under 5 free; lower rates rest of yr. TV; cable. Cafe opp 7 am–midnight. Ck-out 11:30 am. Sundries. Cr cds: MC, V. Ⓟ

✔★**FRANDY.** *(3520 Hwy 132W, Ville Ste-Catherine J0L 1E0) On Hwy 132W, 7 mi W of Champlain Bridge. 514/632-2870.* 18 rms. May–Sep: S $40; D $50–$60; each addl $5; lower rates rest of yr. Crib free. TV. Pool. Cafe nearby. Ck-out noon. Cr cds: A, MC, V. Ⓟ

★**LA SIESTA.** *(180 Taschereau Blvd, Greenfield Park J4V 2H4) SE on Hwy 134, 1½ mi S of Jacques Cartier Bridge. 514/671-7555 , -7556, -8842.* 50 rms, 1–2 story. June–Sep: S, D $42–$58; each addl $5; under 12 free; lower rates rest of yr. Crib free. TV; cable. Cafe 7 am–noon. Rm serv to noon. Ck-out noon. Refrigerators. Cr cds: A, C, D, MC, V. Ⓟ

✔★**NITTOLO'S GARDEN.** *6580 St-Jacques St W (H4B 1V8), 3 mi W. 514/484-3565.* 84 rms, 2 story. S $50–$65; D $55–$70; each addl $5; suites $75; under 12 free. Crib free. TV.

Pool; lifeguard. Cafe 7 am–midnight. Rm serv. Bar 11–3 am. Ck-out noon. Meeting rms. Cr cds: A, C, D, ER, MC, V. (E) (F) (I)

Motor Hotel

✔ ★**LA RÉSIDENCE DU VOYAGEUR.** *847 Sherbrooke East (H2L 1K6).* *514/527-9515.* 28 units, 4 story, 10 kits. June–mid-Sep: S $35–$75; D $40–$80; each addl $5; kit. units $40–$80; under 5 free; wkly rates winter; lower rates rest of yr. TV; cable. Free coffee. Cafe 1 blk. Ck-out noon. Cr cds: ER, MC, V. (E) (F) (I) (J)

Hotel

✔ ★★**ROYAL ROUSSILLON.** *1610 St-Hubert St (H2L 3Z3).* *514/849-3214; res: 800/363-6223 (Québec City).* 147 rms, 7 story. S, D $57–$66; each addl $8. Crib $6. TV; cable. Cafe 7 am–10 pm. Bar 11–1 am. Ck-out 1 pm. Interprovincial bus terminal, subway adj. Some minibars. Cr cds: A, C, D, ER, MC, V. (F)

Inns

✔ ★★**AUBERGE HANDFIELD.** *(555 Chemin du Prince, St-Marc-sur-Richelieu J0L 2E0)* *28 mi SE on CAN 20, exit 112; 6 mi N on Hwy 223.* *514/584-2226.* 55 rms, 2 story. S $42–$97; D $50–$105; each addl $8; under 4 free; theatre & winter package plans. Crib avail. TV. Pool; poolside serv. Cafe 8 am–midnight. Rm serv. Bar 11 am–midnight. Ck-out noon. Meeting rms. Bellhops. Downhill ski 5 mi; x-country ski on site. Theater-boat (late June–early Sep). Marina. Sugar cabin (late Feb–late Apr), sleigh rides. Tennis, golf nearby. Built in 1880. Cr cds: A, C, D, ER, MC, V. (F)

✔ ★**LE CHÂTEAU DE L'ARGOAT.** *524 Sherbrooke St E (H2L 1K1).* *514/842-2046.* 30 rms, 2 story. S $40–$50; D $45–$55; each addl $5; suites $55–$75. Crib $5. TV; cable. Free coffee. Cafe opp 7–10 pm. Ck-out noon. Cr cds: MC, V. (E) (F)

Québec City, Québec

Founded: 1608 **Pop:** 166,474 **Elev:** 239 ft (73 m) **Area code:** 418

Motels

(Rates may be higher during Carnaval)

✔ ★**LE GÎTE.** *5155 Hamel Blvd (Hwy 138) (G2E 2G8).* *418/872-1411.* 40 rms, 5 kits. Mid-June–mid-Sep: S, D $55–$70; each addl $5; kit. units for 2–8, $80–$120; family, wkly rates; some lower rates rest of yr. Crib free. TV; cable. Heated pool. Playground. Bkfst 7 am–noon. Cafe adj open 24 hrs. Ck-out noon. Downhill ski 20 mi; x-country ski 5 mi. Some in-rm whirlpools. Picnic tables. Cr cds: A, MC, V. (F)

✔ ★**ONCLE SAM.** *(5025 W Hamel Blvd, Ste-Foy G2G 1B6)* *5½ mi W on Hwy 138, jct Hwy 540.* *418/872-1488.* 44 rms. Mid-June–mid-Sep: S, D $49–$69; each addl $6–$8; under 6 free; lower rates rest of yr. Crib free. TV; cable. Heated pool. Playground. Ck-out noon. Coin lndry. X-country ski 5 mi. Picnic table. Cr cds: A, MC, V. (F)

★★★**QUÉBEC INN.** *(5175 W Hamel Blvd, Ste-Foy G2G 1B6)* *6½ mi W on Hwy 138.* *418/872-9831; res: 800/463-5777 (PQ).* 135 rms, 2 story. Mid-June–mid-Sep: S, D $55–$95; each addl $10; family rates; AP avail; honeymoon & ski packages; lower rates rest of yr. Crib free. TV; cable, in-rm movies. Indoor pool; poolside serv. Cafe 6 am–midnight. Rm serv. Bar 10–3 am; entertainment, dancing Wed–Sun. Ck-out noon. Meeting rms. Bellhops. Beauty shop. X-country ski 5 mi. Exercise rm; instructor, weights, bicycles, whirlpool, sauna. Balconies. Cr cds: A, ER, MC, V. Ⓕ

🛠 🏊 🤾 🎿 🚫 🐾 SC

✔ ★**ROND POINT.** *(53 Kennedy Blvd, Lévis G6V 6C7) At jct Hwys 132, 173; 1 mi N of CAN 20 exit 325N. 418/833-4920; res: 800/361-6162 (PQ), 800/361-1155 (Maritimes, ON; US).* 126 rms, 2 story. July–mid-Sep: S $46–$64; D $52–$74; each addl $9; suites $96; lower rates rest of yr. Crib $9. TV; cable. Indoor pool. Cafe 7 am–9:30 pm. Rm serv. Bar 4 pm–2 am. Ck-out noon. Meeting rms. Barber. Downhill/x-country ski 20 mi. Miniature golf. Some refrigerators. Some balconies. Cr cds: A, D, ER, MC, V. Ⓕ

🐾 🏊 🤾 SC

Motor Hotel

✔ ★**HOTEL CHÂTEAU LAURIER.** *695 E Grand-Allée (G1R 2K4). 418/522-8108; res: 800/463-4453 (ON, PQ, Maritime, NE US).* 55 rms, 4 story. May–Oct: S $54–$69; D $59–$74; each addl $7; under 12 free; lower rates rest of yr. Crib free. TV; cable. Cafe 7:30–5:30 am. Bar 11–3 am. Ck-out noon. Bellhops. Cr cds: A, ER, MC, V. Ⓕ

🐾 🐾

Hotel

✔ ★ ★**CHÂTEAU BELLEVUE.** *16 rue Laporte (G1R 4M9). 418/692-2573; res: 800/463-2617 (E CAN, E US).* 57 units, 4 story. May–Oct: S $57–$65; D $60–$73; each addl $7; kits. $84; under 12 free; higher rates special events; lower rates rest of yr. Crib free. TV; cable. Cafe nearby. No rm serv. Ck-out noon. Free parking. Some refrigerators. Cr cds: A, ER, MC, V. Ⓕ

🐾 🐾

Saint-Jovite, Québec

Pop: 3,841 **Elev:** 790 ft (241 m) **Area code:** 819

Motor Hotel

✔ ★**LE ST JOVITE.** *1011 Ouimet St (J0T 2H0). 819/425-2751.* 72 rms, 2 story. S $21.50–$54; D $23–$68; each addl $4; suite $79. Crib $5. TV; cable. Heated pool; poolside serv. Cafe 7:30–9:30 am, noon–2 pm, 6–10 pm. Rm serv. Bar 8–1 am. Ck-out noon. Meeting rms. Valet serv. Balconies. Cr cds: A, C, D, ER, MC, V. Ⓕ

Travel Notes

Mobil Travel Guide

Order Form

Mobil Travel Guide:

☐ **California & the West** $9.95
ISBN 0-13-586777-0

☐ **Great Lakes** $9.95
ISBN 0-13-586793-2

☐ **Middle Atlantic** $9.95
ISBN 0-13-586819-X

☐ **Northeast** $9.95
ISBN 0-13-586835-1

☐ **Northwest &
Great Plains** $9.95
ISBN 0-13-586843-2

☐ **Southeast** $9.95
ISBN 0-13-586892-0

☐ **Southwest &
South Central** $9.95
ISBN 0-13-586900-5

☐ **Major Cities** $9.95
ISBN 0-13-586801-7

Special Publications:

☐ **The Road to Walt Disney World** $9.95
ISBN 0-13-586876-9

☐ **Mobil Road Atlas and
Trip Planning Guide** $6.95
ISBN 0-13-586025-3

Lodgings for Less:

☐ **Northeast and Midwest** $5.95
ISBN 0-13-586926-9

☐ **South** $5.95
ISBN 0-13-586934-X

☐ **West** $5.95
ISBN 0-13-586942-0

See other side for a list of states in each volume.

City Guides:

☐ **Mobil Travel Guide: Boston** $5.95
ISBN 0-13-586769-X

☐ **Mobil Travel Guide: Chicago** $5.95
ISBN 0-13-586785-1

☐ **Mobil Travel Guide: New York** $5.95
ISBN 0-13-586827-0

☐ **Mobil Travel Guide:
San Francisco** $5.95
ISBN 0-13-586884-X

☐ **Mobil Travel Guide:
Washington, D.C.** $5.95
ISBN 0-13-586918-8

SHIP TO:

NAME_____

ADDRESS_____

CITY_____STATE_____

ZIP CODE_____TEL_____

If you would like other editions not available
at your local bookstore or Mobil dealer,
please send this form with check or money
order to:

Prentice Hall Mail Order Billing
Rt 59 at Brook Hill Drive
West Nyack, NY 10994

MERCHANDISE TOTAL $_____

SALES TAX   _____

POSTAGE & HANDLING*   _____

TOTAL (CHECK ENCLOSED) $_____

*Please enclose $1.50 for first book, 50¢ for each
additional book (outside the U.S. $2.00 and 50¢
respectively).

Dept. S   9008Z7(9)

Mobil Travel Guide

Lodgings for Less

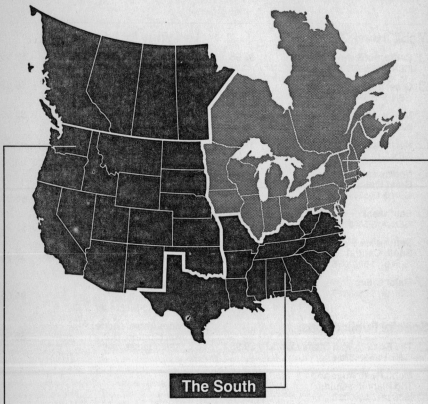

The South

Alabama, Arkansas, Florida, Georgia, Kentucky, Louisiana, Mississippi, Missouri, North Carolina, South Carolina, Tennessee, Texas, Virginia, West Virginia

The West

Arizona, California, Colorado, Idaho, Kansas, Montana, Nebraska, Nevada, New Mexico, North Dakota, Oklahoma, Oregon, South Dakota, Utah, Washington, Wyoming, Canada: Alberta, British Columbia, Manitoba

Northeast and Midwest

Connecticut, Delaware, District of Columbia, Illinois, Indiana, Iowa, Maine, Maryland, Massachusetts, Michigan, Minnesota, New Hampshire, New Jersey, New York, Ohio, Pennsylvania, Rhode Island, Vermont, Wisconsin, Canada: New Brunswick, Nova Scotia, Ontario, Québec

Travel Notes

Travel Notes

Travel Notes

Travel Notes

Travel Notes

Travel Notes

Travel Notes

Travel Notes

Mobil Travel Guide

Lodgings For Less
IDENTIFICATION CARD
Lodging 10% Discount

Bearer Signature   Date

Valid from January 1 to December 31, 1989

Lodgings For Less

10% Lodging Discount

Enjoy cash savings at hotels & motels listed in this Guide.

Many hotels and motels appearing in this Guide are offering a 10% discount for each night's stay at their establishments. Look for the special **$** symbol at the end of each listing to identify all lodging discount participants. This offer may not be used in combination with other discounts or promotions extended by participating establishments. Reservations made through travel agents are not eligible for this discount.

When placing advance reservations always identify yourself as a *MOBIL TRAVEL GUIDE Lodgings For Less* discount customer. You will find toll-free reservation numbers indicated in many lodging listings. Tear out the Identification Card found in the upper right-hand corner and carry it with you in your travels.

Lodgings For Less
10% Discount

A special $ symbol appearing at the end of a listing denotes lodging participation in the 10% discount program. Read the front of this page for information on this offering.

Mobil Travel Guide

Save up to $6
MYSTIC SEAPORT
MYSTIC, CONNECTICUT

Mobil Travel Guide

SUNBEAM FLEET
NATURE CRUISES

Save up to 10%
**SUNBEAM FLEET
NATURE CRUISES**
NEW LONDON (WATERFORD),
CONNECTICUT

Mobil Travel Guide

Save up to $4
**HAGLEY ON THE
BRANDYWINE**
WILMINGTON, DELAWARE

Mobil Travel Guide

Save up to $3
MAGNOLIA MANOR
CAIRO, ILLINOIS

Here's
Chicago!

Mobil Travel Guide

Save up to $6
HERE'S CHICAGO!
CHICAGO, ILLINOIS

Mobil Travel Guide

Save 25%
**CERNAN EARTH AND
SPACE CENTER**
CHICAGO O'HARE AIRPORT AREA
(RIVER GROVE), ILLINOIS

Mobil Travel Guide

Two for the price of one
**FRANK LLOYD WRIGHT
HOME AND STUDIO**
OAK PARK, ILLINOIS

MYSTIC, CONNECTICUT
MYSTIC SEAPORT
With this coupon: Adults $1 off, children 50¢ off regular general admission.
Not to be combined with any other offer.
Valid for family groups of not more than six people from
January 1, 1989 through December 31, 1989.

NEW LONDON (WATERFORD), CONNECTICUT
SUNBEAM FLEET NATURE CRUISES
With this coupon: 10% off each regular adult fare.
Valid for family groups of not more than six people from
May 1, 1989 through September 10, 1989.
Not good with any other discount offer.

WILMINGTON, DELAWARE
HAGLEY ON THE BRANDYWINE
With this coupon: $1 off regular adult admission, 50¢ off all
other categories. Limit four people per coupon.
Valid from January 1, 1989 through December 31, 1989,
except during special events.

CAIRO, ILLINOIS
MAGNOLIA MANOR
With this coupon: 50¢ off each adult or child's regular admission.
Valid for family groups of not more than four people from
January 1, 1989 through December 31, 1989.

CHICAGO, ILLINOIS
HERE'S CHICAGO!
With this coupon: $1 off each regular admission.
Valid for family groups of not more than six people from
January 1, 1989 through December 31, 1989.

CHICAGO O'HARE AIRPORT AREA (RIVER GROVE), ILLINOIS
CERNAN EARTH AND SPACE CENTER
With this coupon: 25% off regular admission.
Valid for family groups of not more than six people from
January 1, 1989 through December 31, 1989.

OAK PARK, ILLINOIS
FRANK LLOYD WRIGHT HOME AND STUDIO
With this coupon: Two admitted for the price of one, except during special events.
Applies to building, tours and recorded walk rentals.
Valid from January 1, 1989 through December 31, 1989.

Mobil Travel Guide

Save up to $6
WILDLIFE PRAIRIE PARK
PEORIA, ILLINOIS

Mobil Travel Guide

Save 50%
**SEVEN ACRES ANTIQUE
VILLAGE AND MUSEUM**
UNION, ILLINOIS

Mobil Travel Guide

Save up to $12
**SQUIRE BOONE CAVERNS
AND VILLAGE**
CORYDON, INDIANA

Mobil Travel Guide

Save up to 50%
HISTORIC FORT WAYNE
FORT WAYNE, INDIANA

HISTORIC
FORT
WAYNE

AMISH ACRES

Mobil Travel Guide

Save up to $6
AMISH ACRES
NAPPANEE, INDIANA

Mobil Travel Guide

Save up to $16
HOLIDAY WORLD
SANTA CLAUS, INDIANA

Mobil Travel Guide

Save up to $6
ADVENTURELAND PARK
DES MOINES, IOWA

Discount Coupon

PEORIA, ILLINOIS
WILDLIFE PRAIRIE PARK
With this coupon: $1 off each regular adult admission.
Valid for family groups of not more than six people from
May 1, 1989 through October 31, 1989.

Discount Coupon

UNION, ILLINOIS
SEVEN ACRES ANTIQUE VILLAGE AND MUSEUM
With this coupon: 50% off regular admission.
Valid for family groups of not more than six people from
April 1, 1989 through October 31, 1989.

Discount Coupon

CORYDON, INDIANA
SQUIRE BOONE CAVERNS AND VILLAGE
With this coupon: Adults $2 off, children $1 off regular admission.
Valid for any size family from
May 24, 1989 through October 31, 1989.

Discount Coupon

FORT WAYNE, INDIANA
HISTORIC FORT WAYNE
With this coupon: One admission free with purchase of one of the same type.
Valid for family groups of not more than six people from
April 15, 1989 through November 25, 1989.

Discount Coupon

NAPPANEE, INDIANA
AMISH ACRES
With this coupon: $1 off each regular admission.
Valid for family groups of not more than six people from
May 1, 1989 through October 31, 1989.

Discount Coupon

SANTA CLAUS, INDIANA
HOLIDAY WORLD
With this coupon: $2 off each regular admission.
Valid for not more than eight people from
April 8, 1989 through October 29, 1989.

Discount Coupon

DES MOINES, IOWA
ADVENTURELAND PARK
With this coupon: $1 off each regular admission.
Valid for family groups of not more than six people from
May 1, 1989 through September 30, 1989.

Mobil Travel Guide

Save up to $6
LIVING HISTORY FARMS
DES MOINES, IOWA

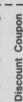

Mobil Travel Guide

Save up to $6
**FORT DODGE HISTORICAL
FORT AND MUSEUM**
FORT DODGE, IOWA

Mobil Travel Guide

Save up to $3
ARGO CRUISES
BOOTHBAY HARBOR, MAINE

Mobil Travel Guide

Save up to $6
HISTORIC ST. MARY'S CITY
ST. MARY'S CITY, MARYLAND

Mobil Travel Guide

Save up to $6
**CHESAPEAKE BAY
MARITIME MUSEUM**
ST. MICHAELS, MARYLAND

Mobil Travel Guide

Save up to $6
**HAMMOND CASTLE
MUSEUM**
GLOUCESTER, MASSACHUSETTS

Mobil Travel Guide

Save up to $6
PLIMOTH PLANTATION
PLYMOUTH, MASSACHUSETTS

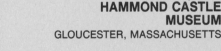

Mobil Travel Guide

Save up to $4.50
**CAPE ISLAND
EXPRESS LINES**
NEW BEDFORD/MARTHA'S
VINEYARD, MASSACHUSETTS

Mobil Travel Guide

Save up to $6
EDAVILLE RAILROAD
SOUTH CARVER,
MASSACHUSETTS

MICHIGAN
SPACE CENTER

Mobil Travel Guide

Save up to 50%
MICHIGAN SPACE CENTER
JACKSON, MICHIGAN

Mobil Travel Guide

Save up to $3
**TOONERVILLE TROLLEY
AND RIVERBOAT TRIP**
SOO JUNCTION, MICHIGAN

Mobil Travel Guide

Save 25%
LUMBERTOWN, USA
BRAINERD, MINNESOTA

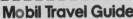

Mobil Travel Guide

Save 30%
**MINNEAPOLIS
PLANETARIUM**
MINNEAPOLIS, MINNESOTA

Mobil Travel Guide

Save up to $7
WATER COUNTRY
PORTSMOUTH, NEW HAMPSHIRE

NEW BEDFORD/MARTHA'S VINEYARD, MASSACHUSETTS
CAPE ISLAND EXPRESS LINES
With this coupon: Adults $1 off, senior citizens 10% off, children 50¢ off regular fare; up to $4.50 total discount.
Valid for family groups of not more than six people from May 15, 1989 through September 30, 1989.

SOUTH CARVER, MASSACHUSETTS
EDAVILLE RAILROAD
With this coupon: $1 off each regular admission.
Valid for family groups of not more than six people from May 1, 1989 through December 31, 1989.

JACKSON, MICHIGAN
MICHIGAN SPACE CENTER
With this coupon: One free admission with one of the same type.
One coupon per person. Void for special events and programs.
Valid from January 1, 1989 through December 31, 1989.

SOO JUNCTION, MICHIGAN
TOONERVILLE TROLLEY AND RIVERBOAT TRIP
With this coupon: 50¢ off each regular admission.
Valid for family groups of not more than six people from June 15, 1989 through October 6, 1989.

BRAINERD, MINNESOTA
LUMBERTOWN, USA
With this coupon: 25% off each regular admission.
Valid for family groups of not more than six people from mid-May, 1989 through mid-September, 1989.

MINNEAPOLIS, MINNESOTA
MINNEAPOLIS PLANETARIUM
With this coupon: 30% off each regular admission.
Valid for family groups of not more than six people from January 1, 1989 through December 31, 1989.

PORTSMOUTH, NEW HAMPSHIRE
WATER COUNTRY
With this coupon: $1 off each regular admission.
Valid for family groups of not more than seven people from Memorial Day, 1989 through Labor Day, 1989.

1   2   3   4   5   6   7

There's Nothing in the World like
Action Park

Mobil Travel Guide

Save up to $30
ACTION PARK
McAFEE (VERNON), NEW JERSEY

Mobil Travel Guide

Save 50%
HISTORIC SPEEDWELL
MORRISTOWN, NEW JERSEY

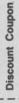

Mobil Travel Guide

Save up to $3
BASEBALL HALL OF FAME
COOPERSTOWN, NEW YORK

Mobil Travel Guide

Save up to $2
**GUINNESS WORLD
OF RECORDS**
NEW YORK, NEW YORK

Mobil Travel Guide

Save up to $4
THE SEAPORT EXPERIENCE
NEW YORK, NEW YORK

THE SEAPORT
EXPERIENCE

Mobil Travel Guide

Save up to $15
SEA WORLD OF OHIO
AURORA, OHIO

ERIEVIEW
PARK

Mobil Travel Guide

Save up to $16
ERIEVIEW PARK
GENEVA-ON-THE-LAKE, OHIO

McAFEE (VERNON), NEW JERSEY
ACTION PARK
With this coupon: Adults and children $5 off on "Pay One Price"
admission Monday-Friday; $2 off on "Pay One
Price" admission weekends.
Valid for family groups of not more than six people from
May 25, 1989 through September 30, 1989.

MORRISTOWN, NEW JERSEY
HISTORIC SPEEDWELL
With this coupon: 50% off each regular admission.
Valid for family groups of not more than six people from
May 1, 1989 through October 30, 1989.

COOPERSTOWN, NEW YORK
BASEBALL HALL OF FAME
With this coupon: 50¢ off each regular admission.
Not good with any other discount program.
Valid for family groups of not more than six people from
January 1, 1989 through December 31, 1989.

NEW YORK, NEW YORK
GUINNESS WORLD OF RECORDS
With this coupon: 50¢ off each regular admission.
Valid for family groups of not more than 4 people from
January 1, 1989 through December 31, 1989.

NEW YORK, NEW YORK
THE SEAPORT EXPERIENCE
With this coupon: Adults 50¢ off, seniors 75¢ off, children 25¢ off
regular admission.
Valid for family groups of not more than four people from
January 1, 1989 through December 31, 1989.

AURORA, OHIO
SEA WORLD OF OHIO
With this coupon: $2.50 off each regular admission.
Valid for family groups of not more than six people from
Memorial Day, 1989 through Labor Day, 1989.

A-110

GENEVA-ON-THE-LAKE, OHIO
ERIEVIEW PARK
General admission free.
With this coupon: Combination Ride & Slide passes $6 each.
Valid for family groups of not more than six people from
May 15, 1989 through September 15, 1989.

Mobil Travel Guide

Save up to $3
**VALLEY GEM
STERNWHEELER**
MARIETTA, OHIO

Discount Coupon

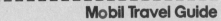

Mobil Travel Guide

Save up to $3
**WANAMAKER, KEMPTON &
SOUTHERN STEAM RR**
HAMBURG (KEMPTON),
PENNSYLVANIA

Discount Coupon

Mobil Travel Guide

Save up to 50%
CLIVEDEN
PHILADELPHIA, PENNSYLVANIA

Discount Coupon

Mobil Travel Guide

Save up to $6
PHILADELPHIA ZOO
PHILADELPHIA, PENNSYLVANIA

(89-01)

Discount Coupon

THE CARNEGIE

Mobil Travel Guide

Save up to $6
**THE CARNEGIE (MUSEUM
OF NATURAL HISTORY),**
PITTSBURGH, PENNSYLVANIA

Discount Coupon

THE INTERNATIONAL
TENNIS HALL OF FAME

Mobil Travel Guide

Save up to $9
**INTERNATIONAL TENNIS
HALL OF FAME**
NEWPORT, RHODE ISLAND

Discount Coupon

Mobil Travel Guide

Save up to $6
SANTA'S LAND
BRATTLEBORO (PUTNEY),
VERMONT

Discount Coupon

MARIETTA, OHIO
VALLEY GEM STERNWHEELER
With this coupon: Adults 50¢ off, children 25¢ off regular admission.
Valid for family groups of not more than six people from
April, 1989 through October, 1989.

HAMBURG (KEMPTON), PENNSYLVANIA
WANAMAKER, KEMPTON & SOUTHERN STEAM RAILROAD
With this coupon: 50¢ off each regular admission.
Valid for family groups of not more than six people from
April 1, 1989 through October 31, 1989.

PHILADELPHIA, PENNSYLVANIA
CLIVEDEN
With this coupon: Adults, two for the price of one regular admission.
Valid for family groups of not more than six people from
April 1, 1989 through December 31, 1989.

PHILADELPHIA, PENNSYLVANIA
PHILADELPHIA ZOO
With this coupon: Adults and children $1 off, senior citizens 50¢ off regular admission.
Valid for family groups of not more than six people from
January 1, 1989 through December 31, 1989.

PITTSBURGH, PENNSYLVANIA
THE CARNEGIE (MUSEUM OF NATURAL HISTORY)
With this coupon: $1 off each regular admission.
Valid for family groups of not more than six people from
January 1, 1989 through December 31, 1989.

NEWPORT, RHODE ISLAND
INTERNATIONAL TENNIS HALL OF FAME
With this coupon: Adults $1.50 off, children 50¢ off regular admission.
Valid for family groups of not more than six people from
January 1, 1989 through December 31, 1989.

BRATTLEBORO (PUTNEY), VERMONT
SANTA'S LAND
With this coupon: $1 off each regular admission.
Valid for family groups of not more than six people from
July 1, 1989 through December 15, 1989.

Discount Coupon

BARABOO, WISCONSIN
CIRCUS WORLD MUSEUM
With this coupon: 20% off each regular admission price.
Valid from May 13, 1989 through September 17, 1989.

Discount Coupon

GREEN BAY, WISCONSIN
RAIL AMERICA—NATIONAL RAILROAD MUSEUM
With this coupon: Adults $1 off, children 50¢ off regular admission.
Valid for family groups of not more than six people from
May 1, 1989 through October 15, 1989.

Discount Coupon

GREEN BAY, WISCONSIN
RIVER QUEEN
With this coupon: $1 off each regular admission.
Valid for family groups of not more than six people from
May 30, 1989 through September 30, 1989.

Discount Coupon

WISCONSIN DELLS, WISCONSIN
TOMMY BARTLETT'S SKI, SKY & STAGE SHOW/
ROBOT WORLD & EXPLORATORY
With this coupon: 20% off each regular general admission.
Valid as follows: SKI, SKY & STAGE SHOW, May 26 - September 9, 1989.
ROBOT WORLD & EXPLORATORY, March 31 - November 19, 1989.
Not good with any other promotion.

Discount Coupon

NIAGARA FALLS, ONTARIO
MINOLTA TOWER
With this coupon: One free admission with paid admission of same type.
Valid for family groups of not more than six people from
January 1, 1989 through December 31, 1989.

Discount Coupon

KINGSTON, ONTARIO
ISLAND QUEEN SHOWBOAT
With this coupon: $1 off each regular adult ticket.
Valid for family groups of not more than six people from
May 13, 1989 through October 8, 1989.

Discount Coupon

QUEBEC CITY, QUEBEC
M/V LOUIS JOLLIET CRUISE
With this coupon: 20% off each regular ticket.
Valid for family groups of not more than six people from
May 1, 1989 through October 15, 1989.